Vertebrate Adaptations

Vertebrate Adaptations

READINGS FROM
**SCIENTIFIC
AMERICAN**

WITH INTRODUCTIONS BY
Norman K. Wessells
STANFORD UNIVERSITY

W. H. Freeman and Company
SAN FRANCISCO

Each of the SCIENTIFIC AMERICAN articles in *Vertebrate Adaptations* is available as a separate Offprint at twenty cents each. For a complete listing of approximately 700 articles now available as Offprints, write to W. H. Freeman and Company, 660 Market Street, San Francisco, California 94104.

Preface

The glamour of modern science often makes us forget the ancient base upon which our knowledge rests. Many of the phenomena of life that are finally yielding to mechanistic interpretation in the twentieth century were first described hundreds, or even thousands, of years ago in the natural history of the time or in anecdotes. Virtually every point noted by Pliny the Elder in the following quotation is elucidated in the material in this book, and many of them are still the subjects of active investigation.

> The swiftest of all animals, not only those of the sea, is the dolphin: it is swifter than a bird and darts faster than a javelin, and were not its mouth much below its snout, almost in the middle of its belly, not a single fish would escape its speed. But nature's foresight contributes delay, because they cannot seize their prey except by turning over on their backs....They have a habit of sallying out on to the land for an unascertained reason, and they do not die at once after touching earth—in fact they die more quickly if the gullet is closed up....For a voice they have a moan like that of a human being....The dolphin is an animal that is not only friendly to mankind but is also a lover of music, and it can be charmed by...the sound of the water-organ....(Pliny, *Natural History,* IX, vii, viii.)

Today we know that the swiftness is due to wrinkles in the skin that permit water to flow over the animal's surface without generating turbulence and drag. The occasional sallies of whales or dolphins onto beaches are thought to result from failure of the echolocating navigation system to receive warning echoes from certain types of shallow, sloping sea bottoms. The "voice" is used in many ways for echolocation and communication. And what better reason than "nature's foresight" ("natural selection," in our parlance) could we conceive to explain these adaptations of a dolphin?

As evidenced throughout this collection of articles, originally published in *Scientific American,* contemporary biology has reached a stage at which the great majority of general properties of living systems can be investigated at the molecular level. Furthermore, we can apply our knowledge of the general properties of vertebrates to the many extraordinary features found only in animals living under very special conditions. The purpose of this book is, in fact, to provide information, both general and specific, about vertebrates, the dominant group of animals on the earth. We will examine the main control systems of vertebrates, and see how those systems are modified and used in unique ways to allow the diversity of life recognized so long ago by Pliny and others.

The collection is designed to supplement courses in animal and vertebrate biology. The vertebrates have received attention from generations of college students, largely because knowledge of these organisms has been considered essential for premedical students. In recent years the traditional "comparative anatomy" courses have begun to be influenced by the impact of molecular biology and comparative physiology. Today, neither students nor their professors are satisfied with a narrow and specialized view of any group of organisms; hence, courses in "vertebrate biology" have become increasingly prevalent, and, I think, the students coming from them have a much more comprehensive understanding of animals and man.

Because it is a supplement, rather than a standard textbook, this collection is purposely incomplete. Its purpose is to fill in some of the gaps and answer some of the questions that might arise from a general survey of vertebrate biology. For those wishing to read further, a special list of recent references for each section is included in the "Biographical Notes and Bibliographies" at the end of the book.

The quotations preceding each Introduction come from Rackham's translation of the *Natural History* by Gaius Plinius Secundus (published by Harvard University Press, 1938–1945). Book and paragraph references are given for each quote.

I am pleased to acknowledge the helpful comments received from Donald Kennedy, Howard A. Bern, George E. Watson, III, J. P. Trinkaus, and Richard D. Palmiter, who are responsible for many good features of the Introductions. Any inaccuracies in the text are my responsibility.

Finally, I wish to thank my wife, Lois, for her enduring help and support while the manuscript was prepared. My appreciation goes also to Jeanne Kennedy, who prepared the index.

September, 1968   NORMAN K. WESSELLS

Contents

Vertebrate Adaptations

An Essay
on Vertebrates

Adaptations are specializations in structure and function that permit animals to survive under a given set of environmental conditions. Whether they are physiological or structural, adaptations are variations upon pre-existing themes: a change in a metabolic pathway occurs, causing a new form of nitrogen excretion; or the shape of a pelvic bone alters, and erect, bipedal locomotion becomes possible. Adaptations develop in the course of generations as responses of continually varying, sexually reproducing organisms to an ever changing environment. Nowhere is this process better illustrated than in the remarkable evolution of vertebrates from filter feeder to abstract thinker.

Many adaptations seem so marvelously complex that to view one individually is, at first glance, to strain credulity. But as one studies the evolution of life he acquires a perspective, with which it is possible to see how the individual building blocks have been altered and used in new ways to yield an organism specialized or "adapted" for some special circumstance. In this introductory essay we will attempt to gain this perspective from a brief, historical survey of the vertebrates. We begin with vertebrate origins.

One of the oldest characteristics unique to those organisms that gave rise to vertebrates was a filter-feeding apparatus with gill slits and cilia. (It is found in some primitive types of organisms alive today—adult tunicates, or sea squirts, amphioxus, and even more primitive, worm-like creatures called *Hemichordates*.) These marine organisms fed by ingesting water, detritus, and suspended food particles through the mouth. The food and detritus were then trapped in mucus, as the water left the body through gill slits located in each lateral wall of the anterior gut (the pharynx). Beating hairlike cilia propelled the stream of water.

Interestingly, the mucus used for trapping the food was secreted by cells that are thought to be a portion of the precursor of the vertebrate

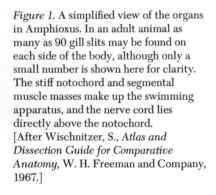

Figure 1. A simplified view of the organs in Amphioxus. In an adult animal as many as 90 gill slits may be found on each side of the body, although only a small number is shown here for clarity. The stiff notochord and segmental muscle masses make up the swimming apparatus, and the nerve cord lies directly above the notochord. [After Wischnitzer, S., *Atlas and Dissection Guide for Comparative Anatomy*, W. H. Freeman and Company, 1967.]

NOTOCHORD   NEURAL TUBE   MUSCLE SEGMENTS

MOUTH   PHARYNGEAL GILL SLITS

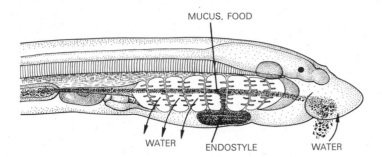

MUCUS, FOOD

WATER   ENDOSTYLE   WATER

Figure 2. The anterior end of a lamprey ammocoete, showing the feeding apparatus. Water, food, and detritus enter the mouth and proceed posteriorly. The water leaves through the gill slits while the food is trapped in the mucus strand rising from the ventral endostyle.
[After Young, J. Z., *The Life of Vertebrates*, Oxford, 1962.]

endocrine gland, the thyroid. Other cells of the same part of the pharynx apparently had the ability to bind iodine into organic molecules, one of which was the hormone thyroxine. This chemical has widespread effects upon both the developmental processes and the adult metabolic functions of today's fishes. Because animals as large and complex as the earliest vertebrates probably required a substantial set of control machinery, we should not be surprised that parts of the endocrine system evolved early in vertebrate history.

A second ancient characteristic of the ancestors of vertebrates was a locomotor complex that differed from that of any other organism. It consisted of segmental masses of muscle extending the length of the body, a stiff central rod (the notochord or, in later forms, the vertebral column) that prevented shortening of the body when muscle contraction occurred, and a nervous control system for coordination of the muscle masses. This combination of structures is seen today in larval tunicates, adult amphioxus, and all vertebrates. Even in the most primitive forms there is a hollow nerve tube, located above the notochord, that shows expansion at the anterior end into a brain. The brain had the beginnings of specialization that resulted from sensory functions (seeing, smelling, tasting) and it was presumably the control center for the central nervous system.

The next major vertebrate adaptation is a muscular, rather than ciliary, filter-feeding apparatus. It is found in the earliest vertebrate fossils, as well as in primitive organisms alive today—the larvae of both lampreys and hagfish (cyclostomes). Lamprey larvae (ammocoetes), for example, do not have cilia, but propel the feeding current by expanding and contracting the pharyngeal cavity. The action thus produced is analogous to the regular movements of the gill cover (operculum) on the sides of common higher fish, such as trout or goldfish. The "suction pump" of ammocoetes is driven by muscles in the wall of the pharynx that pull upon the skeletal support rods between the gill slits. A substantial blood supply serves the gill muscles. One might guess that, in the ancient relatives of the cyclostomes, the presence of this blood near a point of rapid water flow over a body surface (the gill slits) could well provide conditions leading to the formation of the first vertebrate respiratory organ, the "gill."

Although the transition from ciliary to muscular filter feeding does not sound very astounding, its consequences were momentous. Feeding in the new way was apparently much more efficient: larger organisms suddenly appear in the fossil record (see Figure 3), and a smaller percentage of the body is devoted to food gathering by filtering (e.g., the pharynx-gill slit complex has ten or fewer pairs of gill slits, as opposed to fifty or more in amphioxus and other ciliary filter feeders). In the Ordovician period (about

Figure 3. The geological time scale and the appearance of various vertebrate types. The dates in parentheses are estimates, whereas the others are based on analysis of radioactive minerals in the rock strata (see "Radiocarbon Dating" by Edward S. Deevey, Jr., *Scientific American*, February, 1952; Offprint #811). The probable relationship between most of the organisms mentioned in the text is shown. Lines ending in a cross indicate extinction; those ending in an arrow indicate that descendants of that line are alive today. [After Dunbar, Carl O., *Historical Geology*, Wiley, 1960.]

TIME SCALE			DATES	LIFE RECORD
PHANEROZOIC EON	CENOZOIC ERA	PLEISTOCENE EPOCH	(1 MILLION)	
		PLIOCENE EPOCH		
		MIOCENE EPOCH	20 MILLION	
		OLIGOCENE EPOCH	40 MILLION	
		EOCENE EPOCH	60 MILLION	
		PALEOCENE EPOCH	(70 MILLION)	
	MESOZOIC ERA	CRETACEOUS PERIOD	90 MILLION	
		JURASSIC PERIOD	140 MILLION	
		TRIASSIC PERIOD	170 MILLION	
		PERMIAN PERIOD	(200 MILLION) / 230 MILLION	
	PALEOZOIC ERA	PENNSYLVANIAN PERIOD		
		MISSISSIPPIAN PERIOD		
		DEVONIAN PERIOD	300 MILLION	
		SILURIAN PERIOD	350 MILLION	
		ORDOVICIAN PERIOD		
		CAMBRIAN PERIOD	440 MILLION / (500 MILLION)	
CRYPTOZOIC EON				

Life record labels: FROGS, SALAMANDERS, SNAKES, LIZARDS, CYCLOSTOMES, BATS, MAN, OTHER MAMMALS, APES, MONKEYS, MARSUPIALS, BIRDS, INSECTIVORES, WHALES, MONOTREMES, ICHTHYOSAURS, TYRANNOSAURUS, TOOTHED BIRDS, TURTLES, DINOSAURS, THERAPSIDS, BONY FISH, LABYRINTHODONTS, SHARKS, LUNGFISH, JAWED FISH, JAWLESS FISH

450 million years ago), there were a variety of primitive vertebrate fishes, and all of them probably fed by the muscular filter-feeding method or a variation of it. Unfortunately, we have no fossils of the intermediate forms between the ciliary filter feeders and these primitive agnathans (jawless vertebrates). In addition to the muscular filter-feeding apparatus, agnathans possessed many other "vertebrate" characteristics: bone, a skeletal material not found in invertebrates; an internal ear used in sensing orientation in space or body movement; eyes very like those of modern fishes; nasal openings, indicating the organism's ability to smell; lateral-line canals like those of the higher fishes; a light-sensing pineal organ (see page 310); and cranial nerves, some of which led to the gill regions. The circulatory system of these fishes was probably "closed"; that is, it probably consisted of an interconnected set of tubular arteries, capillaries, veins, and heart. Because of the large body size, it seems likely that the vertebrate respiratory pig-

ment, hemoglobin, had to be present. We can only guess about other systems composed of soft parts that were not preserved in the fossil record, but there is no reason not to suppose that endocrine and excretory systems, much like those of modern fish groups, were already present.

The next major advance for the vertebrate stock was also in feeding: it was the transition from filtering food to biting it. Moveable jaws probably arose as modifications of the anterior gill support bones and their musculature. The importance of this step can hardly be exaggerated—for the first time a vertebrate could eat a large invertebrate, or large plant material, or another vertebrate! Immediately, an added complexity of food chains resulted: big fish could eat little fish, or be eaten by bigger fish. No longer were most vertebrates bottom-dwellers, scooping up mud and food. Instead, a remarkable radiation into a variety of early fishes that had jaws (the placoderms) took place. The placoderms and their descendants came to dominate the oceans and the fresh waters of the earth. Their bodies were highly variable in structure, and many new vertebrate organs evolved. Since food was ingested in morsels, a storage and digestion reservoir, the stomach, was necessary. The pursuit of prey and the escape from predators required mechanisms for controlling orientation in the three-dimensional world of water. Thus paired fin systems anterior and posterior to the center of gravity developed, as did changes in body and tail shape. Mechanisms for increasing buoyancy also appeared. As a result of such alterations, an extraordinary diversity of fishes lived in both the marine and fresh waters of the earth during the Devonian period (the "Age of Fishes") which lasted from about 320 to 265 million years ago. Among them were the ancestors of today's sharks, the Elasmobranchs, those of the higher bony fish, the Teleosts, and those of the lines that gave rise to terrestrial vertebrates.

One of the important features of the early history of bony fishes was the development of sacs extending from the anterior gut. Presumably these sacs were vascularized and were one of the respiratory organs of fresh-water fishes. In some salt-water fishes, a sac extending from the gut and similar to a lung in structure became modified into the swim bladder. This is a gas-filled organ that allows bony fishes to remain in neutral buoyancy so that they can hover in the water without expending muscular energy. Other types of fishes had primitive lungs, like those of the first amphibians who made the transition to life on land.

The next major advancements were several that occurred when vertebrates left the water and invaded the land. Adaptations for desiccation control, support of the body, locomotion, and gas exchange had to be evolved. Probably, most attempts at meeting the challenge of life on land failed. Indeed, most of the surviving descendants of the earliest land dwellers—the frogs, toads and salamanders—are even today only marginally emancipated from water.

Frogs and salamanders have moist skins and so are subject to evaporative water loss. Their kidneys are like those of a fresh-water fish—they are ideally suited to eliminate large volumes of dilute urine, but hardly adapted for water conservation. Moreover, because the eggs, sperm and embryos have no protection from drying, at the time of reproduction the organisms must return to the water for breeding. But certain useful advances toward control of desiccation can be seen in these amphibians. The

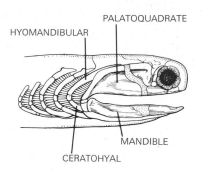

Figure 4. The jaws of an acanthodian placoderm. The upper and lower jaw bones are thought to be modified forms of the gill support bones that are shown posterior to the jaws. [After Romer, A. S., The Vertebrate Body, Saunders, 1962.]

bladder, a storage site for urine from which water can be resorbed, is present for the first time among vertebrates. Coincidentally the structure and function of a portion of the pituitary gland changed, causing the release of a new hormone, vasopressin. This hormone affects the permeability of certain tissues, allowing water to enter the body spaces (through the skin, bladder wall, or kidney tubules). Ready availability of vasopressin is assured because of anatomical changes that have (1) affected the localization of the nerve endings so that release of the hormone occurs in a discrete region, the pars nervosa, and (2) caused the appearance of a special blood supply that drains the portion of the pituitary that contains vasopressin. Finally, although most amphibians still reproduce in bodies of fresh water, behavioral adaptations permit a few to remain away from lakes and streams during breeding. The Javanese tree frog, for example, seals its eggs between two leaves; the egg jelly liquefies and the embryos and larvae live in the pool between the leaves until metamorphosis produces a young frog.

Transition to land posed great mechanical problems for the vertebrate body. No longer was the body supported and pressed on all sides by water: instead, it rested on the ground or was held up by paired derivatives of the pectoral and pelvic fins, the legs. The vertebral column, formerly a simple strut for preventing compression, now tended to move dorsally so that the bulk of the body mass hung below it. Finally, the points at which weight was transferred from the vertebral column to the legs—the pectoral and pelvic girdles—were highly modified and greatly strengthened. We see all these bones in a transitional condition in fossilized early amphibians or in today's salamanders.

The problem of gas exchange on land was especially serious. Primitive lungs simply don't do the job very well. In frogs and salamanders, the work of the simple saccular lungs is supplemented by respiratory exchange across the moist skin. In frogs, about 35 percent of oxygen exchange takes place across the skin and, in salamanders, close to 70 percent. Incidentally, this is the reason why water loss from the skin still occurs in most of today's Amphibia. In addition, Amphibia lack an efficient mechanism for filling and emptying the lungs. A frog swallows bubbles of air just as a lungfish does; unlike all the terrestrial vertebrates, it cannot expand its chest cavity to draw air into the lungs.

Thus we see that the first land vertebrates and most of their surviving amphibian relatives were only partly successful in adapting to the demands of the terrestrial habitat. It was the reptiles, descendants of the ancient amphibians, that succeeded where their predecessors had failed.

Reptiles have a dry and relatively impermeable skin. Their kidneys excrete a small volume of concentrated urine. Their nitrogen metabolism has been modified so that uric acid, rather than urea, is the main end product. Since a molecule of uric acid contains two nitrogen atoms, instead of the single one in urea, only half as many molecules (i.e., osmotically active particles) are produced for a given amount of protein catabolism. Therefore, only half as much osmotic water need be lost from the body as wastes are carried away. In addition, uric acid precipitates out of solution as its concentration is raised in the special storage organs of the reptilian body, so that even more water is freed for resorption into the body.

In the reptiles, an egg that was enclosed in a protective shell evolved.

Figure 5. Structure of urea and uric acid. Note that two molecules of urea occur in the uric acid. Despite its larger size, uric acid is equivalent to urea as an osmotic particle.

The female reproductive ducts covered the fertilized zygote with various protective layers that effectively sealed it from the atmosphere. Then, once the eggs had been laid in a terrestrial environment, they would develop if appropriately incubated so that evaporation was reduced. The male acquired a copulatory organ, which prevented the exposure of sperm and eggs to drying conditions, and insured fertilization of the egg far enough within the female reproductive tract so that there would be time for the zygote to be sealed within the protective coverings.

Other reptilian adaptations centered on the respiratory system. Because the surface of the skin, the epidermis, had become thick, dry, and dead, gases could no longer traverse it, and gas exchange necessarily became restricted to the lungs. This new type of exchange was made possible by the increased structural complexity and surface area of the lungs, and by the newly evolved, expandable rib cage, which filled and emptied the lungs by pumping large volumes of air to and from the respiratory surfaces.

These adaptations freed the reptile from dependence on water—except for the need to drink it—at every stage in its life cycle. Other organ systems also changed radically. The limbs and girdles were modified so that the legs were located more directly beneath the body, raising it higher off the ground. Bends and rotations of the bones at the elbow and knee allowed the limbs to move in an anterior-posterior direction, parallel with the long axis of the body, instead of in sweeping arcs to each side as did the primitive amphibian limbs that protruded outward much like fish fins. With the advent of the reptiles, there occurred for the first time great variation in the shapes and uses of the limbs as these organisms diversified and lived in new ways on the land.

Just as the fishes diverged into an extensive variety of forms after they acquired jaws, so did the reptiles as they overcame the major problems of terrestrial life. During much of the Mesozoic Era (185 to 60 million years ago) they were the dominant forms of animal life on earth.

Nevertheless, reptiles had one significant limitation: their susceptibility to fluctuations in temperature. A terrestrial animal, because it is directly exposed to the atmosphere, is subject to much greater environmental variation than is a marine animal: temperature alters markedly from day to night; seasonal temperature variation in higher latitudes is dramatic; and daily changing weather conditions can produce rapid alterations in the environment. The aquatic vertebrates are not beset by such sudden variations because they are immersed in water, which warms and cools much more slowly than air. For these animals, the only rapid temperature changes would be those encountered in going from one depth of water to another. This basic difference between the two habitats directly affected the adaptations of aquatic and terrestrial vertebrates. A particular lizard so adapted that it could catch insects efficiently on warm summer afternoons might be unable to move rapidly, or function efficiently, in the cool evening or the cold winter. But fishes never having been exposed to the high temperatures of the atmosphere, are physiologically adapted to their relatively constant cold surroundings and can thus function year round.

The inability to tolerate environmental extremes, then, was one reason why the reptiles' utilization of the terrestrial habitat was limited. Add to it the fact that large regions of the earth were, because of the cold, simply beyond their reach, and one can imagine the selective pressure that must have operated to give rise to the two temperature-regulating groups, the birds and the mammals.

All biochemical reactions are somewhat inefficient in that they generate a small amount of heat. Therefore heat is continually being produced by normal animal metabolism. To conserve this heat, birds and mammals acquired feathers or fur to insulate their bodies. Both of these types of insulators consist of dead epidermal cells that require no blood supply. (The presence of superficial vascular networks in the skin is an important cause of heat loss in all vertebrates.) The feathers or hairs are arranged in overlapping layers that trap and immobilize a layer of insulating air next to the skin. To complement these means for conserving heat, three separate control systems evolved—one for heat production, another for heat dissipation, and another for heat retention. And, interestingly, even though birds and mammals arose at different times from different types of reptiles, there developed in all of them the same basic control features that permit maintenance of a constant high body temperature.

In both of these "warm-blooded" groups, the ability to regulate temperature was dependent upon key changes in the blood vascular system and its control machinery. A high-pressure system with rapid blood flow resulted from such changes as the complete separation of the pulmonary (lung) circulatory pathway from the systemic (body) pathway. Equally vital alterations occurred in the protein (globin) portion of hemoglobin, the respiratory pigment of the blood, so that avian and mammalian hemoglobin could bind and carry oxygen at high temperatures (37 degrees centigrade); the respiratory pigment of fishes or amphibians can carry oxygen only at lower temperatures. The most important alteration in avian and mammalian hemoglobin, however, was its new lower affinity for oxygen; this causes a higher oxygen content in the body tissues, which is essential for the high rates of metabolism required by life at 37 to 40 degrees centigrade.

As a result of the many adaptations that had made temperature control possible, a variety of animals appeared. Most could be active for longer periods of the day and, in the temperate regions, for greater parts of the year; some could even live in the polar regions of the earth.

Although feathers of primitive birds were important heat insulators, we don't know whether they originated for this purpose or for that of increasing wing surface to permit short-distance gliding flights. Certainly the feathers contributed to the great difference between avian and mammalian locomotion. They provide a light surface area that makes up much of the aerofoils of wings, the control surface of the tail, and the contouring that assures efficient airflow over the body during flight.

Most organ systems of the avian body have come to resemble those of mammals, but one, the reproductive system, is very different. A bird lays a shelled egg like that of the reptiles; this type of reproduction dictates certain procedures for nesting and for feeding of the young by both parents. In the mammals, a new means of embryo incubation developed. The female reproductive tract and the hormonal system that controls its activity have been altered so that the embryo is retained and nourished within the body. Some advantages of this type of incubation are that the female is mobile during the gestation period, and that the mates do not have to remain together in order to take turns at incubating eggs. (A few species of birds are like mammals in that the female incubates the eggs and cares for the nestlings.) For the mammalian embryo, incubation within the mother's body provided a constant, high temperature. A much longer potential period of gestation became possible because of the availability of an essentially unlimited source of food—the mother's blood—for the embryo. In contrast, all the food for a bird's embryonic development must be put into the yolk before the egg shell is sealed off. Mammals acquired still another convenience, the mammary gland and its hormonal control network. This gland provided a ready source of a constant food type (i.e., a species-specific balance of protein, fats, carbohydrates), and eliminated the necessity of special food gathering to support early life of offspring. We think that mammary glands evolved from sweat glands, structures normally used as a means of lowering elevated body temperature. Thus an organ originally developed for one purpose, temperature regulation, was modified to serve a completely different function.

Other adaptations for life on land affected the animal's ability to gather information from the environment. Changes in the cornea and lens of the eye were particularly important because they enabled the animal living in air to focus light. In fishes the outermost structure of the eye, the cornea, has a refractive index close to that of water (the refractive index is the ratio of the velocity of light in a vacuum to the velocity of light in another medium, such as water or the cornea). Hence the cornea is of little use in bending and focusing light on the retina; consequently, it tends simply to be shaped like the side of the fish so that it offers the least resistance to movement through the water. Fishes do almost all focusing with the lens, by moving it out or in, or occasionally by changing its shape. But in terrestrial vertebrates, the cornea is the critical structure for focusing light because its refractive index (1.376) is so much greater than that of the air (1.00). As C. Ladd Prosser has pointed out, in air the cornea functions as the "coarse" adjustment on a microscope, and the lens as the "fine" adjustment.

Terrestrial adaptions of the ear affected primarily one of the chambers (the lagena) of the internal ear. The lagena has become greatly elongated in most terrestrial vertebrates (in which it is termed the cochlea), and it contains large numbers of sensory hairs that respond to shearing movements of certain membranes. In addition, a "middle" ear developed to amplify and transmit sound from the external ear drum to the membrane system of the internal ear. In fact, these alterations in the ear are among the most complex morphological changes that took place in the transition from aquatic to terrestrial life.

The most striking way in which mammals differ from birds is, of course, in the larger mammalian brain (but see the article by Stettner and Matyniak). In seeking to understand why the mammalian brain, and particularly that of the primates (man and his close relatives), became so large, we must examine many aspects of mammalian biology.

One factor that may have contributed to the expansion of the primate brain is a unique alteration in the reproductive activity of these animals. Virtually all other vertebrates are seasonal breeders: all females mate only when they are in a condition of estrus, or heat, and a condition in which ovulation or release of fertilizable eggs is likely; all females of a given

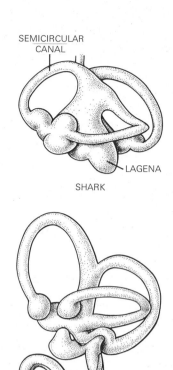

Figure 6. The internal ears of a shark and of a mammal. Note how the lagena is expanded to form the long, coiled cochlea of the terrestrial vertebrate. The semicircular canals are similar in structure and in function; in these and other vertebrates the canals are part of the apparatus that senses acceleration, deceleration, and relative position of the body in the water.

population of a species come into estrus together, and mating occurs at such a time that the young will be born at a season propitious for their survival. In nonhuman primates (and in some other animals), we see an initial alteration in this pattern: females are asynchronous in estrus. They still mate only when ovulation is likely to occur, but as a result of the asynchrony, breeding within a population takes place throughout the year. Only in man do we see the additional step that dissociates mating from ovulation. The nervous and endocrine systems have been modified in such a way that the individual female is a potential breeder all year long. It has been argued, in fact, that this change is the most significant physiological difference between ourselves and the apes. The "competitive" societal organization of the apes could have resulted in large part from the sexual asynchrony of the females. Males repeatedly fight to establish their position in the dominance hierarchy month after month as new females enter estrus and become sexually receptive. Polygamy and harems are the rule in such societies. Mature males tend not to take part in rearing the young, and the oldest, most experienced males are often driven from the group when they are no longer dominant. In man, the dissociation of copulation from reproduction has eliminated at least one condition fostering competition between males—the constant competition for a new sex partner; stable relations between one male and one female can be established, since the female is continually available sexually to the male. It has been proposed that this change established the conditions in which the "cooperative" society of humans could appear. Thus, we can argue that the unique feature of human physiology—the behavior that most distinguishes us from other animals— is sex for pleasure alone, rather than merely for reproduction.

Had such an alteration occurred in the structure of society of prehuman anthropoids, the resultant permanent relationships between males and females, and the cooperative living between old, reproductive, and young non-reproductive animals, could have greatly stimulated development of communication systems, transmittal of experience, and other factors conducive to expanded learning capacity.

Another possible cause contributing to the expansion of the brain might be the evolution of the hand. Indeed, the development of the hand is one of the most intriguing aspects of man's own recent evolutionary history. Several reptiles and mammals (such as *Tyrannosaurus* and the kangaroo) abandoned the usual tetrapod stance for a bipedal one. The forelimbs of these animals became much smaller than those of most other terrestrial vertebrates. The one exception to this tendency has been man. This we take to be a strong piece of indirect evidence that man's primate ancestors lived in the trees. Monkeys and small primates have small, light bodies that they can balance easily above the limbs of trees. As a result, these creatures use four limbs to walk and run on *top* of the branches. The large primates—apes and the early predecessors of man—have larger, heavier bodies that are difficult to balance above narrow branches. These animals developed a new type of locomotion—brachiation—in which they swung with their forelimbs *beneath* the branches. No longer was balance a major problem, but support of the heavy body put new stresses and strains on the forelimbs and pectoral girdle. The results of brachiation are obvious in a gibbon or a chimpanzee: the forelimbs are longer than the hind limbs,

TYRANNOSAURUS   KANGAROO   MAN

the shoulder girdle bones and muscles have been expanded in size to support the weight of the body hanging beneath the forelimb, and the typical mammalian "paw" has been modified for grasping branches. Several million years ago, when our immediate ancestors gradually left the trees to become bipedal terrestrial dwellers, they probably already possessed large forelimbs and hands, which, because of the ways they were used, tended to be preserved as such, rather than shrinking to inconsequence as did those of *Tyrannosaurus*. With these forelimbs and hands, then, man's immediate ancestors acquired their skills in manipulating objects, and it is very possible that this increased dexterity contributed to the expansion of the brain.

So far we have argued that endocrinological and behavioral alterations in sexual activity made development of a cooperative society possible, and that the altered skeleton of hominids permitted bipedal locomotion and use of the hands in new ways. Ecological factors, too, were probably partly responsible for the changes in the societies of prehumans. It is thought that, when early man left the trees to live in the savannah forest-edge habitat, he ate both plant and animal food. Dentition, animal remains, and occasional tools or weapons that have been found support this idea. Some anthropologists have speculated that the practice of hunting large game was the key to cooperation between early hominids. Obvious advantages and consequences of hunting in groups can be imagined. Probably we shall never know whether this type of cooperative food gathering predated and precipitated the altered sex behavior and family structure.

Perhaps the main conclusion to be drawn from this discussion is that cultural and biological evolution of man are intimately linked—feedback from each affects the other so that both change in time. The focus of change, of course, is the brain and its increase in size and complexity. The number of brain associational neurons (intermediate neurons between the sensory

Figure 7. Comparison of Tyrannosaurus, kangaroo, and man. Note that Tyrannosaurus and the kangaroo have much smaller forelimbs than man.

input cells and the motor output nerve cells) grew until ultimately a new property—self-awareness or abstract thought—appeared. We cannot say, as yet, at what point the number and complexity of interactions between neurons became great enough to generate this property, but there is no reason to invoke any nonbiological element to explain it.

Our survey, then, ends with man. We see how an incredibly intricate series of changes, occurring in the course of millions of years, has led to the diversity of vertebrate life and finally to him. In him we can see traces of many of those steps: filter feeding, swimming and its control, feeding mechanisms, the invasion of land, the control of high body temperature, and finally the cultural-biological interplay that led to thought; all have left their marks. Yet these are merely focal points for further study. We have looked at some questions that are still unanswered and at some speculations that are still controversial. As long as they remain so, our survey is not really at an end, but only just begun.

I

Structural Adaptations of Vertebrate Bodies

Almost all species except man and monkeys, both the viviparous and the oviparous, have tails corresponding to the requirements of their bodies, bare with the hairy species, like boars, small with the shaggy ones, like bears, very long with the bristly, like horses. With lizards and snakes when cut off they grow again. The tails of fishes steer their winding courses after the manner of a rudder, and even serve to propel them like a sort of oar by being moved to the right and left. Actual cases of two tails are found in lizards. Oxen's tails have a very long stem, with a tuft at the end, and in asses it is longer than in horses, but it is bristly in beasts of burden. A lion's tail is shaggy at the end, as with oxen and shrewmice, but not so with leopards; foxes and wolves have a hairy tail, as have sheep, with which it is longer. Pigs curl the tail, dogs of low breeds keep it between their legs.

Pliny
NATURAL HISTORY, XI, CXI.

I
Structural Adaptations of Vertebrate Bodies

INTRODUCTION

Life in water, life on land, life in the air—each places very different demands upon the vertebrate body. The muscle-bone complex used for support and locomotion and its neuronal control network have evolved into a bewildering variety of types. In this introduction, we will discuss adaptations for each of the environmental habitats and see how the basic body components changed in time.

The elements of vertebrate swimming are illustrated more diagrammatically in the elongate fish, such as sharks, than in the higher bony fish that are described by Sir James Gray in the first article "How Fishes Swim." When sharks are swimming, their long, thin bodies assume the shape of moving sine waves. This shape results from alternate series of contractions of the muscle masses (myotomes) that make up each side of the fish body. In swimming, a wave of muscle contraction starts in the most anterior muscle mass on one side of the body and then proceeds posteriorly, each myotome contracting in turn. Then, before the first wave proceeds too far, another wave starts at the anterior end on the opposite side of the body. The process continues, first on one side, then on the other, and the result is a bending motion like that of sine waves. This action causes each portion of the sides of the fish to be swept back and forth through the water as if it is a moving inclined plane. Forward propulsion results. In higher fishes, the sine-wave motions are much less obvious, and most of the propulsive thrust comes from the specialized tail region where amplitude of the waves is greatest.

The pattern of the chains of contraction that occur in swimming is largely controlled by nerves in the spinal cord. If the spinal cord of a dogfish shark is severed from the brain, the organism can be made to swim. It will continue to do so for long periods. Some physiologists believe that the whole pattern of coordinated muscle activity is programmed in the network of motor nerves within the spinal cord, and that no sensory input (or exceedingly little) is necessary to coordinate the chains of contractions. Interestingly, the swimming speeds of such "spinal" animals are fairly constant: the spinal cord control system shows little capacity to alter the rate of muscle activity. If small portions of the cord's sensory input are intact, however, appropriate stimuli can evoke violent muscle contraction or faster swimming; such responses do not require presence of a brain. However, the brain (particularly the medulla) is necessary for normal initiation and control of swimming speed. Thus we may view the brain of a normal animal as the control circuit that can start, stop, or modify sets of activity in the motor nerve switchboard of the spinal cord. One might imagine, in

Figure 1. A diagrammatic representation of a shark swimming. The bends in the body are caused by waves of contraction of the muscle masses that start at the front and proceed toward the rear of the fish. The darkened muscle masses are those that are contracted; an instant later, these would be relaxed and the next most posterior muscle masses would be contracted. The next wave of contraction would start on the opposite side (right side in the drawing) of the animal.

fact, that the long neural tube (i.e., the spinal cord) originated in the pre-vertebrates as a motor control system for the segmental muscle masses.

Primitive vertebrate fishes probably propelled themselves as do today's sharks. Like sharks, they possessed asymmetric tails in which the dorsal half was longer and more massive than the ventral half. When such a tail sweeps to and fro through the water, it tends to drive water down and back; the tail, of course, reacts in the opposite direction: it is driven up and forward. The latter force provides propulsion; the former, is a "lift" at the rear end of the body. As a result, the tail tends to rise and the head to sink during swimming. This was the motion of most agnathans, and it was perhaps a useful adaptation for easy movement along the bottom of the sea or fresh water. For free swimming above the bottom, however, turning cartwheels in the water is hardly adaptive! Sharks overcome the difficulty with their broad head, which is flattened ventrally, and a set of wide, flat pectoral fins anterior to the center of gravity. Both flat surfaces tilt up at their anterior ends so they are like planes being pushed through the water; the result is a lift at the front that counteracts that at the rear. By controlling the angle of the anterior lift planes, the fish can direct its movement in the dorsoventral plane. Equivalent fin systems and flattened heads are seen in many types of early agnathan fishes. In addition, in those creatures and in almost all their descendants, there was at least one other pair of fins (the pelvics), located posterior to the center of gravity. The acquisition of these fins was important, not only for fishes but also for terrestrial vertebrates, because the paired fins later became the limbs.

Most of the higher bony fish in the world differ from the sharks or ancestral fishes by having symmetrical tails. The reason is, no doubt, the existence of a swim bladder, which is a source of buoyancy. Unlike sharks that sink if they stop moving forward in water, bony fish can add or remove gas from their swim bladder to keep their body in neutral buoyancy with water at a given depth (i.e., they alter the total specific gravity of their body and so keep its mass exactly equal to the mass of the water it displaces). Clearly, any tendency to drive the body up or down, such as lift from an asymmetric tail, would hardly be advantageous to an organism that would otherwise be stable at one depth. So the tail fin became symmetrical and, because the tail lift was eliminated as a result, the paired fins were freed for functions other than counteracting that lift. Hence, fins came to be used as brakes, tilting rudders, or even wings! One wonders, in fact, what strange and wonderful differences might have taken place in vertebrate evolution if swim bladders and symmetric tails had been present

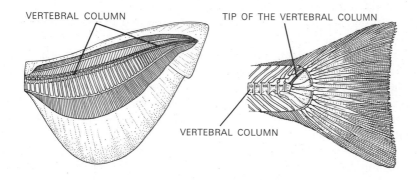

VERTEBRAL COLUMN

TIP OF THE VERTEBRAL COLUMN

VERTEBRAL COLUMN

Figure 2. The caudal "tail" fins of a shark and of a bony fish are seen in these sketches. The asymmetric shape of the shark fin results from an upward bend of the vertebral column and from a large flap of tissue that projects ventrally. The very tip of the bony fish's vertebral column also bends dorsally, perhaps reflecting its evolutionary derivation from an asymmetric tail. Nevertheless, the other bony fin supports are symmetrical so that the whole structure no longer generates a "lift," as does the shark fin.

in the earliest vertebrates so that the paired fins need never have developed.

One of the most surprising features of all aquatic vertebrates is the high rate of speed at which some marine mammals can swim. Seemingly accurate measurements indicate speeds of 18 knots for some dolphins. As Gray points out in his article, this speed is thought to be possible because friction is reduced by laminar flow of water next to the body. Laminar flow patterns can form because the whole skin of dolphins is loose and slack. In addition, the epidermis is thought to be perforated with minute water-filled tubes. When the fish rapidly accelerates or decelerates, or sustains rapid swimming, numerous standing (stationary) waves, or folds, appear in the skin; that is, unlike a stiff, smooth surface, this flexible skin becomes creased at these times. Apparently the creases in the skin conform to the waves of water flowing past the animal. Consequently, the moving water flows smoothly over the surface and does not break up into eddies and swirls that would produce drag. Without such turbulence, the animal can move forward at a much higher rate than would otherwise be possible.

The swimming motion of fishes is still seen in the most primitive terrestrial vertebrates alive today, the salamanders. A salamander uses its limbs for paddling or walking slowly, but, if it is frightened, it tucks them in close to the body and swims or wriggles away by twisting its body in a series of sine-wavelike movements. As was discussed in the introductory essay on vertebrates, it was in the descendants of amphibians that limbs became the prime source of movement on land.

Life on a solid substrate led to major alterations in the vertebral column and the limbs of vertebrates. In the terrestrial vertebrate, the column has shifted toward the dorsal surface, so that most of the body mass hangs below the chain of bones. Because this places great stresses on individual vertebrae, they tend to slip past each other in the dorsoventral plane. To counteract this tendency, individual vertebrae acquired various flanges of bone (zygapophyses, projections from centra, and others) that brace the column and prevent slippage. Particularly in the ancient reptiles (the therapsids) that subsequently gave rise to mammals, the limbs—which had protruded outward somewhat perpendicular to the body axis—gradually moved in under the body: the hind limb turned forward and in, and the knee bent sharply so that the foot still pointed anteriorly; the forelimb initially bent back at the shoulder, so that a compensatory twist was necessary at the elbow; thus, the forearm rotated forward 180 degrees so that the forefoot also pointed anteriorly. These various bends produced the condition from which mammalian limbs radiated. As described so beautifully by Milton Hildebrand in "How Animals Run," a great variety of modifications occurred among the four-footed mammals, while another unique set took place in the arboreal primates and the early relatives of man (see the articles by Napier).

Besides the significant alteration in limbs, there occurred in primates a remarkable evolutionary trend in vision. Insectivores—small shrew-like animals—are close to the stem group of all modern mammals and are particularly close to the primates. Insectivores are usually nocturnal and largely dependent on the senses of smell and of high-sensitivity "rod" vision for orientation. (Rods and cones are the two types of light-sensitive cells in the neural retina of the eye.) But the higher primates, perhaps as a result of life in the trees, move about principally during the day. Sight is

Figure 3. The body movement of a walking salamander. The vertebral column moves back and forth, as does a shark's (see Figure 1). In comparison, when a more advanced terrestrial vertebrate moves, the column remains relatively straight and the limbs move more independently to provide propulsion.
[After Romer, A. S., *The Vertebrate Body*, Saunders, 1962.]

their dominant sense, and they have low-sensitivity "cone" photoreceptor cells and accentuated color vision.

The sharpness, or acuity, of vision of an eye is affected by such factors as the size of the photosensitive elements, the way information from such elements is routed to the brain, and optical properties of the structures through which the light waves pass (see "Eye and Camera," *Scientific American*, August 1950; Offprint 46). In primates, acuity has been maximized by a layer of yellow pigment, the macula lutea, that developed over the fovea of the retina. The macula lutea filters out blue wavelengths of light, which are the ones that produce the greatest chromatic aberration in optical systems. The fovea was already the region of highest acuity in other mammals, because it is structured in a special way: that is, each cone cell is linked directly to an individual nerve cell that carries impulses toward the brain; elsewhere in the retina each neuron leading to the brain may receive input from many light-sensitive cells, and so such neurons "report" on a larger retinal area, thus yielding less acute vision.

Improved depth perception (i.e., binocular vision) has obvious advantages for animals that run or brachiate through the trees. Anatomical alterations that have permitted better depth perception include reduction in the snout, flattening of the face, and movement of the eyes toward one another so that the fields of vision overlap substantially. A particularly intriguing visual adaptation for depth perception was a change in the routes of the optic nerve fibers between the eye and the brain. In most lower vertebrates, optic nerve fibers extend from the eyes across the optic chiasma to the opposite side of the brain. In primates, particularly, this routing has been altered so that many fibers (40 percent of them in man) from the left half of the left eye and the right half of the right eye proceed to the optic chiasma, but then turn outward again to make junctions with brain neurons on the *same* side of the body (fibers from the other halves of each eye continue to cross at the chiasma). The result is that fibers from the left half of each eye go to the left brain, and those from

PRIMITIVE TERRESTRIAL VERTEBRATE

MAMMAL

Figure 4. Representations showing the twists that occurred during evolution of the terrestrial vertebrate limbs. The hind limb bent in at the hip; the knee and the ankle bent. The forelimb rotated back at the shoulder; the upper arm bone rotated outward, and, as the elbow bent, the outer bone of the forearm bent forward and, as this occurred, the outer bone (the posterior bone of the primitive terrestrial vertebrate, shown in the top part of the illustration) twisted over the other forearm bone so that, in the mammal, its lower end is on the inner side of the wrist. As a result, the lower surface of the forepaw is on the ground; otherwise it would face upward. [After Ballard, W. W., *Comparative Anatomy and Physiology*, Ronald, 1964.]

Figure 5. Distribution of optic nerve fibers in a mammal. In a fish, all fibers from each eye would cross the optic chiasma. Note how the lateral geniculate body is subdivided into layers that receive input from the same (I) or opposite (C) retina. [After Grinnell, A. D.; in M. S. Gordon, ed., *Animal Function: Principles and Adaptations*, Macmillan, 1968.

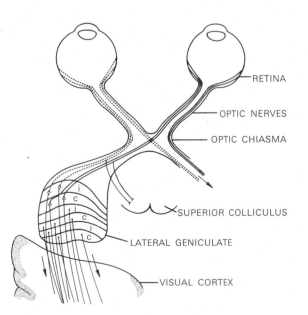

RETINA

OPTIC NERVES

OPTIC CHIASMA

SUPERIOR COLLICULUS

LATERAL GENICULATE

VISUAL CORTEX

the right halves go to the right brain. This means that the same portions of the visual field are sent to the same side of the brain for comparison. In some still unknown way this yields an advantage in assaying depth relationships. In summary, then, alterations in the chemistry of yellow pigment production, in facial structure, and in nerve circuitry all occurred as adaptations in the visual system of the primates.

The series of primate fossils that has appeared since Raymond Dart, the pioneering anthropologist at the University of Witwatersrand, South Africa, discovered the first remains of the *Australopithecines* in 1924, has led to one surprising conclusion about the evolution of man: appearance of an upright stance and "human" hand preceded development of his large brain. In the early *Australopithecines*, who lived some two million years ago, the pelvic girdle and leg structure are indicative of a bipedal stance much like our own, and certainly not of the normal stooping stance of the apes. Coupled with this advanced posture and a prehensile hand was a remarkably small brain, which had a volume of about 510 cubic centimeters (about the same as an adult male gorilla). *Homo habilis,* the next most advanced pre-human who was a contemporary of at least the later *Australopithecines,* had a cranial capacity of 680 cubic centimeters, and the next form, *Homo erectus* (Pithecanthropus) a cranial capacity of 975 cubic centimeters. Thereafter, as the various forms of *Homo sapiens* advanced, the brain volumes increased until the current average size of 1,400 cubic centimeters was reached. Brain volume alone is not a reflection of learning capacity, although it provides an excellent approximation in any single type of organism with similar body shapes, surface areas, etc. Perhaps an even better index might be the number of "excess" cortical neurons, that is, neurons that cannot be accounted for by body size or special adaptation (emphasis on one sensory system, for instance, can lead to expansion of the corresponding portion of the brain). The anthropologist Philip Tobias has estimated the number of excess nerve cells for each of the cranial capacities cited above as follows: *Australopithecus,* 3.5 billion; *H. habilis,* 5.3 billion; *H. erectus,* 7.1 billion; and modern man, 8.6 billion. This trend correlates with a series of increasingly complex behavioral patterns: first, use of tools garnered from the environment, then the manufacture of tools, and finally the complex societal relations of man—each an indication of an increase in learning capacity. The early australopithecine and *habilis* fossils demonstrate clearly that an upright stance and a prehensile hand—both discussed in detail by John Napier in "The Antiquity of Human Walking" and "The Evolution of the Hand"—occurred well before substantial expansion of the brain. In fact, as we outlined in the introductory chapter, it seems likely that the brain expanded as a result of the new habits that early man acquired for life in the forest and in the more open grassy savanna: these habits included walking, grasping, making tools, and finally, getting along in a more and more complex society in which the establishment of a more efficient means of communication would be beneficial. It is remarkable indeed that natural selection should have placed such premium upon increased learning capacity, that in only about 70,000 generations the cerebral cortex expanded from that of a primitive primate to that of early *Homo sapiens.*

Having examined some features of the marine and terrestrial vertebrates, let us turn to the major types that fly. From the reptiles arose the ptero-

ELEVATOR

DEPRESSOR

Figure 6. The major bones and muscle-tendon systems of a bird. The depressor muscles originate from the ventral keel. The elevator muscles start at the upper keel and extend over the shoulder joint to insert on the upper surface of the humerus, the proximal wing bone. [After Darling, Lois and Louis, *Bird*, Houghton Mifflin, 1962.]

saurs and the birds; from the mammals, the bats. We assume that the flight of all three groups was originally gliding. Only when the capacity to generate lift and propulsion had increased, did free flight become possible. The gliding stage can be observed today in some of the "flying" squirrels. Since flight places rigid demands on the construction of any animal body, it is not surprising that the vertebrate organization of these three major flying groups responded to those demands in quite similar ways. Light thin bones, elongate forelimbs and hands, reduced hind limbs, and increased wing surface area are features common to all three groups. The wing of the pterosaur was a large, thin sheet of skin stretched behind an enormously elongate fourth digit. The wing of the bat, too, consists of sheets of skin stretched between digits two through five, all of which are greatly lengthened. The bird wing terminates in a fused set of bones—the second, third, and fourth digits—and the great bulk of the wing aerofoil is made up of the flight feathers. The feathered construction has obvious physiological advantages for temperature control. In addition, it is a more versatile aerodynamic surface: wing "slots" for reducing drag can be created by twisting feathers. Such adjustments are impossible in the continuous sheets of skin in bat or pterosaur wings. This is one of the reasons that bat flight appears so uneven and "fluttery" in comparison with the level flight of most birds. It is the flight of birds that is so remarkable, and the principles that govern it are discussed in the articles "Bird Aerodynamics" by John H. Storer and "Birds as Flying Machines" by Carl Welty.

The driving force of bird flight comes from the huge pectoralis muscles. Their action is a superb example of engineering design. Since greater aerodynamic stability is gained if the center of gravity of a flying body is at or below the level of the wings, the location of a heavy mass of muscle above and between the wings of a bird would certainly present a problem. Thus the muscles that elevate the wings are actually located below the wings. Both the muscles that depress the wings (the pectoralis majors) and those that raise them (the pectoralis minors) are attached to a flange of bone (the keel) that projects downward from the central chest bone, the sternum. The depressor muscle, as might be expected, simply inserts on the ventral surface of the wing to lower it. The elevator muscle, however, ends at a tendon that proceeds dorsally over the shoulder joint to insert on the upper surface of the proximal wing bone. Thus, by a pulley action the muscles located well below the wings can raise them in flight! Bats and fossil pterosaurs, too, have keels from which the flight-depressor muscles originate—this is a good example of the evolutionary process producing the same functional condition at three different times in vertebrate history.

The manner in which adaptations in one body system influence other systems is demonstrated by the effects of flight on temperature control of birds. Feathers, as effective insulators, present a problem to birds that fly by actively flapping the wings. Sweat glands as a means of counteracting rising temperature have never developed in birds, presumably because water poured onto the body surface would mat the feathers and destroy aerodynamic properties. Instead of sweating, birds pant and employ evaporation from the respiratory system for cooling. Particularly large quantities of heat are generated by the flight muscles of the chest. Much of this heat is dissipated by evaporation from the walls of the anterior air sacs. In the duck, for instance, these sacs are ventilated regularly only during flight. The biologists G. W. Salt and E. Zeuthen have calculated that as a pigeon goes from rest to a maximum speed of 43 miles per hour, its metabolism of flight increases about 26-fold. Ventilation of the respiratory system during flight increases 76-fold. This means that a pigeon in flight loses 37.7 kilocalories of heat per hour, and, on the ground, only 0.5 kilocalories per hour. One other factor that is vital to the operation of this adaptive mechanism is the high speed at which air moves through the ducts of the respiratory system (the trachea, the bronchi, and so on); because of it, there is less opportunity for condensation of water—a process that would retain, rather than dissipate, heat—from the humidified air as it leaves the body.

All vertebrate animals have species-recognition signals of some type or other. Birds—with their wonderful colors and songs—exhibit a variety of interesting signals. We will discuss bird song in Part VIII. The colors of bird feathers are caused by pigments made in the body or by certain structural features of the feathers themselves. Melanin pigments yield browns, blacks, and yellows; fat-soluble lipochromes, yellows, oranges, and reds. No blue pigment is found in birds; rather, blue results from refraction and reflection of blue wavelengths by parts of the feather barbs, while other wavelengths are absorbed by melanin-containing cells beneath the reflecting surface. The exquisite shimmering iridescence of a darting hummingbird is the result of similar highly elaborate feather structures.

Color *patterns* are the result of an interplay between genes, dietary constituents, hormones, and such environmental factors as the length of the day or the temperature. Future melanin-containing cells from the embryo of one species may be transplanted to the embryo of another species and there produce patterns and color characteristic of the donor. This occurs even though the structure of the feathers in which the pigment cells come to reside continues to be typical for the host. Changes in day length seem to be the most critical environmental factor in altering hormone levels of the pituitary glands and the gonads of birds. One result of heightened hormone levels is moulting and the appearance of a breeding plumage with characteristic color patterns. The direct effect of sex hormones upon color pattern is shown easily by injections or by castration; thus, a bright red female parakeet of the genus *Eclectus* turns to the typical male green if the ovaries are removed. In this particular bird, the female hormones normally inhibit development of the male pigmentation. In other birds, male or female hormones may act, not as inhibitors, but as stimulators that elicit developmental capabilities of the pigment cells. Many fascinating questions about the distribution of pigmented or structural color-cell groups remain almost completely unanswered.

Much speculation has surrounded the origin of birds and bats. Donald Griffin, whose article on bat radar appears in Part VI, has reasoned as follows. Birds are descendants of reptiles, animals that are most active during the day because of their lack of complete temperature regulation. Birds originated some 150 million years ago and diversified substantially before the first bats appeared. Most of them have remained predominantly diurnal, with vision being their main orienting sense. Bats arose from insectivores, the small nocturnal creatures that regulated temperature and gave rise to all other modern mammalian types. Griffin points out that even today most primitive gliding flight—a stage through which early bats must have passed—occurs at night. The reason, of course, is predation during the day by hawks or other large birds. Therefore, one might guess that the bats retained their original habit of flying at night and thus developed their amazing navigation system, based on sound and the sense of hearing. There was, after all, a tremendously large untapped source of food—the nocturnal flying insects—luring the primitive bats into the air! We have, then, a lovely illustration of how and why two types of vertebrate flying machines should arise and be so different in their sensory-navigational complex.

The last article of this section illustrates another, more general difference between birds and mammals. As discussed previously, the evolution of the mammalian brain has centered largely on the expansion of the cerebral cortex. Birds have remarkably small cerebrums but, paradoxically, can learn and perform complex tasks. The explanation is outlined in "The Brain of Birds" by Laurence Stettner and Kenneth Matyniak, who suggest that another region of the brain, the hyperstriatum, evolved in birds as the center for learning processes. Whether the patterns of neuronal nets will prove to be the same in both the hyperstriatum and the mammalian cortex is still unknown. Nevertheless, the results already obtained suggest that these two types of higher vertebrates followed surprisingly distinct paths in brain evolution. Just as similar structural arrangements can evolve in different vertebrates in response to one problem (e.g., flight), so can quite different portions of the brain evolve to perform the same task, learning. The ways of life are indeed devious and unpredictable!

1

How Fishes Swim

SIR JAMES GRAY · August 1957

The submarine and the airplane obviously owe their existence in part to the inspiration of Nature's smaller but not less attractive prototypes—the fish and the bird. It cannot be said that study of the living models has contributed much to the actual design of the machines; indeed, the boot is on the other foot, for it is rather the machines that have helped us to understand how birds fly and fish swim [see "Bird Aerodynamics," by John Storer, beginning on page 57 in this book]. But engineers may nevertheless have something to learn from intensive study of the locomotion of these animals. Some of their performances are spectacular almost beyond belief, and raise remarkably interesting questions for both the biologist and the engineer. In this article we shall consider the swimming achievements of fishes and whales.

Looking at the propulsive mechanism of a fish, or any other animal, we must note at once a basic difference in mechanical principle between animals and inanimate machines. Nearly all machines apply power by means of wheels or shafts rotating about a fixed axis, normally at a constant speed of rotation. This plan is ruled out for animals because all parts of the body must be connected by blood vessels and nerves: there is no part which can rotate freely about a fixed axis. Debarred from the use of the wheel and axle, animals must employ levers, whipping back and forth, to produce motion. The levers are the bones of its skeleton, hinged together by smooth joints, and the source of power is the muscles, which pull and push the levers by contraction.

The chain of levers comprising a vertebrate's propulsive machine appears in its simplest form in aquatic animals. Each vertebra (lever) is so hinged to its neighbors that it can turn in a single plane. In fishes the backbone whips from side to side (like a snake slithering along the ground), in whales the backbone undulates up and down. A swimming fish drives itself forward by sweeping its tail sidewise; as the tail and caudal fin are bent by the resistance of the water, the forward component of the resultant force propels the fish [see drawing on page 25]. As the tail sweeps in one direction, the front end of the body must tend to swing in the opposite direction, since it is on the opposite side of the hinge, but this movement is usually small—partly because of the high moment of inertia of the front end of the body and partly on account of the resistance which the body offers to the flow of water at right angles to its surface. Thus the head end of the fish acts as a fulcrum for the tail, operating as a flexible lever.

At the moment when the tail fin sweeps across the axis of propulsion, it is traveling rapidly but at a constant speed. During other phases of its motion the speed changes, accelerating as the tail approaches the axis and decelerating after it passes the axis. The whole cycle can be regarded as comparable to that of a variable propeller blade which periodically reverses its direction of rotation and changes pitch as it does so.

How efficient is this propulsion system? Can the oscillating tail of a fish approach in efficiency the steadily running screw propellers that drive a submarine, in terms of the ratio of speed to applied power? To attempt an answer to this question we must first know how fast a fish can swim. Here the biologist finds himself in an embarrassing position, for our information on the subject is far from precise.

As in the case of the flight of birds, the speed of fish is a good deal slower than most people think. When a stationary trout is startled, it appears to move off at an extremely high speed. But the human eye is a very unreliable instrument for judging the rate of this sudden movement. There are, in fact, very few reliable observations concerning the maximum speed of fish of known size and weight. Almost all the data we have are derived from studies of fish under laboratory conditions. These are only small fish, and in addition there is always some question whether the animals are in as good athletic condition as fish in their native environment.

With the assistance of a camera, a number of such measurements have been made by Richard Bainbridge and others in our zoological laboratory at the University of Cambridge. They indicate that ordinarily the maximum speed of a small fresh-water fish is about 10 times the length of the fish's body per second; these speeds are attained only briefly at moments of great stress, when the fish is frightened by a sudden stimulus. A trout eight inches long had a maximum speed of about four miles per hour. The larger the fish, the greater the speed: Bainbridge found, for instance, that a trout one foot long maintained a speed of 6.5 miles per hour for a considerable period [see table on page 28].

It is by no means easy to establish a fair basis of comparison between fish of different species or between different-sized members of the same species. Individual fish—like individual human beings—probably vary in their degree of athletic fitness. Only very extensive observations could distinguish between average and "record-breaking" performances. On general grounds one would expect the speed of a fish to increase

HOW FISH EXERTS FORCE against its medium is illustrated by these two sequences of photographs showing trout out of the water. In the sequence at left the fish has been placed on a board marked with squares; it wriggles but makes no forward progress. In the sequence at right the fish has been placed on a board covered with pegs; its tail pushes against the pegs and moves it across the board.

with size and with the rapidity of the tail beat. Bainbridge's data suggest that there may be a fairly simple relationship between these values: the speed of various sizes of fish belonging to the same species seems to be directly proportional to the length of the body and to the frequency of beat of the tail—so long as the frequency of beat is not too low. In all the species examined the maximum frequency at which the fish can move its tail decreases with increase of length of the body. In the trout the maximum observed frequencies were 24 per second for a 1.5-inch fish and 16 per second for an 11-inch fish—giving maximum speeds of 1.5 and 6.5 miles per hour respectively.

The data collected in Cambridge indicate a very striking feature of fish movement. Evidently the power to execute a sudden spurt is more important to a fish (for escape or for capturing prey) than the maintenance of high speed. Some of these small fish reached their maximum speed within one twentieth of a second from a "standing" start. To accomplish this they must have developed an initial thrust of about four times their own weight.

This brings us to the question of the muscle power a fish must put forth to reach or maintain a given speed. We can calculate the power from the resistance the fish has to overcome as it moves through the water at the speed in question, and the resistance in turn can be estimated by observing how rapidly the fish slows down when it stops its thrust and coasts passively through the water. It was found that for a trout weighing 84 grams the resistance at three miles per hour was approximately 24 grams—roughly one quarter of the weight of the fish. From these figures it was calculated that the fish put out a maximum of about .002 horsepower per pound of body weight in swimming at three miles per hour. This agrees with estimates of the muscle power of fishes which were arrived at in other ways. It seems reasonable to conclude that a small fish can maintain an effective thrust of about one half to one quarter of its body weight for a short time.

As we have noted, in a sudden start the fish may exert a thrust several times greater than this—some four times its body weight. The power required for its "take-off" may be as much as .014 horsepower per pound of total body weight, or .03 per pound of muscle. The fish achieves this extra force by a much more violent maneuver than in ordinary swim-

HOW MEDIUM EXERTS FORCE on the fish is indicated by the arrows on this drawing of a trout. As the tail of the fish moves from right to left the water exerts a force upon it (*two diagonal arrows*). The forward component of this force (*heavy vertical arrow*) drives the fish forward. The lateral component (*broken horizontal arrow*) tends to turn the fish to the side. This motion is opposed by the force exerted by the water on sides of the fish.

ming. It turns its head end sharply to one side and with its markedly flexed tail executes a wide and powerful sweep against the water—in short, the fish takes off by arching its back.

This sort of study of fishes' swimming performances may seem at first sight to be of little more than academic inter-est. But in fact it has considerable prac-tical importance. The problem of the salmon industry is a case in point. The seagoing salmon will lay eggs only if it can get back to its native stream. To reach its spawning bed it must journey upriver in the face of swift currents and sometimes hydroelectric dams. In de-signing fish-passes to get them past these obstacles it is important to know pre-cisely what the salmon's swimming ca-pacities are.

Contrary to popular belief, there is little evidence that salmon generally sur-mount falls by leaping over them. Most of the fish almost certainly climb the falls by swimming up a continuous sheet of water. Very likely the objective of their

SPEED OF FISHES WAS MEASURED in this apparatus at the University of Cambridge. The fish swims in a circular trough which is rotated by the motor at right center. The speed of the trough is adjusted so that the swimming fish is stationary with respect to the observer. The speed of the fish is then indicated on the speedometer at bottom. Above the speedometer is a clock. When the apparatus is started up, the water is made to move at the same speed as the trough by doors which open to let the fish pass.

leap at the bottom of the fall is to pass through the fast-running water on the surface of the torrent and reach a region of the fall where the velocity of flow can be negotiated without undue difficulty. The brave and prodigious leaps into the air at which spectators marvel may well be badly aimed attempts of the salmon to get into the "solid" water!

A salmon is capable of leaping about six feet up and 12 feet forward in the air; to accomplish this it must leave the water with a velocity of about 14 miles per hour. The swimming speed it can maintain for any appreciable time is probably no more than about eight miles per hour. Accurate measurements of the swimming behavior of salmon in the neighborhood of falls are badly needed—and should be possible to obtain with electronic equipment.

At this point it may be useful to summarize the three main conclusions that have been reached from our study of the small fish. Firstly, a typical fish can exert a very powerful initial thrust when starting from rest, producing an acceleration about four times greater than gravity. Secondly, at times of stress it can exert for a limited period a sustained propulsive thrust equal to about one quarter or one half the weight of its body. Thirdly, the resistance exerted by the water against the surface of the moving fish (*i.e.*, the drag) appears to be of the same order as that exerted upon a flat, rigid plate of similar area and speed. Fourthly, the maximum effective power of a fish's muscles is equivalent to about .002 horsepower per pound of body weight.

Such is the picture drawn from studies of small fishes in tanks. It has its points of interest, and its possible applications to the design of fish-passes, but it poses no particularly intriguing or baffling hydrodynamic problems. Recently, however, the whole matter of the swimming performance of fishes was given a fresh slant by a discovery which led to some very puzzling questions indeed. D. R. Gero, a U. S. aircraft engineer, announced some startling figures for the speed of the barracuda. He found that a four-foot, 20-pound barracuda was capable of a maximum speed of 27 miles per hour! This figure not only established the barracuda's claim to be the world's fastest swimmer but also prompted a new look into the horsepower of aquatic animals.

A more convenient subject for such an examination is the dolphin, whose attributes are somewhat better known

than those of the barracuda. (The only essential difference between the propulsive machinery of a fish and that of a dolphin, small relative of the whale, is that the dolphin's tail flaps up and down instead of from side to side.) The dolphin is, of course, a proverbially fast swimmer. More than 20 years ago a dolphin swimming close to the side of a ship was timed at better than 22 miles per hour, and this speed has been confirmed in more recent observations. Now assuming that the drag of the animal's body in the water is comparable to that of a flat plate of comparable area and speed, a six-foot dolphin traveling at 22 miles per hour would require 2.6 horsepower, and its work output would be equivalent to a man—of the same weight as the dolphin—climbing 28,600 feet in one hour! This conclusion is so clearly fantastic that we are forced to look for some error in our assumptions.

Bearing in mind the limitations of animal muscle, it is difficult to endow the dolphin with much more than three tenths of one horsepower of effective output. If this figure is correct, there must be something wrong with the assumption about the drag of the animal's surface in the water: it cannot be more than about one tenth of the assumed value. Yet the resistance could have this low value only if the flow of water were laminar (smooth) over practically the whole of the animal's surface—which an aerodynamic or hydrodynamic engineer must consider altogether unlikely.

The situation is further complicated when we consider the dolphin's larger relatives. The blue whale, largest of all the whales, may weigh some 100 tons. If we suppose that the muscles of a whale are similar to those of a dolphin, a 100-ton whale would develop 448 horsepower. This increase in power over the dolphin is far greater than the increase in surface area (*i.e.*, drag). We should therefore expect the whale to be much faster than the dolphin, yet its top speed appears to be no more than that of the dolphin—about 22 miles per hour. There is another reason to doubt that the whale can put forth anything like 448 horsepower. Physiologists estimate that an exertion beyond about 60 or 70 horsepower would put an intolerable strain on the whale's heart. Now 60 horsepower would not suffice to drive a whale through the water at 20 miles per hour if the flow over its body were turbulent, but it would be sufficient if the flow were laminar.

Thus we reach an impasse. Biologists are extremely unwilling to believe that

LAMINAR AND TURBULENT FLOW are depicted in this diagram of a streamlined body passing through the water. The smooth lines passing around the body indicate laminar flow; the wavy lines, turbulent flow.

SPECIES	LENGTH (FEET)	MAXIMUM OBSERVED SPEED (FEET PER SECOND)	(MILES PER HOUR)	RATIO OF MAXIMUM SPEED TO LENGTH
TROUT	.656 .957	5.552 10.427	3.8 6.5	8.5 11
DACE	.301 .594 .656	5.229 5.552 8.812	3.6 3.8 5.5	17.8 9 13.5
PIKE	.529 .656	6.850 4.896	4.7 3.3	13 7.5
GOLDFISH	.229 .427	2.301 5.552	1.5 3.8	10.3 13
RUDD	.730	4.240	2.9	6
BARRACUDA	3.937	39.125	27.3	10
DOLPHIN	6.529	32.604	22.4	5
WHALE	90	33	20	33

SPEED OF FISHES IS LISTED in this table. The speed of the first five fishes from the top was measured in the laboratory; that of the barracuda, dolphin and whale in nature. The barracuda is the fastest known swimmer. Whale in the table is the blue whale.

fishes or whales can exert enough power to drive themselves through the water at the recorded speeds against the resistance that would be produced by turbulent flow over their bodies, while engineers are probably equally loath to believe that laminar flow can be maintained over a huge body, even a streamlined body, traveling through the water at 20 miles per hour.

Lacking direct data on these questions, we can only speculate on possible explanations which might resolve the contradiction. One point that seems well worth re-examining is our assumption about the hydrodynamic form of the swimming animal. We assumed that the resistance which the animal (say a dolphin) has to overcome is the same as

that of a rigid body of the same size and shape moving forward under a steady propulsive force. But the fact of the matter is that the swimming dolphin is not a rigid body: its tail and flukes are continually moving and bending during each propulsive stroke. It seems reasonable to assume, therefore, that the flow of water over the hind end of the dolphin is not the same as it would be over a rigid structure. In the case of a rigid model towed through the water, much of the resistance is due to slowing down of the water as it flows past the rear end of the model. But the oscillating movement of a swimming animal's tail accelerates water in contact with the tail; this may well reduce or prevent turbulence of flow. There is also another possibility which might be worth investiga-

tion. When a rigid body starts from rest, it takes a little time for turbulence to develop. It is conceivable that in the case of a swimming animal the turbulence never materializes, because the flukes reverse their direction of motion before it has an opportunity to do so.

It would be foolish to urge these speculative suggestions as serious contributions to the problem: they can only be justified insofar as they stimulate engineers to examine the hydrodynamic properties of oscillating bodies. Few, if any, biologists have either the knowledge or the facilities for handling such problems. The questions need to be studied by biologists and engineers working together. Such a cooperative effort could not fail to produce facts of great intrinsic, and possibly of great applied, interest.

DOLPHINS (called porpoises by seamen) were photographed by Jan Hahn as they swam beside the bow of the *Atlantis*, research vessel of the Woods Hole Oceanographic Institution, in the Gulf of Mexico. The speed of these dolphins was about 11 miles per hour.

2

How Animals Run

MILTON HILDEBRAND · May 1960

A man (but not necessarily you or I!) can run 220 yards at the rate of 22.3 miles per hour, and a mile at 15.1 miles per hour. The cheetah, however, can sprint at an estimated 70 miles per hour. And the horse has been known to maintain a speed of 15 miles per hour not just for one mile but for 35 miles.

Other animals are capable of spectacular demonstrations of speed and endurance. Jack rabbits have been clocked at 40 miles per hour. The Mongolian ass is reported to have run 16 miles at the impressive rate of 30 miles per hour. Antelopes apparently enjoy running beside a moving vehicle; they have been reliably timed at 60 miles per hour. The camel has been known to travel 115 miles in 12 hours. Nearly all carnivorous mammals are good runners: the whippet can run 34 miles per hour; the coyote, 43 miles per hour; the red fox, 45 miles per hour. One red fox, running before hounds, covered 150 miles in a day and a half. A fox terrier rewarded with candy turned a treadmill at the rate of 5,000 feet per hour for 17 hours.

I have been attracted by such performances as these to undertake an investigation of how the living running-machine works. The subject has not been thoroughly explored. One study was undertaken by the American photographer Eadweard Muybridge in 1872. Working before the motion-picture camera was invented, Muybridge set up a battery of still cameras to make photographs in rapid sequence. His pictures are still standard references. A. Brazier Howell's work on speed in mammals and Sir James Gray's studies on posture and movement are well known to zoologists. Many investigators have added to our knowledge of the anatomy of running vertebrates, but the analysis of function has for the most part been limited to deductions

from skeletons and muscles. The movements of the running animal are so fast and so complex that they cannot be analyzed by the unaided eye.

In my study I have related comparative anatomy to the analysis of motion pictures of animals in action. The method is simple: Successive frames of the motion picture are projected onto tracing paper, where the movements of the parts of the body with respect to one another and to the ground can be analyzed. The main problem is to get pictures from the side of animals running at top speed over open ground. With an electric camera that exposes 200 frames per second I have succeeded in photographing the movements of a cheetah that had been trained by John Hamlet of Ocala, Fla., to chase a paper bag in an enclosure 65 yards long. However, the animal never demonstrated its top speed, but merely loped along at about 35 miles per hour. I have used the same

STRIDE OF A CANTERING HORSE is shown in these photographs from Eadweard Muybridge's *The Horse in Motion*, published in 1878. The sequence runs right to left across the

camera to make pictures of horses running on race tracks, and I am presently collecting motion-picture sequences of other running animals from commercial and private sources.

All cursorial animals (those that can run far, fast and easily) have evolved from good walkers, and in doing so have gained important selective advantages. They are able to forage over wide areas. A pack of African hunting dogs, for example, can range over 1,500 square miles; the American mountain lion works a circuit some 100 miles long; individual arctic foxes have on occasion wandered 800 miles. Cursorial animals can seek new sources of food and water when their usual supplies fail. The camel moves from oasis to oasis, and in years of drought the big-game animals of Africa travel impressive distances. The mobility of cursorial animals enables them to overcome seasonal variations in climate or in food supply. Some herds of caribou migrate 1,600 miles each year. According to their habit, the predators among the cursorial animals exploit superior speed, relay tactics, relentless endurance or surprise to overtake their prey. The prey species are commonly as swift as their pursuers, but sometimes they have superior endurance or agility.

Speed and endurance are the capacities that characterize all cursorial vertebrates. But one could not make a definitive list of the cursorial species without deciding quite arbitrarily how fast is fast and how far is far. Even then the list would be incomplete, because there are reliable data on speed for only a few animals; in most cases authors quote authors who cite the guesses of laymen. Many cursors are extinct. On the basis of fossils, however, we can surmise that many dinosaurs were excellent runners; that some extinct rhinoceroses, having had long and slender legs, were very fast; and that certain extinct South American grazing animals, having evolved a horselike form, probably had horselike speed.

In order to run, an animal must overcome the inertia of its body and set it into motion; it must overcome the inertia of its legs with every reversal in the direction of their travel; it must compensate for forces of deceleration, including the action of the ground against its descending feet. A full cycle of motion is called a stride. Speed is the product of length of stride times rate of stride. The giraffe achieves a moderate speed with a long stride and a slow rate of stride; the wart hog matches this speed with a short stride and a rapid rate. High speed requires that long strides be taken at a rapid rate, and endurance requires that speed be sustained with economy of effort.

Although longer legs take longer strides, speed is not increased simply by the enlargement of the animal. A larger animal is likely to have a lower rate of stride. Natural selection produced fast runners by making their legs long in relation to other parts of the body. In cursorial animals the effective length of the leg—the part that contributes to length of stride—is especially enhanced. The segments of the leg that are away from the body (the foot, shank and forearm) are elongated with respect to the segments close to the body (the thigh and upper arm). In this evolutionary lengthening process the bones equivalent to the human palm and instep have become the most elongated.

Man's foot does not contribute to the length of his leg, except when he rises on his toes. The bear, the opossum, the raccoon and most other vertebrates that walk but seldom run have similar plantigrade ("sole-walking") feet. Carnivo-

top row and continues across the bottom row. With these and similar photographs Muybridge settled the controversy of whether or not a horse "even at the height of his speed [has] all four of his feet . . . simultaneously free from contact with the ground."

rous mammals, birds, running dinosaurs and some extinct hoofed mammals, on the other hand, stand on what corresponds to the ball of the human foot; these animals have digitigrade ("finger-walking") feet. Other hoofed mammals owe an even further increase in the effective length of their legs to their unguligrade ("hoof-walking") posture, resembling that of a ballet dancer standing on the tips of her toes. Where foot posture and limb proportions have been modified for the cursorial habit, the increased length and slenderness of the leg is striking [see illustration on page 36].

The effective length of the front limb of many runners is also increased by the modification of the structure and function of the shoulder. The shoulder joint of amphibians, reptiles and birds is virtually immobilized by the collarbone, which runs from the breast bone to each shoulder blade, and by a second bone,

the coracoid bone. Because mammals do not have a coracoid bone their shoulder blade has some freedom of movement. In the carnivores this freedom is increased by the reduction of the collarbone to a vestige; in the ungulates the collarbone is eliminated. In both carnivores and ungulates the shoulder blade is oriented so that it lies against the side of a narrow but deep chest rather than against the back of a broad but shallow chest, as it does in man. Thus mounted, the shoulder blade pivots from a point about midway in its length, and the shoulder joint at its lower end is free to move forward and backward with the swing of the leg. The exact motion is exceedingly difficult to ascertain in a running animal, but I have found that it adds about 4.5 inches to the stride of the walking cheetah.

The supple spine of the cat and the dog increases the length of stride of these animals still further. The body of such an animal is several inches longer

when the back is extended than when it is flexed. By extending and flexing its back as its legs swing back and forth the animal adds the increase in its body length to its stride. Timing is important in this maneuver. If the animal were to extend its back while its body was in mid-air, its hindquarters would move backward as its forequarters moved forward, with no net addition to the forward motion of the center of mass of its body. In actuality the running animal extends its back only when its hind feet are pushing against the ground. The cheetah executes this maneuver so adeptly that it could run about six miles per hour without any legs.

With the extra rotation of its hip and shoulder girdles and the measuring-worm action of its back, the legs of the running cursor swing through longer arcs, reaching out farther forward and backward and striking and leaving the ground at a more acute angle than they would if the back were rigid. This clear-

STRIDES OF THE CHEETAH AND THE HORSE in full gallop are contrasted in these illustrations. The sequence and duration of their footfalls, indicated by the horizontal lines under each animal, relate to the time-scale at bottom, which is calibrated in 10ths of a second. The cheetah has two unsupported periods, which account for about half its stride; the horse has one unsupported period, ly increases stride length, but it also aggravates a problem. The body of the animal tends to rise when its shoulders and hips pass over its feet, and tends to fall when its feet extend to the front or rear. Carnivores offset this bobbing motion by flexing their ankles and wrists, thus shortening their legs. Ungulates do the same by sharply flexing the fetlock joint at the moment that the body passes over the vertical leg. The cheetah, a long-striding back-flexer, supplements its wrist-flexing by slipping its shoulder blade up its ribs about an inch, and thus achieves a smooth forward motion.

Since running is in actuality a series of jumps, the length of the jump must be reckoned as another important increment in the length of the stride. Hoofed runners have one major unsupported period, or jump, in each stride: when the legs are gathered beneath the body. The galloping carnivore has two major unsupported periods: when the back is flexed, and again when it is extended. In the horse all of these anatomical and functional adaptations combine to produce a 23-foot stride. The cheetah, although smaller, has a stride of the same length.

Fast runners must take their long strides rapidly. The race horse completes about 2.5 strides per second and the cheetah at least 3.5. It is plain that the higher the rate of stride, the faster the runner must contract its muscles. One might infer that cursorial animals as a group would have evolved the ability to contract their muscles faster than other animals. Within limits that is true, but there is a general principle limiting the rate at which a muscle can contract. Assuming a constant load on the muscle fibers, the rate of contraction varies inversely with any of the muscle's linear dimensions; the larger muscle therefore contracts more slowly. That is why an animal with a larger body has a slower rate of stride and so loses the advantage of its longer length of stride.

The familiar mechanical principle of gear ratio underlies the fast runner's more effective use of its trim musculature. In the linkage of muscle and bone the gear ratio is equal to the distance between the pivot of the motion (the shoulder joint, for example) and the point at which the motion is applied (the foot) divided by the perpendicular distance between the pivot and the point at which the muscle is attached to the bone. Cursorial animals not only have longer legs; their actuating muscles are also attached to the bone closer to the pivot of motion. Their high-gear muscles, in other words, have short lever-arms, and this increases the gear ratio still further. In comparison, the anatomy of walking animals gives them considerably lower gear-ratios; digging and swimming animals have still lower gear ratios.

But while high gears enable an automobile to reach higher speed, they do

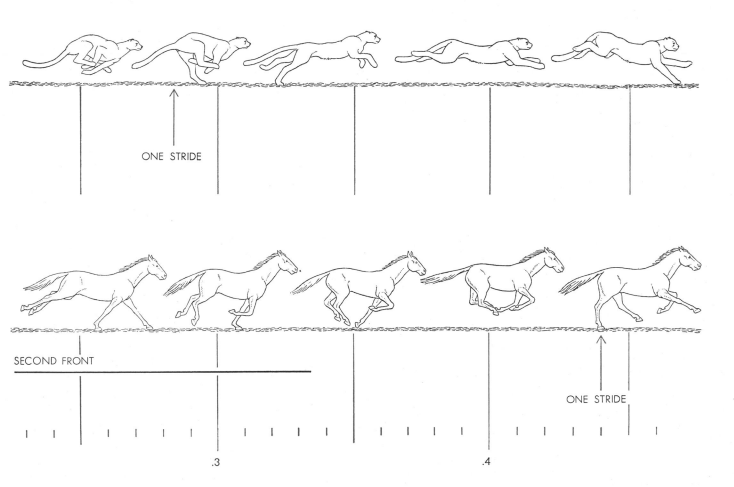

which accounts for about a quarter of its stride. Although both the cheetah and the horse cover about 23 feet per stride, the cheetah attains speeds on the order of 70 miles per hour, to the horse's 43, because it takes about 3.5 strides to the horse's 2.5. The size of the horse has been reduced disproportionately in these drawings for the sake of uniformity in the stride-lines and time-scale.

SWIVELING SHOULDER BLADES of the horse and the cheetah add several inches to their stride length. The faster cheetah gains a further advantage from the flexibility of the spine, which in addi-tion to adding the length of its extension to the animal's stride, adds the speed of its extension to the velocity of its travel. Horse's relatively longer leg partially compensates for its rigid spine.

SPRINGING LIGAMENTS in the legs of horses, shown here, and other hoofed runners reduce the need for heavy muscles. Impact of the foot against the ground (*left*) bends the fetlock joint (*mid-dle*) and stretches an elastic ligament (*shown in color*) that snaps back when the foot leaves the ground (*right*). The springing action at once straightens the foot and gives the leg an upward impetus.

so at the expense of power. The cursorial animal pays a similar price, but the exchange is a good one for several reasons. Running animals do not need great power: air does not offer much resistance even when they are moving at top speed. Moreover, as the English investigators J. M. Smith and R. J. G. Savage have noted, the animal retains some relatively low-gear muscles. Probably the runner uses its low-gear muscles for slow motions, and then shifts to its high-gear muscles to increase speed.

Since the speed at which a muscle can contract is limited, the velocity of the action it controls must be correspondingly limited, even though the muscle speed is amplified by an optimum gear-ratio. A larger muscle, or additional muscles, applied to action around the same joint can produce increased power but not greater speed. Several men together can lift a greater weight than one can lift alone, but several equally skilled sprinters cannot run faster together than one of them alone. The speed of a leg can be increased, however, if different muscles simultaneously move different joints of the leg in the same direction. The total motion they produce, which is represented by the motion of the foot, will then be greater than the motion produced by any one muscle working alone. Just as the total speed of a man walking up an escalator is the sum of his own speed plus that of the escalator, so the independent velocities of each segment of the leg combine additively to produce a higher total velocity.

The trick is to move as many joints as possible in the same direction at the same time. The evolution of the cursorial body has produced just this effect. By abandoning the flat-footed plantigrade posture in favor of a digitigrade or unguligrade one, the cursorial leg acquired an extra limb-joint. In effect it gained still another through the altered functioning of the shoulder blade. The flexible back of the cursorial carnivore adds yet another motion to the compound motion of its legs; the back flexes in such a way that the chest and pelvis are always rotating in the direction of the swinging limbs.

The supple spine of the carnivore contributes to stride rate by speeding up the motion of its body as well as of its legs. The spine is flexed when the runner's first hind foot strikes the ground, and by the time its second hind foot leaves the ground the animal has extended its spine and thus lengthened its body. In the brief interval when its hind

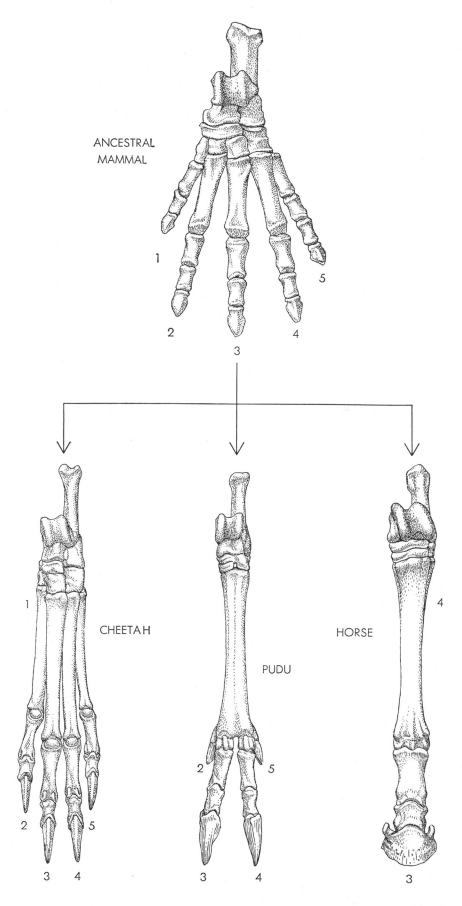

MODERN CURSORIAL FOOT EVOLVED from the broad, five-digited foot of an ancestral mammal (*top*). Lateral digits were lost and metatarsal bones, the longest in the foot, were further elongated. Resultant foot is lighter and longer. Pudu is a deer of the Andes.

feet are planted, the forequarters, riding on the extending spine, move farther and faster than the hindquarters. Similarly when the front feet are on the ground, the hindquarters move faster than the forequarters. So although the speed that the driving legs can impart to the forequarters or hindquarters is limited by their rate of oscillation, the body as a whole is able to exceed that limit. In a sense the animal moves faster than it runs. For the cheetah the advantage amounts to about two miles per hour—enough to add the margin of success in a close chase.

In addition to the obvious tasks of propelling the animal's body and supporting its weight, the locomotor mus-cles must raise the body to compensate for the falling that occurs during the un-supported phases of the stride. The load they must raise is proportional to the mass of the body, which is in turn pro-portional to the cube of any of its linear dimensions. A twofold increase in body length thus increases weight eightfold. The force that a muscle can exert, on the other hand, increases only as the square of its cross section. Thus against an eightfold increase of load, bigger mus-cles can bring only a fourfold increase of force. As body size increases, the capac-ity of the muscles to put the body in for-ward motion and to cause its legs to os-cillate cannot quite keep up with the demands placed upon them. These fac-tors in the nature of muscle explain why the largest animals can neither gallop nor jump, why small runners such as rabbits and foxes can travel as fast as race horses without having marked struc-tural adaptations for speed and why the larger cursorial animals must be highly adapted in order to run at all.

If the bigger runners are to have en-durance as well as speed, they must have not only those adaptations that in-crease the length and rate of their stride, but also adaptations that reduce the load on their locomotor structures and econo-mize the effort of motion. In satisfying this requirement natural selection pro-duced a number of large and fast runners that are able to travel for long distances at somewhat less than their maximum speed. In these animals the mass of the limbs is minimized. The muscles that in other animals draw the limbs toward or away from the midline of the body (the "hand-clapping" muscles in man) are smaller or adapted to moving the legs in the direction of travel, and the mus-cles that manipulate the digits or rotate the forearm have disappeared. The ulna in the forearm and the fibula in the shank —bones involved in these former mo-tions—are reduced in size. The ulna is re-tained at the point where it completes the elbow joint, but elsewhere becomes a sliver fused to its neighbor; the fibula is sometimes represented only by a nub-bin of bone at the ankle.

The shape of the cursorial limb em-bodies another load-reducing principle. Since the kinetic energy that must be alternately developed and overcome in oscillating the limb is equal to half the mass times the square of its velocity, the load on muscles causing such motions can be reduced not only by reducing the mass of the faster-moving parts of the limb but also by reducing the velocity of the more massive parts. Accordingly the fleshy parts of the limb are those close to the body, where they do not move so far, and hence not so fast, as the more distant segments. The lower segments, having lost the muscles and bones involved in rotation and in digit manipulation, are relatively light.

The rigor of design imposed by natu-ral selection is especially evident in the feet of cursorial animals. The feet of other animals tend to be broad and pliable; the bones corresponding to those of the human palm and instep are rounded in cross section and well sepa-rated. In the foot of the cursorial carni-vore, on the other hand, these bones are

ADAPTATION OF THE LEG FOR SPEED is illustrated by the hind-leg bone of the slow badger (*left*), moderately fast dog (*middle*) and highly adapted deer (*right*). The length-ened metatarsus of the latter two has yielded a longer foot and an altered ankle posture that is better suited to running. The thigh bones of all three animals have been drawn to the same scale to show that the leg segments farthest from the body have elongated the most.

crowded into a compact unit, each bone having a somewhat square cross section. In the ungulates the ratio of strength to weight has been improved still further by reduction of the number of bones in the foot. The ungulates have tended to lose their lateral toes; sometimes the basal elements of the other toes are fused into a single bone. This process gave rise to the cannon bone: the shank of the hoofed mammals [see illustration on page 35]. In compensation for the bracing lost as the bones and muscles of their lower limbs were reduced or eliminated, these animals evolved joints that are modified to function as hinges and allow motion only in the line of travel.

The burden on the muscles of hoofed animals is relieved by an especially elegant mechanism built into the foot. When the hoof of the running animal strikes the ground, the impact bends the fetlock joint and stretches certain long ligaments called the suspensory or springing ligaments [see bottom illustration on page 34]. Because the ligaments are elastic, they snap back as the foot leaves the ground, thereby straightening the joint and giving the leg an upward push. Charles L. Camp of the University of California has found that these built-in pogo-sticks evolved from foot muscles at the time that the animals forsook river valleys for the open plains. The exchange was advantageous, for by means of this and the other adaptations, nature has reconciled the limitations of muscle mechanics with the exacting requirements of speed.

POWER AND SPEED are alternatively achieved in the badger (left) and the cheetah (middle) by placement of the teres major muscle. In the cheetah the small distance (b) between the muscle insertion and the joint it moves yields a higher rate of oscillation than in the badger, in which the distance (a) is greater. The higher oscillation rate, coupled with a longer leg (l), yields a faster stride. In the vicuña (right) the gluteus muscle (c) develops about five times the velocity but only a fifth the force of the larger semimembranosus muscle (d). The animal may use the latter to overcome inertia; the former, for high speed. Legs are not in same scale.

3

The Antiquity
of Human Walking

JOHN NAPIER · April 1967

Human walking is a unique activity during which the body, step by step, teeters on the edge of catastrophe. The fact that man has used this form of locomotion for more than a million years has only recently been demonstrated by fossil evidence. The antiquity of this human trait is particularly noteworthy because walking with a striding gait is probably the most significant of the many evolved capacities that separate men from more primitive hominids. The fossil evidence—the terminal bone of a right big toe discovered in 1961 in Olduvai Gorge in Tanzania—sets up a new signpost that not only clarifies the course of human evolution but also helps to guide those who speculate on the forces that converted predominantly quadrupedal animals into habitual bipeds.

Man's bipedal mode of walking seems potentially catastrophic because only the rhythmic forward movement of first one leg and then the other keeps him from falling flat on his face. Consider the sequence of events whenever a man sets out in pursuit of his center of gravity. A stride begins when the muscles of the calf relax and the walker's body sways forward (gravity supplying the energy needed to overcome the body's inertia). The sway places the center of body weight in front of the supporting pedestal normally formed by the two feet. As a result one or the other of the walker's legs must swing forward so that when his foot makes contact with the ground, the area of the supporting pedestal has been widened and the center of body weight once again rests safely within it. The pelvis plays an important role in this action: its degree of rotation determines the distance the swinging leg can move forward, and its muscles help to keep the body balanced while the leg is swinging.

At this point the "stance" leg—the leg still to the rear of the body's center of gravity—provides the propulsive force that drives the body forward. The walker applies this force by using muscular energy, pushing against the ground first with the ball of his foot and then with his big toe. The action constitutes the "push-off," which terminates the stance phase of the walking cycle. Once the stance foot leaves the ground, the walker's leg enters the starting, or "swing," phase of the cycle. As the leg swings forward it is able to clear the ground because it is bent at the hip, knee and ankle. This high-stepping action substantially reduces the leg's moment of inertia. Before making contact with the ground and ending the swing phase the leg straightens at the knee but remains bent at the ankle. As a result it is the

heel that strikes the ground first. The "heel strike" concludes the swing phase; as the body continues to move forward the leg once again enters the stance phase, during which the point of contact between foot and ground moves progressively nearer the toes. At the extreme end of the stance phase, as before, all the walker's propulsive thrust is delivered by the robust terminal bone of his big toe.

A complete walking cycle is considered to extend from the heel strike of one leg to the next heel strike of the same leg; it consists of the stance phase followed by the swing phase. The relative duration of the two phases depends on the cadence or speed of the walk. During normal walking the stance phase constitutes about 60 percent of the cycle and the swing phase 40 percent. Although

WALKING MAN, photographed by Eadweard Muybridge in 1884 during his studies of **human and animal motion, exhibits the characteristic striding gait of the modern human.**

the action of only one leg has been described in this account, the opposite leg obviously moves in a reciprocal fashion; when one leg is moving in the swing phase, the other leg is in its stance phase and keeps the body poised. Actually during normal walking the two phases overlap, so that both feet are on the ground at the same time for about 25 percent of the cycle. As walking speed increases, this period of double leg-support shortens.

Anyone who has watched other people walking and reflected a little on the process has noticed that the human stride demands both an up-and-down and a side-to-side displacement of the body. When two people walk side by side but out of step, the alternate bobbing of their heads makes it evident that the bodies undergo a vertical displacement with each stride. When two people walk in step but with opposite feet leading, they will sway first toward each other and then away in an equally graphic demonstration of the lateral displacement at each stride. When both displacements are plotted sequentially, a pair of low-amplitude sinusoidal curves appear, one in the vertical plane and the other in the horizontal [see illustrations on next page]. General observations of this kind were reduced to precise measurements during World War II when a group at the University of California at Berkeley led by H. D. Eberhart conducted a fundamental investigation of human walking in connection with requirements for the design of artificial legs. Eberhart and his colleagues found that a number of

functional determinants interacted to move the human body's center of gravity through space with a minimum expenditure of energy. In all they isolated six major elements related to hip, knee and foot movement that, working together, reduced both the amplitude of the two sine curves and the abruptness with which vertical and lateral changes in direction took place. If any one of these six elements was disturbed, an irregularity was injected into the normally smooth, undulating flow of walking, thereby producing a limp. What is more important, the irregularity brought about a measurable increase in the body's energy output during each step.

The Evidence of the Bones

What I have described in general and Eberhart's group studied in detail is the form of walking known as striding. It is characterized by the heel strike at the start of the stance phase and the push-off at its conclusion. Not all human walking is striding; when a man moves about slowly or walks on a slippery surface, he may take short steps in which both push-off and heel strike are absent. The foot is simply lifted from the ground at the end of the stance phase and set down flat at the end of the swing phase. The stride, however, is the essence of human bipedalism and the criterion by which the evolutionary status of a hominid walker must be judged. This being the case, it is illuminating to consider how the act of striding leaves its distinctive marks on the bones of the strider.

To take the pelvis first, there is a well-known clinical manifestation called Trendelenburg's sign that is regarded as evidence of hip disease in children. When a normal child stands on one leg, two muscles connecting that leg and the pelvis—the gluteus medius and the gluteus minimus—contract; this contraction, pulling on the pelvis, tilts it and holds it poised over the stance leg. When the hip is diseased, this mechanism fails to operate and the child shows a positive Trendelenburg's sign: the body tends to fall toward the unsupported side.

The same mechanism operates in walking, although not to the same degree. During the stance phase of the walking cycle, the same two gluteal muscles on the stance side brace the pelvis by cantilever action. Although actual tilting toward the stance side does not occur in normal walking, the action of the muscles in stabilizing the walker's hip is an essential component of the striding gait. Without this action the stride would become a slow, ungainly shuffle.

At the same time that the pelvis is stabilized in relation to the stance leg it also rotates to the unsupported side. This rotation, although small, has the effect of increasing the length of the stride. A familiar feature of the way women walk arises from this bit of anatomical mechanics. The difference in the proportions of the male and the female pelvis has the effect of slightly diminishing the range through which the female hip can move forward and back. Thus for a given length of stride women are obliged to rotate the pelvis through a greater

The free foot strikes the ground heel first and the body's weight is gradually transferred from heel to ball of foot as the opposite leg lifts and swings forward. Finally the heel of the stance foot rises and the leg's last contact with the ground is made with the big toe.

WALKING CYCLE extends from the heel strike of one leg to the next heel strike by the same leg. In the photograph, made by Gjon Mili in the course of a study aimed at improvement of artificial legs that he conducted for the U.S. Army, multiple exposures trace the progress of the right leg in the course of two strides. The ribbons of light allow analysis of the movement (*see illustration below*).

SINE CURVE described by the hip of a walking man was recorded on film by means of the experimental system illustrated above. An interrupter blade, passing in front of the camera lens at constant speed, broke the light from lamps attached to the walker into the three rows of dots. The speed of hip (*a*), knee (*b*) or ankle (*c*) during the stride is determined by measuring between the dots.

angle than men do. This secondary sexual characteristic has not lacked exploitation; at least in our culture female pelvic rotation has considerable erotogenic significance. What is more to the point in terms of human evolution is that both the rotation and the balancing of the pelvis leave unmistakable signs on the pelvic bone and on the femur: the leg bone that is joined to it. It is by a study of such signs that the walking capability of a fossil hominid can be judged.

Similar considerations apply to the foot. One way the role of the foot in walking can be studied is to record the vertical forces acting on each part of the foot while it is in contact with the ground during the stance phase of the walking cycle. Many devices have been built for this purpose; one of them is the plastic pedograph. When the subject walks across the surface of the pedograph, a motion-picture camera simultaneously records the exact position of the foot in profile and the pattern of pressures on the surface. Pedograph analyses show that the initial contact between the striding leg and the ground is the heel strike. Because the foot is normally turned out slightly at the end of the swing phase of the walking cycle, the outer side of the back of the heel takes the brunt of the initial contact [*see illustration on opposite page*]. The outer side of the foot contin-

ues to support most of the pressure of the stance until a point about three-fifths of the way along the sole is reached. The weight of the body is then transferred to the ball of the foot and then to the big toe. In the penultimate stage of push-off the brunt of the pressure is under the toes, particularly the big toe. Finally, at the end of the stance phase, only the big toe is involved; it progressively loses contact with the ground and the final push-off is applied through its broad terminal bone.

The use of pedographs and similar apparatus provides precise evidence about the function of the foot in walking, but every physician knows that much the same information is recorded on the soles of everyone's shoes. Assuming that the shoes fit, their pattern of wear is a true record of the individual's habitual gait. The wear pattern will reveal a limp that one man is trying to hide, or unmask one that another man is trying to feign, perhaps to provide evidence for an insurance claim. In any case, just as the form of the pelvis and the femur can disclose the presence or absence of a striding gait, so can the form of the foot bones, particularly the form and proportions of the big-toe bones.

The Origins of Primate Bipedalism

Almost all primates can stand on their hind limbs, and many occasionally walk in this way. But our primate relatives are all, in a manner of speaking, amateurs; only man has taken up the business of bipedalism intensively. This raises two major questions. First, how did the basic postural adaptations that permit walking—occasional or habitual—arise among the primates? Second, what advantages did habitual bipedalism bestow on early man?

With regard to the first question, I have been concerned for some time with the anatomical proportions of all primates, not only man and the apes but also the monkeys and lower primate forms. Such consideration makes it possible to place the primates in natural groups according to their mode of locomotion. Not long ago I suggested a new group, and it is the only one that will concern us here. The group comprises primates with very long hind limbs and very short forelimbs. At about the same time my colleague Alan C. Walker, now at Makerere University College in Uganda, had begun a special study of the locomotion of living and fossil lemurs. Lemurs are among the most primitive offshoots of the basic primate stock. Early in Walker's studies he was struck by the frequency with which a posture best described as "vertical clinging" appeared in the day-to-day behavior of living lemurs. All the animals whose propensity for vertical clinging had been observed by Walker showed the same proportions—that is, long hind limbs and short forelimbs—I had proposed as forming a distinct locomotor group.

When Walker and I compared notes, we decided to define a hitherto unrecognized locomotor category among the primates that we named "vertical clinging and leaping," a term that includes both the animal's typical resting posture and the essential leaping component

in its locomotion. Since proposing this category a most interesting and important extension of the hypothesis has become apparent to us. Some of the earliest primate fossils known, preserved in sediments laid down during Eocene times and therefore as much as 50 million years old, are represented not only by skulls and jaws but also by a few limb bones. In their proportions and details most of these limb bones show the same characteristics that are displayed by the living members of our vertical-clinging-and-leaping group today. Not long ago Elwyn L. Simons of Yale University presented a reconstruction of the lemur-

like North American Eocene primate *Smilodectes* walking along a tree branch in a quadrupedal position [see "The Early Relatives of Man," by Elwyn L. Simons; SCIENTIFIC AMERICAN Offprint 622]. Walker and I would prefer to see *Smilodectes* portrayed in the vertical clinging posture its anatomy unequivocally indicates. The fossil evidence, as far as it goes, suggests to us that vertical clinging and leaping was a major primate locomotor adaptation that took place some 50 million years ago. It may even have been the initial dynamic adaptation to tree life from which the subsequent locomotor patterns of all the living pri-

A   B

DISTRIBUTION OF WEIGHT in the human foot alters radically as action takes the place of rest. When motionless (*A*), the foot divides its static load (half of the body's total weight) between its heel and its ball along the axis *a–b*. The load on the ball of the foot is further divided equally on each side of the axis *c–d*. When striding (*B*), the load (all of the body's weight during part of each stride) is distributed dynamically from the first point of contact (*1, heel strike*) in a smooth flow via the first and fifth metatarsal bones (*2, 3*) that ends with a propulsive thrust (*4, push-off*) delivered by the terminal bone of the big toe.

mates, including man, have stemmed. Walker and I are not alone in this view. In 1962 W. L. Straus, Jr., of Johns Hopkins University declared: "It can safely be assumed that primates early developed the mechanisms permitting maintenance of the trunk in the upright position.... Indeed, this tendency toward truncal erectness can be regarded as an essentially basic primate character." The central adaptations for erectness of the body, which have been retained in the majority of living primates, seem to have provided the necessary anatomical basis for the occasional bipedal behavior exhibited by today's monkeys and apes.

What we are concerned with here is the transition from a distant, hypothetical vertical-clinging ancestor to modern, bipedal man. The transition was almost

QUADRUPEDAL POSTURE needs two sets of muscles to act as the principal extensors of the hip. These are the gluteal group (the gluteus medius and minimus in particular), which connects the pelvis to the upper part of the femur, and the hamstring group. which connects the femur and the lower leg bones. Of these only the biceps femoris is shown in the gorilla musculature at right. The skeletal regions to which these muscles attach are shown in color at left. In most primates the gluteus maximus is quite small.

certainly marked by an intermediate quadrupedal stage. Possibly such Miocene fossil forms as *Proconsul,* a chimpanzee-like early primate from East Africa, represent such a stage. The structural adaptations necessary to convert a quadrupedal ape into a bipedal hom-

inid are centered on the pelvis, the femur, the foot and the musculature associated with these bones. Among the nonhuman primates living today the pelvis and femur are adapted for four-footed walking; the functional relations between hipbones and thigh muscles are

such that, when the animal attempts to assume a bipedal stance, the hip joint is subjected to a stress and the hip must be bent. To compensate for the resulting forward shift of the center of gravity, the knees must also be bent. In order to alter a bent-hip, bent-knee gait into

BIPEDAL POSTURE brings a reversal in the roles played by the same pelvic and femoral muscles. Gluteus medius and gluteus minimus have changed from extensors to abductors and the function of extending the trunk, required when a biped runs or climbs, has been assumed by the gluteus maximus. The hamstring muscles, in turn, now act mainly as stabilizers and extensors of the hip. At right are the muscles as they appear in man; the skeletal regions to which their upper and lower ends attach are shown in color at left.

ILIAC CREST

ILIUM

SACRUM

ACETABULUM

PUBIS

ISCHIUM

COMPONENTS OF THE PELVIS are identified at top; the bones are those of the human pelvis. Below, ilium and ischium of a gorilla (*a*), of *Australopithecus* (*b*) and of modern man (*c*) are seen from the side (the front is to the left in each instance). The ischium of *Australopithecus* is longer than man's; this almost certainly kept the early hominid from striding in the manner of *Homo sapiens*. Instead the gait was probably a kind of jog trot.

prisingly unimportant role in man's ability to stand, or even to walk on a level surface. In standing, for example, the principal stabilizing and extending agents are the muscles of the hamstring group. In walking on the level the gluteus maximus is so little involved that even when it is paralyzed a man's stride is virtually unimpaired. The gluteus maximus comes into its own in man when power is needed to give the hip joint more play for such activities as running, walking up a steep slope or climbing stairs [*see illustration on page 46*]. Its chief function in these circumstances is to correct any tendency for the human trunk to jackknife on the legs.

Because the gluteus maximus has such a specialized role I believe, in contrast to Washburn's view, that it did not assume its present form until late in the evolution of the striding gait. Rather than being the initial adaptation, this muscle's enlargement and present function appear to me far more likely to have been one of the ultimate refinements of human walking. I am in agreement with Washburn, however, when he states that changes in the ilium, or upper pelvis, would have preceded changes in the ischium, or lower pelvis [see "Tools and Human Evolution," by Sherwood L. Washburn; SCIENTIFIC AMERICAN Offprint 601]. The primary adaptation would probably have involved a forward curvature of the vertebral column in the lumbar region. Accompanying this change would have been a broadening and a forward rotation of the iliac portions of the pelvis. Together these early adaptations provide the structural basis for improving the posture of the trunk.

Assuming that we have now given at least a tentative answer to the question of how man's bipedal posture evolved, there remains to be answered the question of why. What were the advantages of habitual bipedalism? Noting the comparative energy demands of various gaits, Washburn points out that human walking is primarily an adaptation for covering long distances economically. To go a long way with a minimum of effort is an asset to a hunter; it seems plausible that evolutionary selection for hunting behavior in man was responsible for the rapid development of striding anatomy. Gordon W. Hewes of the University of Colorado suggests a possible incentive that, acting as an agent of natural selection, could have prompted the quadrupedal ancestors of man to adopt a two-footed gait. In Hewes's view the principal advantage of bipedalism over quadrupedalism would be the free-

man's erect, striding walk, a number of anatomical changes must occur. These include an elongation of the hind limbs with respect to the forelimbs, a shortening and broadening of the pelvis, adjustments of the musculature of the hip (in order to stabilize the trunk during the act of walking upright), a straightening of both hip and knee and considerable reshaping of the foot.

Which of these changes can be considered to be primary and which secondary is still a matter that needs elucidation. Sherwood L. Washburn of the University of California at Berkeley has expressed the view that the change from four-footed to two-footed posture was initiated by a modification in the form and function of the gluteus maximus, a thigh muscle that is powerfully

developed in man but weakly developed in monkeys and apes [*see illustrations on preceding two pages*]. In a quadrupedal primate the principal extensors of the trunk are the "hamstring" muscles and the two upper-leg muscles I have already mentioned: the gluteus medius and gluteus minimus. In man these two muscles bear a different relation to the pelvis, in terms of both position and function. In technical terms they have become abductor muscles of the trunk rather than extensor muscles of the leg. It is this that enables them to play a critical part in stabilizing the pelvis in the course of striding. In man the extensor function of these two gluteal muscles has been taken over by a third, the gluteus maximus. This muscle, insignificant in other primates, plays a sur-

SHAPE AND ORIENTATION of the pelvis in the gorilla and in man reflect the postural differences between quadrupedal and bipedal locomotion. The ischium in the gorilla is long, the ilium extends to the side and the whole pelvis is tilted toward the horizontal (*see illustration on opposite page*). In man the ischium is much shorter, the broad ilium extends forward and the pelvis is vertical.

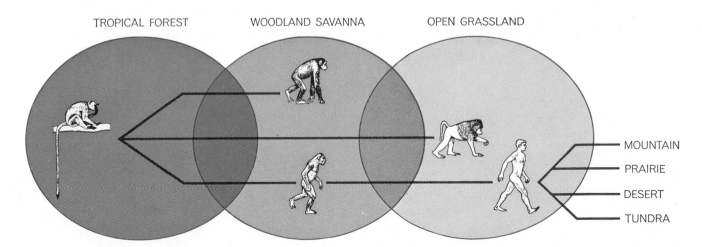

TROPICAL FOREST   WOODLAND SAVANNA   OPEN GRASSLAND

MOUNTAIN
PRAIRIE
DESERT
TUNDRA

ECOLOGICAL PATHWAY to man's eventual mastery of all environments begins (*left*) with a quadrupedal primate ancestor living in tropical forest more than 20 million years ago. During Miocene times mountain-building produced new environments. One, a transition zone between forest and grassland, has been exploited by three groups of primates. Some, for example the chimpanzees, have only recently entered this woodland savanna. Both the newly bipedal hominids and some ground-living quadrupedal monkeys, however, moved beyond the transition zone into open grassland. The quadrupeds, for example the baboons, remained there. On the other hand, the forces of natural selection in the new setting favored the bipedal hominid hunters' adaptation of the striding gait typical of man. Once this adaptation developed, man went on to conquer most of the earth's environments.

ing of the hands, so that food could be carried readily from one place to another for later consumption. To assess the significance of such factors as survival mechanisms it behooves us to review briefly the ecological situation in which our prehuman ancestors found themselves in Miocene times, between 15 and 25 million years ago.

The Miocene Environment

During the Miocene epoch the worldwide mountain-building activity of middle Tertiary times was in full swing. Many parts of the earth, including the region of East Africa where primates of the genus *Proconsul* were living, were being faulted and uplifted to form such mountain zones as the Alps, the Himalayas, the Andes and the Rockies. Massive faulting in Africa gave rise to one of the earth's major geological features: the Rift Valley, which extends 5,000 miles from Tanzania across East Africa to Israel and the Dead Sea. A string of lakes lies along the floor of the Rift Valley like giant stepping-stones. On their shores in Miocene times lived a fantastically rich fauna, inhabitants of the forest and of a new ecological niche—the grassy savanna.

These grasslands of the Miocene were the domain of new forms of vegetation that in many parts of the world had taken the place of rain forest, the dominant form of vegetation in the Eocene and the Oligocene. The savanna offered new evolutionary opportunities to a variety of mammals, including the expanding population of primates in the rapidly shrinking forest. A few primates— the ancestors of man and probably also the ancestors of the living baboons— evidently reacted to the challenge of the new environment.

The savanna, however, was no Eldorado. The problems facing the early hominids in the open grassland were immense. The forest foods to which they were accustomed were hard to come by; the danger of attack by predators was immeasurably increased. If, on top of everything else, the ancestral hominids of Miocene times were in the process of converting from quadrupedalism to bipedalism, it is difficult to conceive of any advantage in bipedalism that could have compensated for the added hazards of life in the open grassland. Consideration of the drawbacks of savanna living has led me to a conclusion contrary to the one generally accepted: I doubt that the advent of bipedalism took place in this environment. An environment neglected by scholars but one far better suited for the origin of man is the woodland-savanna, which is neither high forest nor open grassland. Today this halfway-house niche is occupied by many primates, for example the vervet monkey and some chimpanzees. It has enough trees to provide forest foods and ready escape from predators. At the same time its open grassy spaces are arenas in which new locomotor adaptations can be practiced and new foods can be sampled. In short, the woodland-savanna provides an ideal nursery for evolving hominids, combining the challenge and incentive of the open grassland with much of the security of the forest. It was probably in this transitional environment that man's ancestors learned to walk on two legs. In all likelihood, however, they only learned to stride when they later moved into the open savanna.

Moving forward many millions of years from Miocene to Pleistocene times, we come to man's most immediate hominid precursor: *Australopithecus*. A large consortium of authorities agrees that the shape of the pelvis in *Australopithecus* fossils indicates that these hominids were habitually bipedal, although not to the degree of perfection exhibited by modern man. A few anatomists, fighting a rearguard action, contend that on the contrary the pelvis of *Australopithecus*

STAIR-CLIMBING, like running, is a movement that brings the human gluteus maximus into play. Acting as an extensor of the trunk, the muscle counteracts any tendency for the body to jackknife over the legs. Photographs are from Muybridge's collection.

shows that these hominids were predominantly quadrupedal. I belong to the first school but, as I have been at some pains to emphasize in the past, the kind of upright walking practiced by *Australopithecus* should not be equated with man's heel-and-toe, striding gait.

From Bipedalist to Strider

The stride, although it was not necessarily habitual among the earliest true men, is nevertheless the quintessence of the human locomotor achievement. Among other things, striding involves extension of the leg to a position behind the vertical axis of the spinal column. The degree of extension needed can only be achieved if the ischium of the pelvis is short. But the ischium of *Australopithecus* is long, almost as long as the ischium of an ape [*see illustration on page 44*]. Moreover, it has been shown that in man the gluteus medius and the gluteus minimus are prime movers in stabilizing the pelvis during each stride; in *Australopithecus* this stabilizing mechanism is imperfectly evolved. The combination of both deficiencies almost entirely precludes the possibility that these hominids possessed a striding gait. For *Australopithecus* walking was something of a jog trot. These hominids must have covered the ground with quick, rather short steps, with their knees and hips slightly bent; the prolonged stance phase of the fully human gait must surely have been absent.

Compared with man's stride, therefore, the gait of *Australopithecus* is physiologically inefficient. It calls for a disproportionately high output of energy; indeed, *Australopithecus* probably found long-distance bipedal travel impossible. A natural question arises in this connection. Could the greater energy requirement have led these early representatives of the human family to alter their diet in the direction of an increased reliance on high-energy foodstuffs, such as the flesh of other animals?

The pelvis of *Australopithecus* bears evidence that this hominid walker could scarcely have been a strider. Let us now turn to the foot of what many of us believe is a more advanced hominid. In 1960 L. S. B. Leakey and his wife Mary unearthed most of the bones of this foot in the lower strata at Olduvai Gorge known collectively as Bed I, which are about 1.75 million years old. The bones formed part of a fossil assemblage that has been designated by the Leakeys, by Philip Tobias of the University of the Witwatersrand and by me as possibly the earliest-known species of man: *Homo*

habilis. The foot was complete except for the back of the heel and the terminal bones of the toes; its surviving components were assembled and studied by me and Michael Day, one of my colleagues at the Unit of Primatology and Human Evolution of the Royal Free Hospital School of Medicine in London. On the basis of functional analysis the resemblance to the foot of modern man is close, although differing in a few minor particulars. Perhaps the most significant point of resemblance is that the stout basal bone of the big toe lies alongside the other toes [*see upper illustration on next page*]. This is an essentially human characteristic; in apes and monkeys the big toe is not exceptionally robust and

PELVIC ROTATION of the human female is exaggerated compared with that of a male taking a stride of equal length because the two sexes differ in pelvic anatomy. Muybridge noted the phenomenon, using a pole with whitened ends to record the pelvic oscillations.

PRIMITIVE FOOT, complete except for the back of the heel and the tips of the toes, was unearthed from the lower level at Olduvai Gorge in Tanzania. Attributed to a very early hominid, *Homo habilis,* by its discoverer, L. S. B. Leakey, it is about 1.75 million years old. Its appearance suggests that the possessor was a habitual biped. Absence of the terminal bones of the toes, however, leaves open the question of whether the possessor walked with a stride.

BIG-TOE BONE, also discovered at Olduvai Gorge, is considerably younger than the foot bones in the top illustration but still probably more than a million years old. It is the toe's terminal bone (*bottom view at left, top view at right*) and bore the thrust of its possessor's push-off with each swing of the right leg. The tilting and twisting of the head of the bone in relation to the shaft is unequivocal evidence that its possessor walked with a modern stride.

diverges widely from the other toes. The foot bones, therefore, give evidence that this early hominid species was habitually bipedal. In the absence of the terminal bones of the toes, however, there was no certainty that *Homo habilis* walked with a striding gait.

Then in 1961, in a somewhat higher stratum at Olduvai Gorge (and thus in a slightly younger geological formation), a single bone came to light in an area otherwise barren of human bones. This fossil is the big-toe bone I mentioned at the beginning of this article [*see lower illustration at left*]. Its head is both tilted and twisted with respect to its shaft, characteristics that are found only in modern man and that can with assurance be correlated with a striding gait. Day has recently completed a dimensional analysis of the bone, using a multivariate statistical technique. He is able to show that the fossil is unquestionably human in form.

There is no evidence to link the big-toe bone specifically to either of the two recognized hominids whose fossil remains have been recovered from Bed I at Olduvai: *Homo habilis* and *Zinjanthropus boisei.* Thus the owner of the toe remains unknown, at least for the present. Nonetheless, one thing is made certain by the discovery. We now know that in East Africa more than a million years ago there existed a creature whose mode of locomotion was essentially human.

4

The Evolution of the Hand

JOHN NAPIER · December 1962

At Olduvai Gorge in Tanganyika two years ago L. S. B. Leakey and his wife Mary unearthed 15 bones from the hand of an early hominid. They found the bones on a well-defined living floor a few feet below the site at which in the summer of 1959 they had excavated the skull of a million-year-old man-ape to which they gave the name *Zinjanthropus*. The discovery of *Zinjanthropus* has necessitated a complete revision of previous views about the cultural and biological evolution of man. The skull was found in association with stone tools and waste flakes indicating that at this ancient horizon toolmakers were already in existence. The floor on which the hand bones were discovered has also yielded stone tools and a genuine bone "lissoir," or leather working

tool. Hence this even older living site carries the origins of toolmaking still further back, both in time and evolution, and it is now possible for the first time to reconstruct the hand of the earliest toolmakers.

Research and speculation on the course of human evolution have hitherto paid scant attention to the part played by the hand. Only last year I wrote: "It is a matter of considerable surprise to many to learn that the human hand, which can achieve so much in the field of creative art, communicate such subtle shades of meaning, and upon which the pre-eminence of *Homo sapiens* in the world of animals so largely depends, should constitute, in a structural sense, one of the most primitive and generalized parts of the human body." The im-

plication of this statement, which expresses an almost traditional view, is that the primate forebears of man were equipped with a hand of essentially human form long before the cerebral capacity necessary to exploit its potential had appeared. The corollary to this view is that the difference between the human hand and the monkey hand, as the late Frederic Wood Jones of the Royal College of Surgeons used to insist, is largely one of function rather than structure. Although broadly speaking it is true that the human hand has an extraordinarily generalized structure, the discovery of the Olduvai hand indicates that in a number of minor but nevertheless highly significant features the hand is more specialized than we had supposed.

Tool-using—in the sense of improvisa-

HANDS OF LIVING PRIMATES, all drawn same size, show evolutionary changes in structure related to increasing manual dexterity. Tree shrew (*a*) shows beginnings of unique primate possession, specialized thumb (*digit at right*). In tarsier (*b*) thumb is distinct and can rotate around joint between digit and palm. In capuchin monkey (*c*), a typical New World species, angle between thumb and finger is wider and movement can be initiated at joint at base of palm. Gorilla (*d*), like other Old World species, has saddle joint at base of palm. This allows full rotation of thumb, which is set at a wide angle. Only palm and hand bones are shown here.

tion with naturally occurring objects such as sticks and stones—by the higher apes has often been observed both in the laboratory and in the wild and has even been reported in monkeys. The making of tools, on the other hand, has been regarded as the major breakthrough in human evolution, a sort of status symbol that could be employed to distinguish the genus *Homo* from the rest of the primates. Prior to the discovery of *Zinjanthropus*, the South African man-apes (Australopithecines) had been associated at least indirectly with fabri-

cated tools. Observers were reluctant to credit the man-apes with being tool-makers, however, on the ground that they lacked an adequate cranial capacity. Now that hands as well as skulls have been found at the same site with undoubted tools, one can begin to correlate the evolution of the hand with the stage of culture and the size of the brain. By the same token one must also consider whether the transition from tool-using to toolmaking and the subsequent improvement in toolmaking techniques can be explained purely in

terms of cerebral expansion and the refinement of peripheral neuromuscular mechanisms, or whether a peripheral factor—the changing form of the hand—has played an equally important part in the evolution of the human species. And to understand the significance of the specializations of the human hand, it must be compared in action—as well as in dissection—with the hands of lower primates.

In the hand at rest—with the fingers slightly curled, the thumb lying in the plane of the index finger, the poise of the

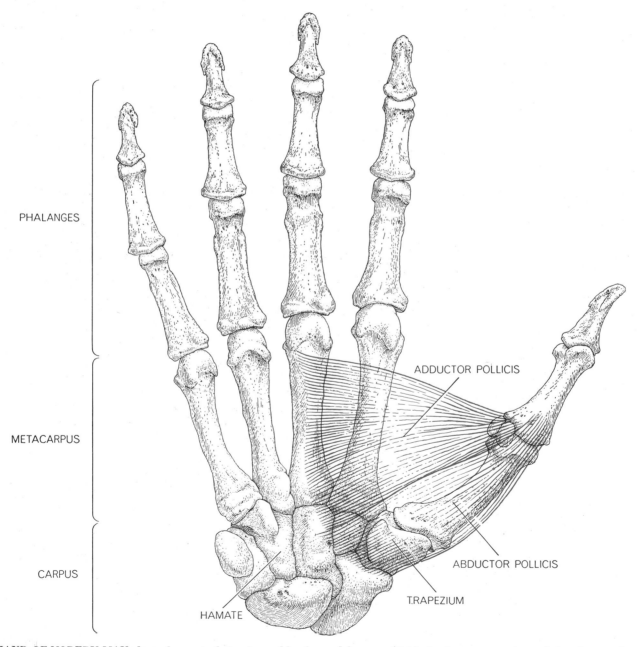

PHALANGES

METACARPUS

CARPUS

ADDUCTOR POLLICIS

ABDUCTOR POLLICIS

T.TRAPEZIUM

HAMATE

HAND OF MODERN MAN, drawn here actual size, is capable of precise movements available to no other species. Breadth of terminal phalanges (end bones of digits) guarantees secure thumb-to-finger grip. Thumb is long in proportion to index finger and is set at very wide angle. Strong muscles (*adductor pollicis* and

abductor pollicis) implement movement of thumb toward and away from palm. Saddle joint at articulation of thumb metacarpal (a bone of the palm) and trapezium (a bone of the carpus, or wrist) enables thumb to rotate through 45 degrees around its own longitudinal axis and so be placed in opposition to all the other digits.

whole reflecting the balanced tension of opposing groups of muscles—one can see something of its potential capacity. From the position of rest, with a minimum of physical effort, the hand can assume either of its two prehensile working postures. The two postures are demonstrated in sequence by the employment of a screw driver to remove a screw solidly embedded in a block of wood [*see illustration below*]. The hand first grips the tool between the flexed fingers and the palm with the thumb reinforcing the pressure of the fingers; this is the "power grip." As the screw comes loose, the hand grasps the tool between one or more fingers and the thumb, with the pulps, or inner surfaces, of the finger and thumb tips fully opposed to one another; this is the "precision grip." Invariably it is the nature of the task to be performed, and not the shape of the tool or object grasped, that dictates which posture is employed. The power grip is the grip of choice when the full strength of the hand must be applied and the need for precision is subordinate; the precision grip comes into play when the need for power is secondary to the demand for fine control.

The significance of this analysis becomes apparent when the two activities are correlated with anatomical structure. The presence or absence of these structural features in the hands of a lower primate or early hominid can then be

POWER GRIP is one of two basic working postures of human hand. Used when strength is needed, it involves holding object between flexed fingers and palm while the thumb applies counterpressure.

PRECISION GRIP is second basic working posture and is used when accuracy and delicacy of touch are required. Object is held between tips of one or more fingers and the fully opposed thumb.

taken to indicate, within limits, the capabilities of those hands in the cultural realm of tool-using and toolmaking. In the case of the hand, at least, evolution has been incremental. Although the precision grip represents the ultimate refinement in prehensility, this does not mean that more primitive capacities have been lost. The human hand remains capable of the postures and movements of the primate foot-hand and even of the paw of the fully quadrupedal mammal, and it retains many of the anatomical structures that go with them. From one stage in evolution to the next the later capability is added to the earlier.

The study of primate evolution is facilitated by the fact that the primates now living constitute a graded series representative of some of its principal chapters. It is possible, at least, to accept a study series composed of tree shrews, tarsiers, New World monkeys, Old World monkeys and man as conforming to the evolutionary sequence. In comparing the hands of these animals with one another and with man's, considerable care must be taken to recognize specializations of structure that do not form part of the sequence. Thus the extremely specialized form of the hand in the anthropoid apes can in no way be regarded as a stage in the sequence from tree shrew to man. The same objection does not apply, however, to certain fossil apes. The hand of the Miocene ancestral ape *Proconsul africanus* does not, for example, show the hand specializations of living apes and can legitimately be brought into the morphological sequence that branches off on the man-ape line toward man.

In the lowliest of the living primates —the tree shrew that inhabits the rain forests of the East Indies and the Malay Archipelago—the hand is little more than a paw. It exhibits in a primate sense only the most rudimentary manual capability. This is the movement of convergence that brings the tips of the digits together by a flexion of the paw at the metacarpophalangeal joints, which correspond in man to the knuckles at the juncture of the fingers and the rest of the hand. The opposite movement—divergence—fans the digits outward and is related to the pedal, or weight-bearing, function of the paw. With its paws thus limited the tree shrew is compelled to grasp objects, for example its insect prey, in two-handed fashion, two convergent paws being the functional equivalent of a prehensile hand. For purposes of locomotion in its arboreal

DIVERGENCE, generally associated with weight-bearing function of hand, is achieved by extension at the metacarpophalangeal joints. All mammalian paws are capable of this action.

CONVERGENCE is achieved by flexion at metacarpophalangeal joints. Two convergent paws equal one prehensile hand; many mammals hold food in two convergent paws to eat.

PREHENSILITY, the ability to wrap the fingers around an object, is a special primate characteristic, related to the emergence of the specialized thumb during evolutionary process.

OPPOSABILITY is ability to sweep thumb across palm while rotating it around its longitudinal axis. Many primates can do this, but underlying structures are best developed in man.

STONE TOOLS to left of center are similar to those found at Olduvai Gorge, Tanganyika, in conjunction with the hand bones of an early hominid. Such crude tools can be made by using the power grip, of which the Olduvai hand was capable. Finely flaked Old Stone Age tools at right can be made only by using the precision grip, which may not have been well developed in Olduvai hand.

habitat, this animal does not require prehensility because, like the squirrel, it is small, it has claws on the tips of its digits and is a tree runner rather than a climber. Even in the tree shrew, however, the specialized thumb of the primate family has begun to take form in the specialized anatomy of this digit and its musculature. Occasionally tree shrews have been observed feeding with one hand.

The hand of the tarsier, another denizen of the rain forests of the East Indies, exhibits a more advanced degree of prehensility in being able to grasp objects by bending the digits toward the palm. The thumb digit also exhibits a degree of opposability to the other digits. This is a pseudo opposability in that the movement is restricted entirely to the metacarpophalangeal joint and is therefore distinct from the true opposability of man's thumb. The movement is facilitated by the well-developed abductor and adductor muscles that persist in the hands of the higher primates. With this equipment the tarsier is able to support its body weight on vertical stems and to grasp small objects with one hand.

The tropical rain forests in which these animals live today are probably not very different from the closed-canopy forests of the Paleocene epoch of some 70 million years ago, during which the first primates appeared. In the wide variety of habitats that these forests provide, ecologists distinguish five major strata, superimposed like a block of apartments. From the top down these are the upper, middle and lower stories (the last being the main closed canopy), the shrub layer and the herb layer on the ground. To these can be added a sixth deck: the subterrain. In the emergence of prehensility in the primate line the three-dimensional arrangement of this system of habitats played a profound role. Prehensility is an adaptation to arboreal life and is related to climbing. In animals that are of small size with respect to the branches on which they live and travel, such as the tree shrew, mobility is not hampered by lack of prehensility. They can live at any level in the forest, from the forest floor to the tops of the tallest trees, their stability assured by the grip of sharp claws and the elaboration of visual and cerebellar mechanisms.

The tree-climbing as opposed to the tree-running phase of primate evolution may not have begun until the middle of the Eocene, perhaps 55 million years ago. What environmental pressure brought about this adaptation can only be guessed at. Thomas F. Barth of the University of Chicago has suggested that the advent of the widely successful order of rodents in the early Eocene may have led to the displacement of the primates from the shrub strata to the upper three strata of the forest canopy. In any case little is known about the form of the primates that made this transition.

In *Proconsul,* of the early to middle Miocene of 20 million years ago, the fossil record discloses a fully developed tree-climbing primate. His hand was clearly prehensile. His thumb, however, was imperfectly opposable. Functionally this hand is comparable to that of some of the living New World monkeys.

True opposability appears for the first time among the living primates in the Old World monkeys. In these animals the carpometacarpal joint shows a well-developed saddle configuration comparable to that in the corresponding joint of the human hand. This allows rotation of the thumb from its wrist articulation. Turning about its longitudinal axis through an angle of about 45 degrees, the thumb can be swept across the palm, and the pulp of the thumb can be directly opposed to the pulp surfaces of one of or all the other digits. This movement is not so expertly performed by the monkeys as by man. At the same time, again as in man, a fair range of movement is retained at the metacarpophalangeal joint, the site of pseudo opposability in the tarsier.

The hands of anthropoid apes display many of these anatomical structures but do not have the same degree of functional capability. This is because of certain specializations that arise from the fact that these apes swing from trees by their hands. Such specializations would seem to exclude the apes from the evolutionary sequence that leads to man. In comparing the hand of monkeys with the hand of man one must bear in mind an obvious fact that is all too often overlooked: monkeys are largely quadrupedal, whereas man is fully bipedal. Variations in the form of the hand from one species of monkey to the next are related to differences in their mode of locomotion. The typical monkey hand is rather long and narrow; the metacarpal, or "palm," bones are short compared with the digits (except in baboons); the terminal phalanges, or finger-tip bones, are slender and the tips of the fingers are consequently narrow from side to side. These are only the most obvious differences between the foot-hand of the Old World monkey and that of man. They serve nonetheless to show how too rigid an application of Frederic Wood Jones's criterion of morphological similarity can mislead one into assuming that the only important difference between the hands of men and monkeys lies in the elaboration of the central nervous system.

It seems likely that the terrestrial phase of human evolution followed on the heels of *Proconsul*. At that time, it is well known, the world's grasslands expanded enormously at the expense of the forests. By the end of the Miocene, 15 million years ago, most of the prototypes of the modern plains-living forms had appeared. During this period, apparently, the hominids also deserted their original forest habitats to take up life on the savanna, where the horizons were figuratively limitless. Bipedal locomotion, a process initiated by life in the trees and the ultimate mechanism for emancipation of the hands, rapidly followed the adoption of terrestrial life. The use of the hands for carrying infants, food and even weapons and tools could not have lagged far behind. As Sherwood L. Washburn of the University of California has suggested on the basis of observations of living higher primates,

tool-using must have appeared at an early stage in hominid evolution. It is a very short step from tool-using to tool-modifying, in the sense of stripping twigs and leaves from a branch in order to improve its effectiveness as a tool or weapon. It is an equally short further step to toolmaking, which at its most primitive is simply the application of the principle of modification to a stick, a stone or a bone. Animal bones are a convenient source of tools; Raymond A. Dart of the University of Witwatersrand in South Africa has advanced the hypothesis that such tools

JUVENILE GORILLA   OLDUVAI HOMINID   MODERN MAN

HAND BONES of juvenile gorilla, Olduvai hominid and modern man are compared. Phalanges (*top row*) decrease in curvature from juvenile gorilla to modern man. Terminal thumb phalanx (*middle row*) increases in breadth and proportional length. Third row shows increase in length of thumb and angle between thumb and index finger. Olduvai bones in outline in third row are reconstructed from other evidence; they were not found.

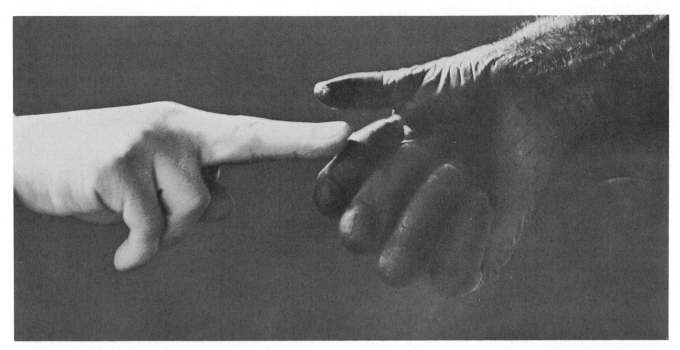

CHIMPANZEE, attempting to grasp experimenter's finger, uses an inefficient precision grip. Because animal's thumb is so short in proportion to the digits, it is compelled to bend the digits forward and grasp the object between the sides of index finger and thumb.

were used by early man-apes as part of an "osteodontokeratic" (bone-tooth-hair) culture.

The tools from the pre-*Zinjanthropus* stratum at Olduvai Gorge are little more than pebbles modified in the simplest way by striking off one or more flakes to produce a chopping edge. This technology could not have required either a particularly large brain or a hand of modern human proportions. The hand bones of the pre-*Zinjanthropus* individuals uncovered by the Leakeys in their more recent excavation of Olduvai Gorge are quite unlike those of modern *Homo sapiens*. But there seems to be no reason, on either geological or anthropological grounds, for doubting that the tools found with them are coeval. Modern man must recover from his surprise at the discovery that hands other than his own were capable of shaping tools.

At this point it may be useful to return to the analysis of the manual capability of modern man that distinguishes the power and the precision grip. When compared with the hand of modern man, the Olduvai hand appears to have been capable of a tremendously strong power grip. Although it was a smaller hand, the relative lengths of the metacarpals and phalanges indicate that the proportion of digits and palm was much the same as it is in man. In addition, the tips of the terminal bones of all the Olduvai fingers are quite wide and the finger tips themselves must therefore have been

broad—an essential feature of the human grip for both mechanical and neurological reasons. The curvature of the metacarpals and phalanges indicates that the fingers were somewhat curved throughout their length and were normally held in semiflexion. Unfortunately no hamate bone was found among the Olduvai remains. This wristbone, which articulates with the fifth metacarpal, meets at a saddle joint in modern man and lends great stability to his power grip.

It seems unlikely that the Olduvai hand was capable of the precision grip in its fullest expression. No thumb metacarpal was found in the Olduvai deposit; hence any inference as to the length of the thumb in relation to the other fingers must be derived from the evidence of the position of the wristbone with which the thumb articulates. This evidence suggests that the Olduvai thumb, like the thumb of the gorilla, was set at a narrower angle and was somewhat shorter than the thumb of modern man, reaching only a little beyond the metacarpophalangeal joint of the index finger. Thus, although the thumb was opposable, it can be deduced that the Olduvai hand could not perform actions as precise as those that can be undertaken by the hand of modern man.

Nonetheless, the Olduvai hand activated by a brain and a neuromuscular mechanism of commensurate development would have had little difficulty in making the tools that were found with it. I myself have made such pebble tools

employing only the power grip to hold and strike two stones together.

The inception of toolmaking has hitherto been regarded as the milestone that marked the emergence of the genus *Homo*. It has been assumed that this development was a sudden event, happening as it were almost overnight, and that its appearance was coincidental with the structural evolution of a hominid of essentially modern human form and proportions. It is now becoming clear that this important cultural phase in evolution had its inception at a much earlier stage in the biological evolution of man, that it existed for a much longer period of time and that it was set in motion by a much less advanced hominid and a much less specialized hand than has previously been believed.

For full understanding of the subsequent improvement in toolmaking over the next few hundred thousand years of the Paleolithic, it is necessary to document the transformation of the hand as well as of the brain. Attention can now also be directed toward evidence of the functional capabilities of the hands of early man that is provided by the tools they made. These studies may help to account for the radical changes in technique and direction that characterize the evolution of stone implements during the middle and late Pleistocene epoch. The present evidence suggests that the stone implements of early man were as good (or as bad) as the hands that made them.

RING-BILLED GULL has a long, narrow wing characteristic of birds that do much gliding over water. The anatomy of the wing is shown at the top of page 60. Birds that do little gliding have shorter and broader wings.

BROWN PELICAN is another gliding bird. The feathers at the tip of its left wing are turned up by a current of air. When the wing beats down during active flight, this same effect occurs and pushes the bird forward.

5

Bird Aerodynamics

JOHN H. STORER · April 1952

THE flight of birds has always excited man's envy and wonder. At first sight the process looks simple enough: a bird seems to lift and drive itself forward by beating its wings against the air in much the same way as a swimmer propels himself through water by flapping his arms. When men first tried to fly, they built their flying machines ("ornithopters") on this principle, with mechanical wings that flapped. But the machines never got off the ground.

For this is not at all the way birds fly. Paradoxically it was the development of the modern propeller plane that finally taught us how birds fly—not the other way around. A bird is actually a living airplane. It flies by the same aerodynamical principles as a plane and uses much of the same mechanical equipment—wings, propellers, steering gear, even slots and flaps for help in taking off and landing.

The slow-motion camera shows that a bird does not push itself along by beating its wings back against the air. On the downstroke the wings move forward, not backward. And when the bird lifts its wings for the next stroke, it does not lose altitude, as might be expected, but sails on steadily on a level course. The easiest way to understand its flight is to consider first how an airplane flies.

The air, like any fluid, has weight, and it presses against every surface of anything submerged in it—downward from above, upward from below and inward from all sides. At sea level the air presses on all surfaces with a force of 14.7 pounds per square inch. The air therefore will supply the force to support flight, provided the flying object can somehow reduce the pressure on its upper surface to less than the lifting pressure, and decrease the pressure against its front surface or increase that from behind. Birds and airplanes do this by means of properly shaped wings and propellers which they manipulate to drive themselves forward at a certain required angle and speed.

We can study the aerodynamical problems involved by blowing a stream of smoke, which makes the air currents visible, against an obstruction in a wind tunnel. When the smoke stream hits the obstruction, it does not flow smoothly around the surface and close up again immediately behind it. Instead, it breaks up and is deflected away from the obstruction so that the air no longer presses against the object's sides with the same force. Moreover, the air stream does not close up again until it has moved some distance past the obstruction, so the pressure on the rear surface of the obstacle also is reduced. There remains a disproportionate pressure on the front surface of the obstacle: what would be known as "drag" if the object instead of the air stream were moving.

Now suppose we place in the air stream an object so shaped that it fills in the spaces that were left vacant when the air was deflected by the first obstruction. The air flows smoothly around this new object, and the pressure is more nearly even on all sides. Drag is reduced. We have "streamlined" the obstacle. By altering this shape just a little, we can change the relative pressures on its different surfaces. Let us flatten the bottom surface slightly, reducing the downward deflection of the air stream. Now the upward pressure of air against the bottom surface is more nearly normal, while the downward pressure on the top surface remains subnormal as before. Presto! We have more pressure from below than from above. If the streamlined model is light enough, the moving air will lift it. We have the beginning of a wing.

If the front edge of this embryo wing is tilted upward just a little so that the air strikes the bottom surface more directly, the lifting force on the wing is increased. The more the wing is tilted, the more lift it will give—up to a certain point. As the angle of tilt approaches the vertical, the pressure against the bottom surface begins to push the wing backward rather than upward. Eventually,

if a plane's wing is tilted too much, the lifting force vanishes, the drag is so great that it stops the plane, and we have what is known as a "stall." The plane must regain the proper angle and speed or it will crash.

In the air a pilot controls the lifting power of his plane both by tilt and by speed: the more speed, the more lift. In taking off or landing, however, he must rely mainly on tilt: to get enough lifting force he must hold his wing at the greatest possible angle against the air, up to the point of stalling. The angle to which he can tilt the wing without stalling can be increased by placing a very small auxiliary wing in front of or behind the main wing. The "slot" formed between the main wing and the small auxiliary airfoil increases the speed of the air flow over the wing and so maintains its lifting power, even after it has passed the normal stalling point.

Once we have a streamlined wing, the next step necessary for flying is to move it through the air fast enough to generate lift. This we accomplish by equipping the machine with propellers, which are actually another set of wings, whose "lift" is exerted forward rather than upward. For mechanical reasons the blades of a propeller function better with a shape and angle slightly different from those of the wings, but the principle on which they work is just the same.

So we have, basically, a single mechanism which, placed in one position, holds an airplane up, and in another, drives it forward. Now we can look at a bird's anatomy and find exactly the same mechanism used in just the same two ways.

THE WING of a bird consists of two parts, which have two very different functions. It is divided into an inner half, operated from the shoulder joint, and an outer half, which is moved separately by a "wrist" midway along the wing. The inner half of the wing is devoted almost exclusively to giving lift. It is held rather rigidly at a slight angle, sloping like the wing of a plane. It also

LANDING American egret demonstrates the use of feathers in its alulas and wing tips to maintain balance and control. The alula is a small bunch of feath- ers on the leading edge of the wing. By opening slots with these feathers and those of the wing tips, the bird can control its lift while losing flying speed.

has the streamlined shape of a plane's wing: its upper feathers are arched to make a curved surface.

At the front edge of the wrist, where the inner and outer wings join, is a small group of feathers called the alula. This is the bird's auxiliary airfoil for help in taking off and landing. The bird can raise the alula to form a slot between that structure and the main wing. Without the alula a bird cannot take off or land successfully.

But where is the propeller? Astonishing as it may seem, every bird has a pair of them, though where they might be is certainly far from obvious. They can be seen in action best in a slow-motion picture of a bird in flight. During the downward beat of the wings the primary feathers at the wing tips stand out almost at right angles to the rest of the wing and to the line of flight. These feathers are the propellers. They take on this twisted form for only a split second during each wing beat. But this ability to change their shape and position is the key to bird flight. Throughout the entire wing beat they are constantly changing their shape, adjusting automatically to air pressure and the changing requirements of the wing as it moves up and down.

This automatic adjustment is made possible by special features of the feather design. The front vane of a wing-tip feather (on the forward side of the quill) is much narrower than the rear vane. Out of this difference comes the force that twists the feather into the shape of a propeller. As the wing beats downward against the air, the greater pressure against the wide rear vane of each of these feathers twists that vane upward until the feather takes on the proper shape and angle to function as a propeller. The degree and shape of its twist is controlled largely by the design of the quill, which is rigid at its base but flattened and flexible toward the end.

With their specialized design the primary feathers are beautifully adapted to meet the varied demands of bird flight. An airplane's propeller rotates around a pivot in one direction; the bird's propeller, in contrast, oscillates rapidly down and up, and it must automatically adapt its shape, position, angle and speed to the changing requirements of the moment. The feathers are not fastened immovably to the bone of the wing but are held by a broad flexible membrane, which allows considerable freedom of movement to each feather. While the bird is flying easily, only the tips of the feathers twist to become propellers. But if the bird is in a hurry and beats its wings more strongly against the air, the whole outer section of the wing, from the wrist out, may be twisted by the greater pressure into one big propeller.

The path of the propeller on the

FLYING egret shows the different functions of the inner and outer halves of a bird wing. In the first two pictures the wings are moving downward. In the third the inner half rises ahead of the outer to maintain lift.

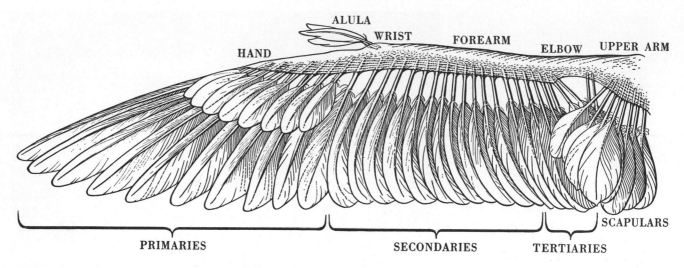

HAND   ALULA   WRIST   FOREARM   ELBOW   UPPER ARM

PRIMARIES   SECONDARIES   TERTIARIES   SCAPULARS

ANATOMY of a herring gull's wing reflects the different functions of its inner and outer halves. The inner half of the wing, from the shoulder to the wrist, is adapted primarily to lift; the outer half, from the wrist to the wing tip, to control and propulsion. Only the principal feathers of the wing are shown in this illustration.

downstroke is downward and forward; on the upstroke, upward and backward. The amount of forward and backward motion varies with the bird's wingbeat. When the bird beats its wings fast, as in taking off, the increased pressure drives the wing tips forward on a more nearly horizontal path; in leisurely flight the movement is more nearly vertical. The inner wing, by maintaining the proper angle, supports the bird's weight through the entire wing beat. This angle is constantly adjusted to maintain a steady lifting force.

In free flight the bird's powerful breast muscles sweep the whole wing up and down from the shoulder. The inner wing does not actually need to move, but it acts as a handle to move the propeller and gives the latter greater speed and power. I have a slow-motion movie of a low-flying white heron skimming some bushes so closely that it did not have room to make a full downward wing beat. The bird held the inner half of each wing extended horizontally and beat the outer half up and down from the wrist. To move the propeller fast enough without the help of the breast muscles must have required great effort. But this flight demonstrated perfectly the true function of each half of the wing. The inner half was the wing of a living airplane, lifting the bird. The outer half was the propeller, driving it forward.

Like an airplane, a bird has special equipment for steering and balancing. It steers by turning its tail, up, down or sidewise. (It can also spread the tail wide to give added lifting surface when needed.) The bird balances itself by means of its wings; if it tips to one side, it can restore itself to an even keel by increasing the lift of that wing, either by beating more strongly with it or by changing its angle.

OF ALL the powers of birds in the air probably none has caused more wonder than their soaring ability. To see a bird rise in the air and sail on motionless wings into the distance until at last it disappears from sight gives one a sense of magic. We now know how it is done, but it is still difficult to realize what is happening as we watch it.

Actually the bird is coasting downhill in relation to the flow of air. It rises because it is riding a rising current of air which is ascending faster than the bird is sinking in the current.

Ascending air currents on which birds can soar or glide arise from two different kinds of situations. One is an obstruction, such as an ocean wave, a shore line or a hillside, which deflects the wind upward. It is common to see a pelican or albatross sailing over the water on motionless wings just above the crest of a moving wave, or a gull hanging motionless against a wind current that rises over a headland, or a hawk soaring on the air current that sweeps up a mountainside.

The second type of rising current is heated air, known as a thermal. A field warmed by the sun heats the air above it, causing it to expand and rise. If the field is surrounded by a cooler forest, the heated pocket of air may rise in the form of a great bubble or of a column. Everyone has seen birds soaring in wide circles over land; usually they are coasting around the periphery of a rising air column. Over the ocean, when the water warms colder air above it, the air rises in a whole group of columns, packed together like the cells of a honeycomb. If the wind then freshens, it may blow the columns over until they lie horizontally on the water. The flat-lying columns of air may rotate around their axes, each in the opposite direction from its neighbor. This has been demonstrated in the laboratory by blowing smoke-filled air over a warmed surface at increasing speed, corresponding to an increase in the wind over the ocean. If you put your two fists together and rotate them, the right clockwise and the left counter-clockwise, you will see that the two

	MILES PER HOUR
Great Blue Heron [cruising]	18-29
Great Blue Heron [pressed]	36
Canada Goose [easy flight]	20
Canada Goose [pressed by plane]	45-60
Mallard [pressed by plane]	55-60
Duck Hawk [pressed by plane]	175-180
Pheasant [average top speed]	60
Woodcock	5-13
Ruby-throated Hummingbird [easy flight]	45-55
Barn Swallow	20-46
Crow	25-60
Sharp-shinned Hawk	16-60
Osprey	20-80

FLYING SPEEDS of 13 species of birds are listed in this table. The conditions under which the observations were made are in parentheses.

inner faces of the fists rise together. Just so two adjoining air cells rotating in opposite directions will push up between them a ridge of rising air. Birds can glide in a straight line along such a ridge.

At the Woods Hole Oceanographic Institution Alfred H. Woodcock studied the soaring of sea gulls at different seasons. During the summer, when the air is warmer than the water, gulls seldom do any soaring. But they do a great deal of it in the fall, when the water is warmer than the air and produces many updrafts. The gull's movements may clearly mark the outlines of the rising air columns. When the wind is relatively light, under 16 miles an hour, the gulls soar in spirals, showing that the columns are standing upright. But as the wind freshens and tilts over the columns, the birds' soaring patterns begin to change; when the wind speed reaches 24 miles per hour, all the gulls soar in straight lines. The spectacle is all but incredible, with the birds sailing into the strong wind on motionless wings and gaining altitude as they go, until they disappear in the distance. I watched it once, and it is a never-to-be-forgotten sight.

How fast do birds fly? A great deal of nonsense has been uttered on this subject. The measurement of a bird's speed capabilities is a very uncertain and tricky thing. The wind, the angle of the bird's flight, whether it is being pressed—these factors and many others affect its speed.

The cruising and top speeds of some common birds are listed in the table at the bottom of the opposite page. Birds vary greatly, of course, in their speed requirements and possibilities. The pheasant and grouse, which have short wings adapted to maneuvering in underbrush, must fly with a rapid wing beat and considerable speed to stay in the air. The same is true of ducks, which do not need large wings because they have an easy landing field on the water. Herons, on the other hand, must be able to land slowly to protect their long, slender legs, which they use for wading to find food. Their big, cumbersome wings are suited for slow landing, but they produce so much friction and drag in the air that herons cannot fly very fast.

As the table shows, 60 miles an hour is fast for a bird, and the fastest known species, the duck hawk, does not exceed 175 to 180 miles per hour. These speeds, of course, are far slower than the speeds of modern planes. They involve very different problems in aerodynamics, and different streamline designs. But some of them do approach the speed of the early planes, and it is interesting to see how closely the designs produced by nature approach the best results of the human engineer.

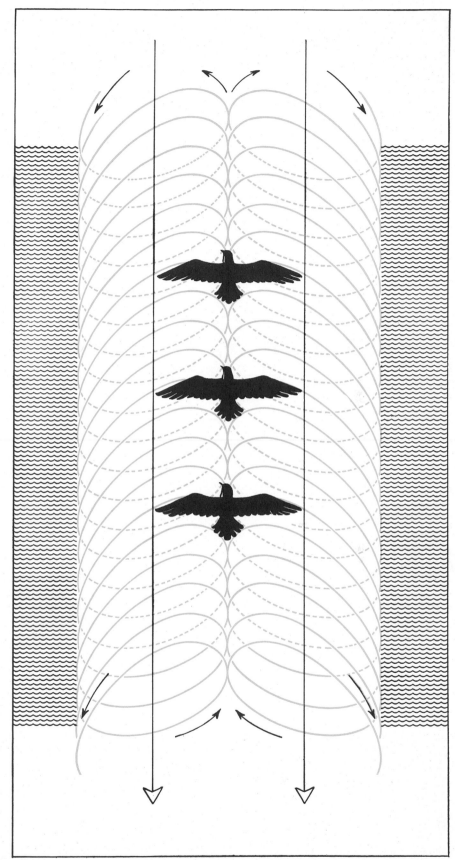

SEA BIRDS sometimes soar against a prevailing wind (*vertical arrows*) by riding an updraft between two counter-rotating cylinders of air. These cylinders result from the fact that when the sea is warmer than the air, many vertical columns of warm air rise from the surface of the water. If the wind freshens, the columns lie parallel to the surface. Birds are not drawn to scale.

6

Birds as Flying Machines

CARL WELTY · March 1955

The great struggle in most animals' lives is to avoid change. A chickadee clinging to a piece of suet on a bitter winter day is doing its unconscious best to maintain its internal status quo. Physiological constancy is the first biological commandment. An animal must eternally strive to keep itself warm, moist and supplied with oxygen, sugar, protein, salts, vitamins and the like, often within precise limits. Too great a change in its internal economy means death.

The spectacular flying performances of birds—spanning oceans, deserts and whole continents—tend to obscure the more important fact that the ability to fly confers on them a remarkably useful mechanism to preserve their internal stability, or homeostasis. Through flight birds can search out the external conditions and substances they need to keep their internal fires burning clean and steady. A bird's wide search for specific foods and habitats makes sense only when considered in the light of this persistent, urgent need for constancy.

The power of flight opens up to birds an enormous gaseous ocean, the atmosphere, and a means of quick, direct access to almost any spot on earth. They can eat in almost any "restaurant"; they have an almost infinite choice of sites to build their homes. As a result birds are, numerically at least, the most successful vertebrates on earth. They number roughly 25,000 species and subspecies, as compared with 15,000 mammals and 15,000 fishes.

At first glance birds appear to be quite variable. They differ considerably in size, body proportions, color, song and ability to fly. But a deeper look shows that they are far more uniform than, say, mammals. The largest living bird, a 125-pound ostrich, is about 20,000 times heavier than the smallest bird, a hummingbird weighing only one tenth of an ounce. However, the largest mammal, a 200,000-pound blue whale, weighs some 22 million times as much as the smallest mammal, the one-seventh-ounce masked shrew. Mammals, in other words, vary in mass more than a thousand times as much as birds. In body architecture, the comparative uniformity of birds is even more striking. Mammals may be as fat as a walrus or as slim as a weasel, furry as a musk ox or hairless as a desert rat,

long as a whale or short as a mole. They may be built to swim, crawl, burrow, run or climb. But the design of nearly all species of birds is tailored to and dictated by one pre-eminent activity—flying. Their structure, outside and inside, constitutes a solution to the problems imposed by flight. Their uniformity has been thrust on them by the drastic demands that determine the design of any flying machine. Birds simply dare not deviate widely from sound aerodynamic design. Nature liquidates deviationists much more consistently and drastically than does any totalitarian dictator.

Birds were able to become flying machines largely through the evolutionary gifts of feathers, wings, hollow bones, warm-bloodedness, a remarkable system of respiration, a strong, large heart and powerful breast muscles. These adaptations all boil down to the two prime requirements for any flying machine: high power and low weight. Birds have thrown all excess baggage overboard. To keep their weight low and feathers dry they forego the luxury of sweat glands. They have even reduced

INTERNAL STRUCTURE of the metacarpal bone of a vulture's wing is shown in this drawing of a longitudinal section. The braces within the bone are almost identical in geometry with those of the Warren truss commonly used as a steel structural member.

their reproductive organs to a minimum. The female has only one ovary, and during the nonbreeding season the sex organs of both males and females atrophy. T. H. Bissonette, the well-known investigator of birds and photoperiodicity, found that in starlings the organs weigh 1,500 times as much during the breeding season as during the rest of the year.

As early as 1679 the Italian physicist Giovanni Borelli, in his *De motu animalium*, noted some of the weight-saving features of bird anatomy: ". . . the body of a Bird is disproportionately lighter than that of man or of any quadruped . . . since the bones of birds are porous, hollowed out to extreme thinness like the roots of the feathers, and the shoulder bones, ribs and wing bones are of little substance; the breast and abdomen contain large cavities filled with air; while the feathers and the down are of exceeding lightness."

The skeleton of a pigeon accounts for only 4.4 per cent of its total body weight, whereas in a comparable mammal such as a white rat it amounts to 5.6 per cent. This in spite of the fact that the bird must have larger and stronger breast bones for the muscles powering its wings and larger pelvic bones to support its locomotion on two legs. The ornithologist Robert Cushman Murphy has reported that the skeleton of a frigate bird with a seven-foot wingspread weighed only four ounces, which was less than the weight of its feathers!

Although a bird's skeleton is extremely light, it is also very strong and elastic—necessary characteristics in an air frame subjected to the great and sudden stresses of aerial acrobatics. This combination of lightness and strength depends mainly on the evolution of hollow, thin bones coupled with a considerable fusion of bones which ordinarily are separate in other vertebrates. The bones of a bird's sacrum and hip girdle, for example, are molded together into a thin, tube-like structure—strong but phenomenally light. Its hollow finger bones are fused together, and in large soaring birds some of these bones have internal trusslike supports, very like the struts inside airplane wings. Similar struts sometimes are seen in the hollow larger bones of the wings and legs.

To "trim ship" further, birds have evolved heads which are very light in proportion to the rest of the body. This has been accomplished through the simple device of eliminating teeth and the accompanying heavy jaws and jaw muscles. A pigeon's skull weighs about

FRIGATE BIRD has a seven-foot wing span, but its skeleton weighs only four ounces. This is less than the weight of its feathers. The skeleton is shown against the outline of the bird.

one sixth as much, proportionately, as that of a rat; its skull represents only one fifth of 1 per cent of its total body weight. In birds the function of the teeth has been taken over largely by the gizzard, located near the bird's center of gravity. The thin, hollow bones of a bird's skull have a remarkably strong re-inforced construction [see photograph on page 65]. Elliott Coues, the 19th-century U. S. ornithologist, referred to the beautifully adapted avian skull as a "poem in bone."

The long, lizard-like tail that birds inherited from their reptilian ancestors has been reduced to a small plate of bone at the end of the vertebrae. The ribs of a bird are elegantly long, flat, thin and jointed; they allow extensive movement for breathing and flying, yet are light and strong. Each rib overlaps its neighbor— an arrangement which gives the kind of resilient strength achieved by a woven splint basket.

Feathers, the bird's most distinctive and remarkable acquisition, are magnificently adapted for fanning the air, for insulation against the weather and for reduction of weight. It has been claimed that for their weight they are stronger than any wing structure devised by man. Their flexibility allows the broad trailing edge of each large wing-feather to bend upward with each downstroke of the wing. This produces the equivalent of pitch in a propeller blade, so that each wingbeat provides both lift and forward propulsion. When a bird is landing or taking off, its strong wingbeats separate the large primary wing feathers at their tips, thus forming wing-slots which help prevent stalling. It seems remarkable that man took so long to learn some of the fundamentals of airplane design which even the lowliest English sparrow demonstrates to perfection [see "Bird Aerodynamics," by John H. Storer, beginning on page 57 in this book].

Besides all this, feathers cloak birds with an extraordinarily effective insulation—so effective that they can live in parts of the Antarctic too cold for any other animal.

The streamlining of birds of course is the envy of all aircraft designers. The bird's awkwardly angular body is trimmed with a set of large quill, or contour, feathers which shape it to the utmost in sleekness. A bird has no ear lobes sticking out of its head. It commonly retracts its "landing gear" (legs) while in flight. As a result birds are far and away the fastest creatures on our planet. The smoothly streamlined peregrine falcon is reputed to dive on its prey at speeds up to 180 miles per hour. (Some rapid fliers have baffles in their nostrils to protect their lungs and air sacs from excessive air pressures.) Even in the water, birds are among the swiftest of animals: Murphy once timed an Antarctic penguin swimming under water at an estimated speed of about 22 miles per hour.

A basic law of chemistry holds that the velocity of any chemical reaction roughly doubles with each rise of 10 degrees centigrade in temperature. In nature the race often goes to the metabolically swift. And birds have evolved the highest operating temperatures of all animals. Man, with his conservative 98.6

AIR SACS connected to the lungs of a pigeon not only lighten the bird but also add to the efficiency of its respiration and cooling. The lungs are indicated by the two dark areas in the center. Two of the air sacs are within the large bones of the bird's upper "arm."

degrees Fahrenheit, is a metabolic slow-poke compared with sparrows (107 degrees) or some thrushes (113 degrees). Birds burn their metabolic candles at both ends, and as a result live short but intense lives. The average wild songbird survives less than two years.

Behind this high temperature in birds lie some interesting circulatory and respiratory refinements. Birds, like mammals, have a four-chambered heart which allows a double circulation, that is, the blood makes a side trip through the lungs for purification before it is circulated through the body again. A bird's heart is large, powerful and rapid-beating [*see table of comparisons on page 6*]. In both mammals and birds the heart rate, and the size of the heart in proportion to the total body, increases as the animals get smaller. But the increases seem significantly greater in birds than in mammals. Any man with a weak heart knows that climbing stairs puts a heavy strain on his pumping system. Birds do a lot of "climbing," and their circulatory systems are built for it.

The blood of birds is not significantly richer in hemoglobin than that of mammals. The pigeon and the mallard have about 15 grams of hemoglobin per 100 cubic centimeters of blood—the same as man. However, the concentration of sugar in their blood averages about twice as high as in mammals. And their blood pressure, as one would expect, also is somewhat higher: in the pigeon it averages 145 millimeters of mercury; in the chicken, 180 millimeters; in the rat, 106 millimeters; in man, 120 millimeters.

In addition to conventional lungs, birds possess an accessory system of five or more pairs of air sacs, connected with the lungs, that ramify widely throughout the body. Branches of these sacs extend into the hollow bones, sometimes even into the small toe bones. The air-sac system not only contributes to the birds' lightness of weight but also supplements the lungs as a supercharger (adding to the efficiency of respiration) and serves as a cooling system for the birds' speedy, hot metabolism. It has been estimated that a flying pigeon uses one fourth of its air intake for breathing and three fourths for cooling.

The lungs of man constitute about 5 per cent of his body volume; the respiratory system of a duck, in contrast, makes up 20 per cent of the body volume (2 per cent lungs and 18 per cent air sacs). The anatomical connections of the lungs and air sacs in birds seem to provide a one-way traffic of air through most of the system, bringing in a constant stream of unmixed fresh air, whereas in the lungs of mammals stale air is mixed inefficiently with the fresh. It seems odd that natural selection has never produced a stale air outlet for animals. The air sacs of birds apparently approach this ideal more closely than any other vertebrate adaptation.

Even in the foods they select to feed their engines birds conserve weight. They burn "high-octane gasoline." Their foods are rich in caloric energy—seeds, fruits, worms, insects, rodents, fish and so on. They eat no low-calorie foods such as leaves or grass; a wood-burning engine has no place in a flying machine. Furthermore, the food birds eat is burned quickly and efficiently. Fruit fed to a young cedar waxwing passes through its digestive tract in an average time of 27 minutes. A thrush that is fed blackberries will excrete the seeds 45 minutes later. Young bluejays take between 55 and 105 minutes to pass food through their bodies. Moreover, birds utilize a greater portion of the food they eat than do mammals. A three-weeks-old stork, eating a pound of food (fish, frogs and other animals), gains about a third of a pound in weight. This 33 per cent utilization of food compares roughly with an average figure of about 10 per cent in a growing mammal.

The breast muscles of a bird are the engine that drives its propellers or wings. In a strong flier, such as the pigeon, these muscles may account for as much as one half the total body weight. On the other hand, some species—*e.g.*, the albatross—fly largely on updrafts of air, as a glider does. In such birds the breast muscles are greatly re-

SKULL OF A CROW achieves the desirable aerodynamic result of making the bird light in the head. Heavy jaws are sacrificed. Their work is largely taken over by the gizzard.

FRONTAL BONE in the skull of a crow is cut through to show its hollow and braced internal construction. The skull of the bird accounts for less than 1 per cent of its total weight.

HEART	PER CENT OF BODY WEIGHT	HEART BEATS PER MINUTE
FROG	.57	22
MAN	.42	72
PIGEON	1.71	135
CANARY	1.68	514
HUMMINGBIRD	2.37	615

HEART WEIGHT and pulse rate are compared for a number of animals. The hearts of birds are relatively large for body size.

duced, and there are well-developed wing tendons and ligaments which enable the bird to hold its wings in the soaring position with little or no effort.

A bird may have strong breast muscles and still be incapable of sustained flight because of an inadequate blood supply to these muscles. This condition is shown in the color of the muscles; that is the explanation of the "white meat" of the chicken and the turkey—their breast muscles have so few blood vessels that they cannot get far off the ground. The dark meat of their legs, on the other hand, indicates a good blood supply and an ability to run a considerable distance without tiring.

After a ruffed grouse has been flushed four times in rapid succession, its breast muscles become so fatigued that it can be picked up by hand. The blood supply is simply inadequate to bring in fuel and carry away waste products fast enough. Xenophon's *Anabasis* relates the capture of bustards in exactly this manner: "But as for the Bustards, anyone can catch them by starting them up quickly; for they fly only a short distance like the partridge and soon tire. And their flesh was very sweet."

In birds the active phase of the breathing cycle is not in inhaling but exhaling. Their wing strokes compress the rib case to expel the air. Thus instead of "running out of breath" birds "fly into breath."

Probably the fastest metabolizing vertebrate on earth is the tiny Allen's hummingbird [see "The Metabolism of Hummingbirds," by Oliver P. Pearson; SCIENTIFIC AMERICAN, January, 1953]. While hovering it consumes about 80 cubic centimeters of oxygen per gram of body weight per hour. Even at rest its metabolic rate is more than 50 times as fast as man's. Interestingly enough, the hovering hummingbird uses energy at about the same proportionate rate as a hovering helicopter. This does not mean that man has equalled nature in the efficiency of energy yield from fuel. To hover the hummingbird requires a great deal more energy, because of the aerodynamic inefficiency of its small wings and its very high loss of energy as dissipated heat. The tiny wings of a hummingbird impose on the bird an almost incredible expenditure of effort. Its breast muscles are estimated to be approximately four times as large, proportionately, as those of a pigeon. This great muscle burden is one price a hummingbird pays for being small.

A more obvious index of the efficiency of bird's fuel consumption is the high mileage of the golden plover. In the fall the plover fattens itself on bayberries in Labrador and then strikes off across the open ocean on a nonstop flight of 2,400 miles to South America. It arrives there weighing some two ounces less than it did on its departure. This is the equivalent of flying a 1,000-pound airplane 20 miles on a pint of gasoline rather than the usual gallon. Man still has far to go to approach such efficiency.

7

The Brain of Birds

LAURENCE JAY STETTNER AND KENNETH A. MATYNIAK · June 1968

In the lexicon of insult few terms are as disparaging as "bird brain." The derivation of the term is obvious. In comparison with the brains of even the most primitive mammals the avian brain seems a pathetic object. The brain of a bird is not only tiny in size but also notably backward in development of the cerebral cortex, the principal organ of intelligence in the higher animals. Yet investigations of the intelligence of animals have shown that the physical aspect of the bird brain is deceiving. Birds have demonstrated in test after test that they are capable of highly intelligent behavior, sometimes surpassing the abilities of mammals with greatly superior cortical development. These findings indicate that studies of the avian brain could be a revealing guide to the sources and evolution of intelligent behavior.

That birds possess certain remarkable sensibilities has of course been noted ever since bird-watching began. Their uncanny powers of navigation in long migrations, their intricate nest-building and their devoted parental behavior have impressed all students of these animals. Still, these activities could be attributed to inborn, stereotyped patterns of behavior rather than to intelligence. They have generally been regarded as "instinctive" in nature, not involving the flexibility and ability to learn that are the earmarks of intellectual activity. The modern studies of the learning abilities of birds by B. F. Skinner of Harvard University and by other investigators, however, cast a completely new light on avian intelligence. Skinner, who used the pigeon as one of his principal subjects in his experimental studies of learning,

found that pigeons were quite flexible in adjusting their behavior to a variety of learning tasks. By now a considerable body of evidence on the learning capacities of birds has been accumulated by a number of investigators, including our group at Wayne State University. Let us review the findings.

It is not easy to devise an experiment that affords a clear test of animal intelligence, and it is still more difficult to design one that will serve for comparative testing of various animals. The Bryn Mawr College psychologist M. E. Bitterman succeeded in working out a relatively simple type of problem that tests an animal's mental flexibility or, in other words, its ability to solve a problem by repeatedly changing or modifying its behavior to meet new conditions [see "The Evolution of Intelligence," by M. E. Bitterman; SCIENTIFIC AMERICAN Offprint 490]. The test is called "multiple reversal." After the animal has learned to choose between two symbols (say a circle rather than a square) in order to obtain a food reward, the "correct" symbol is reversed (from the circle to the square), so that the animal must now switch to choosing the symbol that was previously unrewarded. The experimenter repeats the reversal many times, and the animal's learning is measured by how soon it "catches on" that after the selection of one symbol is no longer rewarded it must switch to the other to gain the reward again. Bitterman found that fishes did not show any improvement in learning such a problem; after each reversal they made about the same number of fruitless selections of the old rewarded symbol before they switched to the new one. Rats, on the other hand, improved as the reversal program proceeded; they made fewer and fewer fruitless trials and eventually learned to switch to

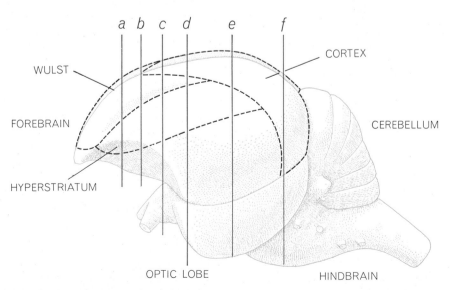

BRAIN OF A BIRD has a small and undeveloped cortex but an extensive striatum that lies above the brain's large optic lobe. The brain illustrated is that of a quail, the bird used in the authors' experiments. Broken lines surround the cortex and two parts of the striatum, the "*Wulst*" and the hyperstriatum. Vertical lines identify the areas seen in transverse section in the illustration on the opposite page, in which the cortex and striatum are contrasted.

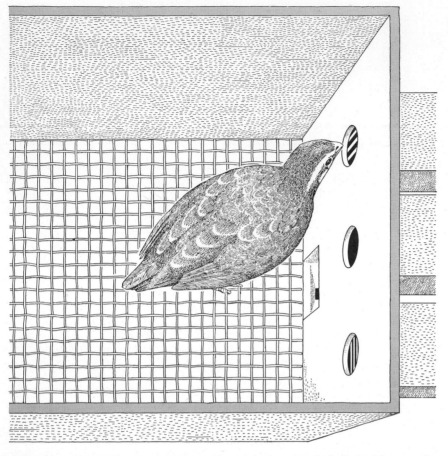

TESTING CHAMBER is seen from above. The images between which the bird learns to discriminate are projected on translucent "pecking plates" that can be reached through the holes in the chamber wall. When the bird pecks the right image, it is rewarded with food.

PECKING PLATE

MULTIPLE PROJECTOR

TO RECORDER

SOLENOID

FEEDING MECHANISM

CUTAWAY VIEW of testing apparatus shows one of three multiple projectors and part of the circuitry connecting the pecking plate with the solenoid-actuated food lift. The bird's correct and incorrect responses to the various projected stimuli are recorded automatically.

the new symbol after only one or two unsuccessful trials at the old.

How do birds do in this test? Bitterman noted that pigeons showed the same "more intelligent" pattern that rats did. And the pigeon is by no means the most proficient learner among the birds. Experiments in our laboratory and by Robert Gossette of Hofstra University have demonstrated that crows, ravens, magpies, myna birds and parrots surpass the pigeon's performance in reversal learning. On the whole, birds do at least as well as many mammals on this measure of learning capacity.

Let us go on to a somewhat more exacting measure: a sophisticated test designed to measure the learning ability of primates rather than of lower mammals such as the rat. In this test, designed by Harry F. Harlow of the University of Wisconsin, the animal must learn a general approach for successful solution of various problems that involve the same principle but are presented in different physical forms. The animal is required to "learn how to learn" the answer; in technical terminology, the subject must form a learning "set." For instance, the animal may be confronted with a bowl and a shoe and receive a food reward if it touches the bowl rather than the shoe. The objects are then shifted about in further trials, and the animal must learn to choose the bowl every time, regardless of its position. After learning this lesson the animal is presented with a series of pairs of objects that entail the same type of recognition. There are a number of forms of the test; the irrelevant variable may be some factor other than the positions of the objects. Harlow has found that in the first presentation it may take a rhesus monkey, for example, some 50 to 60 trials to learn to touch the correct object regardless of position, but in later presentations the animal eventually is able to identify the rewarded object in only one or two trials. Harlow and other investigators have demonstrated that this type of test provides a measure of differences in intelligence among the various primates. Those with a more highly developed cerebral cortex show a greater capacity for forming learning sets. Thus New World cebid monkeys do better than the more primitive marmosets, rhesus monkeys do better than New World monkeys and chimpanzees in turn do better than rhesus monkeys. Learning set has been regarded as a supertest suitable only for primates; the performance of lower mammals on this test is consistently very poor.

How, then, do birds fare on learning

a   *b*   *c*

REWARD   REWARD   REWARD

REVERSAL LEARNING occurs in two steps. At first the animal learns that one visual pattern, in this example horizontal stripes, is rewarded regardless of where it may appear (*"a" and "b"*). Next the previously unrewarded pattern is made rewarding (*c*) and the number of wrong responses before discovery of the reversal is noted. As tests continue, the higher animals learn to reverse more quickly.

set? So far only two representatives—the pigeon and the chicken—have been tested, and both did better than any non-primate mammal had done; in fact, the chickens even outperformed the marmoset!

A still more complex learning task for animals is the "oddity" problem: selection of the odd member among three stimuli, two of which are alike. The complexity is introduced by changing the display or the odd stimulus from one trial to the next. For example, in Trial 1 the presentation may be circle, circle, square in a horizontal row; in Trial 2, square, circle, circle; in Trial 3, square, square, circle, so that the odd member is no longer a square but a circle. The animal cannot attach its response to a particular shape or position; it must take the total situation into account and respond to a relationship. Can birds master such a problem? The answer is yes. Monkeys, cats *and* pigeons have shown the ability to learn to pick out the odd member of a given trio of objects.

The oddity problem can be carried a step further. Is the animal capable of forming a learning set from such an experience, that is, can it generalize the oddity principle by applying it to various stimuli? Having learned to pick the odd figure out of circles and squares, will it also be able to do so when it is presented with, say, two rectangles and a triangle or two shoes and a bowl? To the human mind such a transfer of learning seems so elementary that one might suppose it should not be at all difficult for any animal that is capable of solving the initial oddity problem. It turns out that such is not the case. Even monkeys have some difficulty with the problem; they learn to generalize the oddity prin-

FISH
DECORTICATED RAT
PIGEON
MYNA BIRD
RAT

MULTIPLE-REVERSAL SCORES made by animals representing three vertebrate classes are compared. The lowest class tested, fishes, showed no improvement in learning. The same proved true of rats, members of the highest class tested, when they had suffered brain damage. Normal rats quickly mastered the problem. Pigeons did so almost as quickly as rats, and myna birds outdid pigeons. Data, except those for myna birds, are from studies by M. E. Bitterman of Bryn Mawr College. Robert Gossette of Hofstra University ran the myna tests.

ciple only after they have undergone the experience of solving many different oddity problems in succession. On the other hand, cats, as J. M. Warren of Pennsylvania State University has found, do not form the oddity learning set even after mastering 30 individual oddity problems. What the cat cannot accom-plish, however, the canary can. Nicholas Pastore of Queens College of the City University of New York presented ca-naries with an array of nine three-dimen-sional objects, eight of which were iden-tical. After the birds had learned that selection of the odd object brought a food reward, on later trials with new sets of objects they picked out the odd object in each set at the very first exposure.

Consider next another intellectual ca-pacity: the ability to count or, more pre-cisely, to respond to the property of number. Even primates have consider-able difficulty with this task. Herbert Woodrow of the University of Illinois

ANIMAL DILEMMA was devised by L. V. Krushinsky of Moscow State University. An animal feeds from one of two bowls by reach-ing through a narrow slot in the center of a wide screen (a). The bowls are then moved out of sight behind swinging doors. Seeing the bowl with food in motion, the animal may pursue it or not (b). Movement in the correct direction allows the feeding to resume.

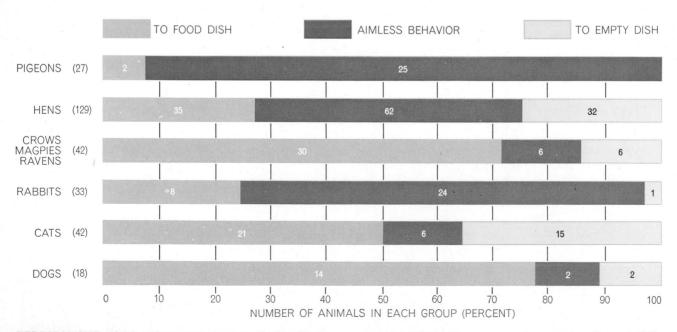

PERFORMANCE of birds and mammals in solving the Krushinsky problem is compared in this graph. Dogs made the best scores, but crows and their relatives were nearly as good as dogs and better than cats or rabbits. Hens outscored rabbits; pigeons did worst.

found, for example, that it took 21,000 trials to teach a monkey to distinguish reliably between the sounding of two tones and the sounding of three. For lower mammals such a task is of course a great deal more formidable. Frank Wesley of Portland State College attempted to teach rats to discriminate a single tone from two tones, but after 3,000 trials had produced no observable progress he gave up.

Birds, on the other hand, consistently master counting problems a great deal more complex than these. For example, the German ethologist Otto Koehler and his co-workers trained pigeons to discriminate four "objects" (or stimuli) from five, and they found in various experiments that ravens and parakeets could learn to "count" up to seven. In one form of these tests a raven was shown a key card with a certain number of spots on it and then was presented with an array of containers, each with a different number of spots on the lid; if the raven chose the lid displaying the same number of spots as the key card did, it was rewarded with a worm. The raven learned to find the matching number up to as many as seven spots, regardless of variation in the sizes, shapes or arrangements of the spots. This ability to respond to number per se, without reference to other properties of the stimulus, seems to be very unusual indeed among animals. For instance, the German zoologist Bernhard Rensch found that an elephant (which presumably ranks high in intelligence among mammals), after learning to discriminate a card with three circles on it from one with four circles, failed completely when the symbols were switched from circles to squares, and it took the animal 440 trials to learn this "new" problem [see "The Intelligence of Elephants," by B. Rensch; SCIENTIFIC AMERICAN Offprint 421]. In contrast, the Wayne State University psychologist Leland Swenson showed that a raven, confronted with a similar switch, solved it readily; the bird, having learned to discriminate one circle from two, scored better than 90 percent in trials in which the symbol was changed from the circle to a square, a triangle or an irregular form.

L. V. Krushinsky of the U.S.S.R., in an ingenious series of experiments at Moscow State University, has uncovered still another facet of avian intelligence. He places two bowls behind a slit in the center of a large screen; one bowl contains food and the animal eats from it. Then both bowls are suddenly moved out of sight, one to the left and one to the right. The problem in this case is one not of learning but of making a modest extrapolation from the visual information available to the animal; if the animal goes around the screen on the side toward which the food bowl has disappeared, it regains the food. Krushinsky has tested dogs, cats, rabbits, pigeons, hens, crows, magpies and ravens on this problem. Rabbits, hens and pigeons do poorly; they tend to move around haphazardly after the food disappears, and most of them do not go behind the screen. Cats go around the screen, but they are as likely to go to the wrong side as to the correct one; it takes many repetitions of the experiment for the cat to catch on and move to the correct side each time. Only dogs, crows and crow relatives solve the problem immediately. A majority of them go promptly and directly to the correct side of the screen the first time they are presented with the case of the disappearing bowls.

Here, then, is another demonstration of a bird's capacity for intelligent behavior. Moreover, the test differentiates among the birds, showing that crows and their relatives are superior to the hen and the pigeon (whose performance is the poorest). The fact that these birds best the cat and match the performance of the dog indicates a surprisingly high level of mental power for a bird brain.

The general tenor of all the results reviewed above is unmistakable. It is true that the total volume of evidence so far is not large, and many more comparative studies will have to be made in order to arrive at an accurate and detailed evaluation of the intellectual capacities of birds. Nevertheless, the consistency of the evidence already established cannot be ignored. It points to the conclusion that birds are capable of intelligent achievements equaling or even exceeding those of many mammals. Even if future studies should reestablish mammalian superiority, it cannot be denied that birds show some mental capabilities that have long been thought to belong solely to animals with a well-developed cerebral cortex.

Krushinsky has recently written: "The last decades have markedly changed the previously widespread idea that the behavior of birds is less plastic than the behavior of mammals." It cannot be said that the new view is shared by scientists generally. Many of them are still reluctant to accept the full implications of the experimental evidence, primarily because the avian cerebral cortex is so obviously primitive. It has therefore become essential to take a closer look at the avian brain to see if it has developed some other structure that may account for the birds' apparent intellectual abilities.

There is little question that among mammals the degree of intelligence depends on the size and complexity of the cerebral cortex. The organ shows a clear picture of evolutionary development going up the mammalian order. In the rat the cortex is smooth (without folds or convolutions) and is comparatively undeveloped in the frontal area; in the dog the cortex has a larger surface, some convolutions and greater frontal development; in the monkey it is still further expanded and more convoluted, and in man the cortex has become so extensive and complex that it is plainly distinguishable from that of all other animals. Within any single species (including man) the intelligence of normal individuals cannot be correlated with differences in their cortical development (at least not on the basis of present knowledge), but where there are major differences in cortical development from one species of mammal to another one finds a clear correlation with the degree of intelligence.

In both mammals and birds the cerebrum, or forebrain, contains two major types of structure: the cortex and a lower portion called the striatum. The two structures were inherited from the reptiles. They developed very differently, however, in the mammals and the birds. In the mammals the cortex became dominant, overgrowing and covering the striatum until, in man, the nerve cells of the striatum are deeply buried and intermingled with cortical fibers that have invaded the forebrain interior. In the birds, on the other hand, the main development has taken place in the striatum, while the cortex has become a thin layer of tissue covering only the top and side surfaces of the forebrain. The striatum in birds is a totally integrated, highly organized mass of nerve nuclei and fiber tracts and makes up most of the bulk of the cerebral hemispheres. In particular, the uppermost part of the striatum, called the hyperstriatum, is a well-developed structure that is not present at all in mammals.

A number of years ago the Harvard Medical School neurologist Stanley Cobb, a pioneer in comparative investigations of the brains of birds, suggested that the cortex played little or no part in the mental processes of birds; in fact, he noted that in their case the anatomy indicated a negative correlation between cortical development and intelligence. He deduced that the principal function of the cortex in birds was in relation to

TRANSVERSE SECTIONS of a quail's forebrain appear in these six micrographs. The outline drawing below each micrograph shows the salient anatomical features. The smallness and shallowness of the cortex, in contrast to the extensive area occupied by various components of the striatum, is evident in sections *b, c* and *d*. The cortex becomes enlarged only toward the rear of the forebrain.

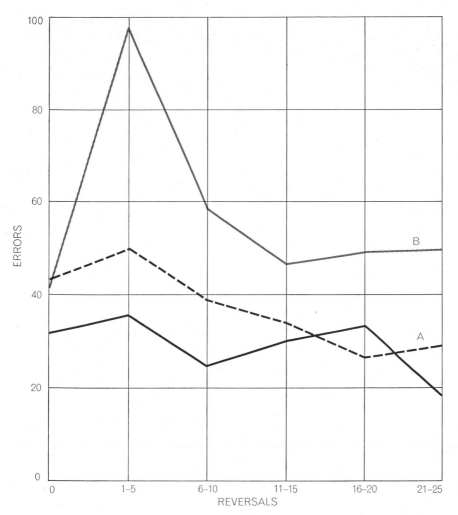

BRAIN DAMAGE resulting from surgical removal of the cortex and of both *Wulst* and cortex produces alterations in the capability of quail to improve reversal learning scores. Solid black line shows improved performance of normal birds over 25 trials. Other lines show performance of birds that were deprived of cortex (*A*) and of both brain tissues (*B*).

the sense of smell, and that as the more advanced avian species came to depend less on this sense the cortex shrank in size and importance. From his many anatomical studies of the brains of birds Cobb concluded that the avian "organ of intelligence" was not the cortex but the hyperstriatum.

Cobb did this on the grounds that examination of the brains of various birds had shown that species considered to be more intelligent have a more highly developed hyperstriatum; for example, in the crow, the parrot and the canary this organ is more prominent than in the chicken, the quail and the pigeon. More precise anatomical evidence supporting the notion that "hyperstriatum is to birds what cortex is to mammals" has recently come from the detailed work on avian brain structure done by Harvey Karten at the Massachusetts Institute of Technology. Karten has described an area of the hyperstriatum that receives the same type of neural connec-

tions in the avian brain as the vision area in the cortex of a mammal's brain.

Various items of evidence involving behavior tend to support these anatomical findings. It has long been known that complete removal of the cortical tissue from a bird's brain does not noticeably impair the animal's motor or sensory abilities, whereas a mammal deprived of its cortex becomes at the least severely handicapped in these respects. Recently H. P. Ziegler of the City University of New York showed that pigeons with extensive damage to their cortex could still perform normally in tests of visual discrimination such as learning to peck at a cross rather than a circle. On the other hand, he found that damage to the hyperstriatum greatly impaired birds' performance in such a test. Krushinsky found in his experiments that the performance of birds on the "around the screen" problem was perfectly correlated with the size of the hyperstriatum; the larger this structure (in proportion to

the total size of the cerebrum), the more readily the bird solved the problem. In contrast, the size of a bird's cortex was not at all correlated with ability to solve the problem.

The next inviting step is to explore the hyperstriatum of birds, with a view to finding out what specific structures within that organ are involved in given levels of learning ability. We have begun such experiments in our laboratory. Since Bitterman's multiple-reversal test had proved to be an effective means of differentiating among different species of animals with respect to their learning ability, and these differences in performance presumably reflected some critical difference in their neurological makeup, we selected the multiple-reversal test for our first experiments. As the initial structure for study we chose a bump on the top of the hyperstriatum called the *Wulst*. (It was so named by German investigators.)

Using bobwhite quail as our subjects, we removed the *Wulst* surgically and proceeded to examine the birds' capabilities. They recovered from the operation very quickly and appeared perfectly normal in their movements, eating and drinking behavior, reactions to people and so on. We first submitted the birds to tests involving only a simple form of learning. They learned to peck at a lighted window for food and to choose between vertical and horizontal stripes. Their behavior in these trials was so normal that we came to the conclusion they would certainly pass the multiple-reversal learning test. On the very first reversal problem, however, the birds showed in dramatic fashion that the operation had indeed seriously impaired some aspect of their intellectual functioning. Every bird that had had its *Wulst* removed displayed tremendous difficulty in learning to reverse its choice; this was true even of two birds that before the operation had been trained to a high level of proficiency in reversal. Evidently the *Wulst* not only contained neurological machinery involved in the reversal learning process but also was involved in the function of memory.

Clearly the birds' difficulties with the reversal test were not due to any impairment of their basic motor, sensory or motivational functions. The brain-damaged birds did not differ from normal ones in their movements, their pecking speed and persistence, their pecking accuracy, their responses to food or their ability to learn to make a simple choice between two different visual stimuli. In fact, in the reversal test they continued to peck consistently at the stimulus that had previously represented a food reward, which convincingly demonstrates that they were able to see the differences between the stimuli.

There are indications that some parts of the avian cortex, as well as the *Wulst*, may be involved in reversal learning. In our original experiments we removed much of the overlying cortical tissue along with the *Wulst*. Later, in order to pin down what tissues were actually involved, we tested birds with only the *Wulst* removed and others with only cortical tissue removed. All the birds that lacked only the *Wulst* showed deficiencies in reversal learning, confirming that it is an important structure in avian learning capacity. Removal of parts of the cortex, on the other hand, left this ability unimpaired in most cases. In some instances, however, cortical excision did impair the ability, although

not as much as excision of the *Wulst* did. We are now investigating the possibility that some part or parts of the cortex are functionally involved with the *Wulst* in the higher learning processes.

The discovery of the intellectual capabilities of the avian hyperstriatum has given us a fascinating new avenue for the investigation of brain processes. As a "thinking machine" that is now found to possess many of the capacities of the mammalian cortex, the hyperstriatum is much more accessible to study than the cortex, and its basic operations should be simpler to unravel. Indeed, the hyperstriatum may turn out to be a kind of Rosetta stone for brain researchers. Investigators of the neurology of higher mental processes have been struggling for many years to decipher the message written in the almost impene-

trable code of the extraordinarily complex mammalian cerebral cortex. In the hyperstriatum we now have another message that says almost the same thing but in a simpler code. By analyzing the simpler code and comparing the two codes, which obviously are related to each other, it should be possible to speed up progress toward understanding the basis of intelligence.

It was the lowly fruit fly that provided the key that opened the door to the modern study of heredity and the eventual decipherment of the genetic code, and the giant axon of the squid similarly has made large contributions to our understanding of the transmission of messages by the nervous system. Perhaps the much maligned bird brain will eventually make a key contribution to the understanding of how the brain works to produce intelligent behavior.

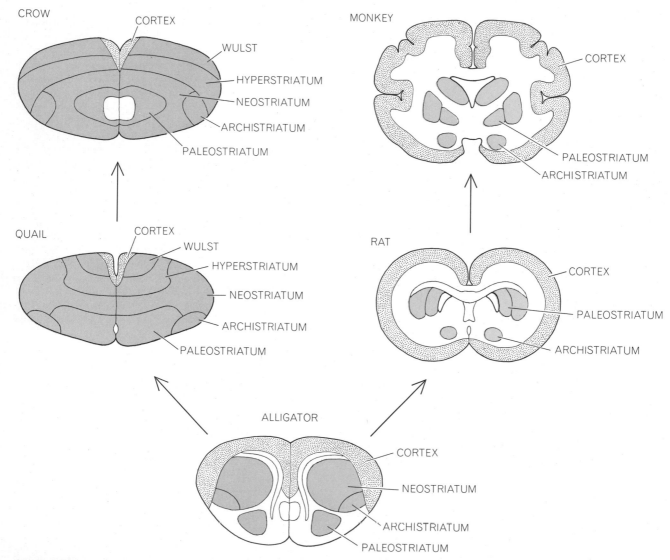

FOREBRAIN EVOLUTION followed separate lines among birds and mammals. Both groups stem from reptilian ancestors, represented here by an alligator's brain seen in transverse section. In it striatal tissue is more abundant than cortical tissue. The trend cli-

maxes in the great enlargement of the hyperstriatum among the birds noted for highly intelligent behavior, such as crows. Among mammals the evolutionary trend progressed in the opposite direction, fostering development of a larger and more complex cortex.

II

Vascular System Biology

The arteries have no sensation, for they even are without blood, nor do they all contain the breath of life; and when they are cut only the part of the body concerned is paralysed...the veins spread underneath the whole skin, finally ending in very thin threads, and they narrow down into such an extremely minute size that the blood cannot pass through them nor can anything else but the moisture passing out from the blood in innumerable small drops which is called sweat.

Pliny
NATURAL HISTORY, XI, LXXXIX.

II
Vascular System Biology

INTRODUCTION

Perhaps the most complex regulatory network in vertebrates involves the control of oxygen and carbon dioxide levels in the body. In homeotherms the temperature-regulating center and its connections impinge in many ways on the breathing and heart-rate systems. In "The Physiology of Exercise" Carleton Chapman and Jere Mitchell introduce the general subject of the vascular system with a general discussion of responses of higher vertebrates to exercise. They touch upon many topics that are treated in greater detail by subsequent articles in this section, and in the sections on respiratory adaptations and temperature.

We know a great deal about the evolution of the blood vascular system in vertebrates. Changes in the routes of flow, in the control machinery, and in the respiratory pigment complement each other throughout vertebrate history. Let us consider, first, some properties of the pigment, hemoglobin.

Each molecule of hemoglobin is a complex of the protein globin and four heme groups; each heme is a porphyrin molecule containing an iron atom. Oxygen binds reversibly to the iron in a manner that varies with the partial pressure of the gas in the neighborhood of the hemoglobin; thus, as partial pressure rises, binding rises, and vice versa. This relationship is described by a sigmoid curve (the oxygen dissociation curve, see page 00) that has a characteristic shape for each vertebrate species. The sigmoid shape reflects the following facts: it is somewhat difficult for the first heme group of a hemoglobin molecule to load the first molecule of oxygen; once the first oxygen is loaded, it is much easier for the second and third groups to load the second and third oxygen molecules, and very easy for the fourth group to load the fourth molecule. This loading pattern results from alterations in the three-dimensional shape of globin. When the first oxygen is bound, the globin changes shape, enabling the remaining hemes to interact with each other and to load more readily. The process is called heme-heme interaction.

The position of the dissociation curve at various partial pressures of oxygen defines the hemoglobin's affinity for oxygen. Curves for most fish bloods show complete loading at relatively low tensions. Such hemoglobin is said to have a "high" affinity for oxygen because it binds the oxygen avidly at low partial pressure. Terrestrial vertebrates (and, in particular, birds and mammals) have curves far to the right (see Figure 1) of those of fish; their hemoglobin has a "low" affinity for oxygen and loads only at the high partial pressure of oxygen in normal air. The low affinity of avian and mammalian hemoglobin for oxygen is of vital importance for high rates of metabolism and elevated body temperature. Low affinity in effect means that the hemoglobin *unloads* its oxygen in the tissues at relatively high partial pressures (pressures at which fish hemoglobin would remain completely loaded). This allows more oxygen to be present around and in cells, a necessity for the high rates of metabolism required for body temperatures of 37 to 40 degrees centigrade.

Dissociation curves are affected by carbon dioxide levels (the Bohr effect, see Chapman and Mitchell), and the protein packing within cells. An increase in carbon dioxide dissolved in blood lowers the pH (some other agents also produce hydrogen ions and lower the pH) and thus decreases hemoglobin's affinity for oxygen; consequently, dissociation occurs more readily in tissue spaces where carbon dioxide is produced by metabolic activity. But in lung alveoli, where carbon dioxide is lost to the air and pH rises, affinity is increased and oxygen is bound more readily to hemoglobin. The Bohr effect was formerly thought to be mediated by the number of reactive sulfhydryl groups (—SH) in the vicinity of the heme moieties on the globin molecule. This now appears to be an oversimplification at best, and it is safest to conclude for the moment that dissociable groups effected by hydrogen ion concentrations affect the heme-oxygen binding interaction in a way that is still undefined.

Alterations in hemoglobins of different vertebrates provide several interesting lessons about the mechanisms of evolution. In terrestrial mammals the degree of the Bohr effect is inversely proportional to the body weight: mouse hemoglobin responds dramatically to increased carbon dioxide by giving up its oxygen very easily, and, as a result, it is a more "efficient" respiratory pigment; the larger the mammal, the less the hemoglobin responds to increased partial pressures of carbon dioxide.

These differences are attributable to the problem of temperature control. The surface area of a mouse is large in relation to its mass; hence, the area from which heat can be lost is great in proportion to the quantity of tissue producing heat. Because the animal cannot remain active (and warm) if oxygen levels fall, the exaggerated Bohr effect works to insure that this emergency does not arise. The proportions are the opposite in an elephant, whose body mass is large in relation to surface area. As a result, there is less chance of precipitous heat loss in the event of subnormal oxygen supply to the tissues. Interestingly, a large aquatic mammal capable of prolonged diving has a much greater Bohr effect than would be predicted on the basis of mass. Humpback whale hemoglobin is the Bohr equivalent of a guinea pig's, for instance, and shows significant

Figure 1. Oxygen dissociation curves for various vertebrates. Fish hemoglobin loads at low partial pressures of oxygen, whereas the pigment of the homeotherms requires much more oxygen in the environment before high percentages of saturation are reached.

decrease in affinity for oxygen under conditions of increasing carbon dioxide. This is obviously a special adaptation that permits rapid oxygen loading while the animal is at the surface, complete unloading as carbon dioxide accumulates during long dives, and tolerance of hydrogen ion production during such dives.

These and other physiological differences in the hemoglobins result from alterations in the amino acids of globin. Globin of mammals has a molecular weight of 64,500 and is composed of four subunits (two alpha units and two beta units). A heme is bound to each subunit. The hemoglobin of the most primitive living vertebrates, the cyclostomes, has a molecular weight of about 17,000, has one heme group, and shows a marked Bohr effect. Although the amino acid composition of cyclostome globin is very different from that of the globin in higher vertebrates, both types of molecules show the important property of undergoing conformational changes when oxygen binding occurs: thus heme-heme interactions take place. This conclusion is based upon the recent discovery of a *sigmoid* dissociation curve for lamprey hemoglobin. (Note that most texts quote the old finding that lamprey hemoglobin has a hyperbolic dissociation curve like that of the storage pigment myoglobin [see page 00]; this is incorrect and was probably the result of early experimentation with very dilute protein solutions.) At first glance, heme-heme interaction in lamprey hemoglobin seems paradoxical because only one heme is found on each molecule. The probable explanation is that hemoglobin aggregates as the protein concentration is raised, and that heme-heme interactions can occur in such aggregates, just as they do between the four subunits of higher vertebrate hemoglobin! It has been proposed that the single gene that produced a globin of 17,000 in cyclostomes, by processes of gene duplication and mutation, gave rise to the set of four genes that produces in higher vertebrates a four-unit globin with a molecular weight of almost 68,000.

In the course of vertebrate evolution, many amino acid substitutions have occurred, affecting the way that globin subunits bind to each other and to hemes, as well as altering dissociable groups near the hemes (the basis of the Bohr effect). These permutations of structure are the variations upon which natural selection has acted to yield hemoglobins adapted to different environments or ways of life.

As the blood pigment changed in the course of time, so did the vascular system and its controls. It seems likely that, in the earliest vertebrates, blood was originally propelled by rhythmic contractions along the main anterior ventral blood vessel. As these organisms increased in size, the pumping function apparently localized in a discrete region that was to become the heart. The walls of the blood vessel in that region acquired cardiac muscle cells and as a result thickened. Such a heart pump works most efficiently if its cavity is expanded somewhat beyond the resting volume before each contraction occurs. The four chambers of the primitive tubular vertebrate heart, such as that in some fish, appear to be stages for accomplishing this purpose by raising the blood pressure. When venous blood returns to the heart of a fish it is under such low pressure that it cannot expand the thick-walled anterior pump, the ventricle. Therefore, the blood first enters a thin-walled chamber, the sinus venosus, where it is propelled forward into a somewhat thicker-walled space, the atrium,

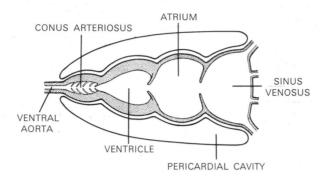

CONUS ARTERIOSUS   ATRIUM   SINUS VENOSUS   VENTRAL AORTA   VENTRICLE   PERICARDIAL CAVITY

Figure 2. The probable arrangement of the heart chambers in a primitive vertebrate. As blood flows from the right to the left through the heart, its pressure is raised by action of the increasingly thick muscular walls (stippled) of the chambers. Back flow is prevented by valves between the chambers. [After Torrey, Theodore W., *Morphogenesis of the Vertebrates*, Wiley, 1967.]

which finally raises blood pressure enough to expand the ventricle. This simplistic interpretation must be modified somewhat, because it does not take into account the elastic recoil of contracting cardiac muscle, a property that also tends to expand the chambers. The intricate workings of the modern heart are recounted in the article "The Heart" by Carl J. Wiggers. Then E. F. Adolph, in "The Heart's Pacemaker," points out that the various chambers each beat at a characteristic rate during the embryonic development of a vertebrate; the anteriormost chamber, which develops first, beats at the slowest rate, the next most posterior chamber develops next and sets the pace with a higher beat, and lastly the most posterior chamber forms and sets the final fast pace. The derivative of this chamber—the sinoatrial node—is the pacemaker in higher vertebrate adult hearts.

If we look at primitive cyclostome adults, we find that the rate of heart beat is determined by the sinus venosus; the beat is wholly myogenic (intrinsic to the muscle cells) in origin and no nerves accelerate or slow the beat. Interestingly, the heart muscle does not respond to direct application of acetylcholine, the agent liberated by the vagus nerve of higher vertebrates to decrease cardiac output. In higher bony fish and sharks, vagal fibers do innervate the heart and their discharge of acetylcholine slows the beat rate and decreases the amplitude of contraction; consequently, less blood is pumped. Finally, in terrestrial vertebrates, the vagus functions as it does in fish, and, in addition, sympathetic nerve fibers discharge noradrenaline, which accelerates the beat and increases its amplitude. Thus, we see three stages of control: myogenic, myogenic plus inhibition, and myogenic plus inhibition and stimulation. Clearly, more precise regulation is possible with such increasingly complex control circuitry. In the embryos of today's birds and mammals, the basic myogenic pattern described above occurs before nerve fibers reach the heart and during that period the cardiac muscle tissue does not respond to application of acetylcholine or noradrenaline. In this way, the developmental sequence within a single embryo reflects the events that occurred during vertebrate evolution.

Although the control of heart beat is the core of vertebrate circulatory regulation, the actual cardiac output (volume of blood pumped) in a mammal is determined to a great degree by the volume of blood returning to the heart through the veins. This quantity is governed by the degree of vasoconstriction of peripheral blood vessels (arterioles, capillaries, veins; see in particular "The Microcirculation of Blood" by Benjamin Zweifach).

Control of venous return is still not completely understood. For example, Edwin Wood ("The Venous System," *Scientific American,* January, 1968; Offprint #1093) has pointed out that when a man stands, return of blood upward through the veins of the leg is difficult because of gravity. Valves spaced along the veins prevent backflow and hold the blood in a series of stages. Nevertheless, a larger percent of total body blood accumulates in the legs. As this occurs, veins elsewhere in the body periphery contract and reduce their volume; this tends to maintain a constant volume of blood returning to the heart and so compensate for the temporary accumulation in the legs. The mechanisms coordinating such venous contraction are not understood, although it seems likely that the sympathetic nervous network is involved. At the cell level, noradrenaline released by sympathetic nerves causes contraction of smooth muscle cells in the walls of veins, thus causing vasoconstriction (remember that the sympathetics also stimulate contraction of cardiac muscle). Other sympathetic fibers innervate smooth muscle cells in the capillary system, where they *usually* evoke vasoconstriction (but, for unknown reasons, some muscle cells respond differently and relax, yielding vasodilation, when noradrenaline is released). The vasomotor center of the medulla in the brain must be the ultimate coordinating switchboard for all of these processes.

Two specialized parts of the circulatory system are discussed in "The Lymphatic System" by H. S. Mayerson and in the article on the rete mirabile, "'The Wonderful Net,'" by P. F. Scholander. Lymph vessels are found in all terrestrial vertebrates (and not just in mammals, as is implied by Mayerson). The higher blood pressures and rates of flow of the partially separate pulmonary circulation of amphibians and reptiles apparently produced leakage of plasma through the walls of blood capillaries. A collecting system evolved to drain the tissue spaces and to return the lost substances to the regular circulatory system. These lymphatic vessels are present in more complex form in birds and mammals.

Rete mirabile and countercurrent flow apparatus are used in many ways by vertebrates. Gases, heat, and some metabolites are commodities passed between the tiny vessels in which fluid flows in opposite directions. The diverse uses of these systems and their sporadic distribution among vertebrates raises interesting questions about genes and the evolutionary process. We assume a genetic basis for the developmental events underlying blood vessel formation and distribution. We have no idea, however, whether the "blood vessel" genes (sequences of DNA) that act during development of the fluke of a whale, are the same as those that bring about the formation of the leg of a heron, or the arm of a sloth—for in each animal, the structure of the rete mirabile is the same—or whether new genes, producing similar structural developments, appeared quite independently during evolution.

We can now add to Scholander's comments about the function of the rete mirabile in the fish swim bladder. The rete itself is responsible for the efficient exchange of gas (oxygen) from the capillary that carries blood away from the lumen of the bladder to the capillary that brings blood to the bladder. But, the extraordinarily high gas content of the bladder must depend upon a special secretion process. It may be due to the lactic acid which is apparently produced metabolically near the point where the capillaries bend from the incurrent to the excurrent direction. Because

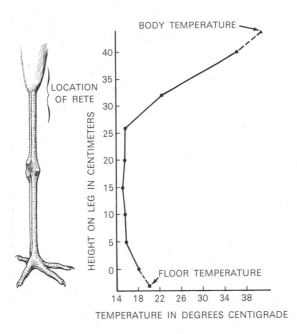

Figure 3. The role of the rete mirabile in conserving body heat is demonstrated by these data on the leg of a stork. The bird was in an environment between 11.5° and 13.0° C. Without the rete bed, the leg would be a major source of heat loss because it lacks insulating feathers. [After Kahl, M. P., Jr., *Physiol. Zool.* **36,** 1963.]

the lactic acid is exchanged between the rete capillaries, as is oxygen, its concentration rises as blood approaches the bend point in the wall of the bladder. This increasing quantity of acid lowers the pH, and because of the Bohr effect, hemoglobin in the blood gives up its oxygen more easily as this point is approached. The lactic acid is also thought to cause "salting out" of oxygen from the blood fluid. In other words, as the concentration of the acid rises, oxygen solubility decreases and transfer from blood fluid to swim bladder lumen is favored. In addition to these effects of lactic acid, the hemoglobin of many fishes with swim bladders shows a "Root effect," whereby the actual quantity of oxygen that can be bound at any one partial pressure of oxygen is decreased as pH falls (i.e., the oxygen dissociation curve does not move to the right as it does in the Bohr effect, but rather the upper segment of the curve is lowered, as shown in Figure 4). Thus, hemoglobin can unload oxygen, even though hundreds of atmospheres of oxygen may be present in the swim bladder.

The last article of this section, "The Ice Fish" by Johan H. Ruud, provides a good illustration of the versatility of vertebrates in taking advantage of special features of the environment. The ice fishes produce no hemoglobin, and, as Ruud suggests, they seem to have an extraordinarily large blood fluid volume that meets the demands of gas transport. Low rates of metabolism in very cold ocean waters demand far less oxygen and produce less carbon dioxide than would metabolism in warmer waters. Cold water also contains more dissolved oxygen than does warm water. This is probably important to ice fish who, because no hemoglobin passes through their gill capillaries, have no pigment to bind oxygen actively and to remove substantial quantities of it from the water. Instead, simple diffusion of oxygen into the blood fluid probably occurs. Consequently, the larger the quantity of dissolved oxygen in sea water, the greater the amounts that can diffuse per unit of time into the flowing blood.

Another group of vertebrates has taken advantage of the high oxygen

Figure 4. Oxygen dissociation curves showing the Bohr and Root effects. In the Bohr effect, the affinity of hemoglobin for oxygen decreases (the curve is displaced to the right). In the Root effect, the maximal quantity of oxygen that can combine with the respiratory pigment and be transported is decreased.

content of cold water in quite another way. In fast-running mountain streams, several types of lungless salamanders are found. These creatures have such extensive capillary nets in their skin that all gas exchange can occur there and no lungs are formed during embryonic development. A peripheral advantage of this modification is that the air-filled lungs are not present to act as buoyancy organs; therefore specific gravity of the body is greater and there is thus less chance of the animal being swept away in the rapidly flowing water currents. But unlike the ice fish, lungless salamanders do utilize hemoglobin and erythrocytes to transport oxygen.

8

The Physiology of Exercise

CARLETON B. CHAPMAN AND JERE H. MITCHELL • May 1965

When Peter Snell of New Zealand ran the mile in three minutes 54.4 seconds and Sixten Jernberg of Sweden covered 50 kilometers on skis in two hours 43 minutes 52.6 seconds, their record performances provided vivid testimony not only to their speed and endurance but also to the prodigious internal adjustments of which the human body is capable. An adult human being at rest gets along on about three-tenths of a liter of oxygen per minute; during maximal exertion the oxygen requirement increases to 10 or more times that amount. Since the body carries no appreciable reserve of oxygen (its entire store would be used up by the muscles in 20 seconds of strenuous exercise), this means that during exertion the body's machinery must step up enormously its intake and distribution of oxygen to the tissues, and it must be able to do so within seconds. On this basic fact hangs a tale that for nearly two centuries has provided physiologists with an absorbing realm of exploration.

The detailed study of muscular exercise began in the 18th century when Antoine Laurent Lavoisier and Pierre Simon de Laplace discovered that the process consumes oxygen and produces carbon dioxide. As investigation progressed it became clear that exercise involves not only the muscles but also many other tissues; that it depends, indeed, on an extraordinary coordination of the respiratory, circulatory and nervous systems, all working together under highly integrated controls. During the 19th century almost every physiologist of the first rank worked on muscular exercise at one time or another. During the 20th century three men—A. V. Hill of Britain, August Krogh of Denmark and Otto Meyerhof of Germany—

have received Nobel prizes largely for work relating to muscle or muscular exercise. Among the Americans who made notable contributions in the physiology of exercise were Edward Cathcart, Francis Benedict, Graham Lusk and D. Bruce Dill. In the years before World War II the Fatigue Laboratory at Harvard University became a world center for the experimental study of muscular exercise.

In recent years investigations of exercise have concentrated on processes in the cell and on physiological systems involved in control. This is not all there is to the study of exercise: in order to ensure an adequate supply of oxygen for the working muscle cell the body must coordinate the interaction of the lungs, the blood (specifically the oxygen-carrying pigment hemoglobin), the heart and circulatory system and finally the muscle cell itself. We shall discuss each component of the system in turn.

Oxygen enters the bloodstream—and carbon dioxide leaves it—by way of the alveoli: the tiny sacs that form the ultimate functional structure of the lungs. The total surface area of this multitude of sacs is normally so large that, as far as the body's needs go, the exchange of gases between the air on one side of the walls of the alveoli and the blood bathing the other side is virtually unlimited. A normal man at rest inhales between six and eight liters of air per minute, from which about .3 liter of oxygen is transferred in the alveoli to the blood. Simultaneously carbon dioxide is given off by the blood and exhaled. When the same man is engaged in maximal muscular activity, he may take in 100 liters of air per minute and extract five liters of oxygen.

The rate of oxygen intake provides an excellent measure of the physical work done. The term "maximal oxygen intake," introduced by Hill in 1924, characterizes the upper limit of performance of an individual in a remarkably predictable way and has proved to be an extremely useful physiological tool. In practice an experimental subject performs a series of work tests on a motor-driven treadmill or bicycle ergometer, each test being at a higher load than the one just preceding. The intake of oxygen per minute rises on a virtually linear curve with work load until maximal intake is attained. Thereafter most people can still increase the work load, but the oxygen intake can rise no further. The maximal oxygen intake in normal individuals, however, has to do not with the capacity of the lungs for ventilation or diffusion but with the maximal pumping capacity of the heart. Maximal oxygen intake is therefore a fair index to circulatory capacity but not to pulmonary capacity.

The outstanding question about the ventilation of the lungs is: How does the control system that so neatly balances oxygen supply against oxygen demand work? As long as 150 years ago it was suspected that mammals had a center for the control of breathing in the medulla oblongata; this center was believed to have the function of maintaining rhythmic respiratory movements regardless of the state of consciousness. Although the respiratory center has long been known to be influenced by higher centers in the brain, the identity of the chemical and hormonal factors that affect it has been elusive. The classical paper on the subject, published in 1905 by John Scott Haldane (father of the late J. B. S. Haldane) and John G. Priestley, held that the respiratory center is primarily subject to the influence of carbon dioxide in the arterial blood flowing into it. The amount of carbon dioxide in the arterial blood in turn is determined by the level of carbon dioxide in the alveoli of the lungs.

Haldane's experiments showed that ventilation can be doubled by increasing the amount of carbon dioxide in inspired air from the usual negligible amounts to about 3 percent. He also considered the possibility that lack of oxygen might stimulate respiration. Ultimately he concluded that the carbon dioxide effect is dominant except under circumstances of extreme lack of oxygen. As far as the Haldane school was concerned the primary function of the respiratory center is to govern ventilation in such a way that the level of carbon dioxide in the alveoli is held as constant as possible.

During physical exercise the production of carbon dioxide in the body rises very rapidly and carbon dioxide is brought to the alveoli in increasing quantities by the venous blood. It was Haldane's view that, as a result of increased amounts of carbon dioxide in the alveoli, the arterial blood becomes more acid. He thought that the acidity stimulates the respiratory center and that excess carbon dioxide is blown off in expired air.

More refined studies later showed that Haldane's chemical-control theory was a considerable oversimplification. It turned out that during exercise and recovery from exercise the rate of ventilation does not rise and fall in direct proportion to the acidity, the carbon dioxide pressure or the oxygen pressure of the arterial blood. Because of these findings various other hypotheses have been offered: that some secondary signal—chemical, hormonal or nervous—acts as the stimulus to the respiratory control center, or that small changes in the carbon dioxide and oxygen pressure can cause large changes in the breathing rate by a multiplying effect. The details of the system are still very much in doubt. Whatever its exact *modus operandi*, the respiratory control mechanism ordinarily prevents carbon dioxide from accumulating in any significant degree and virtually assures an adequate supply of oxygen over a range extending from rest to maximal exertion.

Some interesting possibilities were opened up when Hill studied the effect of breathing pure oxygen during exercise. There seems no reason to doubt that an immediate effect of switching during steady exercise from ordinary air to air enriched with oxygen is to lower considerably the rate of ventilation. The effect is cited to support the view that a change in arterial oxygen pressure has an influence on the regulation of breathing. Athletes who have breathed oxygen-enriched air during exercise have reported a pronounced relief of subjective distress and have evinced a decrease in ventilation. Moreover, the late C. G. Douglas of the University of Oxford and his colleagues showed that oxygen-breathing extended the work capacity of trained athletes. The topic is an important one, not only with respect to competitive athletics but also with respect to the deficient transport of oxygen in disease and at high altitudes. It is being actively investigated in many laboratories.

Another important mechanism employed by the body when it is under fairly severe stress from exercise is its ability to incur an oxygen debt. In theory the mechanism enables the exercising body to live temporarily beyond its capacity for transporting oxygen to active muscles and to compensate for doing so during rest after the exercise. The phenomenon is well documented by the fact that ventilation and oxygen intake do not immediately return to normal resting levels for some time after vigorous exercise stops.

The amount of oxygen debt that can be contracted is limited by the ability of the blood to absorb acid metabolic products without an unduly large change in its acidity. Some degree of oxygen debt is always built up during a short, hard burst of exercise such as a footrace over a distance of 100 yards or a quarter of a mile. Milers or marathon runners, particularly if they are in good physical condition, can cover their distances with a relatively small oxygen debt. The term "steady state" is used by exercise physiologists to define a rate of work that can be performed for considerable periods of time without oxygen debt. Actually most people—probably anyone other than an athlete in training—incur some oxygen debt during exercise at all levels but the very lowest. Waking activity, even if it is quite sedentary, usually involves a continuous process of acquiring and paying off oxygen debt at various rates. During continuous activity, such as walking steadily at three miles per hour for several hours, oxygen debt is built up rapidly at first and then levels off. Thereafter it may remain virtually un-

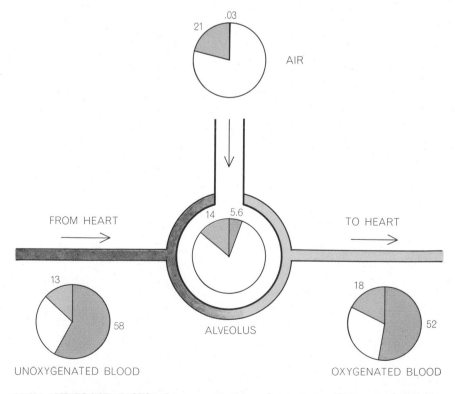

LUNG AND BLOOD GASES in human respiration under resting conditions are shown near and in one of the alveoli, the lung sacs where the blood acquires oxygen and yields carbon dioxide. Numbers give the percentage by volume of oxygen (*color*) and carbon dioxide (*gray*). The remaining percentages are accounted for by substances not involved in respiration.

changed for some hours. During violent activity it builds up rapidly and continuously until the activity ceases.

In any event, the contraction of an oxygen debt, like any other form of deficit financing, has its limits. Ideally the entire process of adaptation to physical stress, including the control of ventilation, is adjusted to the work load so elegantly that the oxygen debt incurred is kept at a minimum. The process of contracting a small oxygen debt is part of the normal mechanism of adaptation to exercise; a large oxygen debt is an emergency mechanism that is invoked only in case of dire need and in most sedentary individuals never comes into play at all.

After ventilation of the lungs the next major link in the system of adaptation to exercise is hemoglobin. Without this remarkable substance mammals would be completely incapable of muscular activity. The ability of hemoglobin to transport and deliver oxygen in the body resides in its iron atoms. Everyone knows that when metallic iron and oxygen combine, as they do in iron ore, it takes a blast furnace to separate them. In hemoglobin, however, iron combines with oxygen transiently and releases it readily to the tissue cells at body temperature.

As Christian Bohr of Denmark (father of the physicist Niels Bohr) first noted in 1904, the absorption and release of oxygen by the hemoglobin contained in the red blood cells are described by an S-shaped curve. Where the partial pressure of oxygen is that of ordinary air, as in the lungs, the hemoglobin of the blood becomes almost completely saturated with oxygen; when pure oxygen is breathed, the hemoglobin is 100 percent saturated. It gives up little of its oxygen as it flows through the arterial system, although the partial pressure of oxygen falls slightly there. When, however, the blood arrives at the capillaries and the surrounding tissues, where the oxygen pressure is substantially lower, the hemoglobin freely surrenders its oxygen and the curve of oxygen-binding bends sharply downward [see illustration on page 88].

Normally arterial blood contains about 18 percent of oxygen by volume, that is, about 18 milliliters of oxygen per 100 milliliters of blood. (Breathing pure oxygen raises this figure to 18.5 milliliters, and it also increases the amount of oxygen dissolved in the blood plasma from .2 milliliter to 1.9 milliliters.) When a person is at rest, the tissues absorb oxygen at a rate that reduces the 18 percent oxygen content of the arterial blood to about 12 percent in the venous blood. The drop is known as the "arteriovenous oxygen difference."

During exercise, on the other hand, the blood may have to give the tissues as much as 15 of its 18 percent of oxygen—about two and a half times more than it surrenders at rest. Several factors facilitate this increased surrender of oxygen by hemoglobin. One, of course, is the depletion of oxygen in the tissues by exercise; this results in a higher gradient between the oxygen pressure in the blood and that in the tissue cells. Another factor is the accumulation of carbon dioxide and acid metabolic products in the exercising muscle fibers, which acts to stimulate the release of oxygen by hemoglobin. Other factors, including the increased temperature of the active muscle cells, may also be involved.

The main point that emerges from this kind of investigation is that the biological properties of hemoglobin play a very important role in enabling the body to adapt to exercise. If the body had to depend solely on dissolving oxygen in a carrier fluid such as blood plasma, even at rest it would have to circulate nearly 300 pounds of fluid per minute—not far from twice the total weight of an average man! Thanks to hemoglobin, a flow of only five liters of blood per minute is enough to supply the body's oxygen needs at rest.

This brings us to the third link in the system of adjustment to exercise: the pumping and circulation of the blood. Comparatively recent developments make it possible to obtain accurate measurements of human cardiac output (the amount of blood pumped per minute) during exercise. It is now established that in a young man the heart can increase its output from about 5.5 liters of blood per minute at rest to nearly five times that figure during maximal exertion. At peak demand for oxygen the heart increases its output both by speeding up its rate of beating and by increasing the volume of blood pumped at each stroke. The pulse rate may double or triple; the stroke volume, which is about 60 to 80 milliliters at each beat when a person is standing at rest, may go as high as 120 milliliters.

The situation at levels of exercise less than maximal is somewhat uncertain. According to the available evidence, it seems likely that under moderate stress the heart may increase either its pulse rate or its stroke volume, depending on the individual's physical training and perhaps on other factors. There is good reason to believe that the heart of a trained athlete increases its stroke volume more readily than that of a sedentary person. Under the stress of emotions such as fear and anger the heart increases its output almost entirely by speeding up its rate of beating. If the nerves controlling the pulse rate are blocked experimentally by drugs, however, the heart will expand its stroke volume. The increase in cardiac output during emotional stress is considerably less than it is under physical stress; even during severe emotional crises it may not rise more than a third over the normal output at rest. The whole subject of the heart's output during stress still leaves much to be learned and is under wide investigation.

The facts we have reviewed so far make clear that the chief limitation on the body's capacity for physical exertion is the cardiac output: the ability of the heart to move blood to the tissues. The heart's capacity for increasing its output fivefold is not enough—even allowing for the ability of hemoglobin to release oxygen more freely—to account for the muscles' consumption of oxygen during violent exercise. An extra margin is provided, however, by a change in the pattern of blood flow. During heavy exercise most of the arterial blood is diverted to the active muscles, where the need for oxygen is most acute.

When the body is at rest, the muscles apparently account for no more than about 20 percent of its total oxygen consumption. Substantial amounts of oxygen go to the brain, the heart, the skin, the kidneys and other organs [see illustration on the next page]. If the muscles' share of the oxygen is about 20 percent, they use at rest only 60 to 70 milliliters of oxygen per minute (the body's total consumption being 300 milliliters per minute). Working at full tilt, as in running or swimming, however, the active muscles need about 3,000 milliliters per minute, or 50 times their resting requirement. The other organs do not require anything like this increase of oxygen; in fact, most of them actually use substantially less oxygen during maximal exertion. (The flow to the skin follows a unique pattern. In light or fairly strenuous exercise there is a substantial increase of blood flow through the skin to dissipate heat generated by the exercise, but when the muscles' need for oxygen becomes acute in maximal exertion, the skin, like the other organs, surrenders most of its claim on the supply of blood.)

The result of this cooperative adaptation by the other organs is that all but a relatively small portion of the cardiac output can go to the active muscles. The absolute amount of oxygen diverted to the muscles by this means is not great: it is no more than about 400 to 500 milliliters per minute. This amount, however, apparently represents a critical margin for the muscles. Experimental drug treatments that block the preferential distribution of blood to the muscles bring about a considerable impairment of the subject's capacity for exertion.

What are the mechanisms that adapt the output of the heart to the muscles' needs during exercise? On this question only fragmentary information is available; obviously it is a difficult question to investigate experimentally. One well-established finding is that the heart muscle itself contains a mechanism for the control of its activity. An experimental preparation of an animal's heart, isolated from any nervous or hormonal influence, still responds to an increase in its rate of filling with blood by increasing the amount it ejects at each beat. This property is known as the Frank-Starling law of the heart, after Otto Frank of Germany and Ernest Henry Starling of Britain, the physiologists who discovered it. Starling called it the "central fortress" of the system whereby the heart adapts itself to varying demands.

Concerning the nervous and hormonal controls of cardiac output certain general facts are known. The heart is powerfully influenced by sympathetic nerves, which stimulate its activity; by parasympathetic nerves (principally the vagus nerves), which depress its activity, and by hormones that reach the heart muscle by way of the bloodstream. These influences, both nervous and hormonal, are in turn triggered by various receptors elsewhere in the circulatory system or by complex factors involving the central nervous system. Typically a receptor at a strategic point in the arterial system (for example in the arch of the aorta) responds to increased pressure by transmitting impulses to integrating centers in the central nervous system. These increase the number of depressor impulses to the heart via the vagus nerves and decrease the

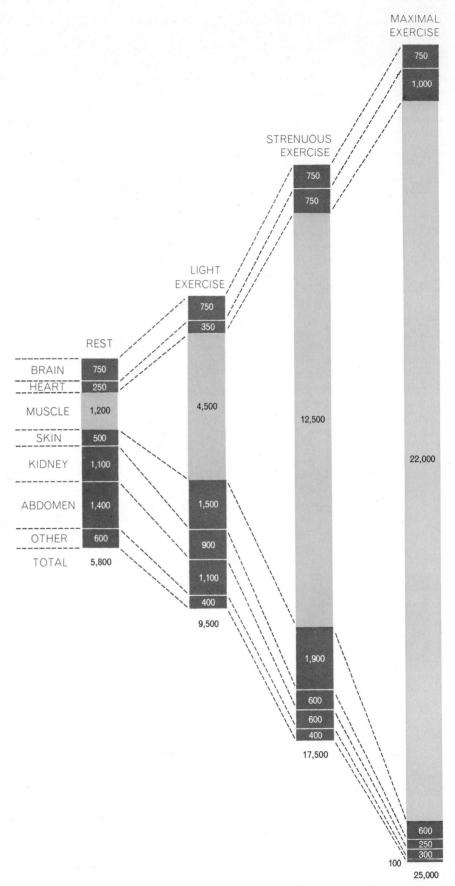

DIVERSION OF BLOOD from certain organs to the muscles is one of the body's major mechanisms for adapting to exercise. Numbers show blood flow in milliliters per minute. The brain is the only organ to which the flow remains almost constant under all conditions.

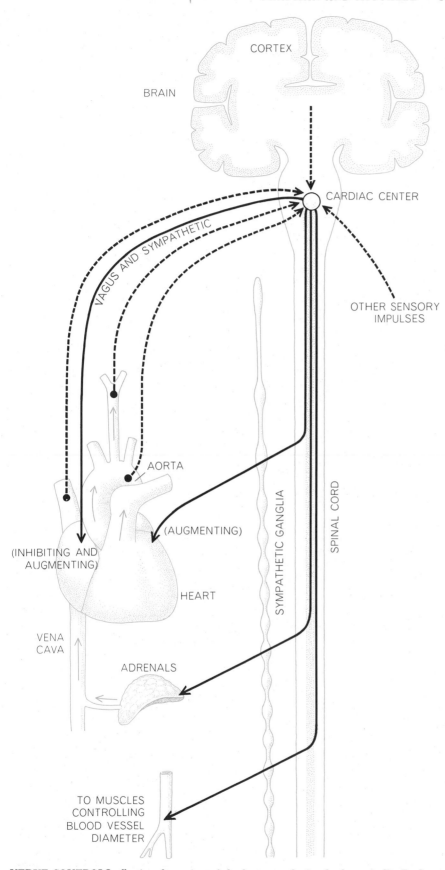

CORTEX

BRAIN

CARDIAC CENTER

VAGUS AND SYMPATHETIC

OTHER SENSORY IMPULSES

AORTA

(AUGMENTING)

SPINAL CORD

SYMPATHETIC GANGLIA

(INHIBITING AND AUGMENTING)

HEART

VENA CAVA

ADRENALS

TO MUSCLES CONTROLLING BLOOD VESSEL DIAMETER

NERVE CONTROLS affecting the action of the heart are depicted schematically. Broken lines represent afferent, or input, nerves; solid lines, efferent, or output, nerves. Some efferent nerves have a sympathetic, or stimulating, effect, in which the sympathetic ganglia participate. Others, such as the vagus, have a parasympathetic, or slowing, effect. Stimuli from cortex, resulting from visual or auditory signals or just from thought, can cause circulatory and muscular systems to begin preparing for exercise before it starts.

number of augmentor impulses via the sympathetic nerves. The net effect is to reduce the rate and force of the heartbeat, thus slowing the flow of blood in the arteries. Conversely, a fall of pressure in the aortic arch gives rise to a signal that stops the sending of impulses to the central nervous system, and so the depression of the heart's activity is diminished.

The eyes and ears may operate in the same way as a blood-pressure receptor. They too, in response to perceptions of the external world, send information in the form of impulses that control the heart's output. The impulses go to the cortex of the brain, which responds by sending appropriate directives to lower centers, whence augmentor or depressor messages are forwarded to the heart. In this way the heart is directed to gear its activity to anticipated needs of the body or to emotional stress.

The ultimate element of the system of adaptation to exercise, and the beneficiary of the marvelously adaptable machinery for supplying oxygen, is of course the muscle cell itself. Compared with many other cell types, the muscle cell is unique in one respect: its tolerance for oxygen deprivation. Certain other types of cell are highly sensitive to even a temporary shortage of oxygen. The cells of the brain, for instance, quickly suffer irreversible damage if the partial pressure of oxygen in the venous blood draining from them falls below 20 millimeters of mercury. Muscle cells, on the other hand, are known to survive even when the venous blood draining from their vicinity shows a partial pressure of oxygen at or near zero!

The extraordinary tolerance of muscle cells for a temporary shortage in the oxygen supply may be accounted for by the presence in these cells of myoglobin. This substance, like hemoglobin, carries oxygen, but it differs from hemoglobin in that it surrenders the oxygen much less readily. The S-shaped curve picturing hemoglobin's uptake and release of oxygen signifies that this behavior varies with the partial pressure of oxygen in hemoglobin's surroundings. As the oxygen pressure rises, the hemoglobin molecules absorb more oxygen; as the pressure falls, hemoglobin gives up its oxygen, and it does so with increasing rapidity as the oxygen pressure in the surroundings drops below 60 millimeters of mercury. (Normally, even during violent exercise, the oxygen pressure in the venous blood coming from active muscles does not fall much below 20 millimeters, at which pressure hemoglobin is about 30 percent saturated with oxygen.) Myoglobin's behavior contrasts sharply with this. Its curve of uptake and retention of oxygen is not S-shaped but hyperbolic, which is to say that after becoming saturated with oxygen the myoglobin molecule does not give up its oxygen until the pressure has fallen to a low level—15 millimeters or less.

Hemoglobin seems designed, therefore, to perform its vital function in surroundings where partial pressures of oxygen range from about 100 down to 20 millimeters (at which level hemoglobin is about 30 percent saturated). Myoglobin, on the other hand, would be of little physiological use (and would relinquish little or no oxygen) if it were confined to the range of partial pressures suitable for hemoglobin. Since myoglobin is found only inside muscle cells, and since there is fair evidence that partial pressures of oxygen in such cells may approach zero during very heavy activity, myoglobin may conceivably serve as a special oxygen store for the cell. According to this view, an intermittently contracting muscle cell might recharge its myoglobin during the resting phase and then, during a succeeding contraction, call on myoglobin oxygen stores when intercellular oxygen pressures fall below 10 millimeters of mercury.

This phenomenon may well account for the fact that mammalian muscles can work more smoothly and effectively when they intermittently contract and relax than when they are kept contracted for an extended period. Actually continuous contraction is probably rare except in laboratory experiments; even in an activity such as weight lifting, which might be thought to keep the muscles under unremitting tension, some of the individual muscle fibrils probably have a chance to relax with each slight shift in grasp and body position.

Myoglobin may also have something to do with the fact that short periods of work alternated with short periods of rest seem to be more efficient—metabolically as well as in work accomplished —than long work periods followed by long rest periods. Another interesting point inviting investigation is the indication that the amount of myoglobin in muscle tissue can be increased by physical training. The physiological significance and functions of myoglobin are a

BOHR EFFECT is evident in curves depicting the release of oxygen by hemoglobin. The curve at left represents a condition of rest; the middle curve, exercise. Arterial blood is indicated in color; venous, in gray. Hemoglobin's release of oxygen increases with declining oxygen pressure in the tissues, a condition that is intensified as exercising muscles use oxygen. Such muscles also produce acid wastes, and acidity entering the blood helps to stimulate the release of oxygen by hemoglobin. This is the Bohr effect, reflected in the shift of the curves to the right. A *p*H reading of 7.4, slightly alkaline, is normal for a man at rest; a slightly acid reading of 6.8 (*light curve*) can occur with heavy exercise.

largely unexplored subject and represent one of the most promising frontiers of research on muscular exercise.

Having looked separately at the main components of the system that effects adaptation to physical stress, let us now put them together and see how the system works as a whole. Nature demands that for survival an organism must be able in an emergency to rise to maximal activity on an instant's notice. Usually, however, the anticipatory warning allows enough time for efficient mobilization of the body's machinery. In man and other mammals a great deal of physiological preparation begins as soon as the individual senses that vigorous physical activity is imminent. The autonomic nervous system becomes active and the adrenal glands release the hormones epinephrine and norepinephrine into the bloodstream. The pulse rate quickens, the heart muscle contracts more forcibly and the output of the heart probably begins to increase slightly. The respiration deepens and may speed up. The voluntary muscles

become tense. The switching of blood flow from other areas to the muscles begins.

When exercise itself starts, there is an immediate jump in the rate of ventilation of the lungs. The cardiac output, pulse rate and stroke volume rise to their maximal level, probably within no more than a minute or two. Simultaneously the hemoglobin starts to surrender more of its oxygen to the muscle tissues, widening the difference between the oxygen content of arterial and venous blood. By the end of the first minute most of the known adaptive mechanisms are working nearly to capacity. Thereafter, with continuation of the exercise, the muscle cells begin to run up an oxygen debt.

If the exercise is pushed to the point of exhaustion, various mechanisms begin to fail. The rhythm of the heart becomes less regular; cardiac output declines; the oxygen content of the arterial blood may fall, and marked pallor —sometimes even blueness—of the lips and fingernails develops. Finally an inordinate rise in the pulse rate and

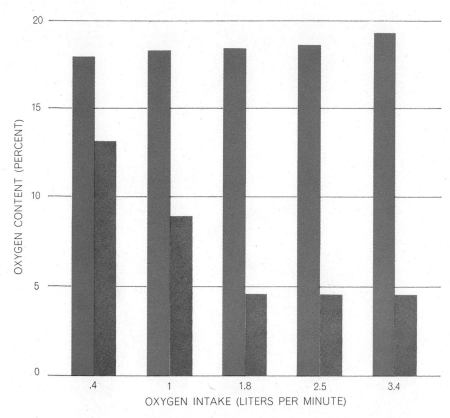

OXYGEN CONTENT (PERCENT)

OXYGEN INTAKE (LITERS PER MINUTE)

ARTERIOVENOUS OXYGEN DIFFERENCE is shown as oxygen intake rises with increasing exercise. Arterial blood is represented in color; venous, in gray. The oxygen content of arterial blood remains almost constant. That of venous blood drops rapidly at first, then levels off as the intake of oxygen and the output of the heart become maximal.

clumsiness of the muscular movements give warning that collapse is imminent.

Research on the physiology of exercise of course has important practical objectives, particularly with respect to what can be accomplished by physical training. The problem is not simply a matter of enabling astronauts to cope

with a landing on the moon. Probably a more useful goal, from the standpoint of the human population at large, is to find training regimes and other measures that will help the body to cope with diseases of the lungs and heart. In many ways the symptoms of chronic heart failure are like those accompanying heavy exercise. The body responds by making

the heart beat faster, by attempting to increase the ventilation of the lungs and by surrendering more oxygen from each liter of blood pumped by the heart to the tissues. By acquiring a better understanding of the mechanisms involved it may be possible to improve the body's adaptation to its needs under a wide variety of conditions.

Could special training techniques and other devices, including drugs, raise man's physical performances to greater heights? The training methods of athletes, from the time of the Greeks to the present, have been largely empirical and rule of thumb. With methods based on fuller physiological knowledge it may well be possible to achieve performances now considered superhuman. One must pay due regard, however, to the limits of the human organism. Once the organism has reached its maximal oxygen intake and cardiac output it cannot go further without drawing on its vital reserves, and this must have its limits of safety.

According to Herodotus, Pheidippides, "a trained runner," covered the 150 miles from Athens to Sparta in two days and two nights. Legend (but not Herodotus) says that a few days later he ran the 22 miles from Marathon to Athens to report the Greek victory over the Persians and fell dead at the end of his run. It may become possible to achieve by artificial means the kind of performance that extreme motivation is said to have made possible for Pheidippides, but only at the same cost. In all likelihood, however, there is room for improvement of human physical achievement, well within the bounds of safety, by rationally based methods.

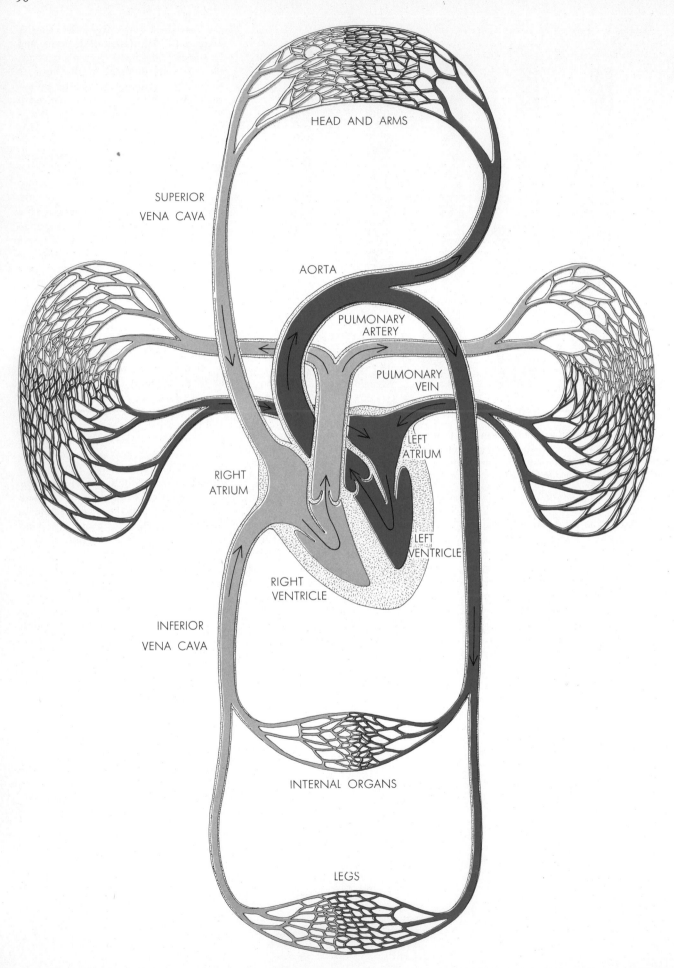

HEAD AND ARMS

SUPERIOR
VENA CAVA

AORTA

PULMONARY
ARTERY

PULMONARY
VEIN

LEFT
ATRIUM

RIGHT
ATRIUM

LEFT
VENTRICLE

RIGHT
VENTRICLE

INFERIOR
VENA CAVA

INTERNAL ORGANS

LEGS

9

The Heart

CARL J. WIGGERS · May 1957

The blood bathes the tissues with fluid and preserves their slight alkalinity; it supplies them with food and oxygen; it conveys the building stones for their growth and repair; it distributes heat generated by the cells and equalizes body temperature; it carries hormones that stimulate and coordinate the activities of the various organs; it conveys antibodies and cells that fight infections—and of course it carries drugs administered for therapeutic purposes. No wonder that William Harvey, the discoverer of the circulation, ardently defended the ancient belief that the blood is the seat of the soul.

The blood cannot support life unless it is kept circulating. If the blood flow to the brain is cut off, within three to five seconds the individual loses consciousness; after 15 to 20 seconds the body begins to twitch convulsively; and if the interruption of the circulation lasts more than nine minutes, the mental powers of the brain are irrevocably destroyed. Similarly the muscles of the heart cannot survive total deprivation of blood flow for longer than 30 minutes. These facts emphasize the vital importance of the heart as a pump.

The work done by this pump is out of all proportion to its size. Let us look at some figures. Even while we are asleep the heart pumps about two ounces

ANATOMY OF THE HEART and its relationship to the circulatory system is schematically depicted on the opposite page. The arterial blood is represented in a bright red; venous blood, in a somewhat paler red. The capillaries of the lungs are represented at left and right; the capillaries of the rest of the body, at top and bottom. The term atrium is now used in preference to auricle.

of blood with each beat, a teacupful with every three beats, nearly five quarts per minute, 75 gallons per hour. In other words, it pumps enough blood to fill an average gasoline tank almost four times every hour just to keep the machinery of the body idling. When the body is moderately active, the heart doubles this output. During strenuous muscular efforts, such as running to catch a train or playing a game of tennis, the cardiac output may go up to 14 barrels per hour. Over the 24 hours of an average day, involving not too vigorous work, it amounts to some 70 barrels, and in a lifetime of 70 years the heart pumps nearly 18 million barrels!

The Design

Let us look at the design of this remarkable organ. The heart is a double pump, composed of two halves. Each side consists of an antechamber, formerly called the auricle but now more commonly called the atrium, and a ventricle. The capacities of these chambers vary considerably during life. In the human heart the average volume of each ventricle is about four ounces, and of each atrium about five ounces. The used blood that has circulated through the body—low in oxygen, high in carbon dioxide, and dark red (not blue) in color—first enters the right half of the heart, principally by two large veins (the superior and inferior venae cavae). The right heart pumps it via the pulmonary artery to the lungs, where the blood discharges some of its carbon dioxide and takes up oxygen. It then travels through the pulmonary veins to the left heart, which pumps the refreshed blood out through the aorta and to all regions of the body [see diagram on opposite page].

The thick muscular walls of the ventricles are mainly responsible for the pumping action. The wall of the left ventricle is much thicker than that of the right. The two pumps are welded together by an even thicker dividing wall (the septum). Around the right and left ventricles is a common envelope consisting of several layers of spiral and circular muscle [see diagrams on page 93]. This arrangement has a number of mechanical virtues. The blood is not merely pushed out of the ventricles but is virtually wrung out of them by the squeeze of the spiral muscle bands. Moreover, it is pumped from both ventricles almost simultaneously, which insures the ejection of equal volumes by the two chambers—a necessity if one or the other side of the heart is not to become congested or depleted. The effectiveness of the pumping action is further enhanced by the fact that the septum between the ventricles becomes rigid just before contraction of the muscle bands, so that it serves as a fixed fulcrum at their ends.

The ventricles fill up with blood from the antechambers (atria). Until the beginning of the present century it was thought that this was accomplished primarily by the contractions of the atria, i.e., that the atria also functioned as pumps. This idea was based partly on inferences from anatomical studies and partly on observation of the exposed hearts of frogs. But it is now known that in mammals the atrium serves mainly as a reservoir. The ventricles fill fairly completely by their elastic recoil from contraction before the atria contract. The contraction of the latter merely completes the transfer of the small amount of blood they have left. Indeed, it has been found that the filling of the ventricles is not significantly impaired when

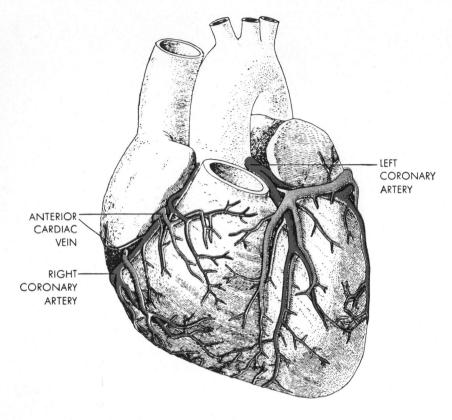

ANTERIOR
CARDIAC
VEIN

RIGHT
CORONARY
ARTERY

LEFT
CORONARY
ARTERY

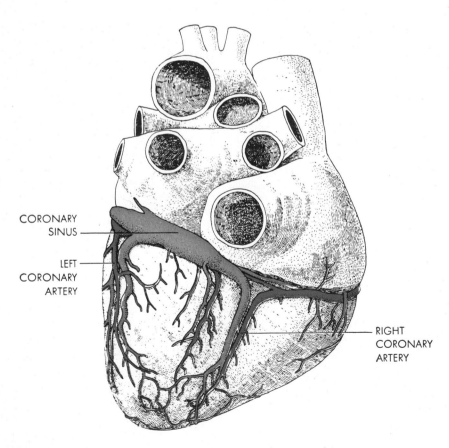

CORONARY
SINUS

LEFT
CORONARY
ARTERY

RIGHT
CORONARY
ARTERY

ARTERIES AND VEINS which carry blood to and from the muscles of the heart are shown from the front (*top*) and back (*bottom*). The arteries are bright red; the veins, pale red.

disease destroys the ability of the atria to contract.

Factors of Safety

Since most of us believe that every biological mechanism must have some purpose, the question arises: Why complicate the cardiac pump with contractions of the atria if the ventricles alone suffice? The answer is that they provide what engineers call a "factor of safety." While the atrial contractions make only a minor contribution to filling the ventricles under normal circumstances, they assume an important role when disease narrows the valve openings between the atria and the ventricles. Their pumping action then is needed to drive blood through the narrowed orifices.

The ventricular pumps also have their factors of safety. The left ventricle can continue to function as an efficient pump even when more than half of its muscle mass is dead. Recently the astounding discovery was made that the right ventricle can be dispensed with altogether and blood will still flow through the lungs to the left heart! An efficient circulation can be maintained when the walls of the right ventricle are nearly completely destroyed or when blood is made to by-pass the right heart. Obviously the heart is equipped with large factors of safety to meet the strains of everyday life.

This applies also to the heart valves. Like any efficient pump, the ventricle is furnished with inlet and outlet valves; it opens the inlet and closes the outlet while it is filling, and closes the inlet when it is ready to discharge. The pressure produced by contraction of the heart muscles mechanically closes the inlet valve between the atrium and ventricle: shortly afterward the outlet valve opens to let the ventricle discharge its blood—into the pulmonary artery in the case of the right ventricle and into the aorta in the case of the left. Then as the muscles relax and pressure in the chambers falls, the outlet valves close and shortly thereafter the inlet valves open. The relaxation that allows the ventricles to fill is called diastole; the contraction that expels the blood is called systole.

While it might seem that competent valves are indispensable for the forward movement of blood, they are in fact not absolutely necessary. The laws of hydraulics play some peculiar tricks. As every farmhand knew in the days of hand well-pumps, if the valves of the pump were worn and leaky, one could

MUSCLE FIBERS of the ventricles are divided into four groups, one of which is shown in each of these four drawings. Two groups of fibers (*two drawings at top*) wind around the outside of both ventricles. Beneath these fibers a third group (*drawing at lower left*) also winds around both ventricles. Beneath these fibers, in turn, a fourth group (*drawing at lower right*) winds only around the left ventricle. The contraction of all these spiral fibers virtually wrings, rather than presses, blood out of the ventricles.

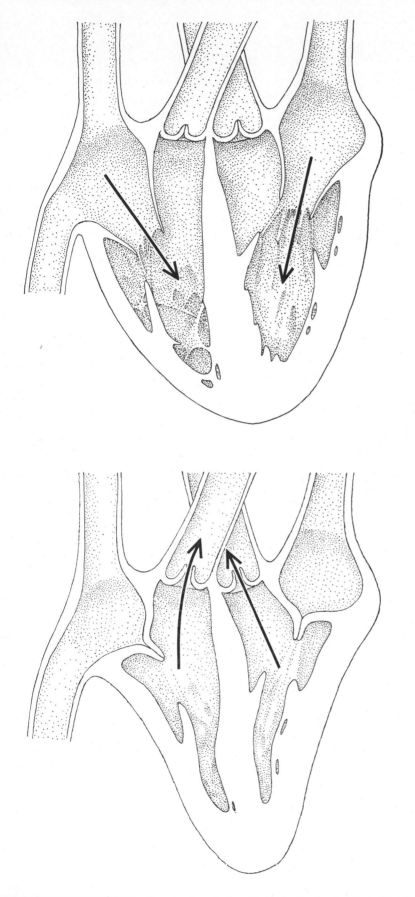

SYSTOLE AND DIASTOLE is the pumping rhythm of the heart. At the top is diastole, in which the ventricles relax and blood flows into them from the atria. The inlet valves of the ventricles are open; the outlet valves are closed. At the bottom is systole, in which the ventricles contract, closing the inlet valves and forcing blood through the outlet valves.

still draw water from the well by pumping harder. Similarly doctors have long been aware that patients can maintain a good circulation despite serious leaks in the heart valves. The factors of safety concerned are partly physical and partly physiological. The physical factor is more vigorous contraction of the heart muscles, aided by a structural arrangement of the deep muscle bands which tends to direct the blood flow forward rather than backward through the leaky valve. The physiological factor of safety is the mechanism known as "Starling's Law." In brief the rule is that, the more a cardiac muscle is stretched, the more vigorously it responds, of course within limits. The result is that the more blood the ventricles contain at the end of diastole, the more they expel. Of course they will fill with an excess of blood when either the inlet or the outlet valves leak. By pumping an extra volume of blood with each beat, the ventricles compensate for the backward loss through the atrial valves. In addition, the sympathetic nerves or hormones carried in the blood may spur the contractile power of the muscles. Under certain circumstances unfavorable influences come into play that depress the contractile force. Fortunately drugs such as digitalis can heighten the contractile force and thus again restore the balance of the circulation even though the valves leak.

Like any sharp closing of a door, the abrupt closings of the heart valves produce sounds, which can be heard at the chest wall. And just as we can gauge the vigor with which a door is slammed by the loudness of the sound, so a physician can assess the forces concerned in the closing of the individual heart valves. When a valve leaks, he hears not only the bang of the valves but also a "murmur" like the sigh of a gust of wind leaking through a broken window pane. The quality and timing of the murmur and its spread over the surface of the chest offer a trained ear considerable additional information. Sometimes a murmur means that the inlet and outlet orifices of the ventricles have been narrowed by calcification of the valves. In that case there is a characteristic sound, just as the water issuing from a hose nozzle makes a hissing sound when the nozzle is closed down.

Blood Supply

In one outstanding respect the heart has no great margin of safety: namely, its oxygen supply. In contrast to many other tissues of the body, which use as little as one fourth of the oxygen brought to them by the blood, the heart uses 80 per cent. The amount of the blood supply is therefore all-important to the heart, particularly when activity raises its demand for oxygen.

Blood is piped to the heart muscles via two large coronary arteries which curl around the surface of the heart and send branchings to the individual muscle fibers [see diagrams on page 92]. The left coronary artery is extraordinarily short. It divides almost immediately into two branches. A large circumflex branch runs to the left in a groove between the left atrium and ventricle and continues as a large vessel which descends on the rear surface of the left ventricle. It supplies the left atrium, the upper front and whole rear portion of the left ventricle. The other branch circles to the left of the pulmonary artery and then runs downward in a furrow to the apex. It supplies the front wall of the left ventricle and a small part of the rear right ventricle. Close to its origin the left coronary artery gives off several twigs which carry blood to the septum. The right coronary artery, embedded in fat, runs to the right in a groove between the right atrium and ventricle. It carries blood to both of them.

From the surface branches vessels run into the walls of the heart, dividing repeatedly until they form very fine capillary networks around the muscle elements. Eventually three systems of veins return the blood to the right heart to be pumped back to the lungs.

In the normal human heart there is little overlap by the three main arteries. If one of them is suddenly blocked, the area of the heart that it serves cannot obtain a blood supply by any substitute route. The muscles deprived of arterial blood soon cease contracting, die and become replaced by scar tissue. Now while this is the ordinary course of events, particularly in young persons, the amazing discovery was made some 20 years ago that the blocking of a main coronary artery does not always result in death of the muscles it serves. It has since been proved that new blood vessels grow in, from other arteries, if a main branch is progressively narrowed by atherosclerosis over a period of months or years. In other words, if the closing of a coronary artery proceeds slowly, a collateral circulation may develop. This biological process constitutes another factor of safety. Recent experiments on dogs indeed indicate that exercise will accelerate the development of collaterals when a major coronary artery is constricted. If this indication is con-

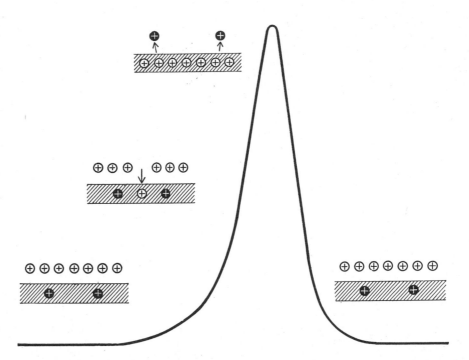

ELECTRICAL IMPULSE IS GENERATED by a cell in the "pacemaker" of the heart, a system of specialized muscle tissue (*see diagram on next page*). At lower left is a cross section of the cell; positively charged potassium ions (*black*) are inside it and a larger number of positively charged sodium ions (*white*) are outside. Because there are more positive charges outside the cell than inside, the inside of the cell is negatively charged with respect to the outside. When the cell is stimulated (*second cross section*), a sodium ion leaks across the membrane. Then many sodium ions rush across the membrane and potassium ions rush out (*third cross section*); this reverses the polarity of the cell and gives rise to an action potential (*peak in curve*). The original situation is then restored (*fourth cross section*)

firmed, it may well be that patients with atherosclerosis will be encouraged to exercise, rather than to adopt a sedentary life.

We have seen that there are many structural and functional factors of safety which enable the heart to respond, not only to the stress and strain of everyday life, but also to unfavorable effects of disease. Their existence has long been recognized; modern research has now thrown some light on the fundamental physiological and chemical processes involved.

The heart's transformation of chemical energy into the mechanical energy of contraction has certain similarities to the conversion of energy in an automobile engine; but there are also essential differences. In both cases a fuel is suddenly exploded by an electric spark. In both the fuel is complex, and the explosion involves a series of chemical reactions. In each case some of the energy is lost as unusable heat. In each the explosions occur in cylinders, but in the heart these cylinders (the heart muscle cells) not only contain the fuel but are able to replenish it themselves from products supplied by the blood. The mechanical efficiency of these cells, *i.e.*, the fraction of total energy that can be converted to mechanical energy, has not been equaled by any man-made

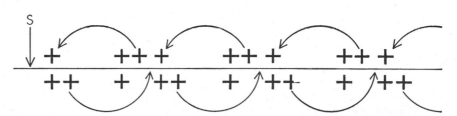

ELECTRICAL IMPULSE IS TRANSMITTED through the pacemaker system not as an electric current but as an electrical chain reaction. When a pacemaker cell is stimulated (S), it discharges and generates a local current which causes the depolarization and discharge of adjacent cells. In effect a wave of positive charge passes through the system (*curved arrows*).

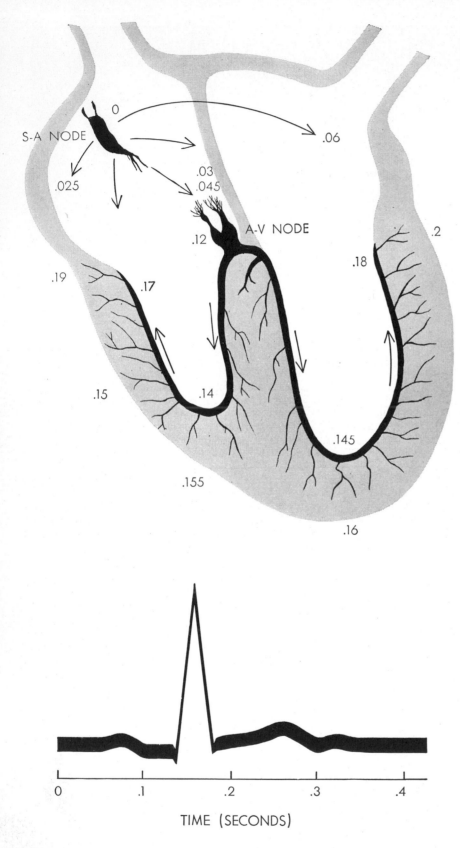

S-A NODE 0

.025

.03
.045

.06

A-V NODE

.12

.18 .2

.19 .17

.15 .14 .145

.155

.16

TIME (SECONDS)

0 .1 .2 .3 .4

PACEMAKER SYSTEM generates and transmits the impulses which cause the contraction of the heart muscles. The impulse is generated in the sino-atrial (S-A) node and spreads across the atria, causing their contraction and stimulating the atrio ventricular (A-V) node. This in turn stimulates the rest of the system, causing the rest of the heart to contract. The numbers indicate the time (in fractions of a second) it takes an impulse to travel from the S-A node to that point. The electrocardiogram curve at bottom indicates the change in electrical potential that occurs during the spread of one impulse through the system.

machine designed in the pre-atomic age. The mechanism responsible for this efficiency is unique and very complex.

Under the microscope we can see that cardiac muscle consists of long, narrow networks of fibers, with connective tissue and tiny blood vessels filling the spaces between. Each muscle fiber is made up of innumerable fibrils embedded in a matrix. It has been demonstrated that these fibrils are responsible for the contraction of the muscle as a whole. By special and clever techniques the fibrils can be washed free of the matrix, and it has been shown that when brought into contact with the energy-rich substance ATP, the fibrils shorten.

Examinations with the polarizing and electron microscopes and with X-rays have produced a fairly good picture of the ultimate design of these microscopic fibers. Each fibril is composed of many smaller filaments, or "protofibrils," just distinguishable under the highest microscopic magnification. The fibrils of a single muscle fiber may contain a total of some 10 million such filaments. The filaments are the smallest units known to stiffen and shorten. It has been possible to extract the actomyosin of which they are composed and to reconstitute filaments by squirting the extracted protein into a salt solution. These synthetic filaments can be made to contract.

The filaments themselves remain straight during contraction; therefore the kinking or coiling necessary for their contraction must take place at a still lower level—the level of molecules. Here the picture is clouded. We know from X-ray diffraction analyses that the molecules composing myosin filaments are arranged as miniature stretched spiral springs or stretched rubber bands. But just how they effect the filaments' contraction can only be guessed. Regardless of the mechanism, there is no doubt that the stiffness and shortening which are the features of contraction are mediated by changes in the molecular arrangement. This rearrangement requires energy. The consensus is that a tiny electric spark delivered to each individual cell causes the explosion of ATP. Not all the energy released is used for shortening of the actomyosin filaments. Some of it is converted to heat and some is used to initiate a series of complex chemical reactions which replenishes the fuel by reconstituting ATP. The explosion of ATP differs from that of gasoline in that no oxygen is required. But oxygen is indispensable for the rebuilding of ATP.

The millions of cardiac cylinders, as

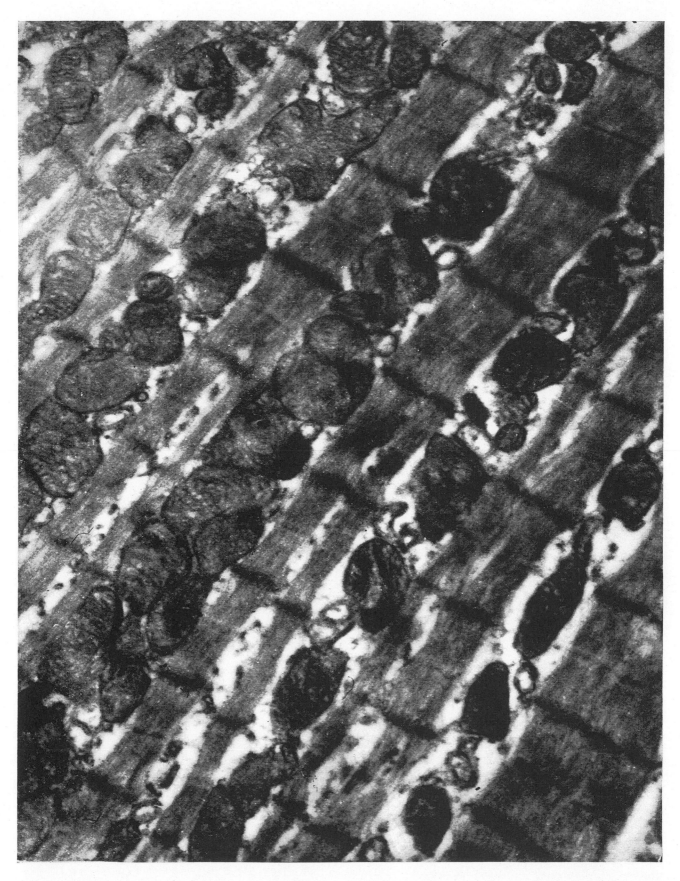

MUSCLE FIBRILS of the heart, which make up its muscle fibers, are revealed in this electron micrograph made by Bruno Kisch of the American College of Cardiology in New York. The fibrils, which are from the heart of a guinea pig, are the long bands running diagonally across the micrograph. The round bodies between the fibrils are sarcosomes, which are found in large numbers in heart muscle and which appear to supply the enzymes that make possible its tireless contractions. The fibrils themselves are made up of protofibrils, which may barely be seen in the micrograph. The micrograph enlarges these structures some 50,000 diameters.

in an automobile engine, must fire in proper sequence to contract the muscle effectively. When they fire haphazardly, there is a great liberation of energy but no coordinated action. This chaotic condition is called fibrillation—i.e., independent and uncoordinated activity of the individual fibrils.

The Beat

What causes the heart to maintain its rhythmic beat? The ancients, performing sacrificial rites, must have noticed that the heart of an animal continues to beat for some time after it has been removed from the body. That the beat must originate in the heart itself was apparently clear to the Alexandrian anatomist Erasistratus in the third century B.C. But anatomists ignored this evidence for the next 20 centuries because they were convinced that the nerves to the heart must generate the heartbeat. In 1890, however, Henry Newell Martin at the Johns Hopkins University demonstrated that the heart of a mammal could be kept beating though it was completely separated from the nerves, provided it was supplied with blood. And many years before that Ernst Heinrich Weber of Germany had made the eventful discovery that stimu-

lation of the vagus nerve to the heart does not excite it but on the contrary stops the heart. In short, it was established that the beat is indeed generated within the heart, and that the nerves have only a regulating influence.

The nature and location of the heart's "pacemaker" remained enigmatic until comparatively recent times. Within the span of my own memory there was considerable evidence for the view that the pacemaking impulses were generated by nerve cells in the right atrium and transmitted by nerve fibers to the heart-muscle cells. At present the evidence is overwhelming that the impulses are actually generated and distributed by a system of specialized muscle tissue consisting of cells placed end to end. Seventy-two times per minute—more or less—a brief electric spark of low intensity is liberated from a barely visible knot of tissue in the rear wall of the right atrium, called the sino-atrial or S-A node. The electric impulse spreads over the sheet of tissue comprising the two atria and, in so doing, excites a succession of muscle fibers which together produce the contraction of the atria. The impulse also reaches another small knot of specialized muscle known as the atrioventricular or A-V node, situated between the atria and ventricles. Here

the impulse is delayed for about seven hundredths of a second, apparently to allow the atria to complete their contractions; then from the A-V node the impulse travels rapidly throughout the ventricles by way of a branching transmission system, reaching every muscle fiber of the two ventricles within six hundredths of a second. Thus the tiny spark produces fairly simultaneous explosions in all the cells, and the two ventricles contract in a concerted manner.

If the heart originates its own impulses, of what use are the two sets of nerves that anatomists have traced to the heart? A brief answer would be that they act like spurs and reins on a horse which has an intrinsic tendency to set its own pace. The vagus nerves continually check the innate tempo of the S-A node; the sympathetic nerves accelerate it during excitement and exercise.

Normally, as I have said, the S-A node generates the spark, but here, too, nature has provided a factor of safety. When the S-A node is depressed or destroyed by disease, the A-V node becomes the generator of impulses. It is not as effective a generator (its maximum rate is only 40 or 50 impulses per minute, and its output excites the atria and ventricles simultaneously), but it suffices to keep the heart going. Patients

HEART SOUNDS indicate the normal and abnormal functioning of the heart valves. The three drawings at the top show the left side of the heart in cross section. The aortic, or outlet, valve is at upper left in each drawing; the mitral, or inlet, valve is at upper right. The first drawing shows the normal closing of the mitral valve; the trace below it records the sound made by this closing. The second drawing shows the partial closing of a leaky mitral valve; the trace below it records the murmur of blood continuing to flow through the valve. The third drawing shows the partial closing of a mitral valve with stiff leaves; the trace below it records a fainter murmur.

have survived up to 20 years with the A-V pacemaker substituting for a damaged S-A node.

There are still lower pacemakers which can maintain a slow heartbeat when the higher ones fail. When all the pacemakers are so weakened that, like an old battery, they are barely able to emit impulses, an anesthetic administered during an operation may stop the heart. In that case the beat can often be restored by rhythmic electric shocks —a system now incorporated in an apparatus for revival of the heart.

The Spark

What sort of mechanism exists in nodal tissues that is able to emit electric sparks with clockwork regularity 104,-000 times a day? We must look first to the blood. The fact that an excised heart does not long continue to beat unless supplied artificially with blood shows that the blood must supply something essential for preservation of its beat. In the 19th century physiologists began to experiment on isolated hearts, first of frogs and turtles and later of rabbits and cats, to determine what constituents of blood could be spared without halting the rhythmic heart contractions. They found that the serum (the blood fluid without cells) could maintain the beat of a mammalian heart, provided the serum was charged with oxygen under pressure. What constituents of the serum, besides the oxygen, were necessary? Attention first focused on the proteins, on the theory that the beating heart required them for nourishment. The heart was, in fact, found to be capable of maintaining its beat fairly well on a "diet" of blood proteins or even egg white or oxygenated milk whey. But the nourishment idea received a blow when it was discovered that the heartbeat could be maintained on a solution of gum arabic! It was then suggested that serum proteins act by virtue of their viscosity. This is an example of how experimenters are sometimes led astray in trying to uncover nature's secrets.

An eventful discovery in 1882 by the English physiologist Sydney Ringer changed the direction of thinking. He showed that a solution containing salts of sodium, potassium and calcium and a little alkali, in the concentrations found in the blood, would sustain the beat of a frog's heart. It was but a step to show that Ringer's solution, when oxygenated, also keeps the mammalian heart beating for a short time. Later it was found that the addition of a biological fuel—glucose or, better yet, lactic acid—would extend the heart's performance.

Summing up the evidence, it was known at the beginning of the present century that the beat of the mammalian heart, and obviously also the generation of the spark, depends primarily on a balanced proportion of sodium, potassium and calcium plus a supply of oxygen and an energy-yielding substance such as glucose.

During the present century the scientific minds have sought to learn how these inorganic elements are involved in the initiation and spread of impulses. In order to understand the intricate mechanisms we must recall what most of us learned in high school: *viz.*, the theory that, when a salt is dissolved in water, the elements are dissociated and become ions charged with positive and negative electricity.

The delicate enclosing membrane of all cells is differentially permeable: that is, ordinarily (at rest) it allows potassium ions to enter the cell but excludes sodium ions. We may say that the potassium ions have admission tickets, while the sodium ions do not. Since sodium ions predominate in the body fluids, the positively charged potassium ions within a cell are greatly outnumbered by positively charged sodium ions around the outside of the cell; the net result is that the outside is more positive than the inside, and the interior can therefore be regarded as negative with respect to the exterior. The potential difference is about one tenth of a volt. Each cell thus becomes a small charged battery. Now in the case of cells of the S-A node, the membrane leaks slightly, allowing some sodium ions to sneak in. This slowly but steadily reduces the potential difference between the inside and the outside of the membrane. When the difference has diminished by a critical amount (usually about six hundredths of a volt), the tiny pores of the membrane abruptly open. A crowd of sodium ions then rushes in, while some of the imprisoned potassium ions escape to the exterior. As a result the relative charges on the two sides of the membrane are momentarily reversed, the inside being positive with respect to the outside. The action potential thus created is the release of the electric spark.

As soon as activity is over, the membrane repolarizes, *i.e.*, reconstitutes a charged battery. How this is accomplished is little understood, beyond the fact that oxidation of glucose or its equivalent is required. The mechanism is pictured as a kind of metabolic pump which ejects the sodium ions that have gained illegal admittance, allows potassium ions to re-enter and closes the pores again. Then the cells are ready to be discharged again.

A little reflection should make it evident that the frequency with which such cells discharge depends on at least two things: (1) the rate at which sodium ions leak into the cell, and (2) the degree to which the potential across the membrane must be reduced in order to discharge it completely. The rate of sodium entry is known to be increased by warming and decreased by cooling, which accounts in part for the more rapid firing of the pacemakers in a patient who has a fever. The magnitude of the potential difference required to discharge the cell depends on the characteristics of the membrane. In this the concentration of calcium ions plays a basic role. Calcium favors stability of the membrane: if its concentration falls below a certain critical value, the rate of discharge by the cells increases; if calcium ions are too abundant, the rate is slowed. The rate of discharge is also affected by other factors. The vagus nerves tend to reduce it, the sympathetic nerves to increase it. The blood's content of oxygen and carbon dioxide, its degree of alkalinity, hormones and drugs—these and other influences can change the stability of the membranes and thus alter the rate of cell discharge.

Transmission of Impulses

The spark from a pacemaker is transmitted to the myriads of cylinders constituting the ventricular pumps by way of the special conducting system. When we say that the impulse travels over this system, this does not mean that electricity flows, as over wires to automobile cylinders. The electric impulse spreads by a kind of chain reaction involving the successive firing of the special transmitting cells. When pacemaker cells discharge, they generate a highly localized current which in turn causes the depolarization and discharge of an adjacent group of cells, and thus the impulse is relayed to the muscle cells concerned with contraction. An advantage of this mechanism is that the strength of the very minute current reaching the contracting fibers is not reduced.

Such a mode of transmission is not unknown in the inanimate world. There is a classic experiment in chemistry which illustrates an analogous process. An iron wire is coated with a microscopic film of iron oxide and suspended in a cylinder of strong nitric acid. Protected by this coating, the iron does not dissolve. But if the coat is breached (by a scratch or by an electric current) at a spot at one end of the immersed wire, a brown bubble immediately forms at this spot and a succession of brown bubbles then traverses the whole length of the wire. An electrical recorder connected to a number of points along the wire shows that a succession of local electric currents is generated down the wire as it bubbles. At each spot the current breaks the iron oxide film and the ensuing chemical reaction generates a new action potential. The contact between bare iron and nitric acid is only momentary, because the break in the film is quickly repaired.

Summarizing, the passage of electric impulses over the conduction system of the heart represents a series of local bioelectric currents, relaying the impulses step by step over special tissue to the contracting cells. On arrival at these cells the electric charges trigger the breakdown of ATP and so release the chemical energy needed for contraction.

Diagnosis

Considering the complexity of the cardiac machinery, it is remarkable that the heartbeat does not go wrong more often. Like a repairman for an automobile or a television set, a physician sometimes has to make an extensive hunt for the source of the disorder. It seems appropriate to close this article with a list of the points at which the machinery is apt to break down.

1. The main (S-A) pacemaker, or in rare instances all the pacemakers, may fail.

2. There may be too many pacemakers. The secondary pacemakers occasionally spring into action and work at cross purposes with the normal one, producing too rapid, too slow, or ill-timed beats.

3. The system for conduction of the pacemaker impulses may break down, leading to "heart block."

4. The heart muscle cylinders may respond with little power because of poor fuel, lack of enough oxygen for building fuel, fatigue or lack of adequate vitamins, hormones or other substances in the blood.

5. Some of the cylinders may be put out of commission by blockage of a coronary artery.

6. The heart valves may leak, and in its gallant effort to compensate, the heart may be overworked to failure.

10

The Heart's Pacemaker

E. F. ADOLPH · March 1967

The heart of a mouse at rest beats about 500 times a minute; in contrast, the elephant's basal heart rate is only 35 beats a minute. In the mouse's lifetime of one to two years its heart totals as many beats as the elephant's does in 25 to 50 years. What governs an animal's heart rate? Obviously it is regulated in part from outside the heart in response to the demands of exercise or stress. But the heart itself has its own pacemaker, regulating its fundamental rhythm and setting limits on its range of rates. Recent experimental investigations in various animals, including observation of the beginnings of the heartbeat in the embryo, have done much to illuminate the operation and regulation of the pacemaker.

The embryonic heart starts beating at a certain age that is characteristic for each animal. In the chick, for instance, the first beats arise at about the 30th hour of the embryo's life [*see top illustration on pages 102 and 103*]. Rhythmic contractions of the heart muscle begin in the right ventricle. A number of hours later the right atrium, or auricle, which meanwhile has taken shape behind the ventricle, also starts to beat. Its beat is faster and it sets the pace, the ventricular cells falling in step with its timing. Finally the venous sinus, which eventually sets apart a group of cells known as the sinoatrial node, develops to the rear of the right atrium, and this structure, beating still faster, takes over the pacemaking function. The sinoatrial node remains the basic pacemaker throughout the animal's life. Other regions of the heart muscle contract rhythmically according to its lead, but most of them lose the capacity to initiate beats of their own accord.

It is an interesting fact that the various muscle cells of the embryo heart differ in their intrinsic beating tempo, yet all are coordinated by the pacemaker. In the tubular heart of a salamander embryo, for example, W. M. Copenhaver of the Columbia University College of Physicians and Surgeons showed by cutting across the heart at various levels that at least eight different intrinsic beating rates can be detected along the length of the heart, each successive region rearward toward the sinus having a faster intrinsic rate. Indeed, when the cells of any embryo heart are separated from one another (by the use of the enzyme trypsin to break down the cement that holds them together), it is found that each cell beats with its own rhythm, depending mainly on the region of the heart from which it came. When, on the other hand, individual cells or fragments of heart tissue are brought together in intimate contact, they synchronize their contractions. Invariably the cell that has the fastest beat takes over the pacemaking. There are indications, however, that the pace is not entirely set by a single cell; the other cells seem to have some influence, and the actual beating rate possibly results from a consensus.

The sinoatrial pacemaker as a whole, consisting of hundreds or thousands of cells, has an intrinsic regulation. Whether in the embryo or maintained in an unchanging chemical medium at a constant temperature, it will beat at a constant rate hour after hour. A disturbance such as deprivation of oxygen can slow the rate, but as soon as normal conditions are restored the pacemaker resumes its basal rhythm. In each species of animal the pacemaker has a certain characteristic rate; for each species there is a "set point"—a standard rate—to which the heart adheres except during disturbing circumstances.

Copenhaver performed experiments with salamander embryos that dramatically tested the autonomy of the pacemaker. Using two different species—the tiger salamander and the spotted salamander—he transplanted the heart from one species to the other before the heart had begun to beat. Which beat would the transplanted heart take up, the donor animal's or the host's? In every case it beat at its own rate, not at that of the host, although in some cases it was pumping the host's blood, and it maintained its own beating pattern throughout the animal's life. The tiger salamander's heart normally beats more rapidly than the spotted salamander's during the first days of life and then slows to less than the spotted salamander's rate; it still showed the same pattern when it was transplanted into a spotted salamander, whether it was grafted in place of the animal's heart or was implanted in the abdomen or tail as a second heart.

The heart of any animal changes its rate with age, usually increasing in rate as the embryo grows and decreasing in later life. In Copenhaver's experiments the transplanted heart, whether it had belonged originally to a tiger salamander or to a spotted salamander, followed its own typical pattern of tempo changes with age. In short, the pacemaker of a given species is endowed not with a particular pace but with a whole program of paces that will develop during its lifetime. This program obviously is implanted in the future pacemaker tissue during the early development of the embryo, when the heart tissue is differentiating. Experiments in the culture of potential heart tissues have shown that such is indeed the case.

How does the pacemaker work? On this central question there are, unfor-

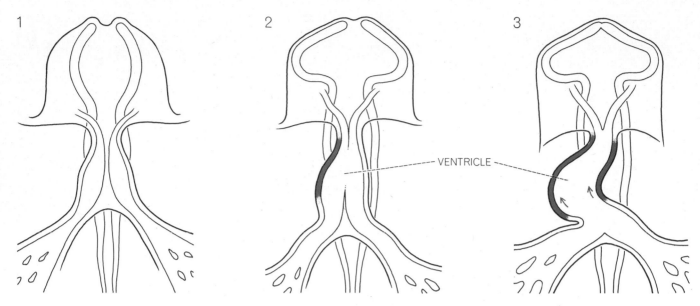

1   2   3

VENTRICLE

PACEMAKING CHANGES in an embryonic chicken heart are depicted in color; arrows show the direction of impulse conduction. At 27 hours (*1*) beating has not begun. The first contractions arise (*2*) in the ventricle. Gradually they originate farther to the rear,

tunately, very few clues so far. The pacemaking cells look distinctly different from other cells. Under the microscope we can see that the cells in the sinoatrial node are more widely separated from one another and have less contractile structure than the cells in other heart tissues. Electrical exploration of the pacemaking cells reveals another distinctive feature [*see upper illustration*

on page 105]. By inserting a microelectrode in an individual cell one finds that during the diastolic, or passive, phase of the beat cycle the inside of the cell loses its negativity gradually until it reaches a transition point, after which it completes its depolarization rapidly (and actually becomes positive for an instant). This pattern of gradual depolarization is peculiar to pacemaker cells.

One is tempted to compare these cells to an electric condenser, which discharges periodically after accumulating charge gradually. The condenser model does not, however, quite fit the process of the cell. Indeed, no model yet suggested has given us much enlightenment on how the pacemaker translates metabolic energy into its rhythmic beat, how it synchronizes the discharges of its many

HUMAN PACEMAKER appears in photomicrographs of two thin slices of heart. At left, in an enlargement of 12 diameters, the sinus node is the dense tissue organized around an artery. At right, in an enlargement of 260 diameters, the internal structure of the node is evident. The darker tissue is the framework of collagen. Within this frame bundles of sinus-node fibers interweave in all directions.

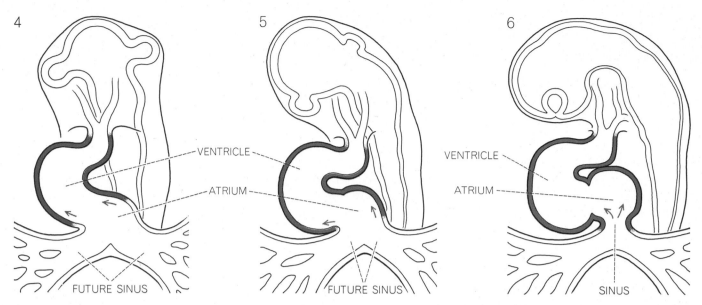

reaching the atrium (5) and finally the sinus (6). Drawings, which slowly turn the embryo from a frontal view at *1* to a view of the left side at *6*, were adapted from *Early Embryology of the Chick*, by Bradley M. Patten, published by the McGraw-Hill Book Company.

cells or how it changes the tempo of its beat as it ages.

Perhaps some enlightenment will come from studies of the pacemakers of invertebrate animals. In the lobster, for instance, the heartbeat is activated by a small group of nerve cells outside the heart. Donald M. Maynard of the University of Michigan studied a species of lobster in which the pacemaker consists of nine nerve cells—four small and five large. He found that any one of the small cells triggers a burst of impulses from all nine, and repetitive bursts from the group are responsible for the rhythmic beats of the heart. How are the discharges from the four small nerve cells regulated? If the interactions of these cells could be unraveled, one might find a clue to the coordinated action of the thousands of cells that constitute the pacemaker in the heart of a vertebrate.

We may well ask: Of what use are the vertebrate pacemaker's thousands of cells? It has been suggested that perhaps only a few of them are pacemaking at any given time and the rest act as reserves. In that case, however, what would prevent one uncontrolled cell from starting a beat of its own? A single cell that began to beat at a pace twice that of the others could throw the entire system into confusion. A more plausible hypothesis is that all the pacemaker cells are under mutual control. So far, however, only feeble evidence of communication among the pacemaker cells has been discovered.

Notwithstanding the lack of information about how natural pacemakers operate, artificial pacemakers have been devised, and they are serving today to keep alive many people with damaged hearts. The best solution to their problem would be the implantation of living pacemaker tissue from a human donor or an animal one. In the embryo of a salamander such a transplant takes beautifully, and the implanted tissue can drive the host's heart quite satisfactorily. Unfortunately in mammals implanted tissue does not wed itself to the heart but simply forms a scar. The only available artificial pacemaker for human use, therefore, is a mechanical one. It consists of a device that produces rhythmic electrical discharges, and wires from this device feed the discharges to the excitable tissues of the heart. The artificial pacemaker can maintain a steady heartbeat; it does not, however, respond to bodily needs that call for a speedup of the beat.

What are the extrinsic, or external, mechanisms that affect the natural pacemaker of the heart, and how do they act? In our laboratory at the University of Rochester School of Medicine and Dentistry we have explored these questions, along with those concerning the intrinsic beat itself, by studying the development of the heart's behavior in animals from the early fetal stage to adulthood.

In the fetus of a rat the heart begins to beat in the 10th day of life. At that stage the heart is still free of any stimulation from nerves, and about the only factors that can change its intrinsic beat are temperature, oxygen and blood supply. From day to day during the growth of the fetus the rate of the intrinsic beat increases. The pacemaker remains relatively insensitive to extrinsic influences, even after nerves grow into the heart on the 16th day, and the insensitivity continues until near birth (on the 22nd day).

By adulthood an animal's heartbeat has become subject to strong influences from the parasympathetic and sympathetic nervous systems. Several investigators, including Raymond C. Truex and David M. Long, then at Hahnemann Medical College, have measured the extent of these influences in the dog. The heart rate of a dog at rest is about 90 beats a minute. If the animal is given a dose of atropine, which blocks parasympathetic nerve impulses from reaching the heart, its rate jumps to 250 beats a minute. Evidently, then, under normal circumstances a flow of impulses from the parasympathetic nerves acts as a restraining influence on the heart rate. On the other hand, the sympathetic nerves have a prodding effect. If these nerves are cut so that no impulses reach the heart, the heartbeats slow to 65 a minute. In short, the sympathetic system acts as an accelerator and the parasympathetic system as a brake, and under normal conditions the two systems counteract each other. When the nerve supply to the heart is completely cut (blocking both systems), the dog's heart beats about 110 times a minute. Perhaps in an adult dog this is the intrinsic rate of the pacemaker itself.

What the experiments show in general is that a continuous interplay normally goes on among the pacemaker and the two nervous systems controlling the heart, whose sources are centered

104

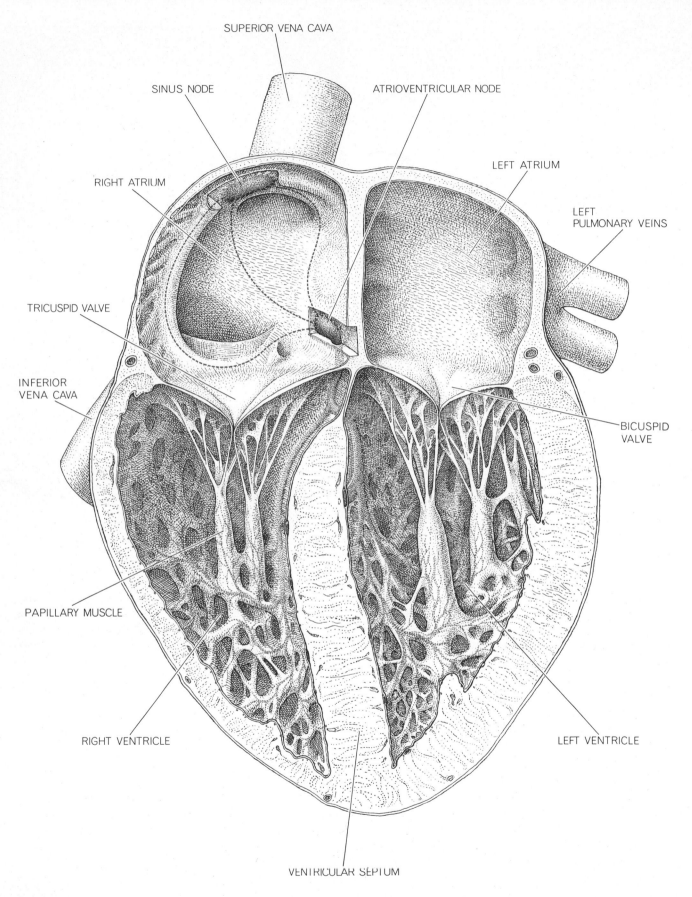

SUPERIOR VENA CAVA

SINUS NODE

ATRIOVENTRICULAR NODE

RIGHT ATRIUM

LEFT ATRIUM

LEFT
PULMONARY VEINS

TRICUSPID VALVE

INFERIOR
VENA CAVA

BICUSPID
VALVE

PAPILLARY MUSCLE

RIGHT VENTRICLE

LEFT VENTRICLE

VENTRICULAR SEPTUM

CUTAWAY VIEW of the human heart, showing the rear portion, depicts the pacemaker and the path of its impulses in color. The pacemaker is the structure near the top of the heart; it is variously called the sinus node and the sinoatrial node. Impulses from the pacemaker spread along the paths indicated by the broken lines to the atrioventricular node, from which they are transmitted to the ventricles. Pacemaker cells differ from both nerve cells and muscle cells; they are usually described as modified muscle cells.

PACEMAKER CELLS appear at an enlargement of 18,000 diameters in this electron micrograph by Thomas N. James of the Henry Ford Hospital in Detroit. The cells, which are the lighter structures, are from the heart of a dog. The darker cells are working myocardial cells, which are not involved in pacemaking. The featureless area at bottom right is one of the capillaries of the heart.

MYOCARDIAL CELLS, which have a muscular function in the heartbeat, differ in structure from pacemaker cells. The latter predominate only in the sinus node. Electron micrograph by James shows parts of three dog myocardial cells enlarged 18,000 diameters.

in the medulla oblongata of the brain-stem. The pacemaker's pace is modified by rhythmic impulses from these nervous systems, and they in turn are guided by activities of the body that call for an increase or a decrease in the pumping action of the heart. Both types of nervous mechanism, however, and hormonal controls as well, work only within fixed limits, which depend on the animal's age and size. In a puppy, for example, the sympathetic nerves exert a much stronger effect on the pacemaker than the parasympathetic nerves do, whereas in the adult dog the reverse is true. Similarly, the pacemaker and the nervous controls combine to give the mouse a more rapid basal beat than the elephant, and an elephant's heart can never beat as fast as that of a mouse.

Precisely what is the ceiling for an animal's heart rate? We investigated the question in the rat by applying rhythmic electric shocks to drive the heart to its maximal capacity. The rats were anesthetized and the driving electric impulses were delivered through fine wire electrodes inserted in the chest. We found that in the fetus the heart's maximal rate was about 350 beats a minute; in a newborn rat, about 450 beats a minute, and in an adult rat, some 750 beats a minute. At these high rates the heart was very inefficient: it pumped little blood because it had no time to fill before each contraction. We can deduce that the limit of tempo set up in the pacemaker may serve as a protective mechanism; if the pacemaker drove the heart too fast, it might produce the uncoordinated, disorderly type of contraction known as fibrillation.

We found further that the hormones isopropyl noradrenalin and thyroxin, whose ability to speed up the heart has long been well known, raised the rats' heart rates to high levels but not to the limits of the heart's capacity. In each case the rate of the rat's heartbeat under maximal prodding rose with age until the animal reached the age of 10 days, after which it leveled off [see lower illustration at right].

The normal heart rate at rest, on the other hand, presents a different picture as the animal ages. Instead of leveling off at the age of 10 days it continues to rise. This rise is attributed mainly to the influence of the maturing nervous system rather than to change in the intrinsic tempo of the pacemaker itself. It was found that administration of a drug that blocks the prodding action of the sympathetic impulses almost eliminated the

ELECTRICAL POTENTIALS in one pacemaker cell (*color*) and two nonpacemaker cells of a rabbit heart were measured by intracellular electrodes. Only cells capable of pacemaking show the gradual changes of polarization indicated by the colored curve for a single beat.

VARIATIONS IN RATE of rats' hearts under different conditions are shown for ages beginning four days before birth and ending at maturity. The colored curve represents the normal rate after birth. Other curves are: *A*, maximal rate when the heart is driven by electric shocks; *B*, rate after administration of stimulating hormones thyroxin and isopropyl noradrenalin; *C*, rate under latter hormone alone; *D*, rate under thyroxin alone, and *F*, rate after administration of the drug propranolol, which blocks accelerating nerve impulses.

heart rate increase with age. Our experiments show that the sympathetic nerves begin to affect the heart rate in rats a day or two before birth, whereas the parasympathetic system does not begin to act on the heart until about 16 days after birth. Thereafter the rate is under the control of the two systems acting competitively, with the sympathetic system apparently exerting slightly more influence than the parasympathetic.

To sum up, it appears that when the heart of the embryo begins to beat, it

functions as an independent organ, driven only by its own inherent pacemaker. As it grows older it becomes receptive to one extrinsic influence after another and through them becomes the servant of many organs and activities of the body. In the adult animal it is capable of a wide range of responses to the body's needs. The full development of its responses and regulation does not come until long after birth, but we can see the beginnings of the arrangements even before the animal is born.

11

The Microcirculation of the Blood

BENJAMIN W. ZWEIFACH · January 1959

When we think of the circulatory system, the words that first occur to us are heart, artery and vein. We tend to forget the microscopic vessels in which the blood flows from the arteries to the veins. Yet it is the microcirculation which serves the primary purpose of the circulatory system: to convey to the cells of the body the substances needed for their metabolism and regulation, to carry away their products—in short, to maintain the environment in which the cells can exist and perform their interrelated tasks. From this point of view the heart and the larger blood vessels are merely secondary plumbing to convey blood to the microcirculation.

To be sure, the entire circulatory system is centered on the heart. The two chambers of the right side of the heart pump blood to the lungs, where it is oxygenated and returned to the chambers of the left side of the heart. Thence the blood is pumped into the aorta, which branches like a tree into smaller and smaller arteries. The smallest twigs of the arterial system are the arterioles, which are too small to be seen with the unaided eye. It is here that the micro-circulation begins. The arterioles in turn branch into the capillaries, which are still smaller. From the capillaries the blood flows into the microscopic tributaries of the venous system: the venules. Then it departs from the microcirculation and is returned by the tree of the venous system to the chambers in the right side of the heart.

The vessels of the microcirculation permeate every tissue of the body; they are never more than .005 inch from any cell. The capillaries themselves are about .0007 inch in diameter. To give the reader an idea of what this dimension means, it would take one cubic centimeter of blood (about 14 drops) from five to seven hours to pass through a capillary. Yet so large is the number of capillaries in the human body that the heart can pump all the blood in the body (about 5,000 cubic centimeters in an adult) through them in a few minutes. The total length of the capillaries in the body is almost 60,000 miles. Taken together, the capillaries comprise the body's largest organ; their total bulk is more than twice that of the liver.

If all the capillaries were open at one time, they would contain all of the blood in the body. Obviously this does not happen under normal circumstances, whereby hangs the principal theme of this article. How is it that the flow of blood through the capillaries can be regulated so as to meet the varying needs of all the tissues, and yet not interfere with the efficiency of the circulatory system as a whole?

It was William Harvey, physician to Charles I of England, who first demonstrated that the blood flows continuously from the arterial system to the venous. In 1661, 33 years after Harvey had published his famous work *De Motu Cordis* (*Concerning the Motion of the Heart*), the Italian anatomist Marcello Malpighi

CAPILLARY from a cat's leg muscle is shown in cross section by this electron micrograph, which enlarges the structure some 20,000 diameters. The band running around the picture is the wall of the capillary. The large, dark object in the center is a single red blood cell. The micrograph was made by George D. Pappas and M. H. Ross of Columbia University.

PULMONARY CAPILLARIES

PULMONARY ARTERY

PULMONARY VEIN

RIGHT HEART

LEFT HEART

VEIN

ARTERY

CAPILLARIES
OF BODY AND ORGANS

CIRCULATORY SYSTEM is schematically outlined. The blood is pumped by the right heart through the pulmonary artery into the capillaries of the lungs. It returns from the lungs through the pulmonary vein to the left heart, which pumps it through the arteries to the capillaries of the internal organs and of the rest of the body. It finally returns to the right heart through the veins.

first observed through his crude microscope the fine conduits which link the two systems. These vessels were named capillaries after the Latin word *capillus*, meaning hair. Since Malpighi's time the capillaries have been intensively examined by a host of microscopists. Their work has established that not all the vessels in the network lying between the arterioles and the venules are the same. Indeed, we must regard the network as a system of interrelated parts. Hence it is preferable to think not of capillaries, but of a functional unit called the capillary bed.

The capillary bed, unlike muscle or liver or kidney, cannot be removed from an experimental animal and studied as an intact unit outside the body of the animal. By their very nature the capillaries are interwoven with other tissues. It is possible, however, to examine the capillary bed in a living animal. For example, one can open the abdomen of an anesthetized rat and carefully expose a thin sheet of mesentery: the tissue that attaches the intestine to the wall of the abdominal cavity. In this transparent sheet the capillary bed is displayed in almost diagrammatic form.

The tube of a capillary is made of a single layer of flat cells resembling irregular stones fitted together in a smooth pavement. The wall of the tube is so thin that even when it is viewed edge-on at a magnification of 1,000 diameters it is visible only as a line. When the wall is magnified in the electron microscope, it may be seen that the wall is less than .0001 inch thick. This so-called endothelium not only forms the walls of the capillaries but also lines the larger blood vessels and the heart, so that all the blood in the body is contained in a single envelope.

In a large blood vessel the tube of endothelium is sheathed in fibrous tissue interwoven with muscle. The fibrous tissue imparts to the vessel a certain amount of elasticity. The muscle is of the "smooth" type, characterized by its ability to contract slowly and sustain its contraction. The muscle cells are long and tapered at both ends; they coil around the vessel. In the tiny arterioles, in fact, a single muscle cell may wrap around the vessel two or three times. When the muscle contracts, the bore of the vessel narrows; when the muscle relaxes, the bore widens.

The muscular sheath of the larger blood vessels does not continue into the capillary bed. Yet as early as the latter part of the 19th-century experimental

physiologists reported that the smallest blood vessels could change their diameter. Moreover, when the flow of blood through the capillary bed of a living animal is observed under the microscope, the pattern of flow constantly changes. At one moment blood flows through one part of the network; a few minutes later that part is shut off and blood flows through another part. In some capillaries the flow even reverses. Throughout this ebb and flow, however, blood passes steadily through certain thoroughfares of the capillary bed.

If the capillaries have no muscles, how is the flow controlled? Some investigators suggested that although the endothelium of the capillaries was not true muscle, it could nonetheless contract. Indeed, it was demonstrated that in many lower animals blood vessels consisting only of endothelium contract and relax in a regular rhythm. However, contractile movements of this kind have not been observed in mammals.

Another explanation was advanced by Charles Rouget, a French histologist. He had discovered peculiar star-shaped cells, each of which was wrapped around a capillary, and he assumed that they were primitive muscle cells which opened and closed the capillaries. Many investigators agreed with him, among them the Danish physiologist August Krogh, who in 1920 won a Nobel prize for his work on the capillary system. It was not possible, however, to prove or disprove the contractile function of the Rouget cells by simple observation.

There the matter rested until methods were developed for performing microsurgical operations on single cells [see "Microsurgery," by M. J. Kopac; SCIENTIFIC AMERICAN, October, 1950]. Now it was possible to probe the cell with extremely fine needles, pipettes and electrodes. Microsurgery established that in mammals neither the capillary endothelium nor the Rouget cells could control the circulation by contraction. The endothelium did not contract when it was stimulated by a microneedle, or by the application with a micropipette of substances that cause larger blood vessels to contract. When one of the star-shaped Rouget cells was stimulated, it became thicker but did not occlude the capillary. When the same stimulus was applied to the recognizable muscle cell of an arteriole, on the other hand, the cell contracted and the arteriole was narrowed.

The microsurgical experiments established an even more significant fact: not

TYPICAL CAPILLARY BED is depicted in this drawing. The blood flows into the bed through an arteriole (A) and out of it through a venule (B). Between the arteriole and the venule the blood passes through thoroughfare channels (C). From these channels it passes into the capillaries proper (D), which then return it to the channels. The arteriole and venule are wrapped with muscle cells; in the thoroughfare channels the muscle cells thin out. The capillaries proper have no muscle cells at all. The flow of blood from a thoroughfare channel into a capillary is regulated by a ring of muscle called a precapillary sphincter (E). The black lines on the surface of the arteriole, venule and thoroughfare channels are nerve fibers leading to muscle cells. At lower left, between the arteriole and venule, is a channel which in many tissues shunts blood directly from the arterial system to the venous when necessary.

all the vessels in the capillary bed entirely lack muscle. For example, if epinephrine, which causes larger blood vessels to contract, is injected into the capillary bed with a micropipette, some of the vessels in the bed become narrower. Even when no stimulating substances are added, the same vessels open and close with the ebb and flow of blood in the capillary bed. It is these vessels, moreover, through which the blood flows steadily from the arterial to the venous system.

So the arterial system, with its muscular vessels, does not end at the capillary bed. The blood is continuously under muscular control as it flows into the venous system. To be sure, the muscle cells along the thoroughfare are sparsely distributed. As the arterial tree branches into the tissues the muscular sheath of the endothelium becomes thinner and thinner until in the smallest arterioles it is only one cell thick. In the thoroughfare channel of the capillary bed the muscle cells are spaced so far apart that the channel is almost indistinguishable from the true capillaries. The major portion of the capillary network arises as abrupt side branches of the thoroughfare channels, and at the point where each of the branches leaves a thoroughfare channel there is a prominent muscle structure: the muscle cells form a ring around the entrance to the capillary. It is this ring, or precapillary sphincter, which acts as a floodgate to control the

A R T E R Y   A R T E R I O L E

WALLS OF BLOOD VESSELS of various kinds reflect their various functions. The wall of an artery consists of a single layer of endothelial cells sheathed in several layers of muscle cells interwoven with fibrous tissue. The wall of an arteriole consists of a single layer of

flow of blood into the capillary network from the thoroughfare channel.

The muscular specialization of the circulatory system is illuminated by its embryonic development. In the early embryo the circulatory system is a network of endothelial tubes through which the primitive blood cells flow in an erratic fashion. The tubes are at first just large enough to pass the blood cells in single file. Attached to the outer wall of the tubes are numerous star-shaped cells which have wandered in from the surrounding tissue.

As the development of the embryo proceeds, those tubes through which the blood flows most rapidly are transformed into heavy-walled arteries and veins. In the process the star-shaped cells evolve through several stages into typical muscle cells. The outer reaches of the adult

circulatory system possess a graded series of muscle-cell types, which are a direct representation of this developmental process. Thus the star-shaped cells of the capillary bed—the Rouget cells—are primitive muscle elements which have no contractile function.

From this point of view the capillary bed can be considered the immature part of the circulatory system. Like embryonic tissue, it has the capacity for growth, which it exhibits in response to injury. It also ages to some extent, and ultimately becomes less capable of dealing with the diversified demands of the tissue cells.

When we put these various facts together, we see the capillary bed not as a simple web of vessels between the arterial and venous systems, but as a

MUSCLE FIBER is richly supplied with capillaries. Lying atop this dissected muscle fiber are two blood vessels, the smaller of which is an artery and the larger a vein. Most of the capillaries run parallel to the fibrils which make up the fiber. The vessels which cut across two or more capillaries are thoroughfare channels. The system is shown in cross section at the right end of the drawing.

CAPILLARY   VENULE   VEIN

endothelial cells sheathed in a single layer of muscle cells. The wall of a capillary consists only of a single layer of endothelial cells. The wall of a venule consists of endothelial cells sheathed in fibrous tissue. The wall of a vein consists of endothelial cells sheathed in fibrous tissue and a thin layer of muscle cells. Thus a layer of endothelial cells lines the entire circulatory system.

physiological unit with two specialized components. One component is the thoroughfare channel, into which blood flows from the arteriole. The other is the true capillaries, which form a secondary network connected to the thoroughfare channel. The precapillary sphincters along the channel open and close periodically, irrigating first one part of the capillary network, then another part. When the sphincters are closed, the blood is restricted to the thoroughfare channel in its movement toward the venous system.

The structure of the physiological unit varies from one tissue to another in accordance with the characteristic needs of the tissues. For example, striated muscle, which unlike the smooth muscle of the blood vessels and other organs contracts rapidly and is under voluntary control, requires over 10 times more blood when it is active than when it is at rest. To meet this wide range of needs each thoroughfare channel in striated muscle gives rise to as many as 20 or 30 true capillaries. Glandular tissues, on the other hand, require only a steady trickle of blood, and each of their thoroughfare channels may give rise to as few as one or two capillaries. In the skin, which shields the body from its outer environment, there are special shunts through which blood can pass directly from the arteries to the veins with minimum loss of heat. Still other tissues require specialized capillary beds. The capillary beds of all the tissues, however, have the same basic feature: a central channel whose muscle cells control the flow of blood into the true capillaries.

But what controls the muscle cells? To answer this question we must draw a distinction between the control of the larger blood vessels and the control of the microcirculation. The muscle cells of the arteries and veins are made to contract and relax by two agencies: (1) the nervous system and (2) chemical "messengers" in the blood. These influences not only cause the vessels to constrict and dilate but also keep the muscle cells in a state of partial contraction. This muscle "tone" maintains the elasticity of the vessels, which assists the heart in maintaining the blood pressure. The operation of the system as a whole is supervised by special regulatory centers in the brain, working in collaboration with sensory monitoring stations strategically located in important vessels.

In the capillary bed, on the other hand, the role of the nervous system is much less significant. Most of the muscle cells in the capillary bed have no direct nerve connections at all. A further circumstance sets the response of the microscopic vessels apart from that of the larger vessels. Whereas the muscle cells of the large vessels are isolated from the surrounding tissues in the thick walls of the vessels, the muscle cells of the arterioles and the thoroughfare channels are immersed in the environment of the very tissues which they supply with blood. This feature introduces another chemical regulatory mechanism: the continuous presence of substances liberated locally by the tissue cells. As a consequence the contraction and relaxation of muscle cells in the microcirculation are under the joint control of messenger substances in the blood and specific chemical products of tissue metabolism.

The chemical substances that influence the function of the blood-vessel muscle cells comprise a subtly orchestrated system which is still imperfectly understood. Among the more important messengers are those released into the bloodstream by the cortex of the adrenal gland. These corticosteroids are essential to all cells in the body, notably maintaining the cells' internal balance of water and salts. (They have also been used with spectacular results in the treatment of degenerative diseases such as arthritis.) When the corticosteroids are deficient or absent, the muscles of the blood vessels lose their tone and the circulation collapses.

Another substance of profound importance to the circulatory system is epinephrine, which is secreted by the core of the adrenal gland (as distinct from its cortex). Epinephrine is one of two principal members of a family of substances called amines; the other principal member is norepinephrine, which is released both by the adrenal gland and by the endings of nerves in the muscles. All the amines cause the contraction of the muscle cells of the blood vessels, with the exception of certain vessels such as the coronary arteries of the heart. Also liberated at the nerve endings is acetylcholine, the effect of which is directly opposite that of the amines: it causes muscle cells to relax.

Many workers have suggested that it is norepinephrine and acetylcholine which control the flow of blood through the small vessels. Our own work at the New York University–Bellevue Medical Center leads us to conclude that such an explanation is too simple. The mechanism could not by itself account for the behavior of the small vessels.

In our view the function of the muscle cells of the small vessels is regulated not only by substances that directly cause them to contract and relax, but also by other substances that simply modify the capacity of the cells to react to stimuli and do work. It is known that a wide variety of substances extracted from tissues cause the small vessels to dilate. We postulate that when the metabolism of tissue cells is accelerated, the cells produce substances of this sort. When such substances accumulate in the vicinity of a precapillary sphincter, they depress the capacity of its muscle cells to respond to stimuli. As a result the sphincter relaxes, and blood flows from the thoroughfare channel into the capillary which nourishes the tissue.

The reaction limits itself, because the blood flow increases to the point where

MESENTERY of a rat is photographed at various magnifications to show the characteristic structures of the microcirculation. The drawings at right label the structures. The magnification of the photomicrograph at top is 100 diameters; of the photomicrograph second from top, 200 diameters; of the third photomicrograph, 1,000 diameters; of the photomicrograph at bottom, 200 diameters.

it is sufficient to meet the nutritional requirements of the tissue cells. This leads to a gradual disappearance of the substances liberated by accelerated metabolism, and to a gradual lessening of the inhibition of the precapillary sphincter. As the muscle cells regain their tone, the sphincter shuts off the capillary.

The muscle cells of the arterioles and the capillary bed are extraordinarily sensitive to chemical stimuli, so sensitive that they respond to as little as a hundredth of the amount of substance required to constrict or dilate a large blood vessel. This sensitivity is dramatically demonstrated by microsurgical experiments on the capillary bed of a living rat. As little as .000000001 gram (.001

microgram) of epinephrine, injected into the capillary bed by means of a micropipette, is sufficient to close its capillary sphincters completely. Such substances reduce the flow of blood through the capillary bed by an orderly sequence of events: first the precapillary sphincters are narrowed, then the thoroughfare channels, then the arterioles, and finally the venules. Substances that cause the blood vessels to dilate, such as acetylcholine, set in motion a similar sequence: first the precapillary sphincters are opened, then the thoroughfare channels, and so on. The sensitivity of the arterioles and the capillary bed to such stimuli contributes to their independent behavior. An amount of substance sufficient to cause dramatic changes in the micro-

circulation simply has no effect on the larger vessels.

The tone of the muscle cells of the microcirculation may well be maintained by norepinephrine continuously discharged from the nerve endings, and by the level of epinephrine circulating in the blood. Our work indicates that the tone is also influenced by the local release of sulfhydryl compounds, which are key substances in the regulation of the oxidations conducted by cells. Now epinephrine and norepinephrine lose their activity when they are oxidized. Thus the actual level of these substances in the vicinity of muscle cells is not only dependent on their formation but also on their removal or destruction. Sulfhydryl compounds have been found to reduce the rate at which epinephrine and norepinephrine are oxidized. In this way the local release of such compounds could regulate the tone of smooth muscle.

Recently it has been suggested that a role in the local control of the microcirculation is played by the so-called mast cells, large numbers of which adjoin the small blood vessels. Various investigators have shown that the mast cells release at least three substances that strongly affect blood vessels: histamine, serotonin and heparin. It has been proposed that these substances, working alone or in certain combinations, are local regulatory factors.

It must be borne in mind that, even though the control of the microcirculation is largely independent of the rest of the circulatory system, the small blood vessels depend upon the nervous controls of the larger blood vessels for the shifting of blood from one organ to another as it is needed. Obviously the nervous controls of the larger vessels and the chemical controls of the microcirculation must be linked in some fashion. Under normal circumstances tissues that are inactive are perfused with a minimal amount of blood to allow the flow to be diverted to the tissues that need it most. During shock and acute infections, on the other hand, the demands of the tissues may be so great that the circulatory system cannot meet them, and the circulation collapses. In such conditions the effect of substances released locally to relax the muscle cells of the capillary bed has superseded the efforts of the nervous system to restrict the blood flow by the release of substances such as norepinephrine. It is ironic that this primitive response, in striving to insure the survival of individual cells, frequently overtaxes the circulation and brings about the death of the organism.

CAPILLARY BEDS OF TWO TISSUES in a living rat are enlarged 200 diameters in these photomicrographs. At top is the capillary bed of a striated muscle; the capillaries run parallel to underlying muscle fibers. At bottom are capillaries in the surface of intestine.

12

The Lymphatic System

H. S. MAYERSON · June 1963

Living tissue is for the most part a collection of cells bathed in a fluid medium. This interstitial fluid constitutes what the French physiologist Claude Bernard named the *milieu intérieur:* the internal environment of the organism that is the true environment of its cells. The interstitial fluid brings nutrients to the cells and carries away waste products; its composition varies in space and time under the control of the co-ordinated physiological processes that maintain homeostasis, the remarkably steady state that characterizes the internal environment of a healthy organism. In the maintenance of the homeostasis of the interstitial fluid the circulation of the blood is obviously of fundamental importance. In the higher vertebrates there is a second circulation that is equally essential: the lymphatic system. Its primary function is to recirculate the interstitial fluid to the bloodstream, thereby helping to create a proper cellular environment and to maintain the constancy of the blood itself. It also serves as a transport system, conducting specialized substances from the cells that make them into the bloodstream. In recent years physiologists, biochemists, physicians and surgeons have been studying the lymphatic system intensively, in health and in disease. Their investigations are providing much new information on how the body functions, explaining some heretofore poorly understood clinical observations and even suggesting new forms of treatment.

The fact that the lymphatic system is an evolutionary newcomer encountered only in the higher vertebrates is significant. In lower animals there is no separation between the internal and external environments; all the cells of a jellyfish, for example, are bathed in sea water. With progression up the evolutionary scale the cells become separated from the external environment, "inside" is no longer identical with "outside" and rudimentary blood circulatory systems make their appearance to conduct the exchange of nutrients and waste products. As the organism becomes more complex the blood system becomes more specialized. The system develops increasing hydrostatic pressure until, in mammals, there is a closed, high-pressure system with conduits of diminishing thickness carrying blood to an extensive, branching bed of tiny capillaries.

At this point in evolution a snag was encountered: the high pressures made the capillaries leaky, with the result that fluid and other substances seeped out of the bloodstream. A drainage system was required and lymphatic vessels evolved (from the veins, judging by embryological evidence) to meet this need.

In man the lymphatic system is an extensive network of distensible vessels resembling the veins. It arises from a fine mesh of small, thin-walled lymph capillaries that branch through most of the soft tissue of the body. Through the walls of these blind-end capillaries the interstitial fluid diffuses to become lymph, a colorless or pale yellow liquid very similar in composition to the interstitial fluid and to plasma, the liquid component of the blood. The lymphatic capillaries converge to form larger vessels that receive tributaries along their length and join to become terminal ducts emptying into large veins in the lower part of the neck. The largest of these great lymphatics, the thoracic duct, drains the lower extremities and all the organs except the heart, the lungs and the upper part of the diaphragm; these are drained by the right lymphatic duct. Smaller cervical ducts collect fluid from each side of the head and neck. All but the largest lymph vessels are fragile and difficult to trace, following different courses in different individuals and even, over a period of time, in the same individual. The larger lymphatics, like large veins, are equipped with valves to prevent backflow.

Along the larger lymphatics are numerous lymph nodes, which are of fundamental importance in protecting the body against disease and the invasion of foreign matter. The lymph nodes serve, first of all, as filtering beds that remove particulate matter from the lymph before it enters the bloodstream; they contain white cells that can ingest and destroy foreign particles, bacteria and dead tissue cells. The nodes are, moreover, centers for the proliferation and storage of lymphocytes and other antibody-manufacturing cells produced in the thymus gland; when bacteria, viruses or antigenic molecules arrive at a lymph node, they stimulate such cells to make antibodies [see "The Thymus Gland," by Sir Macfarlane Burnet; SCIENTIFIC AMERICAN Offprint 138].

Starling's Hypothesis

The present view of the lymphatic circulation as a partner of the blood system in maintaining the fluid dynamics of the body stems from the investigations early in this century by the British physiologist Ernest H. Starling. "Starling's hypothesis" stated that the exchange of fluid between the capillaries and the interstitial space is governed by the relation between hydrostatic pressure and osmotic pressure. Blood at the arterial end of a capillary is still under a driving pressure equivalent to some 40 millimeters of mercury; this constitutes a "filtration pressure" that tends to make plasma seep out of the capillary. Starling

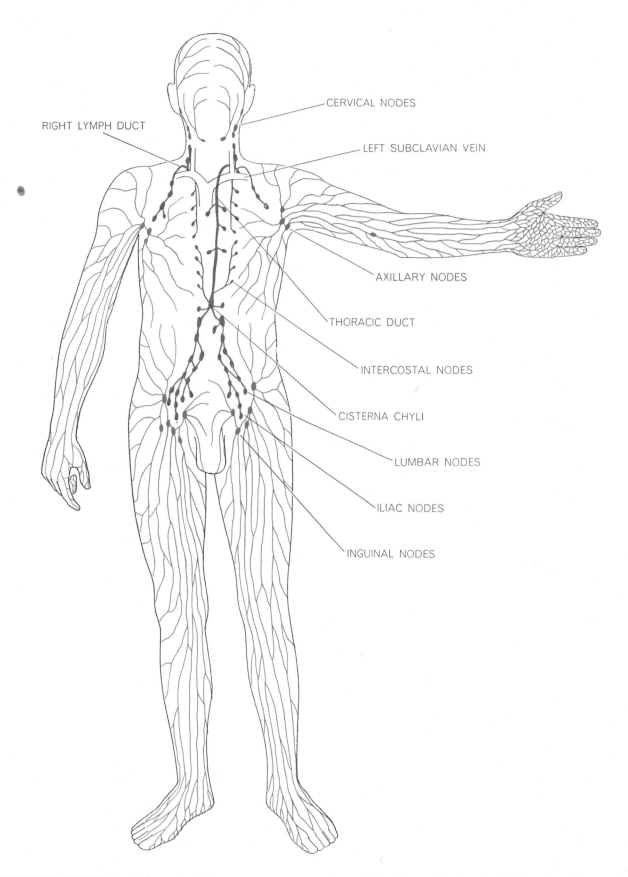

CERVICAL NODES

RIGHT LYMPH DUCT

LEFT SUBCLAVIAN VEIN

AXILLARY NODES

THORACIC DUCT

INTERCOSTAL NODES

CISTERNA CHYLI

LUMBAR NODES

ILIAC NODES

INGUINAL NODES

LYMPHATIC VESSELS drain the entire body, penetrating most of the tissues and carrying back to the bloodstream excess fluid from the intercellular spaces. This diagram shows only some of the larger superficial vessels (*light color*), which run near the surface of the body, and deep vessels (*dark color*), which drain the interior of the body and collect from the superficial vessels. The thoracic duct, which arises at the cisterna chyli in the abdomen, drains most of the body and empties into the left subclavian vein. The right lymph duct drains the heart, lungs, part of the diaphragm, the right upper part of the body and the right side of the head and neck, emptying into the right subclavian vein. Lymph nodes interspersed along the vessels trap foreign matter, including bacteria.

visualized the wall of the capillary as being freely permeable to plasma and all its constituents except the plasma proteins albumin, globulin and fibrinogen, which could leak through only in very small amounts. The proteins remaining in the capillary exert an osmotic pressure that tends to keep fluid in the capillary, countering the filtration pressure. Similar forces are operative in the tissue spaces outside the capillary. At the arterial end of the capillary the resultant of all these forces is ordinarily a positive filtration pressure: water and salts leave the capillary. At the venous end, however, the blood pressure is decreased, energy having been dissipated in pushing the blood through the capillary. Now the osmotic force exerted by the proteins is dominant. The pressure gradient is reversed: fluid, salts and the waste products of cell metabolism flow into the bloodstream [see top illustration on page 118].

It follows, Starling observed, that if the concentration of plasma proteins is decreased (as it would be in starvation), the return of fluid to the bloodstream will be diminished and edema, an excessive accumulation of fluid in the tissue spaces, will result. Similarly, if the capillaries become too permeable to protein, the osmotic pressure of the plasma decreases and that of the tissue fluid increases, again causing edema. Capillary poisons such as snake venoms have this effect. Abnormally high venous pressures also promote edema, by making it difficult for fluid to return to the capillaries; this is often one of the factors operating in congestive heart disease.

A fundamental tenet of Starling's hypothesis was that not much protein leaves the blood capillary. In the 1930's the late Cecil K. Drinker of the Harvard Medical School challenged this idea. Numerous experiments led him to conclude "that the capillaries practically universally leak protein; that this protein does not re-enter the blood vessels unless delivered by the lymphatic system; that the filtrate from the blood capillaries to the tissue spaces contains water, salts and sugars in concentrations found in blood, together with serum globulin, serum albumin and fibrinogen in low concentrations, lower probably than that of tissue fluid or lymph; that water and salts are reabsorbed by blood vessels and protein enters the lymphatics together with water and salts in the concentrations existing in the tissue fluid at the moment of lymphatic entrance." In other words, Drinker believed that protein is continuously filtering out of the blood; the plasma-protein level is maintained only because the lymphatic system picks up protein and returns it to the bloodstream.

Unfortunately Drinker had no definitive method by which to prove that the protein in lymph had leaked out of the blood and was not somehow originating in the cells. Perhaps for this reason his conclusions were not generally accepted. Teachers and the writers of textbooks continued to maintain that "healthy" blood capillaries did not leak protein. It was in an effort to clarify this point that I undertook an investigation of lymph

PULMONARY CIRCULATION

NODE

SYSTEMIC CIRCULATION

NODE

TWO CIRCULATORY SYSTEMS, the blood and the lymphatic (color), are related in this schematic diagram. Oxygenated blood (light gray) is pumped by the heart through a network of capillaries, bringing oxygen and nutrients to the tissue cells. Venous blood (dark gray) returns to the heart and is oxygenated in the course of the pulmonary (lung) circulation. Fluid and other substances seep out of the blood capillaries into the tissue spaces and are returned to the bloodstream by the lymph capillaries and larger lymphatic vessels.

and the lymphatics some 15 years ago. At that time I was working with a clinical group measuring the retention of blood by patients given large infusions. We saw that the patients were retaining the cellular components of the blood quite well but were "losing" the plasma. The loss was clearly into the tissue spaces, not by way of excretion from the kidneys.

If blood capillaries did indeed leak plasma, together with its proteins and other large molecules, then Drinker was correct. If the proteins entered the interstitial fluid, they would stay there, since Starling's measurements and Drinker's findings made it clear that large molecules could not get back into the blood capillaries—unless they were picked up by the lymphatic system. If they leaked from the blood vessels and were in fact returned by the lymphatic vessels, the evolutionary reason for the development of the lymphatic system would be established beyond question. I decided to return to my laboratory at the Tulane University School of Medicine and investigate the problem.

Over the years I have had the enthusiastic assistance of several colleagues—notably Karlman Wasserman, now at the Stanford University Medical School, and Stephen J. LeBrie—and of many students. Time had provided us with two tools not available to Drinker. One was flexible plastic tubing of small diameter, which we could insert into lymphatic vessels much more effectively than had been possible with the glass tubing available earlier. And we now had radioactive isotopes with which to label proteins and follow their course.

Experiments with Proteins

We injected the blood proteins albumin and globulin, to which we had coupled radioactive iodine atoms, into the femoral veins of anesthetized dogs. The proteins immediately began to leave the bloodstream. By calculating the slope of the disappearance curve in each experiment we could arrive at a number expressing the rate of disappearance [see top illustration on page 119]. The average rate of disappearance of albumin, for example, turned out to be about .001; in other words, a thousandth of the total amount of labeled albumin present at any given time was leaking out of the capillaries each minute. If we infused large amounts of salt solution, plasma or whole blood into our dogs, the disappearance rate increased significantly. The same thing happened in animals subjected to severe hemorrhage. In some experiments we simultaneously collected and analyzed lymph from the thoracic duct [see bottom illustration on page 119]. As before, labeled protein left the blood; within a few minutes after injection it appeared in the lymph, at first in small quantities and then at a faster rate. It leveled off, in equilibrium with the blood's protein, seven to 13 hours after injection.

We were able to calculate from our data that in dogs the thoracic duct alone

LACTEALS, the lymphatics of the intestine, were first described by the Italian anatomist Gasparo Aselli in 1622. They were pictured in his *De Lactibus,* the first anatomical work with color plates. This plate shows veins (*A*), *lacteals* (*B*), *mesentery* (*C*), stomach (*D*), small intestine (*F, G, H*) and a lymph node (*L*).

THORACIC DUCT and the major lymph vessels of the lower extremities and trunk that contribute to it are seen in this plate from a French book of 1847, *Atlas d'Anatomie Descriptive du Corps Humain.* The duct arises from a plexus of abdominal vessels and arches up into the lower neck before entering the subclavian vein.

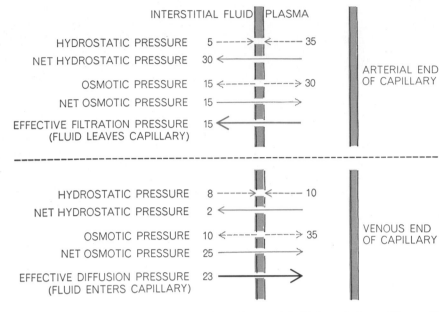

	INTERSTITIAL FLUID	PLASMA	
HYDROSTATIC PRESSURE	5 ----▷ ◁---- 35		
NET HYDROSTATIC PRESSURE	30 ◁—		ARTERIAL END OF CAPILLARY
OSMOTIC PRESSURE	15 ◁---- ----▷ 30		
NET OSMOTIC PRESSURE	15 —————▷		
EFFECTIVE FILTRATION PRESSURE (FLUID LEAVES CAPILLARY)	15 ◁━━━		

HYDROSTATIC PRESSURE	8 ---▷ ◁--- 10		
NET HYDROSTATIC PRESSURE	2 ◁—		
OSMOTIC PRESSURE	10 ◁---- ----▷ 35		VENOUS END OF CAPILLARY
NET OSMOTIC PRESSURE	25 —————▷		
EFFECTIVE DIFFUSION PRESSURE (FLUID ENTERS CAPILLARY)	23 ━━━━▷		

STARLING'S HYPOTHESIS explained the exchange of fluid through the capillary wall. At the arterial end of the capillary the hydrostatic pressure (*given here in centimeters of water*) delivered by the heart is dominant, and fluid leaves the capillary. At the venous end the osmotic pressure of the proteins in the plasma dominates; fluid enters the capillary.

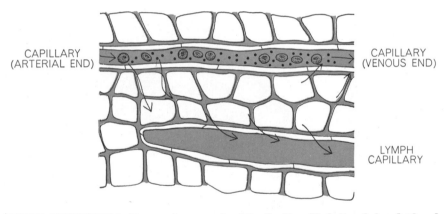

CAPILLARY (ARTERIAL END)
CAPILLARY (VENOUS END)
LYMPH CAPILLARY

FLUID EXCHANGE is diagramed as postulated by Starling. He believed that fluid and salts (*arrows*) left the blood capillaries, mixed with the interstitial fluid and for the most part were reabsorbed by the capillaries. Excess fluid was drained by the lymph vessels. He took it for granted that most of the protein in the blood stayed inside the blood capillaries.

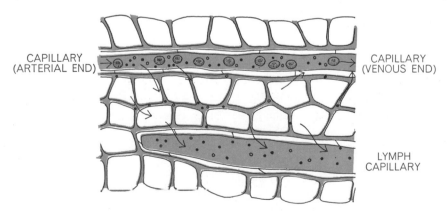

CAPILLARY (ARTERIAL END)
CAPILLARY (VENOUS END)
LYMPH CAPILLARY

PRESENT VIEW of fluid exchange is diagramed. It appears that such large molecules as proteins (*black dots*) and lipids (*open circles*) leave the blood capillaries along with the fluid and salts. Some of the fluid and salts are reabsorbed; the excess, along with large molecules that cannot re-enter the blood capillaries, is returned via the lymphatic system.

returned about 65 per cent of the protein that leaked out of the capillaries. Extension of this kind of experiment to man showed similar rates of leakage. In the course of a day 50 per cent or more of the total amount of protein circulating in the blood is lost from the capillaries and is returned to the bloodstream by the lymphatic system.

The importance of lymphatic drainage of protein becomes clear if one considers its role in lung function, which was elucidated by Drinker. The pulmonary circulation, in contrast to the general circulation, is a low-pressure system. The pulmonary capillary pressure is about a quarter as high as the systemic capillary pressure and the filtration pressure in the pulmonary capillaries is therefore considerably below the osmotic pressure of the blood proteins. As a result fluid is retained in the bloodstream and the lung tissue remains properly "dry."

When pulmonary capillary pressure rises significantly, there is increased fluid and protein leakage and therefore increased lymph flow. For a time the lymph drainage is adequate and the lungs remain relatively dry. But when the leakage exceeds the capacity of the lymphatics to drain away excess fluid and protein, the insidious condition pulmonary edema develops. The excessive accumulation of fluid makes it more difficult for the blood to take up oxygen. The lack of oxygen increases the permeability of the pulmonary capillaries, and this leads to greater loss of protein in a vicious circle. Some recent findings by John J. Sampson and his colleagues at the San Francisco Medical Center of the University of California support this concept. They found that a gradual increase in lymphatic drainage occurs in dogs in which high pulmonary blood pressure is produced and maintained experimentally. This suggests that the lymphatic system attempts to cope with the abnormal situation by proliferating, much as blood capillaries do when coronary circulation is impaired.

Leakage from blood capillaries and recirculation by the lymphatic system is, as I indicated earlier, not limited to protein. Any large molecule can leak out of the capillaries, and it cannot get back to the bloodstream except via the lymphatics. All the plasma lipids, or fatty substances, have been identified in thoracic-duct lymph. Even chylomicrons, particles of emulsified fat as large as a micron (a thousandth of a millimeter) in diameter that are found in blood during the digestion of fat, leak out of the bloodstream and are picked up and recirculated to the vascular system by the lymphatics. As a matter of fact, there is evidence that they may leak out even faster than proteins. The significance of these findings remains to be explained. Aaron Kellner of the Cornell University Medical College has suggested that atherosclerosis, a form of hardening of the arteries in which there is infiltration of the walls of the arteries by lipids, may have its origin in the fact that under normal conditions there is a constant flow of fluid containing lipids and proteins across the blood-vessel lining into the vessel wall. Ordinarily this fluid is removed by the small blood vessels of the wall itself and by the lymphatics. It is conceivable that something may interfere with the removal of lipids and cause them to accumulate in the blood-vessel wall. It is even conceivable that the high capillary filtration that accompanies hypertension may increase the leakage of lipids from capillaries to a level exceeding their rate of removal from the interstitial fluid, which would then bathe even the outer surfaces of the arteries in lipids.

In addition to demonstrating that the lymph returns large molecules from the tissue spaces to the bloodstream, recent investigation has confirmed the importance of lymphatic drainage of excess fluid filtered out of the capillaries but not reabsorbed. Experiments with heavy water show that blood is unquestionably the chief source of the water of lymph. In dogs the amount of lymph returned to the bloodstream via the thoracic duct alone in 24 hours is roughly equivalent to the volume of the blood plasma. Most of this fluid apparently comes from the blood. In some of our experiments we drained the thoracic-duct lymph outside the dog's body and found that the plasma volume dropped about 20 per cent in eight hours and the plasma-protein level some 16 per cent. Translated to a 24-hour basis, the loss would be equivalent to about 60 per cent of the plasma volume and almost half of the total plasma proteins circulating in the blood. Thus the return of lymph plays an essential role in maintaining the blood volume.

One situation in which this function can be observed is the "lymphagogue" effect: the tendency of large infusions into the vascular system to increase the flow of lymph. As we increased the size of infusions in dogs, lymph flow increased proportionally; with large infusions (2,000 milliliters, about the normal blood volume of a large dog) the thoracic-duct lymph flow reached a peak value about 14 times greater than that

LABELED PROTEINS were injected into dogs' veins. Measuring the radioactivity per milliliter of blood withdrawn from an artery showed how quickly the globulin (*gray*) and albumin (*black*) disappeared. The steep slopes represent disappearance, the shallow slopes subsequent metabolism of the proteins. The radioactivity is plotted on a logarithmic scale.

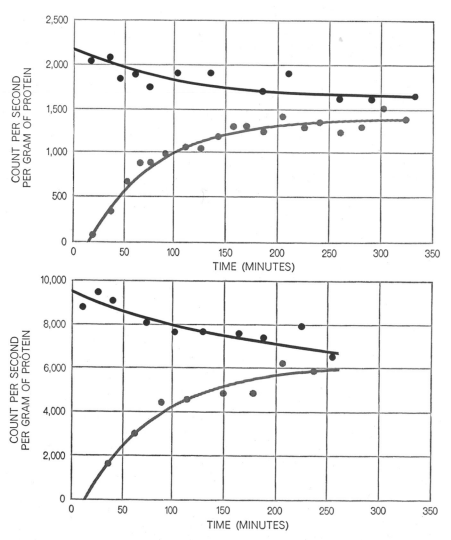

PROTEIN appeared in thoracic-duct lymph (*gray curves*) and increased in the lymph as it disappeared from the blood (*black curves*). The upper graph is for albumin, the lower one for globulin. In time the labeled protein in blood and lymph reached equilibrium.

EFFECT OF INFUSIONS on lymph flow (*graph at left*) and on albumin flow in lymph (*graph at right*) in dogs is illustrated. Each curve shows the ratio of the flow after an infusion of a given size to the flow before the infusion. The curves are for infusions of 250 (*solid black*), 500 (*gray*), 1,000 (*broken black*) and 2,000 (*colored*) milliliters. The larger the infusion, the more leakage.

of the preinfusion level [*see illustration above*]. Most of the excess fluid is excreted by the kidneys in increased urine flow. But the displacement of fluid from the blood circulation into the lymph "saves" some of the fluid. In other words, it can be considered as being a fine adjustment of the blood volume so that not all the fluid is irrevocably lost from the body. Large infusions also increase protein leakage, but again the fact that the protein goes to the lymph and slowly returns to the bloodstream minimizes changes in total circulating protein and the loss of its osmotic effect.

The Mechanism of Filtration

The exact processes or sites of the filtration of large molecules through the capillary wall, and through cell membranes in general, are still unclear. As Arthur K. Solomon has pointed out in these pages [see "Pores in the Cell Membrane," by Arthur K. Solomon; SCIENTIFIC AMERICAN Offprint 76], "some materials pass directly through the fabric of the membrane, either by dissolving in the membrane or by interacting chemically with its substance. But it seems equally certain that a large part of the traffic travels via holes in the wall. These are not necessarily fixed canals; as the living membrane responds to changing conditions inside or outside the cell, some pores may open and others may seal up."

This last point appears to explain our results with infusions in dogs. The massive infusions overfill the closed blood system, raise filtration pressure in the capillaries and result in increased leakage through the capillary walls; lymph flow is copious and the lymph contains more large molecules. Small infusions do not do this. The reason, then, that patients did not do as well as expected after receiving large infusions or transfusions was that the plasma and proteins leaked out through stretched capillary pores. A similar effect accounted for the case of animals subjected to severe hemorrhage: there was not enough blood to oxygenate the capillary walls adequately, the walls became more permeable and the protein molecules passed through.

We found that the rate of leakage for any molecule depends on its size. Globulin, which has a molecular weight of

250,000, leaked more slowly than albumin, which has a weight of 70,000. The third plasma protein, fibrinogen, has a molecular weight of about 450,000 and leaves the blood still more slowly. By introducing into the blood various carbohydrate molecules, which unlike protein molecules do not carry a charge, we were able to demonstrate that it is size and not electrical charge that determines a molecule's rate of movement through the wall.

When, after infusing the carbohydrates, we collected lymph from different parts of the body, we found larger molecules in intestinal lymph than in leg lymph, and still larger molecules in lymph from the liver. This indicated that capillaries in the liver have substantially larger openings than leg capillaries do, and that the vessels of the intestine probably have both large and small openings. There are other indications that liver capillaries are the most permeable of all; for example, apparently both red cells and lymphocytes pass between the blood and the lymph in the liver. Recent studies with the electron microscope confirm the indirect evidence for variations in the size of capillary openings; the structure of the capillaries seems to vary with the organ, and these differences may be related to differences in function.

Transport by the Lymph

When Gasparo Aselli first described lymphatic vessels in 1622, the ones he noted were the lacteals: small vessels that drain the intestinal wall. The dog Aselli was dissecting had eaten recently; the lacteals had absorbed fat from the intestine, which gave them a milky-white appearance and made them far more visible than other lymphatics. The transport of certain fats from the intestine to the bloodstream by way of the thoracic duct is one of the lymphatic system's major functions. Studies in which fatty acids have been labeled with radioactive carbon show that the blood capillaries of the intestine absorb short-chain fatty acid molecules directly, together with most other digested substances, and pass them on to the liver for metabolism. But the lacteal vessels absorb the long-chain fats, such as stearic and palmitic acids, and carry them to the bloodstream via the thoracic duct. The lymphatic system is also the main route by which cholesterol, the principal steroid found in tissues, makes its way into the blood.

Since the lymphatics are interposed between tissue cells and the blood sys-

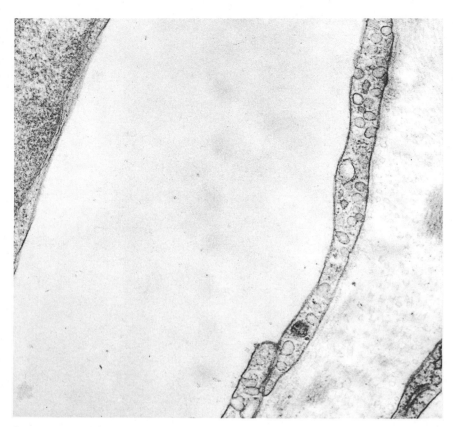

LYMPH CAPILLARY (*lightest area*) of mouse arterial tissue is enlarged 30,000 diameters in this electron micrograph made by Johannes A. G. Rhodin of the New York University School of Medicine. At upper left is part of the nucleus of an endothelial cell of the vessel wall. The thin ends of two other cells overlap near the bottom. The faint shadow in the connective tissue outside the wall is a slight indication of a basement membrane.

"LOOSE JUNCTION" between the overlapping ends of two endothelial cells of a vessel wall is seen in this electron micrograph, also made by Rhodin, of a lymphatic in mouse intestinal tissue. The lymph vessel is at the top, connective tissue at the bottom. In this case there is no sign of a basement membrane outside the wall. The enlargement is 90,000 diameters.

LYMPHANGIOGRAM is an X-ray photograph in which the lymphatic vessels are made visible by injecting into them a radiopaque dye. In the normal leg (*left*) the vessels are straight and well defined. In lymphedema (*right*) there is insufficient drainage of fluid and proteins, in this case because there were too few vessels in the thigh. The extra pressure on the lower-leg vessels increased their number and made them tortuous. These pictures were made by Carl A. Smith of the New York University School of Medicine.

tem it is not surprising to find that they serve as the channel for transport to the bloodstream of substances that originate in tissue cells. The lymph is probably the route by which at least some hormones, many of which are very large molecules, are carried to the blood from the endocrine glands where they are synthesized. Some enzymes, found in lymph in small concentrations, may merely have leaked out of the capillaries. But others are apparently picked up from their cells of origin and carried to the blood by the lymph. Certain enzymes, including histaminase and renin, are present in greater concentrations in lymph than in the blood. The finding on renin, reported by A. F. Lever and W. S. Peart of St. Mary's Hospital Medical School in London, is of particular interest to investigators working on the problem of hypertension. One concept ascribes high blood pressure in some individuals to the production of renin by a kidney suffering from inadequate blood circulation; the renin is thought to combine with a globulin in the plasma to form hypertensin, an enzyme that narrows the arterioles and results in high blood pressure. It has been difficult to establish this concept because no one has been able consistent-

ly to demonstrate the presence of renin in the blood of hypertensive patients. Now that it has been discovered in lymph coming from the kidney it is clear that renin is indeed being formed in these patients, although in amounts so small that it usually escapes detection after being diluted in the blood.

Recently Samuel N. Kolmen of the University of Texas Medical Branch in Galveston has provided what may be a confirmation of the renin concept. He produced hypertension in dogs by removing one kidney and partially constricting the artery supplying the other one. When he shunted the thoracic-duct flow into the dog's gullet or allowed it to escape, the hypertension diminished. The implication is that renin was being kept out of the bloodstream. When Kolmen stopped lymph flow in the shunt, presumably inhibiting the diversion of the renin, the hypertension returned.

The Lymphatic Circulation

To the investigators of the 19th century the lymphatic system was "open-mouthed": its capillaries were assumed to be open to the tissue spaces. More recent evidence has shown that the

lymphatics form a closed system, that fluid enters not through the open ends of vessels but through their walls. The walls of the terminal lymph capillaries, like those of blood capillaries, consist of a single layer of platelike endothelial cells. This layer continues into the larger vessels as a lining but acquires outer layers of connective tissue, elastic fibers and muscle. Although the capillaries of the blood and lymphatic systems are structurally very similar, recent electron micrographs show differences in detail that may help to explain the ease with which the lymph vessels take up large molecules. Sir Howard Florey of the University of Oxford and J. R. Casley-Smith of the University of Adelaide in Australia believe that the most important difference is the poor development or absence in lymph capillaries of "adhesion plates," structures that hold together the endothelial cells of the blood capillaries. They suggest that as a result there are open junctions between adjacent cells in lymph capillaries that allow large molecules to pass through the walls. Johannes A. G. Rhodin of the New York University School of Medicine puts more emphasis on the apparent absence or poor development in lymph capillaries of the "basement membrane" that surrounds blood capillaries.

Certainly it is clear that very large particles do enter the lymphatic vessels: proteins, chylomicrons, lymphocytes and red cells—the last of which can be as much as nine microns in diameter. Bacteria, plastic spheres, graphite particles and other objects have been shown to penetrate the lymphatics with no apparent difficulty. Yet we have found that when we introduce substances directly into the lymphatic system, anything with a molecular weight greater than 2,000 is retained almost completely within the lymphatics, reaching the blood only by way of the thoracic duct. If large particles can get into the lymphatic vessels, why do substances with a molecular weight of 2,000 not get out by the same channels?

I have spent many hours trying to formulate an answer to this question without arriving at a sophisticated concept, and have had to be content with a simple explanation that is at least consistent with the current evidence. Assume that the smallest terminal lymphatics are freely permeable to small and large molecules and particles moving in either direction through intercellular gaps. Compression of these vessels in any way would tend to force their contents in all directions. At least some of the contents would be forced along into the larger lymph vessels, where the presence of valves would prevent backflow. And once the lymph reaches a larger vessel it can no longer lose its large particles through the thick and relatively impermeable wall of the lymphatic.

One can argue that this seems to be a rather inefficient and even casual way of getting the job done. Indeed it is, and this physiological casualness is a characteristic of the lymphatic system as a whole. There is no heart to push the lymph, and although lymphatic vessels do contract and dilate like veins and arteries this activity does not seem to be an important factor in lymph movement. The flow of lymph depends almost entirely on forces external to the system: rhythmic contraction of the intestines, changes in pressure in the chest in the course of breathing and particularly the mechanical squeezing of the lymphatics by contraction of the muscles through which they course.

Lymphatic Malfunction

In spite of the casualness of the lymphatic system, its development, as I have tried to show, was an absolute necessity for highly organized animals. Its importance is most visibly demonstrated in various forms of lymphedema, a swelling of one or more of the extremities due to the lack of lymphatic vessels or to their malfunction. In some individuals the lymphatic system fails to develop normally at birth, causing gradual swelling of the affected part. Lymphangiographic studies, in which the vessels are injected with radiopaque dyes to make them visible in X-ray photographs, show that the lymphatics are scarce, malformed or dilated. Insufficient drainage causes water and protein to accumulate in the tissues and accounts for the severe and often disabling edema. There is evidence that genetic factors may play a role in this

condition. Surgical procedures that destroy lymph vessels may have a similar effect in a local area. Elephantiasis is a specific form of lymphedema resulting from the obstruction of the vessels. It can be caused by infection of the lymphatics or by infestation with a parasitic worm that invades and blocks the vessels.

The lymphedemas have been recognized as such for many years. Recently the view that the lymphatic system is essential to homeostasis—which is to say "good health"—has led to a number of investigations of its role in conditions in which no lymphatic involvement was previously suspected. Our group at Tulane has found that lymphatic drainage of the kidneys is essential in order to maintain the precise osmotic relations

LYMPHEDEMA can cause gross deformity of a limb and even disability. The drawing is based on a photograph of an 11-year-old girl whose leg began to swell at the age of seven, probably because of an insufficiency of lymphatic vessels. The patient's condition was greatly improved by an operation in which the tissue between skin and muscles was removed.

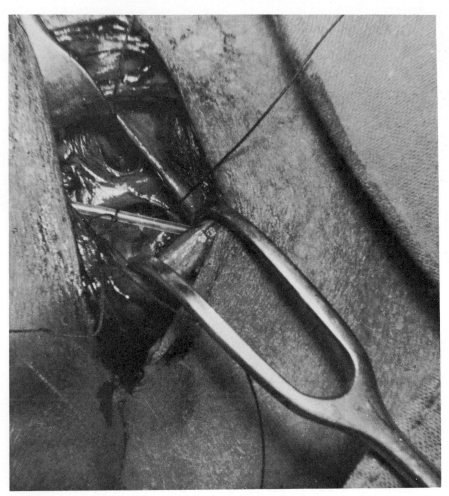

DILATED THORACIC DUCT of a patient with cirrhosis is seen in this photograph made by Allan E. Dumont and John H. Mulholland of the New York University School of Medicine and reprinted from *Annals of Surgery*. The plastic tube just below the duct is a tenth of an inch in diameter. A normal duct would be smaller than the tube.

on which proper kidney function depends. This may explain the dilution of the urine observed in some patients after kidney operations: the lymph vessels may have been damaged, decreasing their capacity for draining proteins and interfering with the reabsorption of water by the kidney tubules.

At the New York University School of Medicine, John H. Mulholland and Allan E. Dumont have been investigating the relation between thoracic-duct flow and cirrhosis of the liver. Their results suggest that the cirrhosis may be associated with increased lymph flow in the liver and that the inability of the thoracic duct to handle the flow may bring on the accumulation of fluid, local high blood pressure and venous bleeding that are frequently seen in cirrhosis patients; drainage of the duct outside the body temporarily relieves the symptoms.

These and other clinical observations are consistent with my feeling that the lymphatic system does a capable job when all is going well but that its capacity for dealing with disturbances is limited. As a phylogenetic late-comer it may simply not have evolved to the point of being able to cope with abnormal stresses and strains. The role of the second circulation in disease states is currently under intensive investigation. As more and more is learned about its primary functions and its reactions to stress, the new knowledge should be helpful in diagnosis and perhaps eventually in the treatment of patients.

13

"The Wonderful Net"

P. F. SCHOLANDER • April 1957

A man standing barefoot in a tub of ice water would not survive very long. But a wading bird may stand about in cold water all day, and the whale and the seal swim in the arctic with naked fins and flippers continually bathed in freezing water. These are warm-blooded animals, like man, and have to maintain a steady body temperature. How do they avoid losing their body heat through their thinly insulated extremities? The question brings to light a truly remarkable piece of biological engineering. It seems that such animals block the loss of heat by means of an elementary physical mechanism, familiar enough to engineers, which nature puts to use in a most effective way. In fact, the same principle is employed for several very different purposes by many members of the animal kingdom from fishes to man.

The principle is known as counter-current exchange. Consider two pipes lying side by side so that heat is easily transmitted from one to the other. Suppose that fluids at different temperatures start flowing in opposite directions in the two pipes: that is, a cold stream flowing counter to a warm [see diagram on next page]. The warmer stream will lose heat to the colder one, and if the transfer is efficient and the pipes long enough, the warm stream will have passed most of its heat to the counter current by the time it leaves the system. In other words, the counter current acts as a barrier to escape of heat in the direction of the warm current's flow. This method of heat exchange is, of course, a common practice in industry: the counter-flow system is used, for example, to tap the heat of exhaust gases from a furnace for preheating the air flowing into the furnace. And the same method apparently serves to conserve body heat for whales, seals, cranes, herons and other animals with chilly extremities.

Claude Bernard, the great 19th-century physiologist, suggested many years ago that veins lying next to arteries in the limbs must take up heat from the arteries, thus intercepting some of the body heat before it reaches the extremities. Recent measurements have proved that there is in fact some artery-to-vein transfer of heat in the human body. But this heat exchange in man is minor compared to that in animals adapted to severe exposure of the extremities. In those animals we find special networks of blood vessels which act as heat traps. This type of network, called *rete mirabile* (wonderful net), is a bundle of small arteries and veins, all mixed together, with the counter-flowing arteries and veins lying next to each other. The retes are generally situated at the places where the trunk of the animal deploys into extremities—limbs, fins, tail and so on. There the retes trap most of the blood heat and return it to the trunk. The blood circulating through the extremities is therefore considerably cooler than in the trunk, but the limbs can function perfectly well at the lower temperature. It has been found that many arctic animals have a leg temperature as low as 50 degrees Fahrenheit or even less.

Anatomists have confirmed that the whale, the seal and the long-legged wading birds possess such retes. However, these networks have also been discovered in the extremities of many tropical animals. It is not surprising to find heat-trapping retes in a water-dwelling animal such as the Florida manatee, for even tropical waters are chilling to a constantly immersed body, but why should the retes appear in tropical land animals like the sloth, the anteater and the armadillo? The answer may be that these animals are hypersensitive to cool air. The sloth, for instance, begins to shiver when the air temperature drops below 80 degrees F. It has to adjust to this situation almost every night, and the retes may well be the means by which it makes the adjustment: that is, the sloth may let its long arms and legs cool to the temperature of the night air, as a reptile does, to preserve its body heat. Recent measurements have shown that it takes a sloth two hours to rewarm a chilled arm from 59 to 77 degrees, whereas an animal without retes, such as a monkey, accomplishes this in 10 minutes.

There is another finding, however, which at first sight is more puzzling. Many animals that spend a great deal of time in cold water or live in the arctic snow seem to lack retes to sidetrack body heat from their poorly insulated legs or feet: Among them are ducks, geese, sea gulls, the fox and the husky (the Eskimo dog). The absence of retes in these animals is not difficult to explain, however, when we consider that all of them are heavily insulated over most of their bodies. Their principal problem lies in getting rid of body heat rather than in conserving it. Consider, for instance, the situation of a husky. It is so well insulated that it can sleep on the snow at 40 degrees below zero without raising its normal rate of metabolism at rest. When this animal gets up after a cold night and begins to run in the warm sun, increasing its metabolic rate 10- or 20-fold because of the exercise, it is immediately faced with the problem of dissipating a good deal of excess heat. Because of its thick fur covering, it can lose heat only through exposed surfaces such as its tongue, face and legs. An arteriovenous network impeding the transport of heat

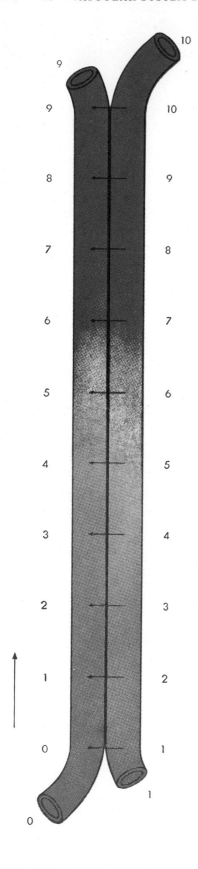

THE PRINCIPLE of counter-current exchange is demonstrated in two pipes lying side by side. Hot water enters one pipe (top right); cold water enters the other (bottom left). The fluids flow in opposite directions. Under ideal conditions heat will diffuse almost completely from one to the other.

to its legs would be a severe handicap. The same is true of the duck and other extremely well-insulated birds, which probably depend upon their webbed feet for heat dissipation.

As I mentioned at the beginning, heat conservation is only one of the functions performed by counter-current networks such as I have described. Indeed, there are more dramatic manifestations of this sort of system in the animal world. Nowhere in nature is counter-current exchange more strikingly developed nor more clearly illustrated than in the swim-bladder wall of deep-sea fishes. Here the function of the "wonderful network" is to prevent the loss of oxygen from the fish's air bladder.

A deep-sea fish keeps its swim bladder filled with gas which is more than 90 per cent oxygen. At depths of 9,000 feet or so it must maintain an oxygen pressure amounting to 200 to 300 atmospheres—nearly double the pressure in a fully charged steel oxygen cylinder. On the other hand, the oxygen pressure in the bladder's surroundings—in the fish's bloodstream and in the sea water outside—is no more than a fifth of an atmosphere. So the oxygen pressure difference across the thin swim-bladder wall is some 200 atmospheres. What is more, blood is constantly streaming along this wall through myriads of blood vessels embedded in it. Oxygen from the bladder, under the enormous pressure of 200 atmospheres, must diffuse into these blood vessels. How is it, then, that the streaming blood does not quickly drain the oxygen from the bladder? The answer, of course, is a counter-current exchange system. Very little oxygen escapes from the swim-bladder wall to the rest of the fish's body, because the outgoing veins, highly charged with oxygen, give it up to adjacent incoming arteries. There is a network of thousands of looping capillaries, so closely intermingled that diffusion of oxygen from veins to arteries goes on at a high rate.

What would be the most efficient arrangement of veins and arteries to give the maximum surface for transfer from one type of vessel to the other? We can treat this as a problem in topology and ask: How can we arrange black and white polygons (representing the cross sections of the blood vessels) so that black always borders white? If we allow only four polygons to meet at each corner, there are two different possible solutions: a checkerboard of squares or a pattern of hexagons with triangles filling the open corners. Under the microscope we observe that evolution has

produced precisely these two patterns in the swim-bladder retes of deep-sea fishes [see photographs and diagrams on page 128].

From the number and dimensions of the capillaries, the speed of the blood flow and other information we can calculate the amount of the oxygen-pressure drop across the rete, or, in other words, how effectively the rete traps oxygen. The calculation indicates that across a rete only one centimeter long, the oxygen pressure is reduced by a factor of more than 3,000. That is to say, the leak of oxygen through the rete is insignificant: translating the situation into terms of heat, if boiling water were to enter such a rete from one end and ice water from the other, the exchange of heat would be all but complete—to within one 10,000th of a degree!

To put it another way, the counter-current exchange in the swim-bladder rete is so efficient that in a single pass a rete one centimeter long is capable of raising a given concentration 3,000-fold, which leaves industrial engineering far behind. In speaking of concentration we include several different kinds: heat, gas pressure, the concentration of a solution and so on. A counter-current exchange system can establish a steep gradient in any of these quantities.

It has recently been suggested that counter-current exchange may be involved in the process whereby the kidneys filter the blood and produce urine. During the process of conversion of blood fluid to urine, the concentration of salts and urea in the fluid may be increased three- or four-fold. Just how is this concentration carried out?

The machines that perform the transformation are the units called nephrons, of which a kidney contains several millions. A nephron consists of a glomerulus capsule (a small ball of capillaries), a long, twisting tubule and a collecting duct [see diagram on page 131]. From the blood in the glomerulus capillaries a filtered fluid passes through the capsule wall into the tubule. The fluid travels along the tortuous course of the tubule,

RETE MIRABILE in the wall of the swim bladder of the deep-sea eel is enlarged 100 times in this photomicrograph. The rete is a bundle of small blood vessels; each of the small light areas in the photomicrograph is a blood vessel seen in cross section. The veins and arteries in the bundle are arranged in such a way that the blood in one vessel flows in a direction opposite that of the blood in an adjacent vessel.

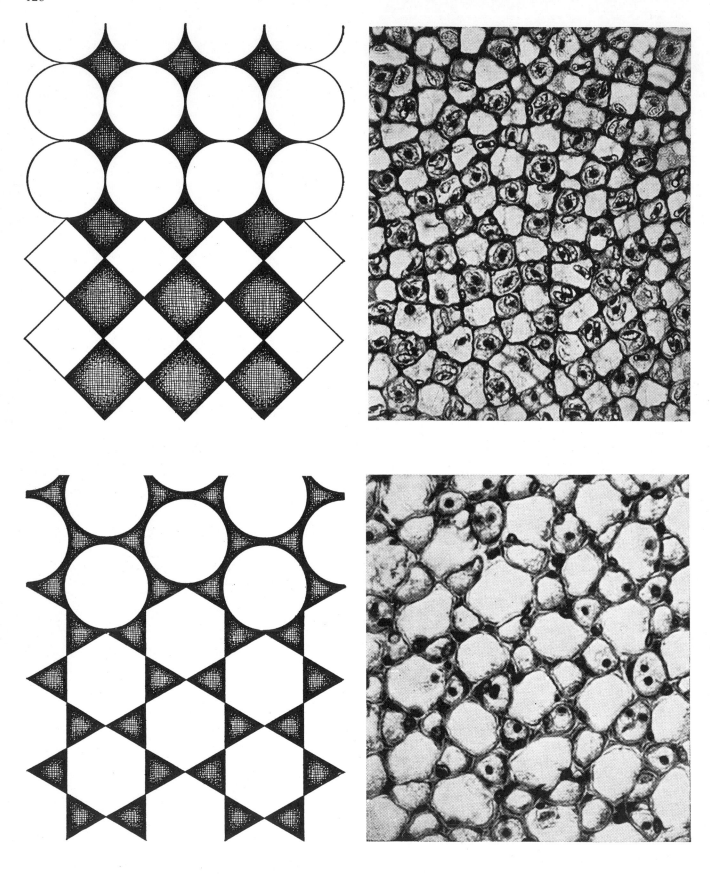

THE APPLICATION of counter-current exchange reaches the ultimate in the swim-bladder retes of deep-sea fishes. Drawings at left show two ways in which veins (*white*) and arteries (*black*) might be arranged to gain the greatest possible area of exchange. One pattern is non-staggered; it gives rise to a checkerboard (*top left*). The other is staggered; it gives rise to stars (*bottom left*). Photomicrographs show the checkerboard in the deep-sea eel (*top right*) and the star pattern in the rosefish (*bottom right*).

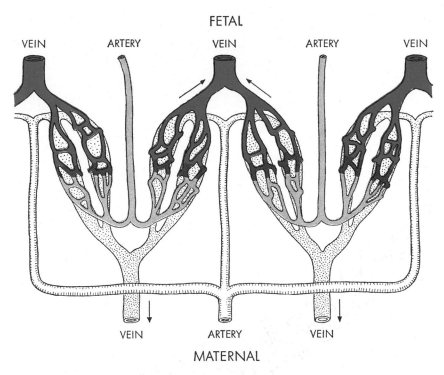

FETAL

VEIN   ARTERY   VEIN   ARTERY   VEIN

VEIN   ARTERY   VEIN

MATERNAL

OXYGEN IS EXCHANGED by counter-current flow in the placenta of the ground squirrel. Oxygen-rich maternal blood (*white*) enters the arteries (*bottom*) and flows counter to the oxygen-poor fetal blood (*gray*). The fetal blood picks up oxygen (*red*) and leaves through the fetal vein (*top*). Oxygen-poor maternal blood (*stippled*) returns to the maternal heart.

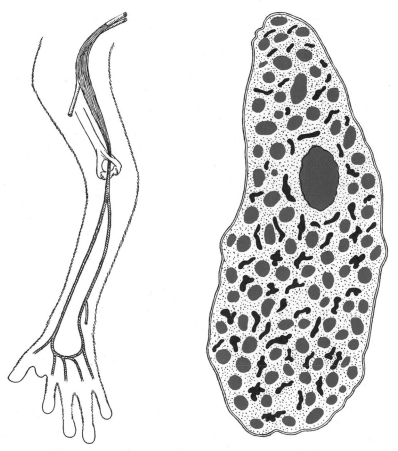

HEAT IS CONSERVED by rete bundles in the loris. They occur where the limbs join the body (*upper left*). Arterial blood enters the upper end of the rete and flows counter to the venous blood. Heat diffuses from the arteries to the veins and is returned to the body. A cross section of the rete (*right*) shows the arrangement of arteries (*red*) and veins (*black*).

doubles back at the loop of Henle [*see diagram*], and by the time it leaves the collecting duct it has become concentrated urine. The conversion does not take place in the glomerulus capsule; it has been established that the fluid emerging from the capsule has essentially the same salt concentration as the blood. The problem is to determine exactly where in the system the change in concentration is produced.

B. Hargitay and Werner Kuhn of the University of Basel recently proposed that it takes place primarily in the loop of Henle. They pointed out that only animals with a Henle loop in the kidney nephron—namely, mammals and birds—can produce a concentrated urine.

The loop of Henle, with its two arms running parallel and fairly close together, is a structure which reminds us of the arteriovenous capillary loops that make up the rete of a fish [*see diagram on page 130*]. Hargitay and Kuhn reasoned that salts or water might migrate from one arm of Henle's loop to the other, and that as a result salts might be concentrated in the bend of the loop. This part of the loop is situated in an internal structure of the kidney called the papilla, which also contains the collecting ducts and adjacent blood capillaries. The investigators assumed that the fluid concentrated in the loop would be transmitted to the ducts and capillaries and become concentrated urine. To test their idea, they first froze rat kidneys and examined small sections of the tissue under a microscope. The sections of tissue in the papilla, around the loop of Henle, proved to have the same melting point as the rats' urine, while the tissue in the cortex (outer part) of the kidney had the same melting point as frozen blood. Since the melting point depends on the salt concentration this finding tended to confirm the idea that the primary site for the concentration of urine is located in the bend of Henle's loop. But it was possible that the brutal freezing process had damaged the tissues so that urine escaped from the collecting ducts and diffused to the area around the loop. To make a clearer test, H. Wirz, a colleague of Hargitay and Kuhn, developed a technique for drawing samples of blood from the capillaries around Henle's loop. This blood proved to have the same melting point as the urine, *i.e.*, its salt concentration was as much as three times higher than that of blood in other parts of the animal's body.

Thus Hargitay and Kuhn seem to have strong support for their thesis that a counter-current exchange in Henle's loop plays a part in the formation of urine by the kidney. But the question still needs further research.

Various other examples of counter-current exchange in animals have been discovered. One of them concerns the breathing of fishes. A fish requires a far more efficient and resourceful breathing apparatus than an animal that lives in the air. Each quart of air contains some 200 cubic centimeters of oxygen, but a quart of sea water has only about five cubic centimeters, and oxygen diffuses through water slowly. The fish therefore has to be remarkably efficient in extracting oxygen from the water that flows over its gills. It can, in fact, take up as much as 80 per cent of the oxygen in the water. Anatomical studies and experiments have proved that fishes employ a counter-current system in this process. The blood in the capillaries of the fish's gill plates flows in the direction counter to the flow of water over its gills. When experimenters reversed the direction of the water current over the gills, fishes extracted only one fifth as much oxygen as they did normally!

In many species of animals the mother and the fetus she is carrying share their blood substances by means of a counter-current exchange system. This apparently is not true of the human animal, for the fetus's capillaries are bathed directly by the mother's blood. But in the rabbit, the sheep, the squirrel, the cow, the cat, the dog and other animals, the mother's blood vessels are intermingled with the fetus's in the placenta, and by counter-current flow they exchange oxygen, nutrients, heat and wastes.

In sum, the principle of counter-current exchange is employed in many and various ways in the world of living

THE WRECKFISH swims at great depths and must therefore keep its swim bladder filled with oxygen at tremendous pressures. It does this by means of counter-current bundles (*solid red*) in the swim-bladder wall (*first and second drawings*). One of these bundles (*third drawing*) and a single counter-current capillary (*fourth drawing*) are schematically depicted. Very little oxygen (*red shading*) escapes beyond the swim-bladder wall because it diffuses (*small arrows*) from the outgoing vein into the adjacent incoming artery. The diagram (*bottom*) represents build-up of pressure (P) by means of a pressure difference (p) between the counter-current artery and vein.

RETE GRADIENTS

things. We cannot fail to be impressed by the marvels of bio-engineering that nature has achieved in its development of "the wonderful net."

THE NEPHRON filters urea and other dissolved substances out of the blood and concentrates them in the urine. It may accomplish this with counter-current exchange. The drawing above is a cross section of the human kidney. At its upper left is a schematic representation of one of the kidney's several million nephrons. In the drawing at left the nephron is enlarged. Arterial blood (*red*) is depicted entering the capillaries of the glomerulus. The dissolved substances filter out of the glomerulus into the proximal tubule. The solution then travels down the tubule and doubles back at the loop of Henle. If the dissolved substances diffused from the ascending tubule into the descending tubule, the urine would be concentrated (*brown shading*) near the bend of the loop. The concentration might then be transmitted to the portion of the collecting ducts located in the papilla.

14

The Ice Fish

JOHAN T. RUUD · November 1965

Shortly after I received my undergraduate degree in zoology I spent a season in the Antarctic aboard the whaling factory ship *Vikingen*. One day in October, 1929, as the ship lay at anchor in a fjord of the South Atlantic island of South Georgia, I walked along the deck and stopped to watch some members of the crew get ready for a fishing trip in the fjord. One of them, an old whale-flenser who had spent several seasons around South Georgia, said to me: "Do you know there are fishes here that have no blood?" Certain that he was trying to pull a greenhorn's leg, I answered: "Oh, yes? Please bring some back with you."

Knowing my animal physiology, I was perfectly sure that such a fish could not exist; in fact, many textbooks firmly state that all vertebrates possess red blood corpuscles containing the respiratory pigment hemoglobin. There are a few trivial exceptions to this rule. The larvae of the common eel do not develop red blood corpuscles until they metamorphose into young adults. The lamprey, the primitive eellike fish that feeds by sucking the blood of other fishes, has a respiratory pigment that is slightly different from hemoglobin.

When the flenser and his friends returned from their day's fishing, I asked them: "Where are your bloodless fish?" As I expected, they replied that they had not caught any. Then, after my return home in 1930, I happened to mention the episode to a fellow student, Ditlef Rustad. Two years earlier Rustad had spent a season in the Antarctic as the biologist on a Norwegian expedition, and much to my surprise he said: "I have seen such a fish." He produced photographs of what he called a "white crocodile fish," which he had examined at Bouvet Island in the South Atlantic. The seemingly bloodless fish proved

to be a member of the chaenichthyid family; the family is one of many in the order Perciformes, or perchlike fishes, the largest and most diverse group of bony fishes. Within this enormous order the chaenichthyids belong to the suborder Notothenioidei, a group of fishes found exclusively in the Antarctic or waters adjacent to it. On the basis of Rustad's photographs the Swedish ichthyologist Orvar Nybelin later declared that the crocodile fish from Bouvet Island was a new species, which he named *Chaenocephalus bouvetensis*. This species was distinct from another species of the same genus: *C. aceratus*, which had been known from South Georgia and other islands in the region. In his description of the new species, published in 1947, Nybelin quoted Rustad to the effect that the blood of the fish was colorless and noted that *C. aceratus* was also said to have colorless blood. So it was that 20 years after Rustad's visit to Bouvet Island the relevant ichthyological literature mentioned for the first time a fact of which whalers in the Antarctic had been aware for half a century. Only one earlier reference to an antarctic fish with colorless blood is known: in 1931 L. Harrison Matthews, now scientific director of the Zoological Society of London, mentioned in his book *South Georgia* that such fishes were found there and also that their gills were white instead of the usual red. The whalers had called the fishes crocodile fish because of the shape of their jaws or ice fish because of their transparency.

In 1948 my attention was directed to the ice fish for a second time. One of my students, Fredrik Beyer, returned that year from the Antarctic, where he had served as the biologist accompanying the "Brattegg" expedition. He

brought back with him some specimens of a third chaenichthyid species— *Champsocephalus esox;* they had been caught with hook and line in the harbor of Punta Arenas, the subantarctic port in the Straits of Magellan. Beyer reported that when the fish were alive they had had creamy white gills and colorless blood.

A further opportunity to look into the riddle of the ice fish came in 1950, when a whaling company operating around South Georgia asked our group at the University of Oslo to undertake

ANTARCTIC ICE FISH caught off the island of South Georgia is a member of the

a survey of the South Georgia "cod"—actually a species of the nototheniid family, which, like the chaenichthyids, belongs to the Notothenioidei. This fish was so common in those waters that the development of a commercial fishery was being considered. Another of my students, Steinar Olsen, undertook the survey; he also promised to keep his eyes open for any species of ice fish he might run into. In 1951 Olsen returned with preserved specimens of three separate species of ice fish—and samples of their blood. The blood was nearly transparent, with a slightly yellowish cast. Under the microscope a few cells could be recognized as white corpuscles, but neither red corpuscles nor any blood pigment could be found.

So far, so good: we had some facts to go on. The ice fish evidently lacked both red blood corpuscles and hemoglobin. But vertebrates ought to have some means of storing oxygen in their blood. On what kind of mechanism did the ice fish rely? The first step toward answering the question would be to determine the oxygen-storage capacity of a freshly drawn sample of blood, and to do this it would be necessary to go to the Antarctic equipped with the appropriate apparatus. My chance came in 1953, when I volunteered as leader

of an international whale-marking expedition.

Our plan was to cruise in antarctic waters for six or seven weeks before the 1953–1954 whaling season began, marking as many whales as possible; our marking party would then be landed at Husvik Harbor on South Georgia just before Christmas to await a vessel due to sail back to Europe sometime in January. This schedule would give me two or three weeks on South Georgia during which I might have an opportunity to catch and study some ice fish.

Everything went as planned; we landed at South Georgia a few days before Christmas and three ice fish—all of them belonging to the local species *C. aceratus*—were brought to me on the first and second day of my visit. This was before I had been able to set up my little laboratory and test my apparatus. The obvious thing to do was to draw the blood from the specimens and store it in a refrigerator until I had everything under control; at the same time I assumed that additional ice fish could be obtained more or less at will.

The gills of *C. aceratus* were indeed creamy white, and the freshly drawn blood was nearly transparent. I found that, if the blood was left undisturbed, it clotted to the consistency of jelly in

two or three minutes. When the blood was spun in a centrifuge, a sediment of white corpuscles settled out of it. This sediment constituted less than 1 percent of the blood by volume; the fluid above it was as clear as water.

After the blood samples had been adequately aerated, I determined their oxygen content; it was .67 percent by volume. This was a surprisingly low value. Ice fish are not small; some are two feet long or longer. It is generally assumed that a good-sized animal must have some reasonably efficient means of storing oxygen in its blood, so that its circulatory system can carry this vital element from the respiratory membranes to the tissues in the body most distant from them. Therefore my first conclusion was that something was wrong either with my apparatus or with the stored blood samples.

To check the apparatus I ran an analysis of the oxygen content of my own blood and the blood of some red-blooded nototheniid fishes; everything came out correct. Since there was no experimental error, the next check required another ice fish. Then my wait for more specimens of ice fish began. They seemed to have disappeared completely from the vicinity of Husvik Harbor; no ice fish entered our fish traps,

species *Chaenocephalus aceratus*. It has the large mouth and slim body characteristic of all 16 species in the family Chaenichthyidae (see *illustration on next two pages*). This species lives on the bottom. It is not a small fish; it grows to a length of about two feet.

and none took my baited hooks. As the day of our marking party's departure for Europe drew near I sent out an appeal to all the other whaling stations on South Georgia. Success! Felix Richards, the physician at the Leith Harbor station, appeared one afternoon in a motorboat carrying a live ice fish in a barrel of seawater.

I went to work immediately with some freshly drawn blood. The average of eight analyses was .72 percent of oxygen by volume—a result essentially

the same as the earlier one. It was evident that the oxygen in saturated ice fish blood is no more than the amount the blood plasma can take up in solution; no other mechanism for the storage of oxygen could possibly be present.

This conclusion raised two related questions. First, how is it possible for a vertebrate of this size to survive in spite of what amounted to a complete anemia? Second, how did this lack of red blood corpuscles and hemoglobin evolve? The questions can be asked

about all 16 species of chaenichthyid fishes. So far, however, the only species for which the oxygen capacity of the blood has been determined is *C. aceratus*. Let us examine what is known of the ecology of this species to see what light it may cast on our two questions.

First, Olsen's studies of 1950 and 1951 on South Georgia showed that although the adults of two other local chaenichthyid species live in the open ocean, feeding on the same shoals of

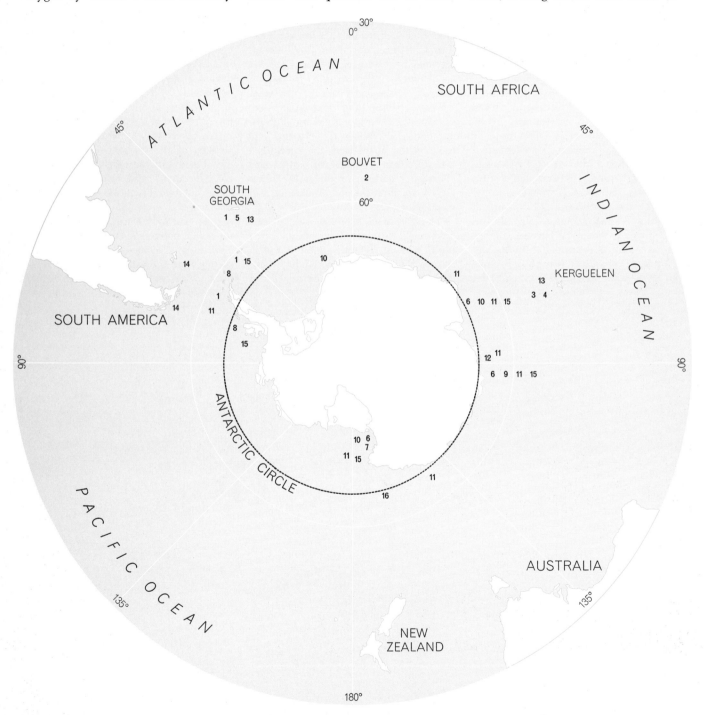

DISTRIBUTION of the various species of ice fish in antarctic and adjacent waters is plotted on this map. The first specimen of this family was taken near Kerguelen Island early in the 19th century and described in 1844 by Sir John Richardson, who placed it in a new genus, *Chaenichthys*. The newest family member is *Chionodraco myersi*, described in 1960 by Hugh H. DeWitt and shrimplike krill that are the staple food of the baleen whales in antarctic waters, the young of these species and both the young and the adults of *C. aceratus* live near the bottom in deep fjords and along the continental shelf. This means that these particular ice fishes have a quite stable environment; these deep waters are well aerated, rich in food and vary in temperature only a few degrees throughout the year (from 2 or 3 degrees above zero centigrade to 1.7 degrees below zero). This steady low temperature is significant because in cold-blooded animals such as fishes the consumption of oxygen roughly doubles with a rise in temperature of 10 degrees C. It appears that even during the cool antarctic summer *C. aceratus* moves from offshore waters to deeper ones, and so avoids the increase in metabolic rate that would result from an increase in the water temperature.

Next, the shape of the ice fish's body —the big head and mouth and the rather narrow body and tail—suggests a sluggish way of life. These antarctic fishes resemble the angler fish, the sculpin or the sea robin of warmer waters; can we assume that their existence is somewhat similar? Imagine an ice fish resting on the bottom waiting for prey—mostly smaller fishes—to come within reach of a quick, snapping movement. The lurking ice fish is nearly invisible; except for a few dark spots arranged in vertical bands its body is transparent, merging almost perfectly with the stems of the surrounding kelp.

CHAENOCEPHALUS
1 C. ACERATUS
2 C. BOUVETENSIS

CHAENICHTHYS
3 C. RHINOCERATUS
4 C. RUGOSUS

PSEUDOCHAENICHTHYS
5 P. GEORGIANUS

CHIONODRACO
6 C. KATHLEENAE
7 C. MYERSI
8 C. HAMATUS

DACODRACO
9 D. HUNTERI

CHAENODRACO
10 C. WILSONI

CRYODRACO
11 C. ANTARCTICUS
12 C. PAPPENHEIMI

CHAMPSOCEPHALUS
13 C. GUNNARI
14 C. ESOX

PAGETOPSIS
15 P. MACROPTERUS

NEOPAGETOPSIS
16 N. IONAH

James C. Tyler. This species and *Cryodraco pappenheimi* are the only two ice fish that are not surely known to have white gills or colorless blood. The outline drawings show the conformation and the relative size of representative species among the 10 genera that comprise the ice fish family; each is shown at one-sixth of natural size. Where several species are named only the first is illustrated.

BLOOD-PRODUCING ORGANS of the spiny-rayed fishes are shown in this drawing of a sectioned yellow perch. They are the front portion of the kidney, the front portion of the alimentary tract, the spleen and, to a lesser extent, the liver. A microscopic examination of 18 spleens taken from specimens of *C. aceratus* revealed no evidence of the development of red blood corpuscles.

The size of its mouth means that quite large prey can be taken with a single bite; thereafter the ice fish can take a long rest while it digests the food that came its way.

What, in terms of oxygen demand, must the ice fish accomplish in the course of a quick meal of this kind? For the first stage of muscular activity no oxygen is required; the dominant chemical event is the production of the waste product lactic acid. It is only later that oxygen is needed, partly for the combustion of the lactic acid and partly for the regeneration of other substances involved in the first stage. This oxygen debt is paid off by drawing on the store of oxygen held in solution in the blood plasma. Thus far in the sequence, at least, the anemic ice fish is no worse off than any other vertebrate.

In vertebrates that have red blood corpuscles the oxygen removed from the blood plasma is readily replenished by drawing on the oxygenated hemoglobin in the red cells. Moreover, the amount of oxygen stored in the oxygenated hemoglobin is usually much greater than the amount dissolved in the plasma. For example, the blood of two specimens of red-blooded nototheniid fishes I examined on South Georgia respectively contained oxygen at the volume levels of 5.99 percent and 6.24 percent. This is an oxygen capacity of the same order of magnitude as that possessed by fishes that live under similar circumstances in arctic waters; in both cases about 90 percent of the available oxygen is bound to the hemoglobin molecules in the red cells.

What can the anemic ice fish substitute for this second store of oxygen on which most vertebrates draw? What alternative mechanism exists for paying the oxygen debt built up in muscles and other tissues? The oxygen removed from the blood plasma can only be replaced by means of a quicker intake of oxygen from the environment, together with a quicker or greater transport of oxygen from the site of intake to the site of consumption. These two generalized mechanisms are exactly the ones on which I believe the ice fish relies.

To consider oxygen transport first, I am fairly confident that compared with other fishes the ice fish has a larger volume of body fluid and blood. The heart of the ice fish is unusually well developed, and the only red muscle to be found in the fish is the dilated part of the aorta called the bulbus arteriosus. This suggests that the circulation of the blood through the ice fish's gills and body is strong and persistent.

As for the intake of oxygen from the surrounding medium, two anatomical facts must be considered. First, the gill chamber of the ice fish appears quite large, but measurements reveal that the gill surface area is not exceptional in size. Moreover, studies soon to be published by Jon Steen and Trom Berg disclose that the epidermal membrane covering the gills is fairly thick; this does not favor a quick exchange of gases.

What may be significant is the second fact: the ice fish is almost completely without scales, which means that respiration can occur through the naked skin over most of its body. A former student, Finn Walvig, has examined the skin's microscopic structure and found the skin richly supplied with blood vessels. The space between these vessels and the surrounding water is so large, however, that the ice fish's skin is also not particularly well suited to the exchange of gases.

We must therefore assume that the ice fish's respiratory exchange of gases is not unusually effective. It remains possible that the ice fish overcomes its oxygen handicap to some extent by circulating an unusually large volume of body fluid; this is known to be the case in other fishes under emergency oxygen conditions. What remains to be determined is to what extent, if any, the ice fish may be dependent on anaerobic (oxygenless) metabolism for its survival.

Thus far I had learned that five of the 16 species of chaenichthyid fishes had white gills and colorless blood. Was this true of the family as a whole? The reader may have already wondered why early descriptions of the various species belonging to this family make no mention of gill color. The explanation is simple. Almost without exception the fish collections brought back from the Antarctic by explorers were preserved in alcohol; this bleaches the specimen's gills and sometimes further discolors them because the alcohol extracts pigments from the body of the specimen. The ichthyologist whose eventual task it is to describe such preserved fishes cannot possibly give any verdict about the original coloration of the gills; indeed, he can be expected to assume that in life they were the usual red color. Only if the man who actually collected the fish and saw it alive has made a note of the gill color—as Rustad did for *C. bouvetensis*—will the describer have the benefit of this information.

Fortunately there are other ways to overcome this absence of data, and I believe I have done so for 11 of the 16 chaenichthyid species. In the course of my work on *C. aceratus* I observed that the clot of blood remaining in the bulbus arteriosus of the fish after death had a consistency and appearance quite different from clots found in the bulbus of red-blooded fishes. The clot in a red-blooded fish is soft and opaque; under the pressure of a needle it disintegrates easily into individual corpuscles, the majority of which can be recognized as red blood cells. A clot removed from the bulbus of an ice fish, on the other hand, is nearly transparent and has a rubber-like consistency; it resists any attempt to break it down into smaller particles. This is exactly what one would expect of clotted blood plasma containing no cells apart from a minute number of white corpuscles.

Through the courtesy of F. C. Fraser, keeper of zoology at the British Museum (Natural History), I was able to remove and examine the clots from the bulbus of 11 separate species of chaenichthyid fishes in the museum's collection. All the clots appeared to be much the same as those I had found in *C. aceratus*. Although such an observation is not conclusive, I felt it was safe to assume that 12 species of chaenichthyid fishes, and probably all the other chaenichthyid species, have in common an almost complete lack of red corpuscles.

Our second basic question—how this anemia arose—must now be examined. Are the chaenichthyid fishes completely unable to produce red corpuscles? Or is the formation of red cells only suppressed and are the few cells that form nonetheless then destroyed so rapidly that they are extremely scarce or totally missing? In a normal bony fish the blood-forming tissues are the kidney, the spleen, the upper end of the alimentary tract and, to a lesser extent, the liver. Because the spleen is easy

SKIN SECTION from the forward edge of an ice fish's pelvic fin reveals the layer just below the epidermis (*top*) that is richly supplied with capillaries and larger blood vessels. Although the number of blood vessels elsewhere in the skin of *C. aceratus* varies, the overall vascular system is well developed. The author suggests that the blood vessels of the skin constitute a second respiratory surface supplementing the ice fish's inefficient gills.

both to dissect out and to preserve, Walvig and I decided to enlist the cooperation of the shore party at Husvig Harbor on South Georgia in collecting a number of ice fish spleens. Walvig analyzed the collection and published his results in 1958; in summary, no cells could be found that appeared to be red corpuscles in the making. This finding reinforced my opinion that the red-cell deficiency is total, at least in the case of *C. aceratus*.

Other findings cast doubt on whether this is true of all chaenichthyid species. The Soviet biologist L. D. Marcinkevic examined seven chaenichthyid species during an Antarctic expedition in 1957. His conclusions were published in 1958; he states that he has found red corpuscles in limited numbers in the fishes' blood vessels and also that he has found evidence of red-cell formation in the liver. Although the scarcity of red cells in Marcinkevic's specimens—they are about half as abundant as white cells—means that they could play no significant part in oxygen transport, the possibility remains that what I have assumed to be a total deficiency may instead be only partial. If such is the case, further investigation may reveal varying degrees of reduction in the number of red corpuscles and the amount of hemoglobin in the separate species of chaenichthyid fishes.

With this theoretical consideration in mind, James C. Tyler of the Academy of Natural Sciences in Philadelphia has proposed that there may exist "white-blooded," or hemoglobin-deficient, species of fish among several other antarctic fish families. In fact, two notothenid species he collected in 1958 and 1959 proved to possess fewer red cells and lower amounts of hemoglobin than is normal among bony fishes. The deficiencies, however, were far from being in a class with those of *C. aceratus* and the other species of the chaenichthyid family I have examined.

Without attempting to guess what future studies will show, I believe that the answer to the question of how these anemic fishes have managed to evolve is to be found in their unique ecological setting. In the case of the ice fish, for example, its major physiological asset—an unusually large volume of blood circulation—by itself would probably not be enough to keep the animal alive in temperate waters. Only when this characteristic is combined with the Antarctic's low and stable water temperature and that environment's abundant supply of food and oxygen is the survival of these peculiar animals possible. In fact, it is hard to imagine any other marine or freshwater environment that would offer a similar chance of survival should another family of anemic fishes begin to evolve elsewhere in the world.

III

Gas Exchange, the Lungs, and Adaptations for Diving

Arcadia also has a marvel in its climbing perch, so called because it climbs out on to the land…so also does a certain kind of fish in the rivers of India, [and here] there is an obvious purpose in getting across into marshes and lakes so as to produce offspring safe, as in those waters there are no creatures to devour their young and the waves are less fierce.

Pliny
NATURAL HISTORY, IX, XXXIV,XXXV.

III

Gas Exchange, the Lungs, and Adaptations for Diving

INTRODUCTION

Almost all vertebrates use gills or lungs as respiratory organs. Individual gill filaments, already alluded to by Scholander in Part II cannot function adequately in air. The reason is simply that adjacent filaments tend to adhere to each other, making it impossible for air to flow between the sheets of tissue and near the blood capillaries where gas exchange occurs. Consequently, all terrestrial vertebrates and fish that obtain oxygen from the air possess lungs or lung-like sacs in which oxygen and carbon dioxide may be exchanged.

Some modern lungfishes respire with gills under normal circumstances and come to the surface to gulp air for their lungs only when oxygen levels of the water fall. The South American lungfish (*Lepidosiren*), on the other hand, is an obligatory lung-breather; because its gills cannot accommodate sufficient respiratory exchange under conditions of normal aeration of the water, the fish must surface periodically to breathe. It seems likely that the simple lungs of modern lungfish are good facsimiles of early vertebrate lungs that appeared long ago in the history of fishes. The circumstance most conducive to the appearance of lungs was probably a fresh-water habitat that was subject to heating and drying; when heating and drying occurred, the amount of dissolved oxygen would decrease, creating an absolute necessity for the ability to breathe air.

The steps by which lungs originally developed remain mysterious. All complex evolutionary changes occur in the course of many generations, with those organisms that happen to possess certain mutations being differentially successful at surviving to reproduce; this is natural selection, and the offspring of such animals are more likely to survive to pass on the mutated genes, assuming that the selective forces remain constant. This reasoning suggests many stages in the appearance of any structure as large and complex as a lung. What came first? A respiratory surface on the gut wall? A diverticulum that secondarily became vascularized? We cannot say. Furthermore, development of the lungs in modern animals tells us little. For many years it was thought that the developmental sequence observed in an animal alive today was a reasonable portrait of the evolutionary history of the species. For instance, in the introduction to Part II we mentioned the similarity between development of the heart and the stages of heart structure and physiology seen in various vertebrates. But in lungs, such a relationship is not so evident. A hollow endodermal diverticulum from the gut forms and grows into special condensed lung mesoderm. The initial single diverticulum branches at its tip; then each branch bifurcates again, and the process continues until the thousands of alveoli (in mammals) or parabronchi (in birds) are formed. Only the terminal product, with thin alveolar walls or minute air capillaries, is capable of normal function and gas exchange. Can this sort of process reflect the evolutionary history of lungs? It is difficult to imagine a function for any organs that would correspond to the early developmental stages of modern lungs. Hence we cannot guess why such early "nonfunctional" stages would be preserved by selection. Nevertheless, we must be cautious, for the developmental sequence may be misleading. The early stages we see today might correspond to former adult stages, if blood vessel formation was precocious in those early vertebrates. If this were so, a single diverticulum might have functioned as a primitive lung. Then in the course of subsequent evolution, a *delay* in vascularization would have provided time for development of a more complex surface area and for the construction of the complex mammalian or avian lung.

Special respiratory surfaces have appeared in isolated types of modern bony fishes. The climbing perch (*Anabas scandens*) possesses a dorsal diverticulum extending from the pharynx; this diverticulum has vascularized walls, and it can accommodate enough exchange to permit the fish to crawl on land for long periods. The mudskipper (mentioned by Scholander in "The Master Switch of Life") is another fish in which aeration takes place across the walls of the oral cavity and pharynx. Its dependence on these respiratory surfaces is illustrated by the fact that, even though it possesses gills, it will drown if kept submerged in a tank of water.

Once vertebrates began living on land, lungs began to increase in surface area. With the appearance of the dry skin in reptiles, all respiratory exchange was restricted to the lungs, so that the necessity for more surface area was greater. The two groups of temperature-regulating animals have radically different gas-exchange structures: mammals have large numbers of minute blind sacs, alveoli; birds, tiny tubes (air capillaries with a diameter of only 10 microns), which have the same function as the alveoli.

Birds also fill their lungs in a different manner than mammals. The expandable rib cage, first seen in reptiles, is still present in birds, but additional filling and emptying is caused by movement of the abdominal muscles. Mammals have a diaphragm—a muscular sheet of tissue that closes off the lung cavity from the abdominal cavity—as well as the expanding rib cage system. The first two articles in this section, "The Lung" by Julius Comroe and "Surface Tension in the Lungs" by John Clements, explain in detail the function of the mammalian lung system.

Recent work on the lipoprotein "surfactant" responsible for controlling the surface tension of mammalian lungs indicates the following: The substance is apparently stored in alveolar cells in special inclusion bodies (which are not mitochondria as implied by early studies and reported by Clements). This conclusion is based on the following kind of correlation: If a guinea pig is exposed to an atmosphere of 15 percent carbon dioxide, the inclusion bodies in the alveolar cells disappear, and concurrently the minimal surface tension of extracts taken from alveolar spaces rises. Then, as recovery from the carbon dioxide treatment occurs, the bodies increase in number and surface tension falls again. Thus, the presence of the surfactant is correlated with the presence of its apparent storage sites in the cells. Other recent work shows that the lipid portion of the lipoprotein surfactant is dipalmityl lecithin. The evolutionary origin of this compound

RESPIRATORY SAC

Figure 1. A diagram of the special respiratory organ of the climbing perch. Equivalent specialized gas exchange sites are found in other bony fish that spend time on land.
[After Young, J. Z., *The Life of Vertebrates*, Oxford, 1962.]

identified in mammalian lungs is still not clear. Surfactant has been found in bird lungs—a surprising finding since birds have tiny tubes that are always open, unlike the mammalian alveolar cavities, which tend to collapse as air is exhaled from the lungs and the diameter of the cavities diminishes. At present it is thought that the surfactant of birds tends to reduce fluid transport into the capillary lumen, and so contributes to keeping the little tubes open for passage of air. Recent experiments have also demonstrated that extracts from some amphibian and reptilian lungs contain fatty substances that lower the surface tension of fluid. How these agents are related to avian and mammalian surfactants is not yet known.

The interrelated control of breathing and heart rate is treated superbly by the various articles in this section. But, because of some very recent results in studies of respiratory control, modification of the material on that subject is necessary here: It now seems probable that the respiratory chemosensitive cells of the brain are not located in the inspiratory and expiratory centers themselves. Instead, they appear to be in the ventro-lateral walls of the medulla of the brain. In these walls, the cells are sensitive to the level of hydrogen ions (H^+) in the cerebrospinal fluid. (The acid level is, of course, related to the partial pressure of carbon dioxide (CO_2) in the fluid by the reactions, $CO_2 + H_2O \rightleftharpoons H_2CO_3 \rightleftharpoons H^+ + HCO_3^-$. Thus, elevated carbon dioxide produces hydrogen ions.) In fact, the pH of the cerebrospinal fluid is kept very constant by active transport regulation, and it shows little change when metabolic events tend to cause large pH changes in the blood. In other words, the brain cells are probably never exposed to the rapid fluctuations of pH that actually control respiratory rate. It seems likely, for this and other reasons, that the medullary chemo-receptor cells have a lesser function in the normal regulation of respiration than has previously been thought; instead, the carotid and aortic chemo-receptors, located in the walls of blood vessels, are thought to respond to the partial pressure of carbon dioxide and oxygen, or to metabolic acidosis or alkalosis, and so act as the main initiators of respiratory reflexes.

Reptiles, birds, and mammals have all given rise to lines of organisms that reentered the water to make it their prime habitat. All of these organisms retained their lungs, failed to develop new gill systems, and continued to breathe air. It seems safe to presume that all such animals possessed the sorts of adaptations outlined by P. F. Scholander in "The Master Switch of Life" and by Suk Ki Hong and Hermann Rahn in "The Diving Women of Korea and Japan." Although the heart beat has been slowed, and the blood flow has been restricted to the brain and heart, there is simply not enough oxygen dissolved in sea water to allow a whale or a penguin to change from lung to gill respiration. And, as was pointed out in the Introduction to Part II, the hemoglobin of a mammal or a bird could not load and serve as a respiratory carrier under such conditions, because the partial pressure of oxygen in water is too low. Quite simply, the high metabolic rate of homeotherms can be supported only by the respiratory efficiency of lungs and air breathing. In spite of the handicap of having to come to the surface periodically, several mammals and a few birds have come to compete successfully with the fishes.

An interesting example of parallel evolution is seen in the prehistoric reptilian ichthyosaurs and in the mammalian dolphins. Of the many reptiles that reentered the water, the ichthyosaurs were the ones that changed

Figure 2. The skeleton of an ichthyosaur reptile. Note the fishlike tail in which the vertebral column turns ventrally. Fishes that gave rise to the first land vertebrates probably had tails in which the column turned upward. The condition seen here reflects the secondary return of this line of reptiles to the water, and an apparent different solution to the problem of tail support. Note that the small hind fin and its supporting pelvic girdle bones no longer articulate with the vertebral column, as they do in land vertebrates. [After Young, J. Z., *The Life of Vertebrates*, Oxford, 1962.]

the most from the terrestrial body plan. They resembled a dolphin in shape: their hind limbs were reduced to small paddles, and their pelvic girdle no longer articulated with the vertebral column; the forelimbs were flat-steering fins containing a large number of "finger" bones that extended outward into the fin blades; the vertebral column consisted of discs similar to those of fish and unlike those of land vertebrates. Ichthyosaurs swam by sweeping their tails back and forth through the water as fishes do. Finally, as might be expected, a shelled egg was not passed from the body, but rather the young were gestated within the female reproductive tract.

Dolphins are streamlined in a similar manner. External protrusions— hair, ear pinnae, penis, scrotum, nipples—are either absent or sunken beneath the body surface. Blubber, besides being the prime insulator, is a contouring material that is important for laminar flow and fast swimming (as discussed in Part I). Unlike ichthyosaurs, dolphins do not swim by moving the tail back and forth; rather, they sweep it up and down with large muscles that are inserted on spines on the tail vertebrae. The centers of the vertebrae are enlarged discs like those of ichthyosaurs, so that the column acts as a compression strut (like that of fish and unlike the "suspension girder" backbone of land mammals). New structures, the tail flukes, serve as propulsive blades that amplify the effects of tail movements. The hind limb is not visible externally, and only remnants of the pelvic girdle remain embedded in the lateral body musculature. As in ichthyosaurs, many finger bones extend outward in the large pectoral fins for support. Both groups of animals have a shortened neck region and nostrils that are located well back from the snout and rather dorsal on the head. Interestingly, the basic sensory systems are different: ichthyosaurs had large eyes and presumably used them as their main sense organ; dolphins and other cetaceans have less prominent eyes and a small optic lobe of the brain, and they use, instead, pulses of high-frequency sound for navigation and communication (discussed in detail in the Introduction to Part VI). In summary, the overwhelming similarities of these groups, which reentered the water millions of years apart, attest to the stringent demands imposed by the aqueous environment as well as to the remarkable plasticity of the vertebrate organization in adapting to a new environment.

15

The Lung

JULIUS H. COMROE, JR. • February 1966

Each year an adult human inhales and exhales between two million and five million liters of air. Each breath consists of about half a liter of air, 20 percent of which is molecular oxygen (O_2); the air swirls briefly through a maze of branching ducts leading to tiny sacs that comprises a gas-exchange apparatus in which some of the oxygen is added to the blood. The apparatus I am describing is of course the lung: the central organ in the system the larger land animals have evolved as a means of supplying each of their cells with oxygen.

Oxygen is essential to most forms of life. A one-celled organism floating in water requires no complex apparatus to extract oxygen from its surroundings; its needs are satisfied by the process of diffusion—the random movement of molecules that results in a net flow of oxygen from regions of abundance to regions of scarcity. Over very short distances, such as the radius of a cell, the diffusion of oxygen is rapid. Over larger distances diffusion is a much slower process; it cannot meet the needs of any many-celled organism in which the distance between the source of oxygen and the most remote cell is greater than half a millimeter.

The evolution of large animals has therefore required the development of various special systems that deliver oxygen from the surrounding medium to each of the animal's cells. In higher vertebrates such as man this system consists of a gas pump (the thorax) and two fluid pumps (the right and left ventricles of the heart). The fluid pumps are linked to networks of capillaries, through the walls of which the actual exchange of gas molecules takes place. The capillary network that receives its blood from the left ventricle distributes oxygen throughout the body. The network that receives its blood from the right ventricle serves a different purpose. In it the actions of the fluid pump and the gas pump are combined to obtain the oxygen needed by the body from the surrounding atmosphere.

This integrated system works in the following manner. The expansion of the thorax allows air to flow into ducts that divide into finer tubes that terminate in the sacs called alveoli. The rhythmic contraction of the right ventricle of the heart drives blood from the veins through a series of vessels that spread through the lung and branch into capillaries [see illustration on opposite page]. These blood-filled pulmonary capillaries surround the gas-filled alveoli; in most places the membrane separating the gas from the blood is only a thousandth of a millimeter thick. Over such a short distance the molecules of oxygen, which are more abundant in the inhaled air than in the venous blood, diffuse readily into the blood. Conversely the molecules of the body's waste product carbon dioxide, which is more abundant in the venous blood than in the inhaled air, diffuse in the opposite direction. In the human lung the surface area available for this gas exchange is huge: 70 square meters—some 40 times the surface area of the entire body. Accordingly gas can be transferred to and from the blood quickly and in large amounts.

The gas exchange that occurs in the lungs is only the first in a series of events that meet the oxygen needs of the human body's billions of cells. The second of the two liquid pumps—the left ventricle of the heart—now distributes the oxygenated blood throughout the body by means of arteries and arterioles that lead to a second gas-exchange system. This second system is in reality composed of billions of individual gas-exchangers, because each capillary is a gas-exchanger for the cells it supplies. As the arterial blood flowing through the capillary gives up its oxygen molecules to the adjacent cells and absorbs the cells' waste products, it becomes venous blood and passes into the collecting system that brings it back to the right ventricle of the heart [see illustration on next page].

The customary use of the term "pulmonary circulation" for that part of the circulatory system which involves the right ventricle and the lungs, and of the term "systemic circulation" for the left ventricle and the balance of the circulatory system, seems to imply that the body has two distinct blood circuits. In actuality there is only one circuit; the systemic apparatus is one arc of it and the pulmonary apparatus is the other. The systemic part of the circuit supplies arterial blood, rich in oxygen and poor in carbon dioxide, to all the capillary gas-exchangers in the body; it also collects the venous blood, poor in oxygen and rich in carbon dioxide, from these exchangers and returns it to the right ventricle. The pulmonary part of the circuit delivers the venous blood to the pulmonary gas-exchanger and then sends it on to the systemic part of the circuit.

This combination of two functions not only provides an adequate exchange of oxygen and carbon dioxide but also

ARTERIAL SYSTEM of the human lung (*opposite page*) is revealed by X-ray photography following the injection of a radio-opaque fluid. The finest visible branches actually subdivide further into capillaries from five to 10 microns in diameter that surround the lung's 300 million air sacs.

146

ALVEOLI

BRONCHI

TRACHEA

PULMONARY
CAPILLARIES

LEFT
VENTRICLE

RIGHT
VENTRICLE

HEART

LUNG

SYSTEMIC
CAPILLARIES

THREE PUMPS operate the lungs' gas-exchange system. One gas pump, the thorax (*see illustration on opposite page*), moves from five to seven liters of air (*color*) in and out of the lungs' air sacs every minute. At top left these alveoli are shown without their covering of pulmonary capillaries, which are shown at center left. One fluid pump, the heart's right ventricle, forces from 70 to 100 cubic centimeters of blood into the pulmonary capillaries at each contraction. This blood (*light gray*) is low in oxygen and high in carbon dioxide; oxygen, abundant in the air, is diffused into the blood while carbon dioxide is diffused from the blood into the air. Oxygenated and low in carbon dioxide, the blood (*dark gray*) then reaches the third pump, the left ventricle, which sends it on to the systemic capillaries (*example at bottom of illustration*) that deliver oxygen to and collect carbon dioxide from all the body's cells.

supplies a variety of nutrients to the tissues and removes the products of tissue metabolism, including heat. Complex regulatory mechanisms ensure enough air flow and blood flow to meet both the body's overall needs and the special needs of any particular part of the body according to its activity.

The Respiratory System

To the physiologist respiration usually means the movement of the thorax and the flow of air in and out of the lungs; to the biochemist respiration is the process within the cells that utilizes oxygen and produces carbon dioxide. Some call the first process external respiration and the second internal respiration or tissue respiration. Here I shall mainly discuss those processes that occur in the lung and that involve exchanges either between the outside air and the gas in the alveoli or between the alveolar gas and the blood in the pulmonary capillaries.

The structure of the respiratory system is sometimes shown in an oversimplified way that emphasizes only the conducting air path and the alveoli. The system is far more complex. It originates with the two tubes of the nose (the mouth can be regarded as a third tube), which join to become one: the trachea. The trachea then subdivides into two main branches, the right bronchus and the left. Each of the bronchi divides into two, each of them into two more and so on; there are from 20 to 22 bronchial subdivisions. These subdivisions give rise to more than a million tubes that end in numerous alveoli, where the gas exchange occurs. There are some 300 million alveoli in a pair of human lungs; they vary in diameter from 75 to 300 microns (thousandths of a millimeter). Before birth they are filled with fluid but thereafter the alveoli of normal lungs always contain gas. Even at the end of a complete exhalation the lungs of a healthy adult contain somewhat more than a liter of gas; this quantity is known as the residual volume. At the end of a normal exhalation the lungs contain more than two liters; this is called the functional residual capacity. When the lungs are expanded to the maximum, a state that is termed the total capacity, they contain from six to seven liters.

More important than total capacity, functional residual capacity or residual volume is the amount of air that reaches the alveoli. An adult human at rest inhales and exhales about half a liter of gas with each breath. Ideally each

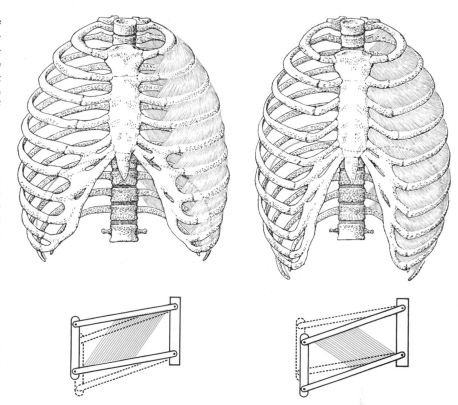

INHALATION takes place when the thorax expands, thus forcing the lungs to enlarge and bringing the pressure of the gas within them below atmospheric pressure. The expansion (*top left*) is principally the work of the diaphragm but also involves the muscles of the rib cage (*detail at bottom left*). Exhalation occurs when passive relaxation reduces the size of the thorax (*top right*), thereby raising the gas in the lungs to greater than atmospheric pressure. Only under conditions of stress do muscles (*detail at bottom right*) aid exhalation.

breath supplies his two-liter reservoir of gas—the functional residual capacity—with a volume of oxygen equal to the volume absorbed from the reservoir by the blood flowing through the pulmonary capillaries. At the same time each breath removes from the reservoir a volume of carbon dioxide equal to the volume produced by the body's cells and yielded to the lungs by the venous blood. The resting adult breathes from 10 to 14 times a minute, with the result that his ventilation—the volume of air entering and leaving the lungs—is from five to seven liters per minute. The maximum human capacity for breathing is about 30 times the resting ventilation rate, a flow of from 150 to 200 liters per minute. Even during the most intense muscular exercise, however, ventilation averages only between 80 and 120 liters per minute; man obviously has a great reserve of ventilation.

The volume of ventilation that is important in terms of gas exchange is less than the total amount of fresh air that enters the nose and mouth. Only the fresh air that reaches the alveoli and mixes with the gas already there is useful. Unlike the blood in the circulatory system, the air does not travel only in

one direction. There are no valves in the bronchi or their subdivisions; incoming and outgoing air moves back and forth through the same system of tubes. Little or no gas is exchanged in these tubes. They represent dead space, and the air that is in them at the end of an inhalation is wasted because it is washed out again during an exhalation. Thus the useful ventilation obtained from any one breath consists of the total inhalation—half a liter, or 500 cubic centimeters—minus that part of the inhalation which is wasted in the dead space. In an adult male the wasted volume is about 150 cubic centimeters.

From an engineering standpoint this dead space in the air pump represents a disadvantage: more ventilation, which necessitates more work by the pump, is required to overcome the 30 percent inefficiency. The dead space may nonetheless represent a net advantage. The use of a single system of ducts for incoming and outgoing air eliminates the need for a separate set of ducts to carry each flow. Such a dual system would certainly encroach on the lung area available for gas exchange and might well result in more than a 30 percent inefficiency.

DIFFUSION PATH from gas-filled air sac to blood-filled capillary can be extremely short. In this electron micrograph of mouse lung tissue, *a* and *b* are air spaces; between these lies a capillary in which there are two red blood cells, *c* and *d*. The large light gray mass is the nucleus of an endothelial cell. The distances from air space *a* to red cell *d* and from air space *b* to red cell *c* are less than half a micron; the diffusion of gases across these gaps is swift.

millions of short, narrow, thin-walled capillaries. Each capillary has a diameter of from five to 10 microns, which is just wide enough to enable red blood cells to pass one at a time. The wall of the capillary is less than .1 micron thick; the capillary's length ranges from .1 to .5 millimeter.

If the pulmonary capillaries were laid end to end, their total length would be hundreds of miles, but the overall capillary network offers surprisingly little resistance to the flow of blood. In order to pump from five to 10 liters of blood per minute through the pulmonary system the right ventricle needs to provide a driving pressure of less than 10 millimeters of mercury—a tenth of the pressure required of the left ventricle for systemic circulation. With only a small increase in driving pressure the pulmonary blood flow can be increased to 30 liters per minute.

Although the total surface area provided by the pulmonary capillaries is enormous, at any instant the capillary vessels contain only from 70 to 100 cubic centimeters of blood. This volume is almost identical with the volume of blood the right ventricle ejects with each contraction. Thus with each heartbeat the reoxygenated blood in the pulmonary capillaries is pushed on toward the left ventricle and venous blood refills the capillaries. In the human body at rest each red blood cell remains in a pulmonary capillary for about three-quarters of a second; during vigorous exercise the length of its stay is reduced to about a third of a second. Even this brief interval is sufficient, under normal conditions, for gas exchange.

Electron microscopy reveals that the membrane in the lung that separates the gas-filled alveolus from the blood-filled capillary consists of three distinct layers. One is the alveolar epithelium, the second is the basement membrane and the third is the capillary endothelium. The cellular structure of these layers renders between a quarter and a third of the membrane's 70 square meters of surface too thick to be ideal for rapid gas exchange; over the rest of the area, however, the barrier through which the gas molecules must diffuse is very thin—as thin as .2 micron. Comparison of the gas-transfer rate in the body at rest with the rate during vigorous exercise provides a measure of the gas-exchange system's capacity. In the body at rest only 200 to 250 cubic centimeters of oxygen diffuse per minute; in the exercising body the system can deliver as much as 5,500 cubic centimeters per minute.

Ventilation of the alveoli is not enough to ensure an adequate supply of oxygen. The incoming air must also be distributed uniformly so that each alveolus receives its share. Some alveoli are very close to the main branchings of the bronchi; others at the top and bottom of the lung are 20 or 30 centimeters away from such a branch. It is a remarkable feat of engineering to distribute the proper amount of fresh air almost simultaneously to 300 million alveoli of varying sizes through a network of a million tubes of varying lengths and diameters.

By the same token, ideal gas exchange requires that the blood be evenly distributed to all the pulmonary capillaries—that none of it should escape oxygenation by flowing through shunts in the capillary bed. Under abnormal circumstances, however, some alveoli are poorly ventilated, and venous blood flowing through the adjacent capillaries is not properly oxygenated. Conversely, there are situations when the flow of blood through certain capillaries is inadequate or nonexistent; in these cases good ventilation of the neighboring alveoli is wasted.

In spite of such deficiencies, the gas exchange can remain effective if the defects are matched (if the same re-

gions that have poor ventilation, for example, also have poor blood flow), so that regions with increased ventilation also have increased blood flow. Two mechanisms help to achieve this kind of matching. First, a decrease in the ventilation of a group of alveoli results in a constriction of the blood vessels and a decrease in the blood flow of the affected region. This decrease is not the result of a nerve stimulus or a reflex but is a local mechanism, probably initiated by oxygen deficiency. Second, a local deficiency in blood flow results in a constriction of the pathways that conduct air to the affected alveoli. The resulting increase in airway resistance serves to direct more of the air to alveoli with a normal, or better than normal, blood supply.

The Pulmonary Circulation

The system that distributes blood to the lungs is just as remarkable as the system that distributes air. As I have noted, the right ventricle of the heart receives all the venous blood from every part of the body; the contraction of the heart propels the blood into one large tube, the pulmonary trunk. Like the trachea, this tube divides and subdivides, ultimately forming hundreds of

The combination of a large diffusion area and a short diffusion path is responsible for much of the lung's efficiency in gas exchange, but an even more critical factor is the remarkable ability of the red blood pigment hemoglobin to combine with oxygen. If plasma that contained no red cells or hemoglobin were substituted for normal blood, the adult human heart would have to pump 83 liters per minute through the pulmonary capillaries to meet the oxygen needs of a man at rest. (Even this assumes that 100 percent of the oxygen in the plasma is delivered to the tissues, which is never the case.) In contrast, blood with a normal amount of hemoglobin in the red cells picks up 65 times more oxygen than plasma alone does; the heart of a man at rest need pump only about five and a half liters of blood per minute, even though the tissues normally extract only from 20 to 25 percent of the oxygen carried to the cells by the red blood corpuscles.

The Mechanics of Breathing

Just as water inevitably runs downhill, so gases flow from regions of higher pressure to those of lower pressure. In the case of the lung, when the total gas pressure in the alveoli is equal to the pressure of the surrounding atmosphere, no movement of gas is possible. For inhalation to occur, the alveolar gas pressure must be less than the atmospheric pressure; for exhalation, the opposite must be the case. There are two ways in which the pressure difference required for the movement of air into the lungs can be created: either the pressure in the alveoli can be lowered below atmospheric pressure or the pressure at the nose and mouth can be raised above atmospheric pressure. In normal breathing man follows the former course; enlarging the thorax (and thus enlarging the lungs as well) enables the alveolar gas to expand until its pressure drops below that of the surrounding atmosphere. Inhalation follows automatically.

The principal muscle for enlarging the thorax is the diaphragm, the large dome-shaped sheet of tissue that is anchored around the circumference of the lower thorax and separates the thoracic cavity from the abdominal cavity. When the muscle of the diaphragm contracts, the mobile central portion of the sheet moves downward, much as a piston moves in a cylinder. In addition, skeletal muscles enlarge the bony thoracic cage by increasing its circumference [see illustration on page 147]. The lungs, of course, lie entirely within the thorax. They have no skeletal muscles and cannot increase their volume by their own efforts, but their covering (the visceral pleura) is closely linked to the entire inner lining of the thorax (the parietal pleura). Only a thin layer of fluid separates the two pleural surfaces; when the thorax expands, the lungs must follow suit. As the pressure of the alveolar gas drops below that of the atmosphere, the outside air flows in through the nose, mouth and tracheo-bronchial air paths until the pressure is equalized.

This kind of pulmonary ventilation requires work; the active contraction of the thoracic muscles provides the force necessary to overcome a series of opposing loads. These loads include the recoil of the elastic tissues of the thorax, the recoil of the elastic tissue of the lungs, the frictional resistance to the flow of air through the hundreds of thousands of ducts of the tracheobronchial tree, and the surface forces created at the fluid-gas interfaces in the alveoli [see "Surface Tension in the Lungs," by John A. Clements, which begins on page 157 in this book].

In contrast to inhalation, exhalation is usually a passive process. During the active contraction of muscles that causes the enlargement of the thorax, the tissues of thorax and lungs are stretched and potential energy is stored in them. The recoil of the stretched tissue and the release of the stored energy produce the exhalation. Only at very high rates of ventilation or when there is an obstruction of the tracheobronchial tree is there active contraction of muscles to assist exhalation.

Artificial ventilation can be produced either by raising external gas pressure or by lowering internal pressure. Body respirators of the "iron lung" type lower the pressure of the air surrounding the thorax in part of their cycle of operation. As a consequence the volume of the thorax increases, the alveolar pressure falls and, since the patient's nose and mouth are outside the apparatus, air at atmospheric pressure flows into his lungs. Later in the cycle the pressure within the respirator rises; the volume of the thorax decreases and the patient exhales.

Other types of artificial ventilation depend on raising the external pressure at the nose and mouth above the atmospheric level. Some mechanical respirators operate by supplying high-pressure

RADIOACTIVE TRACERS such as xenon 133 can assess the performance of the two components in the lungs' gas-exchange system. Inhaled as a gas (left), the xenon will be unevenly distributed if the air ducts are blocked; zones that are poorly ventilated will produce lower scintillation-counter readings than normal ones will. Injected in a solution into the bloodstream (right), the xenon will diffuse unevenly into the air sacs if the blood vessels are blocked. Such faulty blood circulation also causes low readings.

150

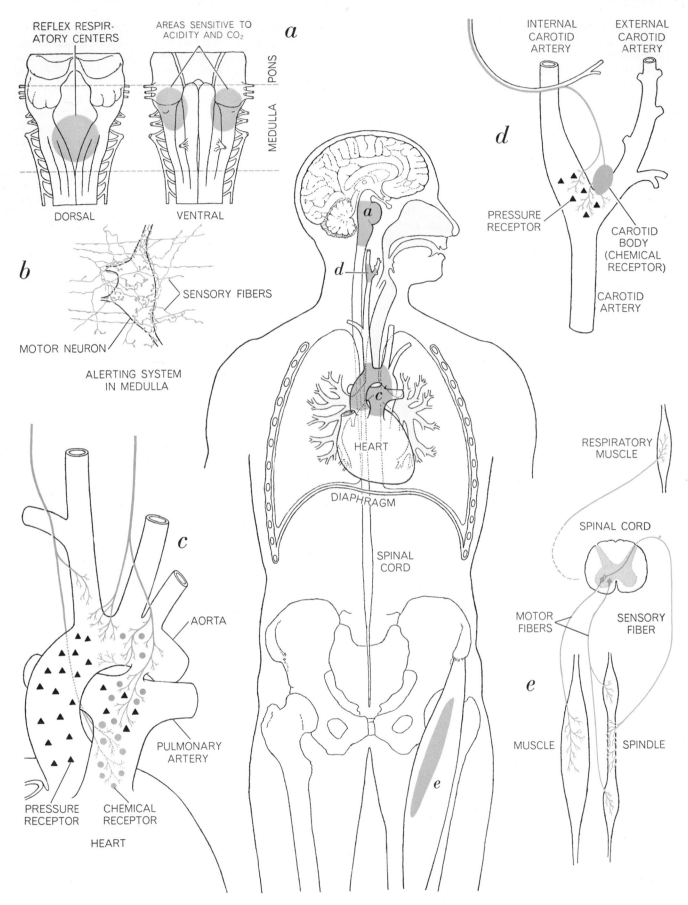

REFLEX RESPIR-
ATORY CENTERS

AREAS SENSITIVE TO
ACIDITY AND CO₂

a

PONS

MEDULLA

DORSAL

VENTRAL

b

SENSORY FIBERS

MOTOR NEURON

ALERTING SYSTEM
IN MEDULLA

INTERNAL
CAROTID
ARTERY

EXTERNAL
CAROTID
ARTERY

d

PRESSURE
RECEPTOR

CAROTID
BODY
(CHEMICAL
RECEPTOR)

CAROTID
ARTERY

c

AORTA

PULMONARY
ARTERY

PRESSURE
RECEPTOR

CHEMICAL
RECEPTOR

HEART

HEART

DIAPHRAGM

SPINAL
CORD

RESPIRATORY
MUSCLE

SPINAL CORD

MOTOR
FIBERS

SENSORY
FIBER

e

MUSCLE

SPINDLE

REGULATION OF BREATHING is controlled not only by the lower brain but also by a variety of other receptor and reflex centers. Portions of the pons and medulla of the lower brain (*a*) react to increases in acidity and carbon dioxide pressure. Other sensitive cells are attached to the aorta and pulmonary artery (*c*) and the carotid artery (*d*). The spindle receptors of skeletal muscles (*e*) also affect breathing, as do such external factors as temperature and vibration and such psychological ones as anxiety and wakefulness.

air at rhythmic intervals to the nose or mouth or more directly to the trachea. In mouth-to-mouth resuscitation the person who administers the air conveys it to the person who receives it by contracting his thorax and pushing air into the other person's lungs. Frogs can push air into their lungs by first filling their cheeks and then contracting their cheek muscles; some people whose respiratory muscles are paralyzed but whose head and neck muscles are not can learn to do this "frog breathing."

Still another way to increase the amount of oxygen available to human tissues is to place a hospital patient in an oxygen tent, in which the concentration of oxygen is increased, or to supply oxygen to him in a hyperbaric chamber, in which the total gas pressure is increased to two or three atmospheres. The extra oxygen that is taken up by the blood under these circumstances may be of help if the patient's clinical problem requires for its correction only more oxygen in the blood and tissues; such is the case, for example, when a patient has an infection caused by anaerobic bacteria. But supplying oxygen in greater than normal amounts does not increase ventilation and therefore cannot eliminate more carbon dioxide, nor does it increase the amount of blood being circulated. In the first instance, help in eliminating carbon dioxide is of prime importance in cases of pulmonary or respiratory disease; in the second, the tissues of patients with circulatory problems need not only more oxygen but also the added glucose, amino acids, lipids, white blood cells, blood platelets, proteins and hormones that can only be obtained from adequate blood flow.

The Measurement of Lung Function

Before the 1950's only a few tests of specific lung function had been devised. These included measurements of the amount of air in the lungs at the end of a full inhalation, the amount in the lungs at the end of a full exhalation, and the maximum amount exhaled after a full inhalation; these three volumes were known respectively as the total lung capacity, the residual volume and the vital capacity. In addition, some measurements had been made of the way in which gas was distributed throughout the tracheobronchial tree during inhalation by means of observing the dilution of a tracer gas such as helium or the exhalation of nitrogen following the inhalation of pure oxygen. Since the 1950's, however, pulmonary physiologists have developed a number of new instruments and test techniques with which to measure objectively, rapidly and accurately not only lung volume and the distribution and diffusion of gases but also the pulmonary circulation and the physical properties of the lung and its connecting air paths.

One such new instrument is the plethysmograph (also known as the body box), which can measure the volume of gas in the lungs and thorax, the resistance to air flow in the bronchial tree and even the blood flow in the pulmonary capillaries. For the first measurement the subject sits in the box (which is airtight and about the size of a telephone booth) and breathes the supply of air in the box through a mouthpiece fitted with a shutter and a pressure gauge. To measure the volume of gas in the subject's lungs at any moment an observer outside the box triggers a circuit that closes the shutter in the mouthpiece and then records the air pressure both in the subject's lungs and in the body box as the subject attempts to inhale; Boyle's law yields a precise measurement of the volume of gas in the subject's lungs.

In order to measure the blood flow in the pulmonary capillaries the subject in the body box is provided with a bag that contains a mixture of 80 percent nitrous oxide and 20 percent oxygen. At a signal the subject inhales a single breath of this mixture and holds the breath for a few seconds. Nitrous oxide dissolves readily in the blood; as its molecules diffuse from the alveoli to enter the blood flowing through the pulmonary capillaries, the total number of gas molecules in the alveoli obviously decreases. But the nitrous oxide that dissolves in the blood does not increase the volume of the blood; therefore the total gas pressure must decrease as the nitrous oxide molecules are subtracted. Knowing the total volume of gas in the lungs, the volume of nitrous oxide and the solubility of nitrous oxide in the blood, one can calculate the flow of blood through the pulmonary capillaries instant by instant. These calculations can be used both to measure the amount of blood pumped by the heart—and thus to arrive at an index of cardiac performance—and to detect unusual resistance to blood flow through the pulmonary capillaries.

To measure resistance to air flow in the bronchial tree the subject in the body box is instructed to breathe the air about him without any interruption while the observer continuously records changes in pressure in the box. One would expect that in a closed system the mere movement of 500 cubic centimeters of gas from the supply in the box into the lungs of a subject also in the box would not bring about any overall change in pressure. In actuality the pressure in the box increases. The reason is that gas can flow only from a region of higher pressure to a region of lower pressure. The subject cannot inhale unless the pressure of the gas in his lungs is lower than the pressure of the gas in the box; therefore the molecules of gas in his lungs during inhalation must occupy a greater volume than they did in the box before inhalation. The expansion of the subject's thorax, in turn, compresses—and thus is the equivalent of adding to—the rest of the gas in the body box; the effect is reversed as the thorax contracts during exhalation. An appropriately calibrated record of these pressure changes makes it possible for the pressure of the gas in the subject's alveoli to be calculated at any moment in the respiratory cycle. This test can be used to detect the increased resistance to air flow that arises in patients with bronchial asthma, for example, and to evaluate the effectiveness of antiasthmatic drugs.

Another useful instrument for the study of lung function is the nitrogen meter, developed during World War II by John C. Lilly at the University of Pennsylvania in order to detect leaks in or around aviators' oxygen masks. The instrument operates as an emission spectroscope, continuously sampling, analyzing and recording the concentration of nitrogen in a mixture of gases; its lag is less than a tenth of a second. Pulmonary physiologists use the nitrogen meter to detect uneven distribution of air within the lung. Assume that when one breathes ordinary air, the lungs contain 2,000 cubic centimeters of gas, 80 percent of which is nitrogen. If one next inhales 2,000 cubic centimeters of pure oxygen, and if this oxygen is distributed uniformly to the millions of alveoli, each alveolus should now contain a gas that is only 40 percent nitrogen instead of the former 80 percent. If, however, the 2,000 cubic centimeters of oxygen are not evenly distributed, some alveoli will receive less than their share, others will receive more, and the composition of the alveolar gas at the end of the oxygen inhalation will be decidedly nonuniform. In the alveoli that receive the most oxygen the proportion of nitrogen may be reduced to 30 percent; in those that receive little oxygen the proportion of nitrogen may remain as high as 75 percent.

It is impossible to put sampling

152

TURBINATES

TRAPPED
PARTICLES

LYMPH NODE

BRONCHIOLE

LYMPHATIC
CAPILLARIES

MUCUS

CILIA

MUCOUS
GLAND

ALVEOLI

b

a

c

BAFFLE SYSTEM protects the lung's interior from intrusion by particles of foreign matter. Hairs in the nose and the convolutions of the turbinate bones (*a*) entrap most particles larger than 10 microns in diameter. Particles of from two to 10 microns in diameter usually settle on the walls of the trachea, the bronchi or the bronchioles, where the escalator action of mucus-covered cilia (*b*) carries them up to the pharynx for expulsion. Particles smaller than two microns in diameter reach the lung's air sacs (*c*). Some are engulfed by scavenger cells; others are carried to the nearest lymph node. Any that remain may cause fibrous tissue to form.

needles into thousands of alveoli in order to determine what mixture of gas each of them contains, but the nitrogen meter easily samples and analyzes the gas leaving the alveoli as the subject exhales. The first part of the exhaled gas comes from the outermost part of the tracheobronchial tree; it contains pure oxygen that has not traveled far enough down the conducting air path to mix with any alveolar gas. The second part of the exhalation shows a rapidly rising concentration of nitrogen; it represents alveolar gas that has washed some pure oxygen out of the conducting air path during exhalation and has mixed with it in the process. Once the conducting air path has been washed clear of oxygen, the remainder of the exhalation will be entirely alveolar gas. Analysis of the amount of nitrogen in the third part of the exhalation quickly shows whether or not the oxygen is distributed uniformly. If the distribution is uniform, the nitrogen-meter record for this part of the exhalation will be a horizontal line: from beginning to end the alveolar gas will be 40 percent nitrogen. If, on the other hand, the distribution is uneven, the nitrogen-meter record for the third part of the exhalation will rise continuously because the first part of the alveolar gas will come from well-ventilated areas of the lung and the last from poorly ventilated ones. In less than a minute the nitrogen meter can separate individuals with uneven ventilation from individuals whose ventilation is normal.

Having discovered by means of the nitrogen meter that a subject suffers from uneven ventilation somewhere in his lungs, the pulmonary physiologist can now use radioactive gases to determine exactly   here the unevenness lies. The subject inhales a small amount of a relatively insoluble radioactive gas such as xenon 133 and holds his breath. A battery of three radiation counters on each side of the thorax measures the amount of radioactivity in the alveolar gas contained in the upper, middle and lower portions of each lung. Well-ventilated lung areas show a high level of radioactivity; poorly ventilated areas, a low level.

Radiation-counter readings can also be used to measure the uniformity of blood flow through the pulmonary capillaries. In order to do this the radioactive xenon is dissolved in a saline solution and the solution is administered intravenously. As it flows through the pulmonary capillaries the xenon comes out of solution and enters the alveolar gas. A high local concentration of xenon is an indication of a good flow of blood in that area; a low concentration indicates the contrary.

Another use of radioactive tracers to check on blood circulation involves the deliberate clogging of some fine pulmonary blood vessels. Radioactive albumin is treated so that it forms clumps that are about 30 microns in diameter—a size somewhat larger than the pulmonary capillaries or the vessels that lead into them. When the clumps are administered intravenously, they cannot enter blood vessels that are obstructed by disease; instead they collect in the parts of the lung with good circulation, where they block some of the fine vessels for a few hours. The whole thorax can now be scanned for radioactivity; in 10 or 20 minutes the activity of the albumin produces a clear image in which the regions of the lung with good pulmonary blood flow are clearly delineated.

Still another test, which measures the rate of gas exchange across the alveolar membrane, is made possible by the fact that hemoglobin has an extraordinary capacity for combining with carbon monoxide. The subject inhales a very low concentration of this potentially toxic gas. The carbon monoxide molecules diffuse across the capillary membranes and combine with the hemoglobin in the red blood cells. Assuming a normal amount of blood in the pulmonary capillaries, the rate at which the carbon monoxide disappears from the alveolar gas is directly proportional to its rate of diffusion. Unlike the somewhat similar test involving nitrous oxide, the carbon monoxide test measures only the rate of gas diffusion, not the rate of capillary blood flow. The affinity between the gas and the hemoglobin is so great that, even if the circulation of the blood were briefly halted, the stagnant red blood cells could still absorb carbon monoxide. A slow rate of carbon monoxide diffusion therefore indicates that the alveolar membranes have become thickened or that some abnormal fluid or tissue is separating many of the alveoli from the pulmonary capillaries.

The Regulation of Ventilation

The blood and air pumps that feed the lung's gas-exchange apparatus must be able to vary their performance to suit environments that range from sea level to high altitudes and activities that range from complete rest to violent exercise. Whatever the circumstances, exactly the right amount of oxygenated blood must be provided to meet the body's needs; to achieve this result responsive decision centers in the body, controlling both respiration and circulation, must not only be supplied with the necessary information but also possess the capacity to enforce decisions.

The first of these respiratory control centers was discovered by César Legallois of France in 1811. He found that if the cerebrum, the cerebellum and part of the upper brainstem were removed from a rabbit, the animal's breathing remained rhythmic, but that if a small region of the lower medulla was damaged or removed, breathing ceased. In the century and a half since Legallois' time physiologists have continued to accord this region of the brain —a group of interconnected nerve cells in the lower medulla—the paramount role in the control of respiration. This is not, however, the only region of the brain concerned with the regulation of breathing; there are chemically sensitive regions near the lateral surfaces of the upper medulla that call for an increase in ventilation when their carbon dioxide pressure or their acidity increases. Some other parts of the medulla, the cerebral cortex and the part of the brain called the pons can also influence respiration.

In addition to these areas in the brain a variety of respiratory receptors, interconnecting links, pathways and reflexes are found elsewhere in the body. Chemically sensitive cells in the regions of the carotid artery and the aorta initiate reflexes that increase respiration when their oxygen supply is not sufficient to maintain their metabolic needs or when the local carbon dioxide pressure or acidity increases. Stretch-sensitive receptors in the major arteries act through reflexes to increase or decrease respiration in response to low or high arterial blood pressure. Other receptors in the circulatory system, sensitive both to chemical stimuli and to mechanical deformation, can set off reflexes that slow or stop breathing. Respiration can also be regulated by the degree of inflation or deflation of the lungs, by the individual's state of wakefulness or awareness, by the concentration of certain hormones in the blood and by the discharge of the special sensory receptors known as spindles in skeletal muscles (including the respiratory muscles themselves).

We still do not know how some or all of these central and peripheral components interact to achieve the most important (and the most frequent) change in ventilation: the change that takes place when the body's metabolic activity increases. We know that during exercise both the body's oxygen consumption and its carbon dioxide production increase, and that so does the rate of ventilation. It is therefore logical to assume that ventilation is regulated by receptors somewhere in the body that are sensitive to oxygen or to carbon dioxide or to both. A puzzling fact remains: mild and even moderate exercise simply does not decrease the amount of oxygen or increase the amount of carbon dioxide in the arterial blood, yet the respiration rate rises. What causes this increase, which is enough to satisfy both the ordinary needs of the body and the extraordinary needs of exercising muscles? No one knows.

The Upper Respiratory Tract

In the course of taking from four to 10 million breaths a year each individual draws into the alveoli of his lungs air that may be hot or cold, dry or moist, possibly clean but more probably dirty. Each liter of urban air, for example, contains several million particles of foreign matter; in a day a city-dwelling adult inhales perhaps 20 billion such particles. What protects the lungs and the air ducts leading to them from air with undesirable physical characteristics or chemical composition? Sensory receptors in the air ducts and the lungs can initiate protective reflexes when they are suitably stimulated; specialized cells can also engulf foreign particles that have penetrated far into the lung. The main task of protecting the lungs, however, is left to the upper respiratory tract.

The nose, the mouth, the oropharynx, the nasopharynx, the larynx, the trachea and those bronchi that are outside the lung itself together constitute the upper respiratory tract. Although the obvious function of this series of passages is to conduct air to and from the lung, the tract is also a sophisticated air conditioner and filter. It contains built-in warning devices to signal the presence of most pollutants and is carpeted with a remarkable escalator membrane that moves foreign bodies upward and out of the tract at the rate of nearly an inch a minute. Within quite broad limits the initial state of the air a man breathes is of little consequence; thanks to the mediation of the upper respiratory tract the air will be warm, moist and almost free of particles by the time it reaches the alveoli.

The first role in the conditioning process is played by the mucous membrane of the nose, the mouth and the pharynx; this large surface has a rich blood supply that warms cold air, cools hot air and otherwise protects the alveoli under a wide range of conditions. Experimental animals have been exposed to air heated to 500 degrees centigrade and air cooled to −100 degrees C.; in both instances the trip through the respiratory tract had cooled or warmed the air almost to body temperature by the time it had reached the lower trachea.

The upper respiratory tract also filters air. The hairs in the nose block the passage of large particles; beyond these hairs the involuted contours of the nasal turbinate bones force the air to move in numerous narrow streams, so that suspended particles tend to approach either the dividing septum of the nose or the moist mucous membranes of the turbinates. Here many particles either impinge directly on the mucous membranes or settle there in response to gravity.

The filter system of the nose almost completely removes from the air particles with a diameter larger than 10 microns. Particles ranging in diameter from two to 10 microns usually settle on the walls of the trachea, the bronchi and the bronchioles. Only particles between .3 micron and two microns in diameter are likely to reach the alveolar ducts and the alveoli. Particles smaller than .3 micron, if they are not taken up by the blood, are likely to remain in suspension as aerosols and so are washed out of the lungs along with the exhaled air.

Foreign bodies that settle on the walls of the nose, the pharynx, the trachea, the bronchi and the bronchioles may be expelled by the explosive blast of air that is generated by a sneeze or a cough, but more often they are removed by the action of the cilia. These are very primitive structures that are found in many forms of life, from one-celled organisms to man. Resembling hairs, they are powered by a contractile mechanism; in action each cilium makes a fast, forceful forward stroke that is followed by a slower, less forceful return stroke that brings the cilium into starting position again. The strokes of a row of cilia are precisely coordinated so that the hairs move together as a wave. The cilia of the human respiratory tract do not beat in the open air; they operate within a protective sheet of the mucus that is secreted by glands in the trachea and the bronchi. The effect of their wavelike motion is to move the entire mucus sheet—and anything trapped on it—up the respiratory tract to the pharynx, where it can be swallowed or spat out.

The ciliary escalator is in constant operation; it provides a quiet, unobtrusive, round-the-clock mechanism for the removal of foreign matter from the upper respiratory tract. The speed of this upward movement depends on the length of the cilia and the frequency of their motion. Calculations show that a cilium that is 10 microns long and that beats 20 times per second can move the mucus sheet 320 microns per second, or 19.2 millimeters per minute. Speeds of 16 millimeters per minute have actually been observed in experiments.

In spite of all such preventive measures some inhaled particles—particularly those suspended in fluid droplets—manage to pass through the alveolar ducts and reach the alveoli. How do these deeper surfaces, which have no cilia or mucous glands, cleanse themselves? The amoeba-like lymphocytes of the bloodstream and their larger relatives the macrophages engulf and digest some particles of foreign matter. They can also surround the particles in the air ducts and then ride the mucus escalator up to the nasopharynx. Other particles may pass into lymphatic vessels and come to rest in the nearest lymph nodes. Some remain permanently attached to the lung tissue, as the darkened lungs of coal miners demonstrate. Many such intrusions are essentially harmless, but some, for example particles of silica, can result in the formation of tough fibrous tissue that causes serious pulmonary disease.

The filtration mechanism of the upper respiratory tract can thus be credited with several important achievements. It is responsible for the interception and removal of foreign particles. It can remove bacteria suspended in the air and also dispose of bacteria, viruses and even irritant or carcinogenic gases when they are adsorbed onto larger particles. Unless the filter system is overloaded, it keeps the alveoli practically sterile. This, however, is not the only protection the lungs possess. Among the reflex responses to chemical or mechanical irritation of the nose are cessation of breathing, closure of the larynx, constriction of the bronchi and even slowing of the heart. These responses are aimed at preventing potentially harmful gases from reaching the alveoli and, through the alveoli, the pulmonary circulation.

In many animals, for instance, the act of swallowing results in reflex closure of the glottis and the inhibition of respiration. Because the pharynx is a passageway both for air and for food and water, this reflex prevents food or water from entering the respiratory passages during the journey from the mouth to the esophagus. Because the reflex does not operate during unconsciousness it is dangerous to try to arouse an unconscious person by pouring liquids such as alcohol into his mouth.

When specific chemical irritants penetrate beyond the larynx, the reflex response is usually a cough combined with bronchial constriction. Like the swallowing reflex, the cough reflex is depressed or absent during unconsciousness. It also is less active in older people; this is why they are more likely to draw foreign bodies into their lungs.

Bronchial constriction is a response to irritation of the air paths that is less obvious than a cough. When the concentration of dust, smoke or irritant gas is too low to elicit the cough reflex, this constrictive increase in air-path resistance is frequently evident. Smoking a cigarette, for example, induces an immediate twofold or threefold rise in air-path resistance that continues for 10 to 30 minutes. The inhalation of cigarette smoke produces the same effect in smokers and nonsmokers alike. It does not cause shortness of breath, as asthma does; the air-path resistance must increase fourfold or fivefold to produce that effect. Nor has the reflex anything to do with nicotine; no increase in air-path resistance is caused by the inhalation of nicotine aerosols, whereas exactly the same degree of resistance is induced by smoking cigarettes with a normal (2 percent) or a minimal (.5 percent) nicotine content. The reflex is evidently triggered by the settling of particles less than a micron in diameter on the sensory receptors in the air path.

Other air pollutants—irritant gases, vapors, fumes, smokes, aerosols or small particles—may give rise to a similar bronchial constriction. It is one of the ironies of man's urban way of life that exposure to the pollutants that produce severe and repeated bronchial constriction results in excessive secretion of mucus, a reduction in ciliary activity, obstruction of the fine air paths and finally cell damage. These circumstances enable bacteria to penetrate to the alveoli and remain there long enough to initiate infectious lung disease. They are also probably a factor in the development of such tracheobronchial diseases as chronic bronchitis and lung cancer. Thus man's advances in material culture increasingly threaten the air pump that helped to make his evolutionary success possible.

PULMONARY VEIN

BRONCHIOLE

PULMONARY
ARTERY

ALVEOLI

ALVEOLI are the air spaces in the lungs through which oxygen enters the blood and carbon dioxide leaves. A surface-active agent coats the moist alveoli and regulates the elasticity and tension of the lungs as a whole. In this schematic diagram nearly all the smaller blood vessels have been omitted except where capillary networks embedded in the alveolar walls show through from the backs of two alveoli seen in cross section. The average alveolus expands and contracts more than 15,000 times a day during breathing.

16

Surface Tension in the Lungs

JOHN A. CLEMENTS · December 1962

By far the most extensive surface of the human body in contact with the environment is the moist interior surface of the lungs. To carry on the exchange of carbon dioxide and oxygen between the circulating blood and the atmosphere in sufficient volume to sustain life processes requires approximately one square meter of lung surface for each kilogram of body weight. In the normal adult this amounts to the area of a tennis court. Such an area is encompassed in the comparatively small volume of the chest by the compartmentation of the lungs into hundreds of millions of tiny air spaces called alveoli. These air spaces are connected by confluent passages through the bronchial tree and the trachea to the atmosphere and are thus, topologically speaking, outside the body. Within the walls of the alveoli the blood is spread out in a thin sheet, separated from the air by a membrane about one micron (.001 millimeter) thick.

Since the primary function of the lungs is to present the inner surface of the alveoli to the air, it is not surprising to learn that the vital process of respiration is critically dependent on the physical properties of this surface. There is, of course, much more to the anatomy and physiology of the lungs. In recent years, however, the attention of investigators has been drawn increasingly to the role that is played by surface tension: the manifestation of the universal intermolecular forces that is observed in the surfaces of all fluids. The surface tension in the outermost single layer of molecules in the film of tissue fluid that moistens the surface of the lungs has been found to account for one-half to three-quarters of the elasticity with which the air spaces expand and contract in the course of the 15,000 breaths that are drawn into the lungs of the average individual each day.

As this knowledge suggests, it has also been found that the body has a way of regulating the surface tension of the lungs. Certain cells in the walls of the alveoli secrete a sort of detergent or wetting agent. This "surface-active" substance tends to weaken the surface tension. Its presence in the monomolecular layer on the surface of the film of moisture coating the air spaces serves to stabilize the dynamic activity of the lungs. It equalizes the tension in the air spaces as they expand and contract; it

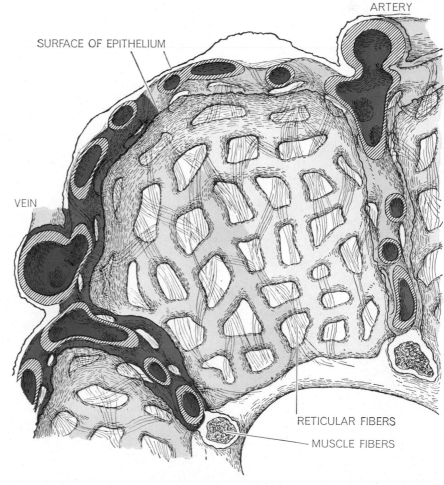

SINGLE ALVEOLUS is actually microscopic in size. The alveolar wall has been rendered transparent in this schematic cross section so that the rich network of blood capillaries and fibers that support the alveolus can be seen. The surface-active substance that plays a key role in stabilizing lung function normally coats the epithelium of every healthy alveolus.

158

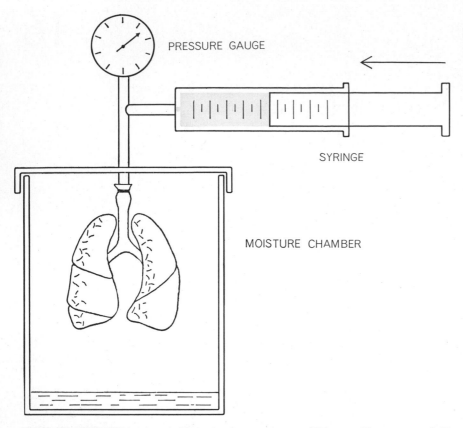

PRESSURE GAUGE

SYRINGE

MOISTURE CHAMBER

LUNG ELASTICITY is measured by using large syringe to fill lungs with a gas or a fluid (*color*). Lungs taken at autopsy are placed in a moist chamber and attached to a manometer, or pressure gauge. Karl von Neergaard of Zurich made the first such measurement in 1929.

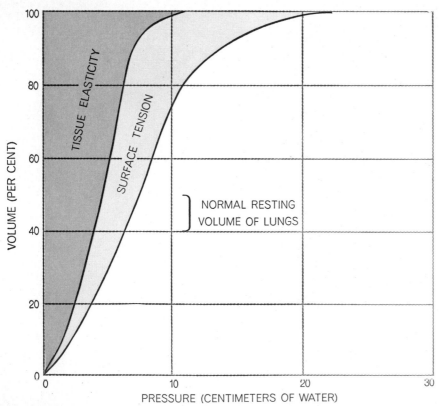

ELASTICITY CURVES are obtained by plotting pressure needed to expand the lungs against volume of lungs. The lungs show much less elasticity when filled with fluid than they do when filled with gas. Surface tension plays a significant role only when lungs are filled with gas. The amount of elasticity contributed by surface tension shows up as the difference between the curves at any particular volume of the lungs. It rises as the lungs expand.

brings about an even distribution of pressure between large and small alveoli, and by decreasing the over-all pressure it reduces the muscular effort required for respiration. This substance has the further function of assisting the osmotic forces acting across the surface of the lungs and so keeping the film of moisture on the surface from drawing fluid into the air spaces.

The critical importance of the surface-active agent becomes apparent when it is not there to do its work. Its absence explains some of the symptoms in the complex organic disease of the newborn recorded variously as fatal respiratory distress, hyaline-membrane disease or atelectasis. The collapse of the lungs and the filling of the air spaces with fluid observed in this disease is promoted by abnormally high surface tension in the alveoli. Some 25,000 newborn infants die of the disease in the U.S. each year. A similar syndrome, although it is not always fatal, has recently appeared as a complication attending heart surgery in some patients whose lungs have been temporarily disengaged from the respiratory function by diversion of the blood through a "heart-lung" machine.

The contribution of surface tension to the elasticity of the lungs was first demonstrated in 1929 by Karl von Neergaard of the University Clinic in Zurich. He distended lung preparations alternately with air and with saline solution and compared the pressures required to do so with each. This experiment, since repeated many times by other workers, showed that it takes a higher pressure to distend the lungs with air. The interpretation of this experiment calls for a more precise definition of a surface: it is an interface between two substances and it is established by the relative cohesion of their constituent molecules. Thus when the fluid on the surface of the lungs forms an interface with air, it exhibits a stronger surface tension than it does at an interface with saline solution. In fact, the tissue fluid forms essentially no interface at all with saline solution of the right concentration and the surface tension is reduced to almost zero. Distention of the lungs with saline solution can therefore be used to measure the elastic properties of the tissue alone, uncomplicated by the effects of surface tension. Since inflation with air yields a measure of both the tissue and the surface-tension components, the effect of surface tension can be derived by subtracting the pressure required to distend the lungs with saline solution from the pressure required to inflate them to the same volume with air.

The technique has recently provided conclusive evidence that surface tension is abnormally high in the fatal respiratory distress of the newborn. After autopsy the lungs of such infants can be expanded at almost normal pressures with saline solution but require three to four times the normal pressure for air inflation. Moreover, the alveoli collapse at abnormally high air pressures during deflation.

In everyday experience with surface tension there is little to suggest that it has such formidable power. It has barely measurable effects on the properties of solids, showing up for example in the measurement of the elasticity of fine-drawn wires. Its action is more prominent in the behavior of liquids, as in the shaping of raindrops or the providing of a platform for certain aquatic insects. But it seems no more than an incidental effect of the geometry that accounts for it. Whereas the molecules in the bulk of a liquid experience forces of mutual attraction that are balanced in all directions, the molecules at the surface are attracted more strongly to their neighbors below the surface and are attracted only weakly to the sparser population of molecules in the air above the surface.

MAXWELL FRAME, used to demonstrate surface tension, consists of U-shaped wire with separate wire across open end. Liquid film (*color*) pulls at cross wire. Force needed to prevent cross wire from moving to bottom of U (*black arrow*) is proportional to the tension.

Because the net pull is downward, the surface particles tend to dive and the surface shrinks to the least possible area.

The resultant force of cohesion at the interface between a liquid and the air can be demonstrated with the help of a Maxwell frame, named for the 19th-century physicist James Clerk Maxwell. This is a U-shaped wire, with the open end of the U closed by a cross wire that can slide along the legs of the U. A film of liquid stretched out on the frame tends to pull the cross wire to the bottom of

the U. The force necessary to resist this pull—to maintain a constant area of film—provides a measure of the surface tension. Since the film in this experiment has two surfaces, the measured force must be divided by twice the width of the U; the result is usually expressed in dynes per centimeter. (A dyne is the force required to accelerate a one-gram mass one centimeter per second.) The surface tension of pure water at body temperature is equal to about 70 dynes per centimeter; that of blood plasma and

SURFACE BALANCE measures change in surface tension as area of film of surface-active agent on water increases and decreases. Surface tension pulls down on platinum strip (*attached to gauge*). Water alone produces pull of about 70 dynes per centimeter. A detergent in the water makes surface tension about 30 dynes per cen-

timeter but the tension does not change as barrier moves slowly back and forth. Surface-active agent from lungs forms a film on the water and makes the surface tension about 40 dynes per centimeter (*left*). As barrier moves toward strip, compressing the agent, tension drops (*right*). Surface tension rises as the barrier moves back.

CHANGE IN SURFACE TENSION with area, as measured by surface balance, is large when surface-active agent from normal lungs covers the water. Moving barrier made several trips back and forth during test. The tension at first drops rapidly as barrier moves in (*arrow pointing to left*), and it rises rapidly as barrier moves back (*arrow pointing to right*).

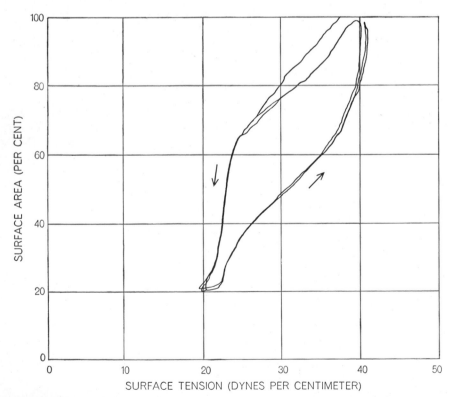

CHANGE IS SMALL when the alveolar coating comes from lungs of newborn infant who succumbed to acute respiratory distress. In such a case the surface tension is about 18 dynes per centimeter. Relative lack of surface activity plays a key role in the fatal disease.

tissue fluid, to about 50 dynes per centimeter.

The results conform with the observation that surface tension does not exert very strong forces. At this point, however, geometry enters the picture again. According to a formula of Pierre Simon de Laplace, the 18th-century astronomer and mathematician, the force exerted in a given surface is equal to twice the tension divided by the radius of the surface. In a flat surface with, so to speak, infinite radius the force is zero. Given the tiny dimensions of the average-sized alveolus, calculation shows that the surface tension of tissue fluid should exert a considerable force. At 50 dynes per centimeter in a surface with a radius of only .05 millimeter, it would produce a force of 20,000 dynes per square centimeter. Expressed as pressure this is equal to 20 centimeters of water.

This computation explains why surface tension influences the elasticity of the lungs so greatly. It does not, however, agree with the actual values for the surface tension in normal lungs obtained by comparison of the pressures required to distend the lungs with liquid and to inflate them with air. At functional or intermediate lung volume, in fact, the calculated effect of surface tension turns out to be from five to 10 times too large. In other words, the surface tension of the tissue fluid would have to be closer to five or 10 dynes per centimeter instead of 50 dynes per centimeter. At larger lung volumes the measured pressure comes into closer agreement with the calculated pressure, indicating a surface tension for the lung tissue of about 40 dynes per centimeter. In short, the surface tension of the tissue is unexpectedly low in the lungs, and it varies with the inflation and deflation of the air spaces.

With these suggestive clues in hand, investigators began to look into the tissue fluid of the lungs for the presence of a surface-active agent. Soaps or detergents are familiar examples of substances of this kind. Their molecules have weaker forces of mutual attraction for one another and for molecules of other species. They tend to accumulate in excess at surfaces and interfaces when mixed in solutions. Acting as bridges between dissimilar substances such as oil and water or water and air, they wet, penetrate and disperse oily substances and stabilize emulsions and foams. The concentration of their weaker attractive forces at an interface reduces the surface tension. At a number of laboratories the presence of a surface-active agent was soon demonstrated in the tissue fluid extracted from the lungs. The extraction can be accomplished in a number of ways: by rinsing the alveoli with saline solution via the air passages; by generating a foam in the alveoli; and by filtration from minced whole tissue. Each of these procedures yields an extract that contains a powerful surface-active agent on which accurate measurements can be made.

The laboratory technique for detecting the presence of this agent and measuring its effect on the surface tension of the tissue fluid provides a nice demonstration of its mode of operation in the alveoli. The extract is placed in a shallow tray and a .001-inch-thick platinum strip is suspended in it from the arm of a sensitive electrobalance or strain gauge. The pull of the surface on the strip provides a measure of the surface tension. A motor-driven barrier slowly sweeps the surface from the far end of the tray, reducing the area of liquid surface in which the platinum strip is hanging to 10 or 20 per cent of its initial size. Since the surface-active agent in the extract spontaneously forms a film at the surface, it is concentrated in the area in front of the barrier. As the concentration builds up, the surface tension falls to low values.

Extracts from normal lungs show a change in surface tension, when measured this way, from about 40 dynes per square centimeter to two dynes per square centimeter—in excellent agreement with the surface tension as estimated in the lung itself. In contrast, the surface tension does not fall below 18 dynes per square centimeter in extracts from the lungs of newborn infants that have succumbed to hyaline-membrane disease.

The change in surface tension with the change in surface area is the key to the action of the surface-active agent in the lung. In an expanded air space the layer of surface-active agent is attenuated, and surface tension is increased accordingly. The increase in tension is partly offset, however, by the increase in the radius of the air space, and the increase in force or counterpressure exerted by the surface tension is diminished. As the air space contracts to perhaps half its expanded size, the increasing concentration of the surface-active agent reduces the surface tension, balancing the Laplace equation in the other direction and again decreasing the pressure in the air space. Similarly, between

LUNGS OF FROGS contain quite large air spaces that are not threatened by pressure of surface tension created by a liquid that coats the inner lining. Therefore a surface-active agent is not necessary, and none has been found. One lung is shown in longitudinal section at right. Color indicates blood vessels. The diagrams on this page are highly schematic.

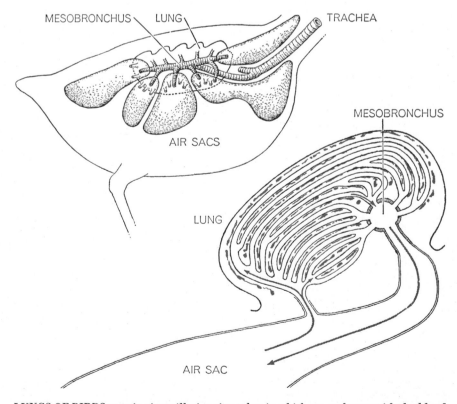

LUNGS OF BIRDS contain air capillaries, tiny tubes in which gas exchange with the blood takes place. Air passes through lungs into and out of large air sacs. Since there is little change in lung volume, surface tension does not need to be adjusted. Surface-active agent has not been found in the lungs of birds. A cross section of a bird lung is seen at right.

the smallest alveolus and the largest, which may be three or four times larger, differences in the concentration of the surface-active agent in the interface of tissue fluid and air bring about a homogeneous distribution of pressure. The performance of hundreds of millions of alveoli, of random size, is thereby smoothed and co-ordinated.

The action of the alveolar surface-active agent in balancing the forces that

FATTY ACIDS

GLYCEROL

PHOSPHATE

CHOLINE

LECITHIN MOLECULE consists of long-chain fatty-acid groups that are not strongly attracted to water, as well as glycerol and electrically charged, or polar, phosphate and choline groups that are attracted to polar molecules of water. The fatty acid is thought to stand up out of the water when the molecule is part of a surface layer. Lecithin is strongly surface-active; it is a constituent of the substance that coats the alveoli.

otherwise tend to draw fluid out of the capillaries into the alveolar air spaces is also important. The blood pressure in the capillaries, the osmotic pull of the tissue fluid in and on the alveolar membrane, and the surface tension of this fluid all work to move fluids outward. One force, the osmotic pull of the blood plasma, opposes this combination of forces. The maintenance of a favorable balance of forces is assisted by the reduction in surface tension through the action of the surface-active agent. In hyaline-membrane disease, with surface tension sustained at as much as 45 dynes per centimeter, the leakage of fluid from the capillaries blocks the exchange of oxygen and carbon dioxide between blood and air; the process is limited in the end only by engorgement of the air spaces or by their collapse.

Chemical analysis has shown that the surface-active agent of the lungs is a lipoprotein, that is, a compound molecule made up of protein and fatty constituents. The latter are of an appropriately soapy kind, lecithin being the predominant component. A member of the same chemical family that has been made synthetically, a substance called dipalmitoyl lecithin, shows the same surface activity. Dipalmitoyl lecithin has even been isolated from the lung fluid. It is tempting, therefore, to attribute the surface activity of the lung material to dipalmitoyl lecithin. Against this conclusion, however, it can be shown that the active material isolated from the extract of tissue fluid is the intact lipoprotein molecule. Its activity is destroyed by attempts to segregate the lipids from the protein or to isolate any one of the lipid components from the whole. At present the most reasonable opinion is that the native material is a complex of protein and lipids, particularly dipalmitoyl lecithin, and that both are essential to its activity.

The discovery of this remarkable substance in the lung fluid of man has prompted a search for it in other animals. So far it has turned up in all the other mammals that have been tested (the mouse, rat, guinea pig, rabbit, cat, dog and cow), but not in any amphibian (frog and toad), reptile (snake and crocodile) or bird (pigeon and chicken). There appears to be some rationale for this distribution among species. Amphibians and reptiles depend on their environment to supply a major portion of the heat that sustains their metabolism; weight for weight they do not require as much exchange of respiratory gases as

mammals and therefore do not need as much lung surface. Accordingly they have relatively large air spaces in their lungs, and their lung function is not seriously threatened by the action of surface tension. Birds, on the other hand, have small air spaces, more comparable in size to those in the lungs of mammals. But the bird lung is ventilated in a peculiar way. Instead of the tidal ventilation, which alternately inflates and deflates the air spaces of mammals, the exchange of respiratory gases is accomplished by drawing air through the lungs into large air sacs that are separate from the lungs. In this way the change of volume in the air spaces is minimized. The air spaces can remain at or near their maximum volume, and the lungs are stabilized by the elasticity of the lung tissue itself.

In mammals the lung tissues apparently begin to secrete the critical surface-active material late in embryonic development. This is true, at least, of the two species in which the question has been investigated. In the mouse, which has a gestation period of 20 days, surface activity in the lungs appears suddenly at 17 or 18 days. The lungs of the human fetus develop the activity somewhat more gradually, during the fifth to the seventh month of gestation. This is the interval during which prematurely born infants become increasingly viable.

Since it is now reasonably certain that the secretion of a surface-active material is an adaptation peculiar to mammals, investigators are finding new significance in an observation made in 1954 by Charles Clifford Macklin of the University of Western Ontario. He showed that the walls of the alveoli in mammalian lungs contain special cells that he called granular pneumonocytes. He even suggested that the "granules" discharged by these cells "regulated the surface tension" of the alveoli, but he did not enlarge on this idea further. Under the electron microscope it now appears that the granules of Macklin are cellular particles called mitochondria and possibly the products of mitochondria from certain cells in the alveolar membrane. Mitochondria are associated with the metabolic and synthetic activities of all cells; they appear in high concentration in those tissue cells that have specialized secretory functions [see "Energy Transformation in the Cell," by Albert Lehninger; SCIENTIFIC AMERICAN Offprint 69]. Some of the granules can be identified as true mitochondria, with the fine structure that characterizes them in other cells. Others appear to be mitochondria-like bodies involved in a process of transformation by which they lose their fine structure and become relatively featureless. Most remarkable of all, the electron-microscope pictures show these same forms passing through the cell membrane from the cytoplasm into the air space. This process could be the means by which the surface-active substance is secreted into the tissue fluid that coats the surface of the alveoli.

Various stages of the process have been observed in the cells of a half-dozen species of mammals but never in the amphibians or birds in which it has been looked for. In mammals, moreover, it has been found that this peculiar transformation of the mitochondria appears in the lung tissues along with surface activity at the same stage of fetal development.

With this background of evidence established by classical physiology and the most modern techniques of cell biology, the way seems to be cleared for investigation of the hormonal, neural, nutritional, environmental and genetic factors that may influence the production, function and elimination of the alveolar surface-active agent. Diabetes, for example, is associated with derangement of lipid, or fat, metabolism. In view of the importance of the lipid fraction of the surface-active agent one wonders if diabetes in the mother may not be a factor predisposing the fetus to respiratory distress at birth, particularly since the syndrome occurs more frequently among infants born to diabetic mothers. The experience with patients in heart surgery suggests another line of investigation. From the rapid decrease in surface activity and the collapse of the lung that sometimes follows the bypassing of the pulmonary circulation, it can be surmised that the production of the agent depends on blood flow and that distribution of the flow affects the distribution of air in the lungs. The question of neural control is raised by experiments with small animals, in which cutting of the vagus nerve is followed by decline in surface activity, the accumulation of fluid and finally collapse of the air spaces. Pure oxygen, atmospheric pollutants and some industrial chemicals have been shown to affect the alveolar surfaces. Animals in which hormonal activity is high—young animals, females in estrus and animals that have been treated with cortisone—are particularly subject to the toxic effects of pure oxygen on the lungs. Occasionally massive collapse of the lungs follows general anesthesia, with no indication of obstruction to the air passages. It is not too much to hope that problems of this kind can be brought within the reach of effective treatment by the next advances in the understanding of the mechanism that regulates the surface tension in the lungs.

MITOCHONDRIAL TRANSFORMATION can be seen in this electron micrograph by Robert E. Brooks of the University of Oregon. It shows part of an alveolar epithelial cell enlarged approximately 45,000 diameters. Toward upper right a transformed mitochondrion seems to be emerging into the air space. To its left is a normal mitochondrion, and to the left of that, one is beginning to change, losing fine structure. Mitochondria probably produce lung agent; transformed mitochondria may carry it to the surface.

17

The Master Switch
of Life

P. F. SCHOLANDER · December 1963

In the higher animals breathing and the beating of the heart seem synonymous with life. They implement the central process of animal metabolism: the respiratory gas exchange that brings oxygen to the tissues and removes carbon dioxide. Few events are more dangerous to life than an interruption of breathing or circulation that interferes with this exchange. It is not that all the tissues of an animal need to be continuously supplied with fresh oxygen; most parts of the human body display a considerable tolerance for asphyxia. The tissues of an arm or a leg can be isolated by a tight tourniquet for more than an hour without damage; the kidney can survive without circulation for a similar period and a corneal transplant for many hours. The heart and the brain, however, are exquisitely sensitive to asphyxia. Suffocation or heart failure kills a human being within a few minutes, and the brain suffers irreversible damage if its circulation ceases for more than five minutes.

One might expect that the body would respond with heroic measures to the threat of asphyxia. It does indeed. The defense is a striking circulatory adaptation: a gross redistribution of the blood supply to concentrate the available oxygen in the tissues that need it most. The identification of this defense mechanism has resulted from studies, extending over a number of years, of animals that are specialized to go for an unusual length of time without breathing: the diving mammals and diving birds. Only recently has it become clear that this "master switch" of life is the generalized response of vertebrate animals to the threat of asphyxia from any one of a number of quite different circumstances.

A cat or a dog or a rabbit—or a human being—dies by drowning in a few minutes. A duck, however, can endure sub-mersion for 10 to 20 minutes, a seal for 20 minutes or more and some species of whales for an hour or even two hours. How do they do it? The simplest explanation would be that diving animals have a capacity for oxygen storage that is sufficient for them to remain on normal aerobic, or oxygen-consuming, metabolism throughout their dives. As long ago as the turn of the century the physiologists Charles R. Richet and Christian Bohr realized that this could not be the full story. Many diving species do have a large blood volume and a good supply of oxygen-binding pigments: hemoglobin in the blood and myoglobin in the muscles. Their lungs, however, are not unusually large. Their total store of oxygen is seldom even twice that of comparable nondiving animals and could not, it was clear, account for their much greater ability to remain submerged.

At the University of Oslo during the 1930's I undertook a series of experiments to find out just what goes on when an animal dives. For this purpose it was necessary to bring diving animals into the laboratory, where they could be connected to the proper instruments for recording in detail the physiological events that take place before, during and after submergence. Over the years my colleagues—Laurence Irving in particular—and I have worked with many mammals and birds. We have found seals to be ideal experimental animals: they tame easily and submit readily to a number of diving exercises. At first we confined them to a board that could be lowered and raised in a bathtub full of water. Lately my colleague Robert W. Elsner at the Scripps Institution of Oceanography has trained seals to "dive" voluntarily, keeping their noses under water for as long as seven minutes.

Our first experiments at Oslo confirmed the earlier discovery, by Richet and others, of diving bradycardia, or slowing of the heart action. When the nose of a seal submerges, the animal's heartbeat usually falls to a tenth or so of the normal rate. This happens quickly, indicating that it occurs by reflex action before it can be triggered by any metabolic change. The initiation of bradycardia is affected by psychological factors. It can be induced by many stimuli other than diving, such as a sharp handclap or a threatening movement on the part of the investigator when the seal is completely out of the water. Conversely, bradycardia sometimes fails to develop in a submerged seal if the animal knows it is free to raise its head and breathe whenever it likes. In long dives, however, the slowing down is always pronounced. It is significant that the impulse is so strong it ordinarily continues for the duration of the dive, even when the animal works hard—a situation that would normally cause a rise in the heart rate.

Bradycardia occurs in every diving animal that has been studied. It has been reported in such diverse species as the seal, porpoise, hippopotamus, dugong, beaver, duck, penguin, auk, crocodile and turtle. The same thing happens in fishes when they are taken out of the water. And when such nondivers as cats, dogs and men submerge, bradycardia develops too, although it is often less pronounced than in the specialized divers.

When the heart of a seal beats only five or six times a minute, what happens to the blood pressure? We found that the central blood pressure—in the main artery of a hind flipper, for instance—stays at a normal level. The shape of the pressure trace, however, reveals that

SEAL DIVES IN LABORATORY by being ducked in a bathtub full of water. The animal is strapped loosely to a weighted board. Its head is covered by a mask connected to a device for recording respiration. When the board is tilted down (*broken line*), the mask fills with water and the seal's nose is submerged. An artery in a hind flipper is shown cannulated for removal of blood samples.

VOLUNTARY DIVING eliminates any possibility that restraint affects the seal's responses. This harbor seal (*Phoca vitulina*) is being trained to keep its nose under water until the experimenter lowers his warning finger and instead displays the reward, a fish.

0 MINUTES

2 MINUTES

TIME (SECONDS)

TIME

DIVING BRADYCARDIA, the slowing of the heart rate that occurs in vertebrates when they submerge, is quite apparent in this electrocardiogram of a diving seal. Three segments of the record are shown, made at the beginning of, during and at the end of an

whereas the pressure rise with each beat is normal, the subsequent drop in pressure is gradual and prolonged. This indicates that, although the systolic phase of the heartbeat is almost normal, the diastolic phase, during which the blood is forced through the aorta, encounters resistance: the peripheral blood vessels are constricted. Measurements in a small toe artery in the seal's flipper show that the pressure there drops when the dive begins, falling rapidly to the much lower level maintained in the veins. In other words, we found that the circulation in the flippers shuts down to practically nothing during a dive [*see bottom illustration on opposite page*].

For another clue to circulation we measured the level of lactic acid in the muscles and blood of a diving seal. Lactic acid is the end product of the anaerobic metabolic process from which muscles derive energy in the absence of oxygen. The concentration of this metabolite in muscle tissue rises sharply during a dive but the concentration in the blood does not; then, when the seal begins to breathe again, lactic acid floods into the bloodstream. The same sequence of

events has been found to occur in most other animals, showing that the muscle circulation remains closed down as long as the dive continues. Similarly, oxygen disappears from muscle tissue a few minutes after a seal submerges, whereas the arterial blood still contains plenty of oxygen—enough to keep the myoglobin saturated if the muscles are being supplied with blood [*see illustrations on page 168*]. Other experiments revealed that in the seal both the mesenteric and the renal arteries, supplying the intestines and kidneys respectively, close down during diving. All these findings made it apparent that a major portion of the peripheral circulation shuts off promptly on submergence. This was evidently the reason the heart slows down.

At this point our results tied in nicely with some conclusions reached by Irving, who was then at Swarthmore College. His efforts had been stimulated by pioneering studies of circulatory control conducted in the 1920's by Detlev W. Bronk, then at Swarthmore, and the late Robert Gesell of the University of

Michigan. Bronk and Gesell had discovered in 1927 that in a dog rendered asphyxic by an excess of carbon dioxide and a lack of oxygen the muscle circulation slowed down as the blood pressure remained normal and the brain circulation increased. Irving noted in 1934 that this phenomenon might explain a diving animal's resistance to asphyxia, and he proceeded to measure blood flow in a variety of animals by introducing heated wire probes into various tissues and recording the rate at which their heat was dissipated. His data indicated that during a dive the flow in muscle tissue is reduced but the brain blood flow remains constant or even increases. He decided that the essence of the defense against asphyxia in animals would prove to be some mechanism for the selective redistribution of the circulation, with preferential delivery of the decreasing oxygen store to those organs that can least endure anoxia: the brain and the heart.

When the blood flow closes down in most tissues during a dive, what happens to energy metabolism? This is best studied during a quiet dive, with a seal or

CENTRAL BLOOD PRESSURE stays at about a normal level during a seal's dive (*color*); the rate of increase in pressure during a contraction is also normal. The slow pressure drop between contractions, however, suggests constriction of peripheral blood vessels.

8 MINUTES

3   4   5   0   1   2   3   4   5

(SECONDS)   TIME (SECONDS)

eight-minute dive, the duration of which is shown in color. The heart slows down at the start of the dive. The rate remains as low as seven or eight per minute during the dive and then returns to a normal 80 or so per minute as soon as the seal breathes again.

duck trained to remain inactive while under water. The oxygen stores are large enough to provide only a quarter of the energy expended in a predive resting period of the same length. The next question was: Do anaerobic processes, including lactic acid production, substitute fully for the lack of oxygen? Muscle on anaerobic metabolism incurs an "oxygen debt" that must be paid off when oxygen becomes available. The excess oxygen intake on recovery from a dive is a measure of that debt. If an animal consumed energy at the same rate during a dive as before it, this excess intake would be enough to equal a normal oxygen-consumption rate during the dive. We found that it was characteristic in quiet dives, however, for the seal or duck to exhibit an oxygen debt much smaller than this. In the case of the sloth, a tree-living animal that is curiously tolerant of submersion, there was no apparent oxygen debt at all [see illustration on page 169]. The implication was that metabolism must slow down.

We could not settle this definitely by studying the oxygen debt alone; it was conceivable that the debt was being paid off so slowly it eluded us. Temperature measurements, however, confirmed the impression of decreased metabolism. We often noticed that after long dives (20 minutes or so) the seal would be shivering during the recovery period. We found that the animal lost body temperature at a rapid rate while submerged. Now, this could not be because of increased heat loss, since there was no substantial change in the thermal contact between the seal and the water; only the nostrils were submerged for the dive. Moreover, the reduction of circulation meant that heat conductivity was lessened, not increased. The loss in body temperature therefore meant an actual decrease in heat production—a slowing down of metabolism. Apparently the lack of blood in the tissues simply jams the normal metabolic processes by mass action; the flame of metabolism is damped and burns lower. It is quite logical that submergence should bring about a progressive reduction in energy metabolism, considering that the suspension of breathing ultimately terminates in death, or zero metabolic activity.

In most dives under natural conditions, of course, this general metabolic slowing down is masked. The animal is actively gathering food, and its muscles probably expend energy at several times the resting rate for the total animal. After a few minutes the muscles have used up the private store of oxygen in their myoglobin, and then they depend on anaerobic processes resulting in lactic acid formation. After such dives there is a substantial oxygen debt reflecting the amount of exercise; it is therefore impossible to detect the subtle lowering of metabolism that must still occur in the nonactive tissues deprived of circulation.

It has been fascinating, and of particular interest from the point of view of evolution, to discover the very same asphyxial defense in fishes taken out of the water—diving in reverse, as it were. The response is found in a variety of fishes, including many that would never leave the water under normal conditions. It is most striking in the aquatic versions of diving mammals and diving birds: the fishes that routinely make excursions out of the water, such as the fly-

PERIPHERAL PRESSURE, taken in a small toe artery, drops appreciably during a seal's dive (colored area). From near the central blood-pressure level (broken line) it falls almost to the venous level, which indicates a closing down of circulation in the flipper.

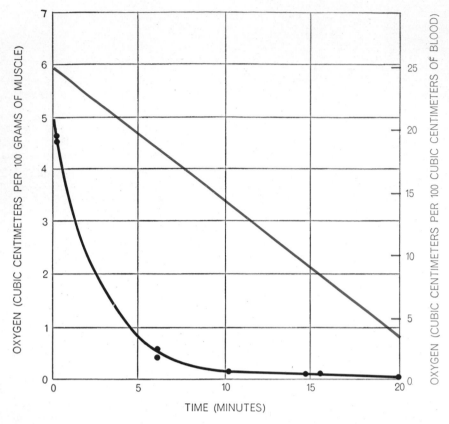

OXYGEN concentration is traced in the muscle (*black curve*) and arterial blood (*colored curve*) of a harbor seal during a dive. The sharp drop in muscle oxygen while the blood is still more than half-saturated suggests that there is no appreciable blood flow in muscle.

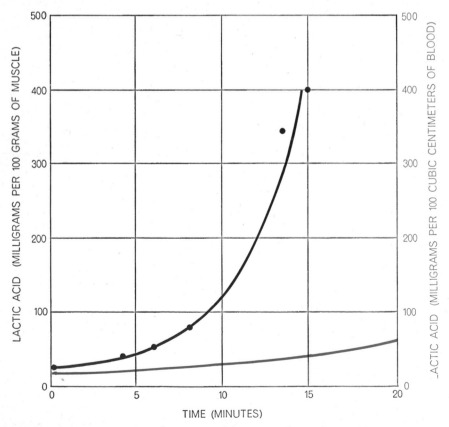

LACTIC ACID concentration confirms lack of blood flow in muscle. Lactic acid builds up in the muscle as the oxygen there is used up, but little enters the blood. The blood lactic acid level rises sharply only after the muscle circulation is restored when breathing resumes.

ing fish. It would be interesting to obtain an electrocardiogram of a flying fish taking off on a natural flight, but this would call for a rather tricky technique. When the leap is simulated, however, by lifting a flying fish out of the water, a profound bradycardia develops immediately.

Another fish that survives on land for some time is the grunion, an amazing little member of the herring family that frequents the coast of California. These fish spawn only on a few nights with maximum tides during the spring. They ride up the beach on a long wave at high tide. As the water recedes the female digs into the sand tail first and deposits her eggs; the male curves around her and fertilizes them. When they have finished, the fish ride out to sea again on another high wave. The spawning procedure can last five or 10 minutes or even longer and is accompanied by much thrashing about; in spite of this activity there is a profound bradycardia during the entire period. Walter F. Garey and Edda D. Bradstreet of the Scripps Institution have studied the lactic acid sequence in grunions caught on the beach and kept overnight in a laboratory tank. The fish are placed in a dish and prodded to keep them wriggling; blood and muscle are sampled during this period and after return to the water. Garey and Miss Bradstreet found that during the anaerobic period lactic acid increases rapidly in the muscles; practically none appears in the circulation until the fish is back in the water. Then, as the peripheral circulation opens up again, lactic acid is flushed out of the muscles and suddenly appears in the blood [*see upper illustration on page 171*].

Whereas fishes such as the grunion dive in reverse, the mudskipper (*Periophthalmus*) performs a double reverse. It spends most of its time out of the water in mangrove swamps at the edge of tropical seas, perching on a mangrove root and slithering, if it is frightened, into a burrow in the mud. These mudholes are frequently devoid of oxygen. By dint of heroic and slippery investigations in northern Australian mangrove swamps, Garey has determined that the heart of a mudskipper in its mudhole develops a pronounced bradycardia. It would seem, then, that the creature has turned evolution around: it is more at home as an air-breathing animal than as a proper fish!

In view of the strikingly similar responses to asphyxia in so many quite different vertebrate animals, it would be strange if human beings did not conform to the common scheme. Indeed, a number of recent studies of human divers, of birth anoxia in babies and of several pathological conditions have turned up exactly the same pattern.

My associates and I obtained valuable information by examining the native pearl divers of northern Australia, who are trained from boyhood to make deep dives. (We found, incidentally, that these experts seldom stay down for longer than a minute; many individual divers can remain submerged for twice as long, but this is evidently too strenuous as a regular practice.) A diver develops bradycardia within 20 to 30 seconds whether he remains quiet or swims about. The arterial blood pressure is normal or even elevated; just as in the seal, the diastolic pressure drop is slowed down, apparently by constriction of the peripheral blood vessels. As we expect-

ed, there is little or no rise in the lactic acid level in the blood during the dive, but there is an acute rise in the recovery period. In all these respects human divers respond like other vertebrates. In one respect, however, human beings may be unique: Pathological arrhythmias, or irregularities of the heartbeat, are alarmingly common in man after only half a minute's dive and such arrhythmias have so far not been observed in animals.

In our laboratory at the Scripps Institution, Elsner has been able to demonstrate ischemia, or lack of blood flow, in the muscles of an extremity simply by having a volunteer submerge his face in a basin of water. An electrocardiograph measures the heart rate, and the flow of blood into the calf is measured by plethysmography. In this technique a cuff placed around the thigh

is inflated just enough to occlude the return of blood through the veins while leaving the arteries open to supply blood to the lower part of the leg. As the calf fills with blood its circumference is measured and traced by a recording device. As soon as the subject immerses his face his heart slows down. At the same time there is a sharp decrease in the extent to which the calf expands when the venous return is obstructed; the constriction of the small arteries diminishes and may virtually stop blood flow into the calf. As soon as the subject lifts his face out of the water and breathes, the arterioles open up again and the calf expands [*see illustrations on page 172*]. If a subject is merely told to hold his breath without submerging his face, all these effects are less pronounced. As in the case of the seal that is free to breathe at will, psychological

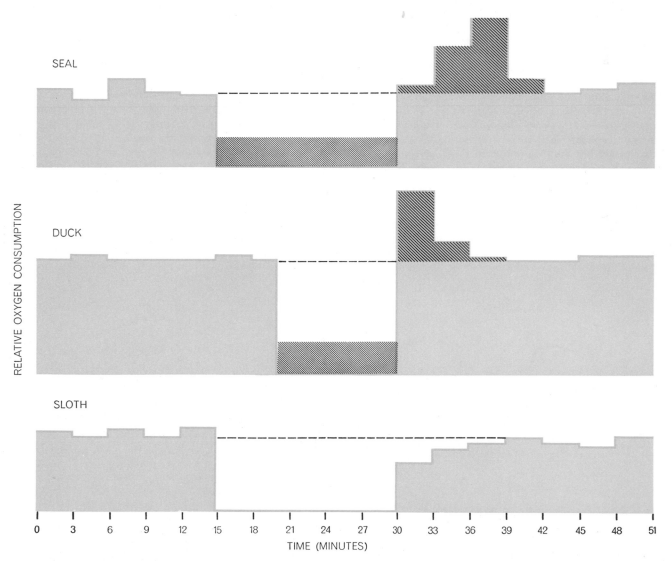

METABOLIC SLOWING DOWN during a dive is demonstrated in three animals by the record of oxygen consumption in successive three-minute periods. In the seal and duck the amount of excess oxygen intake after the dive (*hatching on color*) represents the oxygen debt incurred by anaerobic metabolism during the dive. This debt (*hatching on white*) is clearly not enough to have sustained an energy expenditure at a normal rate (*broken lines*) during the dive. The sloth seems to incur no oxygen debt while diving.

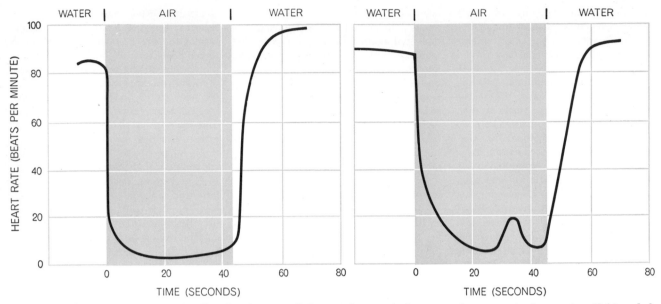

FISH OUT OF WATER develops bradycardia just as a diving animal does when it submerges. These two graphs show the sharp decrease in heart rate that occurs in the grunion (*left*) and the flying fish (*right*) when they are temporarily taken out of water.

factors seem to influence the physiological response to asphyxia.

Physicians have been aware that bradycardia sometimes occurs in babies before, during and immediately after birth and that this can be a sign of asphyxia induced by obstruction or final interruption of the placental blood flow. This concept has been strengthened by lactic acid measurements in newborn infants by Stanley James of the Columbia University College of Physicians and Surgeons. Judging by his data, a normal birth is always followed by a sharp rise in the blood lactic acid. This rise is sharper and higher in babies that have survived a difficult delivery and show clini-

cal symptoms of birth distress; in other words, the longer the period of anoxia, the greater the lactic acid build-up [*see lower illustration on page 171*]. Newborn animals in general have a short period of increased resistance to asphyxia. The sequence of events in babies suggests that selective ischemia is an important asphyxial defense even in newborn infants.

Various pathological conditions that decrease cardiac output, such as arrhythmias and coronary occlusions, are sometimes followed by such apparently unrelated complications as damage to the kidneys or even gangrenous sores in the intestine. Donald D. Van Slyke

and his collaborators at the Rockefeller Institute for Medical Research found in 1944 that severe shock in dogs resulted in decreased kidney function and tissue damage—and that the same symptoms appeared if they simply clamped the renal artery of a healthy dog. Pointing out the analogy to the peripheral vasoconstriction we had reported in diving animals, Van Slyke concluded that under stress the blood supply to the brain is maintained, if necessary, at the cost of restriction of circulation to other areas: the organism, as he said recently, is reduced to "a heart-lung-brain preparation."

More recently Eliot Corday and his

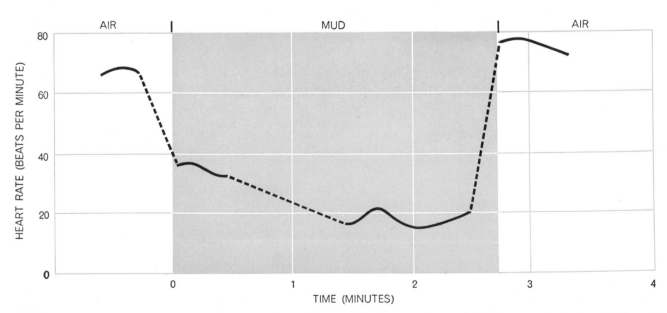

MUDSKIPPER is a curious fish that has become acclimated to breathing air. While it is out of water, its heart rate is normal; when it enters its mud-filled burrow, it develops bradycardia. Broken lines join the various segments of this fragmentary record.

colleagues at the University of California at Los Angeles have found that the same events account for certain gangrenous lesions of the intestine. They impaired the circulation of dogs in various ways, inflicting cardiac arrhythmias by electrical stimulation or decreasing the blood pressure by bleeding the animals. With modern blood-flow-metering techniques and blood-pressure measurements they were able to demonstrate a widespread vasoconstriction that tends to sustain the blood pressure near a normal level but leaves the kidney, the gastrointestinal tract, the muscles and the skin with greatly reduced circulation. These workers again recognized the sequence as a mechanism for maintaining an adequate blood supply to the most sensitive organs.

A quite different physiological event that seems to depend on the same circulatory switch as the prime control is hibernation. In all the relatively few species of mammals and birds that hibernate the body temperature is lowered in the presence of an unfavorable thermal environment. In most animals hibernation is seasonal but in others the temperature drops in a daily cycle. The dormant state is characterized, in any case, by a body temperature only a degree or so warmer than the surroundings; along with this there is a correspondingly low metabolic rate, perhaps a tenth or less of the resting rate in the waking condition. The heart rate is very low—only a few beats per minute—but the central blood pressure remains quite high in relation to this bradycardia. Again the pressure trace shows the slow diastolic emptying of the arteries that suggests a peripheral vasoconstriction. There is good evidence that hibernation is a controlled state; when a decrease in the ambient temperature brings a threat of freezing, the animal increases its heat production and usually emerges from hibernation.

The transition periods during which the animal enters or emerges from hibernation are of particular interest. When a ground squirrel or woodchuck goes into hibernation, the heart rate slows down before the body temperature starts to drop, indicating that the drop in metabolic rate is caused—as in asphyxial defense—by a primary vasoconstriction. Arousal from hibernation is easier to study because it can be precipitated at will by disturbing the animal. This triggers an immediate acceleration of the heartbeat to as much as 100 times the hibernating rate. There follows an intense shivering of the front part of the body, which warms up much more quickly than the rest of the body does as measured by the rectal temperature. Midway through arousal the blood flow in the forelegs of the squirrel is sometimes 10 times greater than in the hind legs. The uneven distribution of metabolic and circulatory activity is apparently accomplished by a dilation of the blood vessels that begins in the forward parts. When the vessels in the rest of the animal finally dilate, the over-all metabolic rate sometimes rises as high as when the animal exercises. The entire sequence is consistent with the idea that the onset and termination of hibernation are triggered in the first instance by

MUSCLE ISCHEMIA, or lack of blood, in grunions results in a lactic acid build-up in muscle while the fish is out of the water. As seen here, the lactic acid does not rise much in the blood until the muscle circulation is restored when the fish re-enters the water.

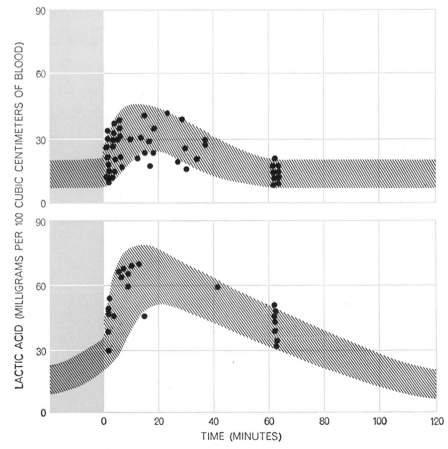

SIMILAR ISCHEMIA apparently protects a baby during the delivery period (*color*). When breathing begins, the muscle circulation opens up and lactic acid floods the blood. The lactic acid build-up is smaller in a normal delivery (*top*) than in a long, difficult one (*bottom*).

vasomotor impulses controlling the size of the small blood vessels. The circulation then throttles metabolism in the tissues to a rate compatible with the blood flow. Going into hibernation seems to call for the same primary vasoconstriction that operates in asphyxial defense.

Any mechanism that operates in many kinds of animals across a wide range of circumstances must be of fundamental physiological significance. In our current work at the Scripps Institution we are trying to learn more about the details of blood flow in animals by im-

planting ultrasonic measuring devices on arteries and veins. We hope to discover just how the autonomic nervous system responds to environmental changes and the threat of anoxia and what sequence of events actually throws the circulatory switch.

HUMAN DIVING is investigated in the laboratory by having a volunteer immerse his face in a basin of water. In this case the circulation in the lower leg is being measured by plethysmography.

The inflatable cuff on the thigh occludes the veins draining the calf but leaves the arteries open. By measuring the circumference of the calf one can determine the blood flow into the lower leg.

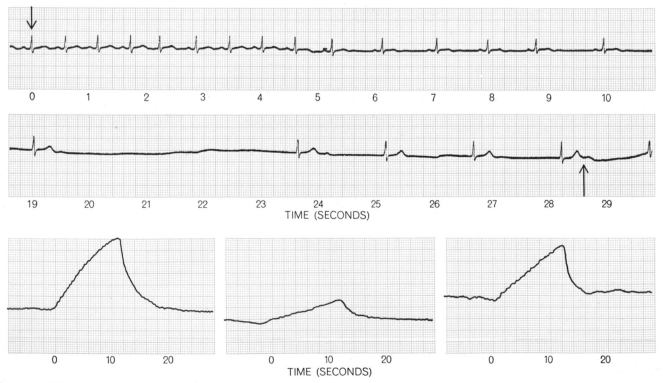

FACE IMMERSION results in bradycardia. The electrocardiogram (*two top strips*) records an extreme case (*arrows mark start and end of dive*). Plethysmographic records (*bottom*) show changes in

calf circumference when venous return is occluded for some 12 seconds before (*left*), during (*center*) and after (*right*) face immersion. Blood flow into calf is clearly much reduced during dive.

18

The Diving Women of Korea and Japan

SUK KI HONG AND HERMANN RAHN · May 1967

Off the shores of Korea and southern Japan the ocean bottom is rich in shellfish and edible seaweeds. For at least 1,500 years these crops have been harvested by divers, mostly women, who support their families by daily foraging on the sea bottom. Using no special equipment other than goggles (or glass face masks), these breath-holding divers have become famous the world over for their performances. They sometimes descend to depths of 80 feet and can hold their breath for up to two minutes. Coming up only for brief rests and a few breaths of air, they dive repeatedly, and in warm weather they work four hours a day, with resting intervals of an hour or so away from the water. The Korean women dive even in winter, when the water temperature is 50 degrees Fahrenheit (but only for short periods under such conditions). For those who choose this occupation diving is a lifelong profession; they begin to work in shallow water at the age of 11 or 12 and sometimes continue to 65. Childbearing does not interrupt their work; a pregnant diving woman may work up to the day of delivery and nurse her baby afterward between diving shifts.

The divers are called ama. At present there are some 30,000 of them living and working along the seacoasts of Korea and Japan. About 11,000 ama dwell on the small, rocky island of Cheju off the southern tip of the Korean peninsula, which is believed to be the area where the diving practice originated. Archaeological remains indicate that the practice began before the fourth century. In times past the main objective of the divers may have been pearls, but today it is solely food. Up to the 17th century the ama of Korea included men as well as women; now they are all women. And in Japan, where many of the ama are male, women nevertheless predominate in the occupation. As we shall see, the female is better suited to this work than the male.

In recent years physiologists have found considerable interest in studying the capacities and physiological reactions of the ama, who are probably the most skillful natural divers in the world. What accounts for their remarkable adaptation to the aquatic environment, training or heredity or a combination of both? How do they compare with their nondiving compatriots? The ama themselves have readily cooperated with us in these studies.

We shall begin by describing the dive itself. Basically two different approaches are used. One is a simple system in which the diver operates alone; she is called cachido (unassisted diver). The other is a more sophisticated technique; this diver, called a funado (assisted diver), has a helper in a boat, usually her husband.

The cachido operates from a small float at the surface. She takes several deep breaths, then swims to the bottom, gathers what she can find and swims up to her float again. Because of the oxygen consumption required for her swimming effort she is restricted to comparatively shallow dives and a short time on the bottom. She may on occasion go as deep as 50 or 60 feet, but on the average she limits her foraging to a depth of 15 or 20 feet. Her average dive lasts about 30 seconds, of which 15 seconds is spent working on the bottom. When she surfaces, she hangs on to the float and rests for about 30 seconds, taking deep breaths, and then dives again. Thus the cycle takes about a minute, and the diver averages about 60 dives an hour.

The funado dispenses with swimming effort and uses aids that speed her descent and ascent. She carries a counterweight (of about 30 pounds) to pull her to the bottom, and at the end of her dive a helper in a boat above pulls her up with a rope. These aids minimize her oxygen need and hasten her rate of descent and ascent, thereby enabling her to go to greater depths and spend more time on the bottom. The funado can work at depths of 60 to 80 feet and average 30 seconds in gathering on the bottom—twice as long as the cachido. However, since the total duration of each dive and resting period is twice that of the cachido, the funado makes only about 30 dives per hour instead of 60. Consequently her bottom time per hour is about the same as the cachido's. Her advantage is that she can harvest deeper bottoms. In economic terms this advantage is partly offset by the fact that the funado requires a boat and an assistant.

There are variations, of course, on the two basic diving styles, almost as many variations as there are diving locations. Some divers use assistance to ascend but not to descend; some use only light weights to help in the descent, and so on.

By and large the divers wear minimal clothing, often only a loincloth, during their work in the water. Even in winter the Korean divers wear only cotton bathing suits. In Japan some ama have recently adopted foam-rubber suits, but most of the diving women cannot afford this luxury.

The use of goggles or face masks to improve vision in the water is a comparatively recent development—hardly a century old. It must have revolutionized the diving industry and greatly increased the number of divers and the size of the harvest. The unprotected human eye suffers a basic loss of visual acuity in water because the light passing through water undergoes relatively little refraction when it enters the tissue of the cornea, so that the focal point of the image is considerably behind the retina [see top

JAPANESE DIVING WOMAN was photographed by the Italian writer Fosco Maraini near the island of Hekura off the western coast of Japan. The ama's descent is assisted by a string of lead weights tied around her waist. At the time she was diving for aba- lone at a depth of about 30 feet. At the end of each dive a helper in a boat at the surface pulls the ama up by means of the long rope attached to her waist. The other rope belongs to another diver. The ama in this region wear only loincloths during their dives.

illustration on page 179]. Our sharp vision in air is due to the difference in the refractive index between air and the corneal tissue; this difference bends light sharply as it enters the eye and thereby helps to focus images on the retinal surface. (The lens serves for fine adjustments.) Goggles sharpen vision in the water by providing a layer of air at the interface with the eyeball.

Goggles create a hazard, however, when the diver descends below 10 feet in the water. The hydrostatic pressure on the body then increases the internal body pressures, including that of the blood, to a level substantially higher than the air pressure behind the goggles. As a result the blood vessels in the eyelid lining may burst. This conjunctival bleeding is well known to divers who have ventured too deep in the water with

only simple goggles. When the Korean and Japanese divers began to use goggles, they soon learned that they must compensate for the pressure factor. Their solution was to attach air-filled, compressible bags (of rubber or thin animal hide) to the goggles. As the diver descends in the water the increasing water pressure compresses the bags, forcing more air into the goggle space and thus raising the air pressure there in proportion to the increase in hydrostatic pressure on the body. Nowadays, in place of goggles, most divers use a face mask covering the nose, so that air from the lungs instead of from external bags can serve to boost the air pressure in front of the eyes.

The ama evolved another technique that may or may not have biological value. During hyperventilation before

their dives they purse their lips and emit a loud whistle with each expiration of breath. These whistles, which can be heard for long distances, have become the trademark of the ama. The basic reason for the whistling is quite mysterious. The ama say it makes them "feel better" and "protects the lungs." Various observers have suggested that it may prevent excessive hyperventilation (which can produce unconsciousness in a long dive) or may help by increasing the residual lung volume, but no evidence has been found to verify these hypotheses. Many of the Japanese divers, male and female, do not whistle before they dive.

Preparing for a dive, the ama hyperventilates for five to 10 seconds, takes a final deep breath and then makes the plunge. The hyperventilation serves to

GEOGRAPHIC DISTRIBUTION of the ama divers along the seacoasts of South Korea and southern Japan is indicated by the colored areas. The diving practice is believed to have originated on the small island of Cheju off the southern tip of the Korean peninsula.

5 SECONDS

15 SECONDS

5 SECONDS

UNASSISTED DIVER, called a *cachido,* employs one of the two basic techniques of ama diving. The *cachido* operates from a small float at the surface. On an average dive she swims to a depth of about 15 to 20 feet; the dive lasts about 25 to 30 seconds, of which 15 seconds is spent working on the bottom. The entire diving cycle takes about a minute, and the diver averages 60 dives per hour.

15 SECONDS

30 SECONDS

15 SECONDS

ASSISTED DIVER, called a *funado,* uses a counterweight to descend passively to a depth of 60 to 80 feet. She averages 30 seconds in gathering on the bottom but makes only about 30 dives per hour. At the end of each dive a helper in the boat pulls her up.

remove a considerable amount of carbon dioxide from the blood. The final breath, however, is not a full one but only about 85 percent of what the lungs can hold. Just why the ama limits this breath is not clear; perhaps she does so to avoid uncomfortable pressure in the lungs or to restrict the body's buoyancy in the water.

As the diver descends the water pressure compresses her chest and consequently her lung volume. The depth to which she can go is limited, of course, by the amount of lung compression she can tolerate. If she dives deeper than the level of maximum lung compression (her "residual lung volume"), she becomes subject to a painful lung squeeze; moreover, because the hydrostatic pressure in her blood vessels then exceeds the air pressure in her lungs, the pulmonary blood vessels may burst.

The diver, as we have noted, starts her dive with a lungful of air that is comparatively rich in oxygen and comparatively poor in carbon dioxide. What happens to the composition of this air in the lungs, and to the exchange with the blood, during the dive? In order to investigate this question we needed a means of obtaining samples of the diver's lung air under water without risk to the diver. Edward H. Lanphier and Richard A. Morin of our group (from the State University of New York at Buffalo) devised a simple apparatus into which the diver could blow her lung air and then reinhale most of it, leaving a small sample of air in the device. The divers were understandably reluctant at first to try this device, because it meant giving up their precious lung air deep under water with the possibility that they might not recover it, but they were eventually reassured by tests of the apparatus.

We took four samples of the diver's lung air: one before she entered the water, a second when she had hyperventilated her lungs at the surface and was about to dive, a third when she reached the bottom at a depth of 40 feet and a fourth after she had returned to the surface. In each sample we measured the concentrations and calculated the partial pressures of the principal gases: oxygen, carbon dioxide and nitrogen.

Normally, in a resting person out of the water, the air in the alveoli of the lungs is 14.3 percent oxygen, 5.2 percent carbon dioxide and 80.5 percent nitrogen (disregarding the rare gases and water vapor). We found that after hyperventilation the divers' alveolar air con-

KOREAN DIVING WOMAN from Cheju Island cooperated with the authors in their study of the physiological reactions to breath-hold diving. The large ball slung over her left shoulder is a float that is left at the surface during the dive; attached to the float is a net for collecting the catch. The black belt was provided by the authors to carry a pressure-sensitive bottle and electrocardiograph wires for recording the heart rate. The ama holds an alveolar, or lung, gas sampler in her right hand. The Korean ama wear only light cotton bathing suits even in the winter, when the water temperature can be as low as 50 degrees Fahrenheit.

sists of 16.7 percent oxygen, 4 percent carbon dioxide and 79.3 percent nitrogen; translating these figures into partial pressures (in millimeters of mercury), the respective proportions are 120 millimeters for oxygen, 29 for carbon dioxide and 567 for nitrogen.

By the time the *cachido* (unassisted diver) reaches the bottom at a depth of 40 feet the oxygen concentration in her lungs is reduced to 11.1 percent, because of the uptake of oxygen by the blood. However, since at that depth the water pressure has compressed the lungs to somewhat more than half of their pre-dive volume, the oxygen pressure amounts to 149 millimeters of mercury—a greater pressure than before the dive. Consequently oxygen is still being transmitted to the blood at a substantial rate.

For the same reason the blood also takes up carbon dioxide during the dive. The carbon dioxide concentration in the lungs drops from 4 percent at the beginning of the dive to 3.2 percent at the bottom. This is somewhat paradoxical; when a person out of the water holds his breath, the carbon dioxide in his lungs increases. At a depth of 40 feet, however, the compression of the lung volume raises the carbon dioxide pressure to 42 millimeters of mercury, and this is greater than the carbon dioxide pressure in the venous blood. As a result the blood and tissues retain carbon dioxide and even absorb some from the lungs.

As the diver ascends from the bottom, the expansion of the lungs drastically reverses the situation. With the reduction of pressure in the lungs, carbon dioxide comes out of the blood rapidly. Much more important is the precipitous drop of the oxygen partial pressure in the lungs: within 30 seconds it falls from 149 to 41 millimeters of mercury. This is no greater than the partial pressure of oxygen in the venous blood; hence the blood cannot pick up oxygen, and Lanphier has shown that it may actually lose oxygen to the lungs. In all probability that fact explains many of the deaths that have occurred among sports divers returning to the surface after deep, lengthy dives. The cumulative oxygen deficiency in the tissues is sharply accentuated during the ascent.

Our research has also yielded a measure of the nitrogen danger in a long dive. We found that at a depth of 40 feet the nitrogen partial pressure in the compressed lungs is doubled (to 1,134 millimeters of mercury), and throughout the dive the nitrogen tension is sufficient to drive the gas into the blood. Lanphier has calculated that repeated dives to

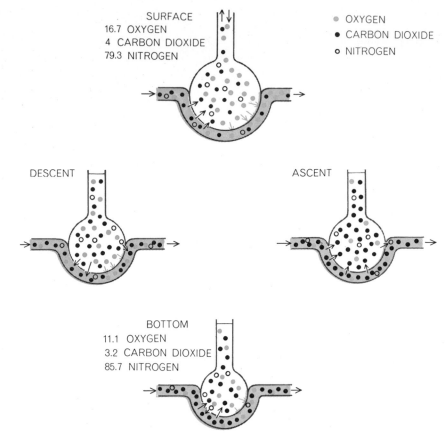

GASES EXCHANGED between a single alveolus, or lung sac, and the bloodstream are shown for four stages of a typical ama dive. The concentrations of three principal gases in the lung at the surface and at the bottom are given in percent. During descent water pressure on the lungs causes all gases to enter the blood. During ascent this situation is reversed.

AVERAGE HEART RATE for a group of Korean ama was measured before, during and after their dives. All the dives were to a depth of about 15 feet. The average pattern shown here was substantially the same in the summer, when the water temperature was about 80 degrees Fahrenheit, as it was in winter, when water temperature was about 50 degrees F.

GOGGLES SHARPEN VISION under water by providing a layer of air at the interface with the eyeball (*c*). Vision is normally sharp in air because the difference in refractive index between air and the tissue of the cornea helps to focus images on the retinal surface (*a*). The small difference in the refractive index between water and corneal tissue causes the focal point to move considerably beyond the retina (*b*), reducing visual acuity under water.

EVOLUTION OF GOGGLES has resulted in several solutions to the problem presented by the increase in hydrostatic pressure on the body during a dive. The earliest goggles (*a*) were uncompensated, and the difference in pressure between the blood vessels in the eyelid and the air behind the goggles could result in conjunctival bleeding. The problem was first solved by attaching air-filled, compressible bags to the goggles (*b*). During a dive the increasing water pressure compresses the bags, raising the air pressure behind the goggles in proportion to the increase in hydrostatic pressure on the body. In some cases (*c*) the lungs were used as an additional compensating gas chamber. With a modern face mask that covers the nose (*d*) the lungs provide the only source of compensating air pressure during a dive.

depths of 120 feet, such as are performed by male pearl divers in the Tuamotu Archipelago of the South Pacific, can result in enough accumulation of nitrogen in the blood to cause the bends on ascent. When these divers come to the surface they are sometimes stricken by fatal attacks, which they call *taravana*.

The ama of the Korean area are not so reckless. Long experience has taught them the limits of safety, and, although they undoubtedly have some slight anoxia at the end of each dive, they quickly recover from it. The diving women content themselves with comparatively short dives that they can perform again and again for extended periods without serious danger. They avoid excessive depletion of oxygen and excessive accumulation of nitrogen in their blood.

As far as we have been able to determine, the diving women possess no particular constitutional aptitudes of a hereditary kind. The daughters of Korean farmers can be trained to become just as capable divers as the daughters of divers. The training, however, is important. The most significant adaptation the trained diving women show is an unusually large "vital capacity," measured as the volume of air that can be drawn into the lungs in a single inspiration after a complete expiration. In this attribute the ama are substantially superior to nondiving Korean women. It appears that the divers acquire this capacity through development of the muscles involved in inspiration, which also serve to resist compression of the chest and lung volume in the water.

A large lung capacity, or oxygen intake, is one way to fortify the body for diving; another is conservation of the oxygen stored in the blood. It is now well known, thanks to the researches of P. F. Scholander of the Scripps Institution of Oceanography and other investigators, that certain diving mammals and birds have a built-in mechanism that minimizes their need for oxygen while they are under water [see "The Master Switch of Life," by P. F. Scholander, which begins on page 164 in this book]. This mechanism constricts the blood vessels supplying the kidneys and most of the body muscles so that the blood flow to these organs is drastically reduced; meanwhile a normal flow is maintained to the heart, brain and other organs that require an undiminished supply of oxygen. Thus the heart can slow down, the rate of removal of oxygen from the blood by tissues is reduced, and the animal can prolong its dive.

Several investigators have found recently that human subjects lying under water also slow their heart rate, although not as much as the diving animals do. We made a study of this matter in the ama during their dives. We attached electrodes (sealed from contact with the seawater) to the chests of the divers, and while they dived to the bottom, at the end of a 100-foot cable, an electrocardiograph in our boat recorded their heart rhythms. During their hyperventilation preparatory to diving the divers' heart rate averaged about 100 beats a minute. During the dive the rate fell until, at 20 seconds after submersion, it had dropped to 70 beats; after 30 seconds it dropped further to some 60 beats a minute [*see bottom illustration on page 178*]. When the divers returned to the surface, the heart rate jumped to slightly above normal and then rapidly recovered its usual beat.

Curiously, human subjects who hold their breath out of the water, even in an air pressure chamber, do not show the same degree of slowing of the heart. It was also noteworthy that in about 50 percent of the dives the ama showed some irregularity of heartbeat. These and other findings raise a number of puzzling questions. Nevertheless, one thing is quite clear: the automatic slowing of the heart is an important factor in the ability of human divers to extend their time under water.

In the last analysis the amount of time one can spend in the water, even without holding one's breath, is limited by the loss of body heat. For the working ama this is a critical factor, affecting the length of their working day both in summer and in winter. (They warm themselves at open fires after each long diving shift.) We investigated the effects of their cold exposure from several points of view, including measurements of the heat losses at various water temperatures and analysis of the defensive mechanisms brought into play.

For measuring the amount of the body's heat loss in the water there are two convenient indexes: (1) the increase of heat production by the body (through the exercise of swimming and shivering) and (2) the drop in the body's internal temperature. The body's heat production can be measured by examining its consumption of oxygen; this can be gauged from the oxygen content of the lungs at the end of a dive and during recovery. Our measurements were made on Korean diving women in Pusan harbor at two seasons of the year: in August,

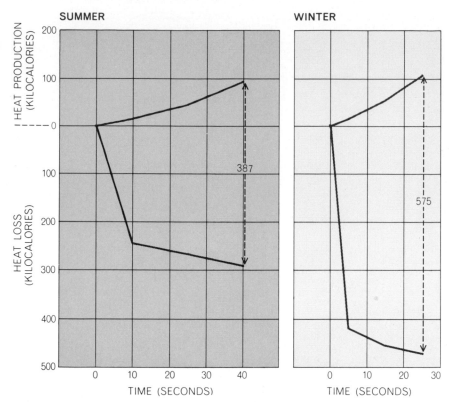

BODY HEAT lost by ama divers was found to be about 400 kilocalories in a summer shift (*left*) and about 600 kilocalories in a winter shift (*right*). The curves above the abscissa at zero kilocalories represent heat generated by swimming and shivering and were estimated by the rate of oxygen consumption. The curves below abscissa represent heat lost by the body to the water and were estimated by changes in rectal temperature and skin temperature.

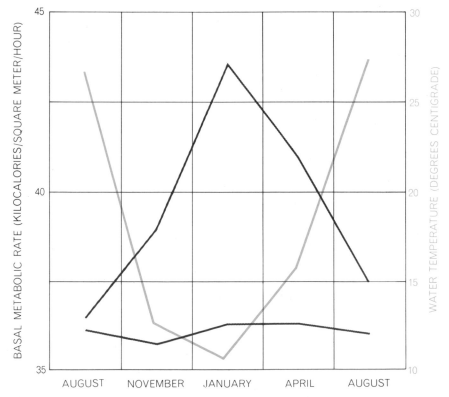

BASAL METABOLIC RATE of ama women (*top gray curve*) increases in winter and decreases in summer. In nondiving Korean women (*bottom gray curve*) basal metabolic rate is constant throughout the year. The colored curve shows the mean seawater temperatures in the diving area of Pusan harbor for the same period covered by the other measurements.

when the water temperature was 80.6 degrees F., and in January with the water temperature at 50 degrees.

In both seasons at the end of a single diving shift (40 minutes in the summer, 25 minutes in winter) the deep-body temperature was found to be reduced from the normal 98.6 degrees F. to 95 degrees or less. Combining this information with the measurements of oxygen consumption, we estimated that the ama's body-heat loss was about 400 kilocalories in a summer shift and about 600 kilocalories in a winter shift. On a daily basis, taking into consideration that the ama works in the water for three long shifts each day in summer and only one or two short shifts in winter, the day's total heat loss is estimated to be about the same in all seasons: approximately 1,000 kilocalories per day.

To compensate for this loss the Korean diving woman eats considerably more than her nondiving sisters. The ama's daily food consumption amounts to about 3,000 kilocalories, whereas the average for nondiving Korean women of comparable age is on the order of 2,000 kilocalories per day. Our various items of evidence suggest that the Korean diving woman subjects herself to a daily cold stress greater than that of any other group of human beings yet studied. Her

extra food consumption goes entirely into coping with this stress. The Korean diving women are not heavy; on the contrary, they are unusually lean.

It is interesting now to examine whether or not the diving women have developed any special bodily defenses against cold. One such defense would be an elevated rate of basal metabolism, that is, an above-average basic rate of heat production. There was little reason, however, to expect to find the Korean women particularly well endowed in this respect. In the first place, populations of mankind the world over, in cold climates or warm, have been found to differ little in basal metabolism. In the second place, any elevation of the basal rate that might exist in the diving women would be too small to have much effect in offsetting the large heat losses in water.

Yet we found to our surprise that the diving women did show a significant elevation of the basal metabolic rate—but only in the winter months! In that season their basal rate is about 25 percent higher than that of nondiving women of the same community and the same economic background (who show no seasonal change in basal metabolism). Only one other population in the world has been found to have a basal metabolic rate

as high as that of the Korean diving women in winter: the Alaskan Eskimos. The available evidence indicates that the warmly clothed Eskimos do not, however, experience consistently severe cold stresses; their elevated basal rate is believed to arise from an exceptionally large amount of protein in their diet. We found that the protein intake of Korean diving women is not particularly high. It therefore seems probable that their elevated basal metabolic rate in winter is a direct reflection of their severe exposure to cold in that season, and that this in turn indicates a latent human mechanism of adaptation to cold that is evoked only under extreme cold stresses such as the Korean divers experience. The response is too feeble to give the divers any significant amount of protection in the winter water. It does, however, raise an interesting physiological question that we are pursuing with further studies, namely the possibility that severe exposure to winter cold may, as a general rule, stimulate the human thyroid gland to a seasonal elevation of activity.

The production of body heat is one aspect of the defense against cold; another is the body's insulation for retaining heat. Here the most important factor (but not the only one) is the layer of fat

BETWEEN DIVES the ama were persuaded to expire air into a large plastic gas bag in order to measure the rate at which oxygen is consumed in swimming and diving to produce heat. The water temperature in Pusan harbor at the time (January) was 50 degrees F. One of the authors (Hong) assists. Data obtained in this way were used to construct the graph at the top of the preceding page.

under the skin. The heat conductivity of fatty tissue is only about half that of muscle tissue; in other words, it is twice as good an insulator. Whales and seals owe their ability to live in arctic and antarctic waters to their very thick layers of subcutaneous fat. Similarly, subcutaneous fat explains why women dominate the diving profession of Korea and Japan; they are more generously endowed with this protection than men are.

Donald W. Rennie of the State University of New York at Buffalo collaborated with one of the authors of this article (Hong) in detailed measurements of the body insulation of Korean women, comparing divers with nondivers. The thickness of the subcutaneous fat can easily be determined by measuring the thickness of folds of skin in various parts of the body. This does not, however, tell the whole story of the body's thermal insulation. To measure this insulation in functional terms, we had our subjects lie in a tank of water for three hours with only the face out of the water. From measurements of the reduction in deep-body temperature and the body's heat production we were then able to calculate the degree of the subject's overall thermal insulation. These studies revealed three particularly interesting facts. They showed, for one thing, that with the same thickness of subcutaneous fat, divers had less heat loss than nondivers. This was taken to indicate that the divers' fatty insulation is supplemented by some kind of vascular adaptation that restricts the loss of heat from the blood vessels to the skin, particularly in the arms and legs. Secondly, the observations disclosed that in winter the diving women lose about half of their subcutaneous fat (although nondivers do not). Presumably this means that during the winter the divers' heat loss is so great that their food intake does not compensate for it sufficiently; in any case, their vascular adaptation helps them to maintain insulation. Thirdly, we found that diving women could tolerate lower water temperatures than nondiving women without shivering. The divers did not shiver when they lay for three hours in water at 82.8 degrees F.; nondivers began to shiver at a temperature of 86 degrees. (Male nondivers shivered at 88 degrees.) It appears that the diving women's resistance to shivering arises from some hardening aspect of their training that inhibits shiver-triggering impulses from the skin. The inhibition of shivering is an advantage because shivering speeds up the emission of body heat. L. G. Pugh, a British physiologist

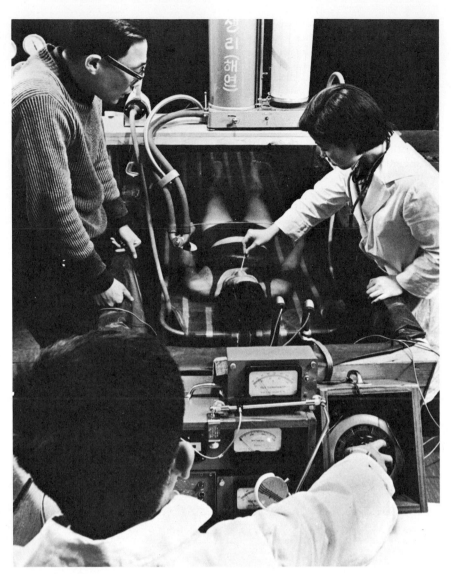

AMA'S THERMAL INSULATION (mainly fat) was measured by having the subjects lie in a tank of water for three hours. From measurements of the reduction of deep-body temperature and the body's heat production the authors were able to calculate the degree of the subject's overall thermal insulation. Once again Hong (*left*) keeps a close eye on the operation.

who has studied long-distance swimmers, discovered the interesting additional fact that swimmers, whether fat or thin, lose heat more rapidly while swimming than while lying motionless in the water. The whole subject of the body's thermal insulation is obviously a rather complicated one that will not be easy to unravel. As a general conclusion, however, it is very clearly established that women are far better insulated than men against cold.

As a concluding observation we should note that the 1,500-year-old diving occupation in Korea and Japan is now declining. The number of divers has dwindled during the past few decades, and by the end of this century the profession may disappear altogether, chiefly because more remunerative and less arduous ways of making a living are arising. Nonetheless, for the 30,000 practitioners still active in the diving profession (at least in summer) diving remains a proud calling and necessary livelihood. By adopting scuba gear and other modern underwater equipment the divers could greatly increase their production; the present harvest could be obtained by not much more than a tenth of the present number of divers. This would raise havoc, however, with employment and the economy in the hundreds of small villages whose women daily go forth to seek their families' existence on the sea bottom. For that reason innovations are fiercely resisted. Indeed, many villages in Japan have outlawed the foam-rubber suit for divers to prevent too easy and too rapid harvesting of the local waters.

IV

Water Balance and Its Control

IV

Water Balance and Its Control

INTRODUCTION

The body of higher vertebrates is about 60 percent water. Somewhat less than half of the water is extracellular, and in it are dissolved a variety of organic and inorganic molecules. Because animals are open systems in that they take in and give off water and many other types of molecules each day, a regulating system that maintains the constancy of the bond water and its constituents has evolved. As summarized by A. V. Wolf ("Body Water," *Scientific American,* November, 1958), the relation among the quantity of water an animal drinks, the volume of urine it produces, and evaporative loss is so controlled that the total amount of body water is kept within a few percent of its average value. Control of salt content and the balance between different salt ions is equally strict. The core of the system is, of course, the kidney and its physiology.

The functional units of the kidney—the nephrons—appeared early in vertebrate evolution. Each nephron was originally a duct that drained the body cavity (the coelom) to the exterior. In later forms, a cluster of blood capillaries that adjoined a portion of the duct evolved, and the connection between the duct and coelom was closed off. Thereafter, the ducts drained fluid and molecules that filtered from the blood capillaries into the cavity of the ducts. The most primitive kidney we know today is in lamprey larvae, in which a glomus (a tangle of blood vessels) is located in the wall of the coelom near the opening of each nephron. Similar glomi and nephrons are present in adult hagfish (another cyclostome), whose body fluids have the same osmotic pressure as sea water. Some regulation within the hagfish occurs, however, because the ratio between various ions in the body is different from the ratio between those ions in sea water. In adult lampreys and all higher vertebrates the glomus is inserted into the end, or funnel, of the nephron, and in these organisms it is called the glomerulus. The adult lampreys and all fresh-water fishes require an active regulatory system because their blood is hypertonic (i.e., has a higher osmotic pressure) to the fresh water in which they live. This system must eliminate the water that tends to enter the body because of the osmotic gradient, and yet retain the salts, which tend to flow out from the body (because they tend to flow from a region of high concentration—the body fluids—to one of low concentration—the watery habitat).

The glomerular portion of the nephron is the site at which water, salts, and some organic molecules (those having a molecular weight of 68,000 or less) are forced through the wall of the glomerular capillary and nephron capsule. This filtration is directly dependent upon blood pressure in the glomerulus. As the filtrate flows from the capsule and through the tubular portion of the nephron, water, glucose, small proteins, chloride ions and some other molecules are reabsorbed to varying degrees, while other substances—such as urea, magnesium ions, and potassium ions—are secreted into the filtrate by tubule cells. The end product, of course, is the urine. The system functions at a remarkable rate in man: about 175 quarts of fluid per day pass from the blood into the capsules of the kidney nephrons and all but one or two quarts are resorbed by the tubules. Homer Smith (*Scientific American*, January, 1953; Offprint #37) points out that 2.5 pounds of salt enter the capsules with the water, but only a third of an ounce is lost in urine.

As outlined by Scholander in "The Wonderful Net" (Part II), the ability of the mammalian kidney to produce urine hypertonic to blood is dependent upon a countercurrent flow system that transfers sodium ions (Na^+) from one portion of the kidney tubule to the other; consequently, high sodium concentration can be maintained in the medullary (central) part of the kidney. Refer to Figure 1 for help in visualizing the following relationships. First, for clarity, we must trace the route of urine flow: nephron capsule, proximal tubule, descending loop, ascending loop, distal tubule, and, finally, collecting duct. Most of the active transport of sodium ions takes place across the thick-walled ascending loops. The sodium ions removed from these loops are added to the intercellular fluid and then transferred back to the descending loops; thus, the sodium ions tend to move in a circle—descending loop to ascending loop to intercellular fluid to descending loop. The result is to create a very high concentration of sodium ions within and between these loops, that is, in this whole "medullary" portion of the kidney. Consider the effects on water flowing down the kidney tubule: because of the high sodium ion concentration, water tends to move through the walls of both the descending and ascending loops; the result is to reduce the *volume* of urine that ultimately leaves the top of the ascending loop and enters the distal tubule and collecting duct. Furthermore, since sodium ions have also left the urine as it passes up-

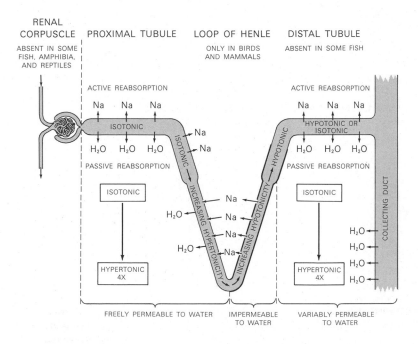

Figure 1. A diagrammatic representation of a nephron unit, showing the manner in which hypertonic urine is produced. [After Pitts, Robert F., *The Physiological Basis of Diuretic Therapy*, Charles C. Thomas, 1959.]

ward through the ascending loop, the concentration of the urine is lowered; that is, it becomes dilute. Next, the urine flows down through the thin-walled collecting ducts that actually pass among the medullary descending and ascending loops; recall that the extracellular sodium ion concentration is very high there (four times that of blood, in man). The result is to remove more water from the urine in the collecting ducts. This, of course, raises the concentration of the urine (until it is hypertonic to the blood). In the end, a small volume of highly concentrated urine is produced and sent on to the bladder.

The control system for kidney function is marvelously complex and depends upon activity of both nerve and endocrine cells. Primary control resides in the brain, where osmoreceptor cells of the hypothalamus control the release of antidiuretic hormone (vasopressin). These nerve cells respond to alterations in the osmotic pressure of blood plasma flowing through the brain and make compensatory adjustments in quantities of vasopressin released in the posterior pituitary.

The hormone affects mammalian kidney nephrons (particularly distal tubules and collecting ducts) and the bladder wall to increase resorption of water. In other organisms, it also decreases glomerular filtration rate. Interestingly, this peptide hormone can work physiologically only if it is applied to the connective tissue or basal side of the tissue. The biochemical mechanism of action appears to be a stimulated production of cyclic-AMP (adenosine-3',5'-phosphate), which in turn alters properties of cell permeability. In amphibians, vasopressin also reduces the permeability barrier to sodium ions and so causes increased retention of salts as well as conserving water.

An important element of chemical regulation of physiological processes is the short half-life of chemical mediators in the body; if the half-life were not short, the control machinery would be relatively insensitive to altering conditions in the body. Vasopressin of various vertebrates has a half-life that varies between 1 and 24 minutes; under most circumstances the shorter times (1 to 4 minutes) apply. The half-life is governed by destruction of the peptide; two-thirds is removed from the blood and inactivated by the kidney and the remaining one-third is destroyed in the liver.

Several other coordinating agents control urine content. Aldosterone produced by the cortex of the adrenal gland, controls resorption of sodium ions by the distal tubules of the nephrons. Aldosterone secretion is regulated by angiotensin II, a substance produced in the kidney when an enzyme called renin is released from cells of the juxtaglomerular apparatus. Renin acts on α-2-globulin, one of the proteins in serum, to change it into angiotensin I. Then another blood protein, the "converting enzyme," splits two amino acids from this decapeptide to produce the active octapeptide, angiotensin II. Besides affecting aldosterone release, this agent causes contraction of smooth muscle cells in the walls of blood capillaries, both in the kidney and elsewhere in the body. It seems significant that the posterior pituitary hormones vasopressin and oxytocin, both of which produce contraction of smooth muscles in various other organs of the body, also are composed of eight amino acids.

Angiotensin II has a vital function in a feedback-control loop of the mammalian nephron. The apparatus of this loop is composed of the first portion of the distal tubule (see Figure 1), the cells of which are called the macula densa cells, and the renin-containing cells of the blood vessels approaching the glomerulus. Although in the figure the two kinds of cells appear far apart, in an intact kidney the various parts of the nephron are in fact twisted about one another, and, specifically, the macula densa cells of the tubule and the renin-containing cells of the blood vessels really interdigitate with one another; thus, they can interact easily. The sodium concentration, either of the tubular fluid (i.e., the urine) near the macula densa cells or of the resorbed fluid in the same regions, is somehow measured. This sodium concentration effects release of renin by the blood vessel cells and thus, indirectly, the production of angiotensin I and II. It is angiotensin II that controls the blood pressure (or rate of flow) in the glomerulus. And, as we said before, the glomerular filtration rate is dependent upon blood pressure. Therefore, the loop is complete: the quantity of sodium entering the distal tubular portion of the nephron ultimately determines the filtration rate back in the glomerulus. Thus, a sodium-sensitive feedback loop coordinates glomerular and tubular function, and operates through proteins produced by the kidney (renin) and by the liver (globulin and converting enzyme).

It is often said that the length of the loop of Henle (comprising the ascending and descending loops described above) is the unique feature of mammalian and avian nephrons that permits production of urine that is hypertonic to blood. Recent observations have disproved that generalization. A number of terrestrial birds (such as the Savannah sparrow and the house finch) that lack functional salt glands (see "Salt Glands" by Knut Schmidt-Nielsen) have been investigated, and they possess extraordinarily large numbers of relatively short loops of Henle. Yet hypertonic urine is produced by these kidneys. Thus the same physiological ability can be derived from either anatomical arrangement—the long loops or the large numbers of short loops.

Those birds and reptiles that cannot produce a hypertonic urine possess a salt-secreting gland near the eyes. More recent work by Schmidt-Nielsen and his collaborators shows that this gland is necessary because of an indirect effect of the final water resorption that occurs in the cloaca (the final chamber through which kidney and intestinal products pass). Water is taken back into the body through the walls of the cloaca, thus drying out the feces and uric acid. Cations tend to move with the water and they must be excreted elsewhere; this excretion is the function of the salt glands of the head. Physiologically the salt-secreting glands act like kidney tubules in response to vasopressin and hypothalamic control.

Another interesting adaptation of various vertebrates is the ability to retain large quantities of urea in the body fluids. Sharks, their relatives, and various amphibia that live in saline environments build up high concentrations of urea in order to counteract the osmotic gradient resulting from higher salt concentrations in the sea outside the body. The urea molecules act as osmotic particles that raise internal osmotic pressure and reduce the tendency for water to leave the body. The same functional end point is seen in the spadefoot toad (*Scaphiopus couchi*), which can lose as much as 60 percent of its body water by dehydration as it lies buried in sand for long periods. As this occurs, urea concentrations rise, but the tissues can tolerate them. Consequently, the organism, which may already be in mild distress because of water loss, does not have to lose still more water as urine. The means by which cells of different kinds of vertebrates become tolerant of high urea concentrations is unknown.

19

The Desert Rat

KNUT AND BODIL SCHMIDT–NIELSEN · July 1953

THERE IS a common impression that no higher animal can live long without drinking water. Certainly this is true of man and many other mammals; we need water at frequent intervals, and in a very hot, dry desert a man without water cannot last more than a day or so. An animal such as the camel can survive somewhat longer, but sooner or later it too must drink to refill its supply.

Yet we know that the waterless desert is not uninhabited. Even in desert areas with no visible drinking water within scores of miles, one will often find a fairly rich animal life. How do these animals get the water they must have to live? The body of a desert mammal has about the same water content (65 per cent of body weight) as that of a drinking animal, and it generally has no more tolerance to desiccation of the tissues, sometimes less. For many desert animals the answer is simple: they get their water in their food. These animals live on juicy plants, one of the most important of which is cactus. The pack rat, for example, eats large quantities of cactus pulp, which is about 90 per cent water. Thus it is easy to account for the survival of animals in areas where cacti and other water-storing plants are available.

There are, however, animals which can live in areas altogether barren of juicy vegetation. An outstanding example is a certain general type of desert rodent which is found in all the major desert areas of the world—in Africa, in Asia, in Australia and in the southwestern U. S. Although the rats of this type seem to have evolved independently in the several areas and are not related to one another, all of them are similar in appearance and habits and all seem to be able to live with a minimum of water. How they do so has long been a puzzle to biologists.

During the past few years we have investigated intensively a rodent of this type—the so-called kangaroo rat that lives in deserts of the U. S. Southwest. In a field laboratory in Arizona and in biological laboratories at Swarthmore College, Stanford University and the University of Cincinnati we have studied the kangaroo rat's habits and physiology, and we now have a good understanding of how this rodent is able to get along on a diet so dry that other animals would soon die of thirst.

THE LITTLE kangaroo rat is not actually related to the kangaroo, though it looks a great deal like one. It hops along on long hind legs, and it has a long, strong tail which it uses for support and steering. It lives in a burrow in the ground by day and comes out for food only at night. The animal thrives in the driest regions, even in the bare sand dunes of Death Valley. Water to drink, even dew, is rarely available in its natural habitat. The kangaroo rat apparently has only a short range of movement—not more than a few hundred yards—and

BANNERTAILED KANGAROO RAT (*Dipodomys spectabilis*) from the Santa Rita Range of Arizona is photographed in the laboratory. It is called the kangaroo rat because of its powerful hind legs and long tail.

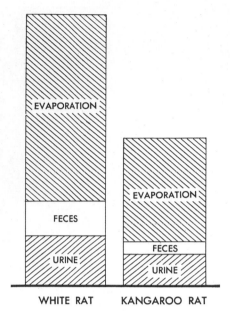

WATER LOSSES of the kangaroo rat (*right*) and the white rat (*left*) are compared at zero humidity.

therefore does not leave its dry area to find juicy plants. Stomach analyses have shown that it seldom or never consumes any succulent vegetation. Its food consists of seeds and other dry plant material. In the laboratory it will live indefinitely without water and with no other food but dry barley seeds.

The first question to be answered was whether the kangaroo rat stores water in its body to carry it over long dry periods. It was found that the animal's water content was always about the same (some 65 per cent of body weight), in the rainy season or the dry season, or after it had been kept on dry food in the laboratory for several weeks. During eight weeks on nothing but dry barley in the laboratory some of the animals increased their body weight, and their water percentage was as high as at the beginning of the experiment; they had actually increased the total amount of water in their bodies. Furthermore, kangaroo rats which were

given watermelon as well as barley to eat showed no higher water percentage in their bodies than animals maintained on a dry diet. They must therefore have eliminated the excess of water at the same rate as it was taken in. Altogether the experiments made clear that the kangaroo rat does not store water or live through dry periods at the expense of its body water.

There is only one way the kangaroo rat can get any substantial amount of water on its dry diet. That is by oxidizing its food. The oxidation of hydrogen or a substance containing hydrogen always forms water. Obviously the amount of water an animal forms in its metabolism will depend upon the hydrogen content of its food. The amount is simply a matter of chemistry and is the same in all animals. Oxidation of a gram of carbohydrate (starch or sugar) yields .6 of a gram of water; of a gram of fat, 1.1 grams of water; of a gram of protein, .3 of a gram of water. Protein produces relatively little water because a considerable part of its hydrogen is not oxidized but is excreted with nitrogen as urea.

Now the experimental diet of dry barley on which the kangaroo rats lived yields 54 grams of water for each 100 grams of barley (dry weight) consumed. If there is any moisture in the air, the barley will also contain a little absorbed water—about 13 grams per 100 grams when the relative humidity is 50 per cent at 75 degrees Fahrenheit. The kangaroo rat consumes 100 grams of barley in a period of about five weeks. Thus during that period its total intake of water is between 54 and 67 grams, depending on atmospheric conditions.

THIS is an astonishingly small amount of water for an animal of its size to subsist on. It can maintain its water balance only if its water losses are correspondingly small. The next step, therefore, was to find out how the animal manages to keep its water loss so low, if indeed it does. We proceeded to measure its losses of water through the three

routes by which an animal eliminates water; in the urine, in the feces and by evaporation from the skin and the respiratory passages.

There is an animal, the African lungfish, which can get along for long periods without excreting any urine at all. When the stream or pond in which it is living dries up, it burrows into the mud and stays there until the next rain. The eminent authority on the kidney, Homer W. Smith [SCIENTIFIC AMERICAN Offprint 37], has found that during this time the urea content of the fish's blood may rise to the extravagant level of 4 per cent. Can the kangaroo rat similarly accumulate waste products and avoid urinating during a dry spell? We investigated and found that it could not: the urea and salt content of its blood did not rise when it was on a dry diet or fall when it had a moist diet. And it continued on its dry diet to excrete urea as usual.

However, we learned that it could get rid of its waste products with a very small output of water. The kangaroo rat has an amazingly efficient kidney. The concentration of urea in its urine can be as high as 24 per cent, whereas in man the maximum is about 6 per cent. Thus the kangaroo rat needs only about one fourth as much water to eliminate a given amount of urea as a man would. Its excretion of salts is similarly efficient. The animal can excrete urine about twice as salty as sea water!

The reason that a human being cannot tolerate drinking sea water is that the body is dehydrated in the process of getting rid of the salts. The saltiness of the kangaroo rat's urine suggested that this animal might be able to drink sea water and get a net water gain from it. Of course it was not easy to induce the kangaroo rat, which normally does not drink, to imbibe sea water. But we were able to make it do so by feeding it a high protein diet (soy beans) which formed very large amounts of urea and forced the rat to drink to avoid dehydration. The animal's kidney proved able to excrete both the excess of urea and the salts in the sea water. Drinking sea water actually enabled the animal to maintain its water balance. So far as is known, no other mammal can drink sea water with impunity.

From the known efficiency of the kangaroo rat's kidney we calculated that the animal uses 13 grams of water to excrete the waste products formed from 100 grams of dry barley. Measurement of the water content of its feces, which are exceptionally dry, showed that it loses about three grams of water by this route in metabolizing 100 grams of dry barley. There remained, then, the question of how much water the kangaroo rat loses by evaporation.

Very little escapes through its skin. Rodents have no sweat glands except on the toe pads, and the kangaroo rat has

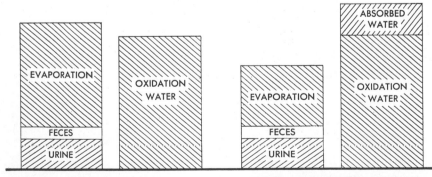

WATER BALANCE of the kangaroo rat is shown under two different conditions of humidity. The first and third bars indicate water loss; the second and fourth, water gain. The term "absorbed water" refers to water in food.

fewer sweat glands than most rats. All mammals lose a little water from the skin even where there are no sweat glands, and there is reason to believe that the kangaroo rat suffers less loss by this route than other mammals. It does, however, lose a considerable amount of water by evaporation from its respiratory tract. In the extremely dry desert air this loss could be serious. At zero humidity the loss by evaporation from the skin and respiratory tract would amount to some 44 grams of water during the five weeks in which the rat metabolizes 100 grams of barley. At a relative humidity of 50 per cent and a temperature of 75 degrees the loss by evaporation would be about 25 grams.

W E CAN NOW add up the balance sheet of the kangaroo rat's water intake and outgo. At zero humidity its total intake on a diet of dry barley would be 54 grams, and the total loss would be 61 grams (14 in the urine, 3 in the feces and 44 by evaporation). At 50 per cent relative humidity at 75 degrees the intake would be 67 grams and the outgo only 43 grams. Thus it seems clear that the kangaroo rat cannot survive on a barley diet in completely dry air, for under those conditions it has a water deficit in spite of its marvelous mechanisms for water conservation. Actual tests showed that the minimum atmospheric conditions under which the animal can maintain its water balance on the dry diet is 10 to 20 per cent relative humidity at 75 degrees.

The desert atmosphere is often somewhat drier than this, but the explanation of the kangaroo rat's survival is that it is a night animal. During the day it stays in its burrow, where the air is always a little more humid than outside, even when the soil seems to be completely dry. To measure the temperature and humidity in the burrow we used a tiny

WEIGHT CHANGES of kangaroo rats fed either fresh water, sea water or no water showed that they could drink sea water without ill effects. Although kangaroo rats normally drink no water, they were induced to do so by a protein-rich diet that required water for the excretion of urea.

instrument which included a humidity-sensitive hair hygrometer. The instrument makes a record on a smoked glass disk, which can be read afterward under a microscope. The recorder was tied to the rat's tail, and the animal dragged it into the burrow. It was secured by a thin wire so that the animal could not run away with the instrument. After 12 hours we opened the burrow and read the record. We found that in early summer in the Arizona desert the relative humidity inside the kangaroo rat's burrows ranged from 30 to 50 per cent, and the temperature from about 75 to 88 degrees. At night, in the desert outside the burrows, the relative humidity varied from 15 to 40 per cent and the temperature from about 60 to 75 degrees. The protection

of the burrow by day provides just enough margin to enable the kangaroo rat to maintain its water balance and live in the driest of our deserts.

The same protection allows the kangaroo rat to survive the desert heat. A mammal such as man avoids overheating only by evaporating large quantities of water. The kangaroo rat cannot do this, nor can it tolerate a body temperature of much more than 100 degrees. It does not sweat or increase evaporation from its respiratory passages by panting, as a dog does. If it were exposed to the daytime heat in the desert, it would soon perish. The adaptations that permit it to thrive in the hot desert are its nocturnal habits and its extraordinary facilities for water conservation.

The Physiology of the Camel

KNUT SCHMIDT–NIELSEN · December 1959

The camel's ability to go without water for long periods is proverbial. Naturalists since Pliny the Elder have ascribed this talent to a built-in reservoir on which the animal can draw in time of need. Thus the English zoologist George Shaw wrote in 1801: "Independent of the four stomachs which are common to the ruminating animals, the Camels have a fifth bag which serves them as a reservoir for water. . . . This particularity is known to Oriental travelers, who have sometimes found it necessary to kill a Camel in order to obtain a supply of water."

Such tales appear even in modern zoology textbooks (though some writers have shifted the camel's reservoir from its stomach to its hump). There is remarkably little evidence for them. A few years ago I became interested in camel physiology and leafed through every book on the subject I could find. I accumulated a large amount of information on the camel's anatomy, its diseases and its evolution, but discovered that scientific knowledge of its water metabolism was almost nonexistent.

The camel's tolerance for drought is real enough. It can travel across stretches of desert where a man on foot and without water would quickly die of thirst. This fact poses some interesting questions for the physiologist. No animal can get along completely without water. Land animals in particular lose water steadily through their kidneys and from the moist surfaces of their lungs; mammals cool themselves in hot surroundings by evaporating water from their skins or oral membranes.

Desert animals have evolved a variety of mechanisms to minimize these losses. The kangaroo rat, for example, produces urine which contains so little water that it solidifies almost as soon as it is excreted. The animal avoids the heat and thus decreases evaporation by passing the daylight hours in a relatively cool burrow [see "The Desert Rat," by Knut and Bodil Schmidt-Nielsen, which begins on page 189 in this book].

The camel can hardly escape the heat by burrowing. Does it emulate the desert rat by excreting a highly concentrated urine? Does it store water in its stomach, or anywhere else? For that matter, just how long can a camel go without water?

Our laboratory at Duke University was obviously no place to seek answers to these questions. Accordingly my wife and I, together with T. R. Houpt of the University of Pennsylvania and S. A. Jarnum of the University of Copenhagen, undertook to study camels in the Sahara Desert. The information we were seeking was not only of scientific interest but might also be of practical importance. In many arid lands the camel is the chief domestic animal. It serves not only as a beast of burden but also as a source of milk, meat, wool and leather. A better understanding of camel physiology might benefit the economy of these areas, which include some of the most poverty-stricken regions on earth.

The expedition required a year's planning, because we had to be completely independent of outside supplies in setting up our desert laboratory. Late in 1953 we arrived at the oasis of Béni Abbès, located in the desert south of the Atlas Mountains. To many Americans the word "oasis" suggests a few date palms clustered around a well. Béni Abbès, however, is a community of several thousand people. Its location over an underground river flowing down from the mountains ensures water for drinking and some irrigation.

Camels are valuable beasts in the Sahara, and we had considerable difficulty in securing animals for experimental purposes. With the aid of our native assistant, Mohammed ben Fredj, I managed after considerable haggling to purchase one animal and later to rent two others. Meanwhile we sought to track down the source of some of the abundant camel folklore.

Explorers have often reported that their camels have gone without water for as long as several weeks. Is this possible? Under certain circumstances it is. Much desert exploration has been conducted in winter, because the desert summers are unbearably hot. During the winter the camel can often meet its need for water by browsing on bushes and succulent plants, which flourish after a rain and contain considerable water. Indeed, we found that in the Sahara grazing camels are not watered at all in winter. Some that had not drunk for as much as two months refused water when we offered it to them. When we examined such animals that had been butchered for meat, we found that all their organs contained the normal amount of water.

Thus the camel's drought tolerance in winter seems entirely ascribable to its diet. Even a man would have no difficulty in abstaining from drinking in cool weather if he fed largely on juicy fruits and vegetables. During the winter months the only way to dehydrate a camel is to restrict it to a fodder of dry grass and dried dates (not the soft, sweet dates of the grocery but a hard, fibrous and bitter variety). Even when we kept our camels on this completely dry diet, they could go for several weeks without drinking, though they lost water steadily through their lungs and skin and through the formation of urine and feces. We were able to measure these losses quite accurately simply by weighing the beasts, because unlike most animals deprived of water they continued to eat normally and thus did not lose weight in the usual sense. When we finally offered them water, they would in a few minutes drink enough to bring their weight back to normal. In no case did they drink more water than they had previously lost. Evidently they were not storing up a surplus but replacing a deficit.

Our studies of butchered camels supported this conclusion; we could find no evidence for special water-storing organs. The camel's first stomach, or rumen, does have pouches that are not found in the stomachs of other ruminants. These pouches have been called water sacs by some investigators, but their total fluid capacity is only about a gallon, and they contain coarsely masticated fodder rather than water. The main part of the rumen and the other stomachs contained considerable fluid, but less than the stomachs of other ruminating animals do. Chemical analysis revealed the similarity of the fluid to digestive juices; in salt content it resembled blood rather than water. Though it could furnish no significant reserve of water for the camel, it might well save the life of a thirsty man. The stories of travelers who killed their camels for water may thus be true. However, a man would have to be terribly thirsty to resort to such an expedient, because the fluid is usually a foul-smelling greenish soup. As for other possible sites of water storage, we found that neither the hump nor any other part of the animal's body contained an unusual quantity of fluid.

The tale that the camel stores water has probably gained color from the animal's remarkable capacity for rapid and copious drinking. During a later experiment one of our camels drank more than 27 gallons of water in 10 minutes. Camels are always watered before a long desert journey, and if they have not been watered for some days they will drink greedily. The uncritical observer could easily conclude that the animals are storing water in anticipation of future needs.

Some writers have alleged that the camel's fatty hump, though it contains no water reservoir, nonetheless provides the animal with a reserve of water as well as of food. Their logic is simple enough. All foods contain hydrogen and therefore produce water when they are oxidized in the body; the desert rat obtains all its water from this source. Fat contains a greater proportion of hydrogen than any other foodstuff and yields

CAMEL CAN LOSE WATER amounting to more than 25 per cent of its body weight. A dehydrated camel (*top*) appears emaciated but can still move about; a similarly dehydrated man would be unconscious or dead. The animal can quickly drink back its water losses and resume its normal appearance (*bottom*). Photographs were made about 10 minutes apart.

a correspondingly larger amount of water: about 1.1 pounds of water for each pound of fat. Thus a camel with 100 pounds of fat on its back might seem to be carrying 110 pounds—more than 13 gallons—of water. But in order to turn the fat into water the camel must take in oxygen through its lungs; in the process it loses water by evaporation from the lung surfaces. Calculation of the rate of loss indicates that the animal will lose more water by evaporation than it can gain through oxidation.

If the camel possesses no special reserves of water, it must have evolved methods for economizing on water expenditure. Its kidney functions in particular seemed worth investigating. All vertebrates rely on the kidney to rid their bodies of nitrogenous wastes (in mammals primarily urea). Few animals can tolerate any accumulation of these substances in the body. The kangaroo rat conserves water by eliminating a urine very rich in urea, and we were not surprised to find the camel following its example. When we kept our camels on dry fodder, their urine output declined and its urea content rose. In the case of one young animal, however, the urea output dropped sharply along with the volume of urine. The animal did not retain the urea in its blood, because the concentration of urea in the blood plasma also fell. Even the injection of urea into the bloodstream did not raise its concentration in the urine.

Further work revealed that the low level of urea had to do with nutrition rather than water conservation. The dry fodder contained too little protein to meet the nutritional needs of a young and growing camel. Under these circumstances the animal was apparently able to reprocess "waste" urea into new protein. From recent studies of sheep we have found that they share the camel's ability to use nitrogenous compounds over and over again. Experiments with cows by other investigators suggest that these ruminants may husband nitrogen in the same manner [see "The Metabolism of Ruminants," by Terence A. Rogers; SCIENTIFIC AMERICAN, February, 1958].

To determine the maximum efficiency with which the camel can excrete urea, we tried to put one of our camels on a high-protein diet. Unfortunately the camel's taste in food is exceedingly conservative. When we sought to trick the animal into increasing its protein intake by feeding it dates stuffed with raw peanuts, it balked at the first date and refused to accept any more for the rest of the day. Over a period of weeks we gradually accustomed it to the adulterated food, but we were forced to abandon the experiment when we found that we had exhausted the entire stock of peanuts in the oasis!

The kidney of the desert rat has a remarkable capacity for concentrating not only urea but also salt, and one would expect the camel's kidney to operate with similar efficiency. We were not able to test this hypothesis because

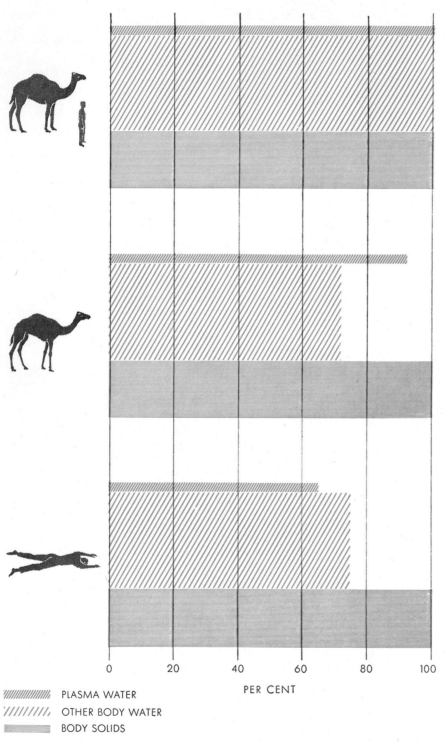

PER CENT

////////// PLASMA WATER

//////// OTHER BODY WATER

▬▬▬▬ BODY SOLIDS

CAMEL SURVIVES DEHYDRATION partly by maintaining the volume of its blood. Under normal conditions (*top*) plasma water in both man and camel accounts for about a 12th of total body water. In a camel that has lost about a fourth of its body water (*center*) the blood volume will drop by less than a 10th. Under the same conditions a man's blood volume will drop by a third (*bottom*). The viscous blood circulates too slowly to carry the man's body heat outward to the skin, so that his temperature soon rises to a fatal level.

neither the fodder nor the local wells contained much salt. We were told, however, that camels in other areas could and did drink "bitter waters" containing enough magnesium sulfate (epsom salt) to sicken a man. Camels in coastal regions were said to browse on seaweed along the shore; these plants would of course have a salt content equal to that of sea water. It seems quite possible that the camel can approach the performance of the desert rat, whose efficient kidney permits it to drink sea water without harm.

Even the most efficient kidney cannot explain the camel's ability to get along on low water-rations during the desert summer. In this season the temperature soars to 120 degrees Fahrenheit or more. Since higher animals cannot survive body temperatures much

over 100 degrees, they must either seek shelter, as do many small desert creatures, or cool themselves by evaporation of water from the mouth (panting) or from the skin (sweating). On a hot desert day a man may produce more than a quart of sweat an hour.

A man losing water at this rate rapidly becomes intensely thirsty. If the loss passes 5 per cent of his body weight (about a gallon), his physical condition rapidly deteriorates, his perceptions become distorted and his judgment falters. A loss of 10 per cent brings on delirium, deafness and insensitivity to pain.

In cool surroundings a man may cling to life until he has lost water up to 20 per cent of his body weight. In the desert heat, however, a loss of no more than 12 per cent will result in "explosive heat death." As the blood loses water it becomes denser and more viscous. The thickened blood taxes the pumping capacity of the heart and slows the circulation to the point where metabolic heat is no longer carried outward to the skin and dissipated. The internal temperature of the body suddenly increases, and death quickly follows.

How does the camel fare under similar conditions? We kept one camel without water for eight days in the heat of the desert summer. It had then lost 220 pounds—about 22 per cent—of its body weight. It looked emaciated; its abdomen was drawn in against its vertebrae, its muscles were shrunken and its legs were scrawny and appeared even longer than usual. But even though the animal would not have been able to do heavy work or travel a long distance, it was not in serious condition. It had no difficulty in emptying bucket after bucket of water and quickly recovered its normal appearance. Later experiments showed that camels can lose more than 25 per cent of their body weight without being seriously weakened. The lethal limit of dehydration is probably considerably higher, but for obvious humanitarian reasons we did not attempt to determine it.

How does a camel that has lost water amounting to a quarter of its body weight—more than a third of the water in its system—manage to avoid the explosive heat death that would overtake a man long before this point? It can do so because it maintains its blood volume despite the water loss. We were able to

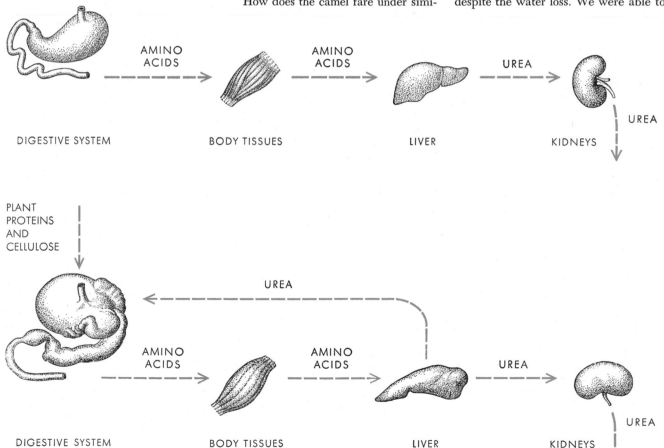

UNUSUAL NITROGEN METABOLISM helps the camel to get along on low-grade fodder. In man (top) nitrogenous metabolic wastes are constantly excreted in the form of urea. In the camel (bottom) urea may return via bloodstream to the stomach, where in combination with broken-down cellulose it is reprocessed into new protein. Sheep and perhaps cattle husband nitrogen similarly.

calculate the blood volume before and after dehydration by injecting a non-poisonous dye into the bloodstream and measuring its concentration when it had become evenly distributed. In the case of a young camel that had lost about 11 gallons of water the reduction in blood volume was less than a quart. The water had been lost not from the blood but from the other body fluids and from the tissues.

One might suppose that the camel has some special physiological mechanism for maintaining its blood volume. In theory, however, a man should be able to do the same thing. When he lacks water, the osmotic pressure of the proteins in his blood plasma should draw it from the rest of his body. Since this does not happen, the real question is not how the dehydrated camel maintains its

"FLEXIBLE" BODY TEMPERATURE partly accounts for the camel's ability to conserve water. Colored curves show variations in body temperature for a camel and a donkey over a 20-day period during the desert summer; a typical temperature curve for a man is shown for comparison. Solid gray curves show variations in air temperature during the same period; the broken curves indicate the additional heat load due to radiation from the sun and ground. The camel's temperature can rise to 105 degrees before the animal begins to sweat freely; during the night its temperature drops as low as 93 degrees, thereby delaying the next day's rise. The camel blood volume but why a dehydrated man does not.

The camel not only tolerates dehydration much better than a man but also loses water much more slowly. One reason is that it excretes only a small volume

14   15   16   17   18   19   20

survived though watered (*shading*) only at the beginning and end of the period. Donkey, with a less flexible temperature, sweated more and drank more often. In the desert summer man must drink every day.

of urine—in summer often as little as a quart a day. The animal saves much more water, however, by economizing on sweat.

In the burning heat of the desert an inanimate object such as a rock may reach a temperature of more than 150 degrees F. A camel in such an environment, like a man, maintains a tolerable body temperature by sweating. But where the temperature of the man remains virtually constant as the day grows hotter, the temperature of the camel increases slowly to about 105 degrees. As the temperature of the camel rises, the animal sweats very little; only when its temperature reaches 105 degrees does it sweat freely. The camel's elevated temperature also lessens its absorption of heat, which of course depends on the difference between the temperature of its body and that of the environment.

The camel lowers the heat load on its body still further by letting its temperature fall below normal during the cool desert night. At dawn its temperature may have dropped as low as 93 degrees. Thus much of the day will elapse before the animal's body heats up to 105 degrees and sweating must set in. As a result of its flexible body temperature the camel sweats little except during the hottest hours of the day, where a man in the same environment perspires almost from sunrise to sunset.

These remarkable temperature fluctuations—about 12 degrees for the camel as against two degrees for a man—might seem to indicate a failure of normal heat regulation. This, however, is not so. The camel's body temperature never rises above 105 degrees. Moreover, if the camel has free access to water, the fluctuations are much smaller: about four degrees, comparable to the fluctuations during the cool winter months.

These findings may have implications for animal husbandry in the tropics. Cattle breeders have long sought ways of adapting the highly productive European dairy and beef animals to hot climates. In the process they have generally assumed that animals whose body temperature rises in hot weather will adapt poorly to heat. Although this assumption is often correct, the camel's example suggests that the reverse may sometimes be true.

People in desert areas and outside them have long appreciated the excellent insulating properties of camel hair. The camel employs camel-hair insulation to lower its heat load still fur-

ther. Even during the summer, when the camel sheds much of its wool, it retains a layer several inches thick on its back where the sun beats down. When we sheared the wool from one of our camels, we found that the shorn animal produced 60 per cent more sweat than an unshorn one. To Americans, who wear light clothing during the summer, the idea that a thick layer of wool is advantageous in the desert may seem unreasonable. The Arabs, however, typically dress in several layers of loose clothing, frequently made of wool. I have seen a nomad returning from the desert shed one thick wool burnous after another. We ourselves quickly learned that Arab dress was more comfortable than "civilized" garments.

The camel's hump also helps indirectly to lessen the heat load on the animal. Nearly all mammals possess a food reserve in the form of fat, but in most of them the fat is distributed fairly uniformly over the body just beneath the skin. In having its fat concentrated in one place the camel lacks insulation between its body and its skin, where evaporative cooling takes place. The absence of insulation facilitates the flow of heat outward, just as the insulating wool slows the flow of heat inward.

To clarify the relative importance of insulation and temperature fluctuation in lowering the camel's need for water, we repeated several of our experiments on a donkey. Because the donkey, like the camel, is a native of the arid lands of Asia, it should presumably have developed similar devices for conserving water.

We found that the donkey could tolerate as much water loss as the camel—up to 25 per cent. The donkey, however, lost water three times more rapidly than the camel does; thus it could not go as long without drinking. In one experiment a camel went for 17 days without drinking, while the donkey had to be watered at least once every four days. The difference in water loss seems partly due to the fact that the body temperature of the donkey is more stable than that of the camel. The donkey begins to sweat when its temperature has risen only slightly. Furthermore, the donkey's coat is quite thin in comparison with the camel's and thus does not provide so effective a barrier against heat from the environment.

The donkey outdoes the camel in one respect: its drinking capacity. A camel that has lost 25 per cent of its body weight can drink back the loss in about

10 minutes; a donkey can perform the same feat in less than two minutes. A man drinks much more slowly; after a day in the desert he will not completely make up his water losses for several hours or until he has eaten (when he tends to drink with his food).

The drinking capacity of both camel and donkey doubtless came about by evolutionary adaptation in the wild state. Water holes are rare in an arid land, and predators often lie in wait near them. The animal that can quickly replenish its water losses and depart is likely to live longer than one that must linger by the water to satisfy its needs.

HEAT FLOW IN CAMEL AND MAN is compared in these schematic cross sections of a small portion of body surface. Colored curves show temperature; heat flow, suggested by arrows, increases with the slope of the curves. Camel (*top*) can eliminate heat from its body with an average skin temperature of about 103 degrees; its wool slows the heat flow from the environment. Man (*bottom*), with a lower body temperature and an insulating layer of fat beneath the skin, must maintain a lower skin temperature (that is, must evaporate more sweat) to obtain the same flow of heat from his interior. The lack of insulation between his skin and the air raises heat flow from the air, necessitating still more evaporation.

21

Salt Glands

KNUT SCHMIDT–NIELSEN · January 1959

As the writers of stories about castaways are apt to point out, a man who drinks sea water will only intensify his thirst. He must excrete the salt contained in the water through his kidneys, and this process requires additional water which is taken from the fluids of his body. The dehydration is aggravated by the fact that sea water, in addition to common salt or sodium chloride, also contains magnesium sulfate, which causes diarrhea. Most air-breathing vertebrates are similarly unable to tolerate the drinking of sea water, but some are not so restricted. Many birds, mammals and reptiles whose ancestors dwelt on land now live on or in the sea, often hundreds of miles from any source of fresh water. Some, like the sea turtles, seals and albatrosses, return to the land only to reproduce. Whales, sea cows and some sea snakes, which bear living young in the water, have given up the land entirely.

Yet all these animals, like man, must limit the concentration of salt in their blood and body fluids to about 1 per cent—less than a third of the salt concentration in sea water. If they drink sea water, they must somehow get rid of the excess salt. Our castaway can do so only at the price of dehydrating his tissues. Since his kidneys can at best se-

PETREL EJECTS DROPLETS of solution produced by its salt gland through a pair of tubes atop its beak, as shown in this high-speed photograph. The salt-gland secretions of most birds drip from the tip of the beak. The petrel, however, remains in the air almost continuously and has apparently evolved this "water pistol" mechanism as a means of eliminating the fluid while in flight.

crete a 2-per-cent salt solution, he must eliminate up to a quart and a half of urine for every quart of sea water he drinks, with his body fluids making up the difference. If other animals drink sea water, how do they escape dehydration? If they do not drink sea water, where do they obtain the water which their bodies require?

The elimination of salt by sea birds and marine reptiles poses these questions in particularly troublesome form. Their kidneys are far less efficient than our own: a gull would have to produce more than two quarts of urine to dispose of the salt in a quart of sea water. Yet many observers have seen marine birds drinking from the ocean. Physiologists have held that the appearance of drinking is no proof that the birds actually swallow water, and that the low efficiency of their kidneys proves that they do not. Our experiments during the past two years have shown that while the physiologists are right about the kidneys, the observations of drinking are also correct. Marine birds do drink sea water. Their main salt-eliminating organ is not the kidney, however, but a special gland in the head which disposes of salt more rapidly than any kidney does. Our studies indicate that all marine birds and probably all marine reptiles possess this gland.

The obvious way to find out whether birds can tolerate sea water is to make them drink it. If gulls in captivity are given only sea water, they will drink it without ill effects. To measure the exact amount of sea water ingested we administered it through a stomach tube, and found that the birds could tolerate large quantities. Their output of urine increased sharply but accounted for only a small part of the salt they had ingested. Most of the salt showed up in a clear, colorless fluid which dripped from the tip of the beak. In seeking the source of this fluid our attention was drawn to the so-called nasal glands, paired structures of hitherto unknown function found in the heads of all birds. Anatomists described these organs more than a century ago, and noted that they are much larger in sea birds than in land birds. The difference in size suggested that the glands must perform some special function in marine species. Some investigators proposed that the organs produce a secretion akin to tears which serves to rinse sea water from the birds' sensitive nasal membranes.

We were able to collect samples of the secretion from the gland by inserting a thin tube into its duct. The fluid turned out to be an almost pure 5-per-cent solution of sodium chloride—many times saltier than tears and nearly twice as salty as sea water. The gland, it was plain, had nothing to do with rinsing the nasal membranes but a great deal to do with eliminating salt. By sampling the output of other glands in the bird's head, we established that the nasal gland was the only one that produces this concentrated solution.

The nasal glands can handle relatively enormous quantities of salt. In one experiment we gave a gull 134 cubic centimeters of sea water—equal to about a tenth of the gull's body weight. In man this would correspond to about two gallons. No man could tolerate this much sea water; he would sicken after drinking a small fraction of it. The gull, however, seemed unaffected; within three hours it had excreted nearly all the salt. Its salt glands had produced only about two thirds as much fluid as its kidneys, but had excreted more than 90 per cent of the salt.

The fluid produced by the salt gland is about five times as salty as the bird's blood and other body fluids. How does the organ manage to produce so concentrated a solution? Microscopic examination of the gland reveals that it consists of many parallel cylindrical lobes, each composed of several thousand branching tubules radiating from a central duct like bristles from a bottle brush. These tubules, about a thousandth of an inch in diameter, secrete the salty fluid.

A network of capillaries carries the blood parallel to the flow of salt solution in the tubules, but in the opposite direction [see *illustration on opposite page*]. This arrangement brings into play the principle of counter-current flow, which seems to amplify the transfer of salt from the blood in the capillaries to the fluid in the tubules. A similar arrangement in the kidneys of mammals appears to account for their efficiency in the concentration of urine [see " 'The Wonderful Net' " by P. F. Scholander, beginning on page 125 in this book]. No such provision for counter-current flow is found in the kidneys of reptiles, and it is only slightly developed in birds.

Counter-current flow, however, does not of itself account for the gland's capacity to concentrate salt. The secret of this process lies in the structure of the tubules and the cells that compose them.

The microscopic structure of a salt-gland tubule resembles a stack of pies with a small hole in the middle. Each "pie" consists of five to seven individual

STRUCTURE of salt gland is essentially the same in all sea birds. In the gull the glands lie above the bird's eyes, as shown at left. Cross section of a gland (*a*) shows that it consists of many lobes (*b*). Each of these

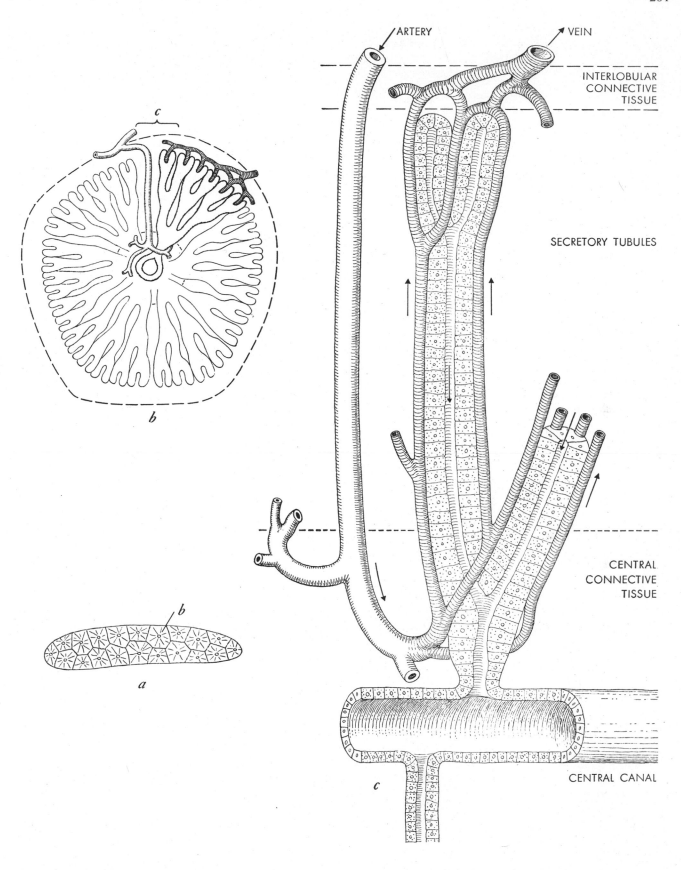

ARTERY

VEIN

INTERLOBULAR
CONNECTIVE
TISSUE

SECRETORY TUBULES

c

b

b

a

c

CENTRAL
CONNECTIVE
TISSUE

CENTRAL CANAL

lobes contains several thousand branching tubules which radiate from a central duct like the hairs of a bottle brush. Enlargement of a single tubule (*c*) reveals that it is surrounded by capillaries in which blood flows counter to the flow of salt secretion in the tubule. This counter-current flow, which also occurs in the kidneys of mammals, facilitates the transfer of salt from the blood to the tubule. The tubule wall, only one cell thick, consists of rings of five to seven wedge-shaped cells. These rings, stacked one on top of another, encircle a small hole, or lumen, through which the salty secretion flows from the tubule into the central canal of the lobe.

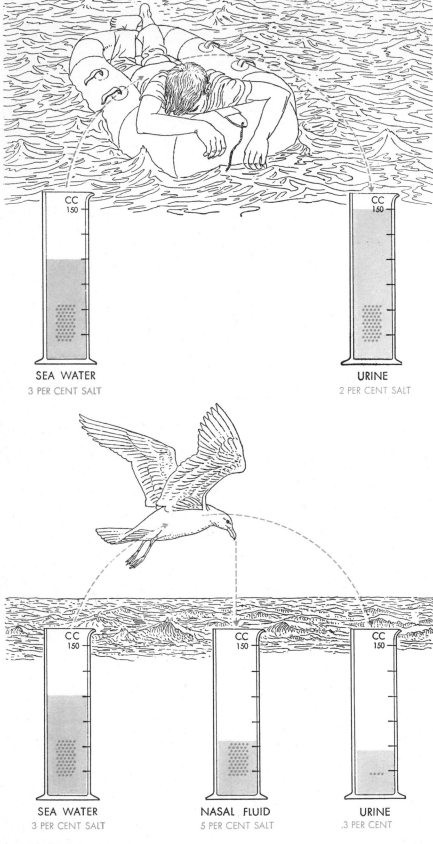

SEA WATER
3 PER CENT SALT

URINE
2 PER CENT SALT

SEA WATER
3 PER CENT SALT

NASAL FLUID
5 PER CENT SALT

URINE
.3 PER CENT

cells arranged like wedges. The hole, or lumen, funnels the secretion into the central duct. When we inject dye into the lumen, colored fluid seeps out into a system of irregular crevices in the walls of the tubule. More detailed examination with the electron microscope reveals a similar, interlocking system of deep folds which extend inward from the outer surface of the tubule. This structure may be important in that it greatly multiplies the surface area of the cell. It is worth noting that cells with similar, though shallower, folds are found in the tubules of the mammalian kidney.

Evidently some physiological mechanism in the cell "pumps" sodium and chloride ions against the osmotic gradient, from the dilute salt solution of the blood to the more concentrated solution in the lumen. Nerve cells similarly "pump" out the sodium which they absorb when stimulated [see "The Nerve Impulse and the Squid," by Richard D. Keynes; SCIENTIFIC AMERICAN, December, 1958]. Of course the mechanisms in the two processes may be quite different. In the tubule cells the transport of sodium and chloride ions seems to involve the mitochondria, the intracellular particles in which carbohydrates are oxidized to produce energy.

The similarities between the salt gland and the mammalian kidney should not obscure their important differences. For one thing, the salt gland is essentially a much simpler organ. The composition of its secretions, which apart from a trace of potassium contain only sodium chloride and water, indicates that its sole function is to eliminate salt. In contrast, the kidney performs a variety of regulatory and eliminative tasks and produces a fluid of complex and variable composition, depending on the animal's physiological needs at a particular time.

The salt gland's distinctive structure, elegantly specialized to a single end, enables it to perform an almost unbelievable amount of osmotic work in a short time. In one minute it can produce up to half its own weight of concentrated salt solution. The human kidney can produce at most about a twentieth of its weight in urine per minute, and its normal output is much less.

Another major difference between the two glands is that the salt gland functions only intermittently, in response to the need to eliminate salt. The kidney, on the other hand, secretes continuously, though at a varying rate. The salt gland's activity depends on the concentration of salt in the blood. The injection of salt solutions into a bird's bloodstream causes

SALT EXCRETION IN MEN AND BIRDS is compared in these drawings. Castaway at top cannot drink sea water because in eliminating the salt it contains (*colored dots*) he will lose more water than he has drunk. His kidney secretions have a salt content lower than that of sea water. Gull (*below*) can drink sea water even though its kidneys are far less efficient than a man's. It eliminates salt mainly through its salt, or "nasal," glands. These organs, more efficient than any kidney, secrete a fluid which is nearly twice as salty as sea water.

the gland to secrete, indicating that some center, probably in the brain, responds to the salt concentration. The gland responds to impulses in a branch of the facial nerve, for electric stimulation of this nerve causes the gland to secrete.

While the structure and function of the salt gland is essentially the same in all sea birds, its location varies. In the gull and many other birds the glands are located on top of the head above the eye sockets [see illustrations on this page]; in the cormorant and the gannet they lie between the eye and the nasal cavity. The duct of the gland in either case opens into the nasal cavity. The salty fluid flows out through the nostrils of most species and drips from the tip of the beak, but there are some interesting variations on this general scheme. The pelican, for example, has a pair of grooves in its long upper beak which lead the fluid down to the tip; the solution would otherwise trickle into the pouch of the lower beak and be reingested. In the cormorant and the gannet the nostrils are nonfunctional and covered with skin; the fluid makes its exit through the internal nostrils in the roof of the mouth and flows to the tip of the beak.

LOCATION OF SALT GLAND (color) varies in different species of marine birds and reptiles. In the gull (A) the gland's secretions emerge from the nostril and drip from the beak; in the cormorant (D) the fluid flows along the roof of the mouth. The pelican (B) has grooves along its upper beak which keep the fluid from dripping into its pouch; the petrel (C) ejects the fluid through tubular nostrils. In the turtle (E) the gland opens at the back corner of the eye; in the marine iguana (F) it opens into the nasal cavity.

CROSS SECTION OF SALT-GLAND TUBULE is shown magnified about 5,700 diameters in this electron micrograph made by William L. Doyle of the University of Chicago. To emphasize the cell-structure the specimen was kept in a solution which shrank and distorted the cells and their nuclei. Most of the material of the cells lies in folded, leaflike layers; cells with a somewhat similar structure are found in the kidney tubules of mammals.

The petrel displays an especially interesting mechanism for getting rid of the fluid. Its nostrils are extended in two short tubes along the top of its beak. When its salt glands are working, the bird shoots droplets of the fluid outward through the tubes [see illustration on page 199]. This curious design may reflect a special adaptation to the petrel's mode of life. Though the bird remains at sea for months at a time, it rarely settles down on the water to rest. Presumably the airstream from its almost continuous flight would hamper the elimination of fluid from the bird's nostrils, were it not for the water-pistol function of the tubes.

Our studies so far have demonstrated the existence of the salt gland in the herring gull, black-backed gull, common tern, black skimmer, guillemot, Louisiana heron, little blue heron, double-crested cormorant, brown pelican, gannet, petrel, albatross, eider duck and Humboldt penguin. These species, from a wide variety of geographical locations, represent all the major orders of marine birds. There is little doubt that this remarkable organ makes it possible for all sea birds to eliminate salt and live without fresh water.

The discovery of the salt gland in sea birds prompted us to look for a similar organ in other air-breathing sea animals.

In *Alice's Adventures in Wonderland* the Mock Turtle weeps perpetual tears because he is not a real turtle; real turtles, at least the marine species, also weep after a fashion. A. F. Carr, Jr., a distinguished specialist in marine turtles, gives us a vivid account of a Pacific Ridley turtle that came ashore to lay its eggs. The animal "began secreting copious tears shortly after she left the water, and these continued to flow after the nest was dug. By the time she had begun to lay, her eyes were closed and plastered over with tear-soaked sand and the effect was doleful in the extreme." Thus Carr makes it clear that the turtle's tears do not serve to wash its eyes free of sand, an explanation that otherwise might seem reasonable. The suggestion that the turtle weeps from the pangs of egg-laying is even wider of the mark.

With the loggerhead turtle as our subject, we have found that the sea turtle's tears come from a large gland behind its eyeball. The tears have much the same composition as that of the salt-gland secretions of the sea bird. Thus it would seem more than likely that the turtle's "weeping" serves to eliminate salt. The salt gland of the turtle has a structure similar to that of the gland in sea birds, with tubules radiating from a central duct, and it seems that this structure is essential for the elaboration of a fluid with a high salt concentration. The similarity is the more striking because the location of the gland in the turtle indicates that it has a different evolutionary origin. Still a third independent line of evolution may be represented by the salt gland in the Galápagos marine iguana, the only true marine lizard.

Anatomical studies of the other marine reptiles—the sea snakes and the marine crocodiles—have established that their heads contain large glands whose function may be similar to that of the salt gland. When we succeed in obtaining living specimens of these creatures, we expect to determine whether their glands have the same function.

Investigations of marine mammals thus far indicate that these animals handle the elimination of salt from their systems in a more conventional manner. The seal and some whales apparently satisfy their need for water with the fluids of the fish on which they feed. The elimination of such salt as these fluids contain requires kidneys of no more than human efficiency. But other whales, and walruses, whose diet of squid, plankton or shellfish is no less salty than sea water, must surely eliminate large quantities of excess salt even if they do not drink from the ocean itself. Our knowledge of their physiology suggests that their kidneys, which are more powerful than ours, can eliminate all the salts in their food. Some mammalian kidneys do function at this high level. The kangaroo rat, whose desert habitat compels it to conserve water to the utmost, can produce urine twice as salty as the ocean, and thrives in the laboratory on a diet of sea water and dried soybeans [see "The Desert Rat," by Knut and Bodil Schmidt-Nielsen, beginning on page 189 in this book].

We should like to study salt excretion in whales, but these animals are obviously not easy to work with. We have undertaken, however, some pilot studies on seals. When we injected them with salt solutions that stimulate the salt glands of birds and reptiles, they merely increased their output of urine. Methacholine, a drug which also stimulates the salt gland, gave equally negative results. Whatever the seal's need to eliminate salt, its kidneys are evidently adequate to the task. We must therefore assume that the salt gland has evolved only in the birds and reptiles, animals whose kidneys cannot produce concentrated salt solutions.

V

Temperature
Adaptations

...the males [bears] lie in hiding for periods of forty days and the females four months. If they have not got caves, they build rainproof dens by heaping up branches and brushwood, with a carpet of soft foliage on the floor. For the first fortnight they sleep so soundly that they cannot be aroused even by wounds; at this period they get fat with sloth to a remarkable degree....As a result of these days of sleep they shrink in bulk and they live by sucking their forepaws....No evidence of food and only the smallest amount of water is found in the belly at this stage, and...there are only a few drops of blood in the neighborhood of the heart and none in the rest of the body.

Pliny
NATURAL HISTORY, VIII, LIV.

V

Temperature
Adaptations

INTRODUCTION

Fishes and amphibians are poikilotherms—animals whose temperature varies with that of the environment. They are adapted in a variety of ways to their normal environmental temperature range, and, as we will see, they show ability to become acclimated to different temperatures by a number of biochemical modifications.

Reptiles, too, are poikilotherms, but, as Charles M. Bogert points out in "How Reptiles Regulate Their Body Temperature," they behave in special ways in order to raise and regulate their body temperature at least part of the time. The hormonal and neuronal mechanisms contributing to this capacity in reptiles are still present in birds and mammals, and are part of the more complex control machinery used for true homeothermy. (Homeotherms are animals whose temperature is high and is held constant despite fluctuations in environmental temperature.) Most important of the reptilian properties is a group of cells, apparently located in the hypothalamus, that responds to temperature by altering blood pressure and the rate of heart beat. In fact, the vascular system occupies a critical position among those adaptations that permit temperature regulation. Reptiles are sometimes called "ectotherms" because they derive most of their heat from outside the body; the blood fluid transports heat from the surface to the internal regions of the body. Because of its ubiquitous flow, moving blood fluid is also the best means of providing the organism with a continuous, rapidly responding source of information about overall body temperature. In birds and mammals, control of vasoconstriction of peripheral blood vessels has become the primary means of regulating the degree of heat conservation (the insulation derived from feathers or fur is not considered a regulator). The foregoing, then, emphasizes the central role of the vascular system in temperature relations and homeothermy.

Since temperature control originated relatively late in the history of vertebrates, most other physical properties of the internal environment were already under regulatory control. Development of the capacity to govern temperature seems to have involved utilizing a number of existing organ systems for the secondary purpose of participating in thermal control. A lizard, for example, when it is frightened, shows a brief shivering tremor as a means of increasing heat production. It never shivers when exposed to chilling conditions, but the same sort of shivering is used by birds and mammals to generate heat in cold environments. The biologist V. H. Hutchison has shown that the Indian python goes one step further. The female coils about a cluster of eggs and incubates them at elevated temperature by continually contracting her body musculature. The heat generated is sufficient to maintain a body and egg temperature of as much as 7 degrees centigrade above ambient. To perform this feat the female functions like a homeotherm as environmental temperature falls: it increases its consumption of oxygen and so is able to produce the extra heat needed for constancy of internal temperature. Nonincubating pythons and all other poikilotherms show rather strict proportionality of oxygen utilization to temperature, so that the quantities of oxygen used fall rapidly as the environment cools.

Still another example of reptiles employing a temperature-regulatory activity has been described by George A. Bartholomew. Several types of lizards breathe faster and faster as their body warms (thus meeting the need for more oxygen). In addition, some large lizards take special deep, rapid breaths, utilizing in particular the floor of the mouth and the neck, as temperature rises above 38 degrees centigrade. This increases the volume of air pumped and the amount of evaporation from the respiratory system. Obviously, here is an equivalent to panting, one of the emergency measures used by birds and mammals for cooling the body. There are many such neuronal or endocrine-controlled processes, which originated in reptiles but are now included in the temperature-regulating arsenal of the homeotherm.

From a study of the monotremes (the spiny anteater *Echidna*, or the duckbill platypus *Ornithorhynchus*), the most primitive living mammals, we attain further insight into the development of homeothermy. These "prototherian" animals diverged from the early mammals long before the marsupial and placental insectivores appeared. *Echidna* can maintain its body temperature between 20 and 30 degrees centigrade as the ambient environmental temperature falls toward 0 degrees. It is able to do this by increasing its rate of heat production; the metabolic rate is raised as the environment chills, and the heat produced is conserved by fur, which serves as an insulator. It is said that no vasoconstriction occurs to aid in heat retention. The result is quite different if ambient temperature rises much above 30 degrees centigrade: regulation breaks down and heat death can result. This ensues because *Echidna* lacks sweat glands and the panting reflex; it is essentially unable to combat rising body temperature except by decreasing heat production. Obviously animals with such primitive control abilities are limited in their activity; thus, monotremes commonly hibernate during cool weather and remain inactive and out of the sun in hot weather.

Marsupials (the Metatheria) are more like the placentals (the Eutheria) than the monotremes are because they have a higher normal body temperature (about 33 degrees centigrade) and are able to control it over a wider range of ambient temperature. Sweat glands, panting, and peripheral vasoconstriction are all present, so that control in both upper and lower danger zones is feasible.

Properties of the eutherian temperature-regulatory system are described by Laurence Irving in "Adaptations to Cold" and by T. H. Benzinger in "The Human Thermostat." The evolution of the system was the result of the ability certain neurons acquired to respond to altered temperature. The output from the medulla of the brain that elicits a coordinated response to compensate for such a temperature change is dependent upon sensory information from the body periphery, from deep body-temperature sensors, and from the hypothalamic sensor cells themselves.

Figure 1. The rates of discharge of mammalian hot and cold temperature-sensing cells. Note that the cold receptor is virtually quiet when 37° C is approached.
[After Zotterman, Y., *Ann. Rev. Physiol.* **15**, 1953.]

The activity of temperature-sensing nerves is typified by the following data on the responses of *cold* receptors in the skin of monkeys. A characteristic discharge rate of nerve impulses from the cold receptor is found for each temperature. Under conditions of constant ambient temperature this rate is nearly maximal when surface temperature of the skin is between 20 and 35 degrees centigrade. Discharge falls to zero as temperature rises from 35 to 40 degrees centigrade. When the temperature drops from about 40 degrees centigrade to 20 degrees, a peak discharge of 150 impulses per second is attained. A change as small as 0.5 degrees centigrade alters the discharge rates of these nerves, and even smaller increments affect the rates of some other temperature sensors. It is not clear how changing temperature evokes nerve discharge in such cells as these, or in the temperature sensors of the central nervous system.

A variety of biochemical adaptations to temperature are seen in various vertebrates. The amazing heat-generating brown fat of immature or hibernating mammals is described in "The Production of Heat by Fat" by Michael Dawkins and David Hull. This type of heat production is dependent upon the activity of different kinds of differentiated cells (brown or white fat cells) of one organism.

Some biochemical adaptations to temperature may vary between closely related species. An example of this type is seen in lizards that "prefer" different normal body temperatures ranging from 30 to 38.8 degrees centigrade. Differences are seen in myosin ATPase, an important enzyme in ATP metabolism during muscle contraction. Paul Licht of the University of California has shown that the temperature optimum for the enzyme differs between the species and correlates nicely with preferred body temperatures. Interestingly, lizards preferring high normal temperatures tend to have narrow preferred temperature ranges and the optima for their enzyme is similarly narrow; in contrast, animals preferring cooler conditions have more widely ranging preferred body temperatures and myosin ATPases with broad optima. It seems reasonable to assume that these functional differences in the enzymes are probably due to minor variations in the structure of the protein chains (i.e., they reflect the sorts of mutations discussed already for vertebrate hemoglobins).

Another type of temperature adaptation is the alteration of proteins within single cells. It can be seen in animals that are placed at new temperatures in the laboratory so that they become acclimated. In goldfish, for instance, Peter Hochachka of the University of British Columbia suggests that heart lactic dehydrogenase enzymes (LDH) increase in activity during acclimation to cold. This augmented activity is thought to result from a larger quantity of enzyme; and in fact several biologists have proposed that the quantity of enzymes in poikilotherms adapted to cold may be greater than that in animals habituated to higher temperatures. Quite a different alteration is seen in the liver of an animal adapted to a high temperature. One of the LDH protein subunits is no longer demonstrable, suggesting that the synthetic pattern of acclimated cells is altered. So, depending on tissue type and other factors, quantities of protein or type of protein may be varied in response to altered temperature.

A related well-known example is that of the fats found at different levels in the long legs of caribou, animals that often stand in the snow. As one proceeds from the thigh to the foot the degree of saturation of fatty acids decreases; this means that the melting point of the fat is lowered and the fat remains soft and pliable despite low temperature. If normal fats, with melting points as much as 30 centigrade degrees higher, were present in the foot, the tissues would be quite stiff and immobile. In some vertebrates this type of property also varies with season of the year, with unsaturated fats being manufactured during winter months and not in the seasons of warm weather.

Other differences are seen in the extremities of homeotherms that are exposed to temperature extremes, and, in particular, to cold extremes. In birds and mammals, for instance, most neurons stop conducting impulses at temperatures of about 15 to 20 degrees centigrade. In contrast, in cold-adapted legs, the peripheral nerves continue to function at 3 degrees centigrade. This is truly amazing when one realizes that such differences may be found within *single* long nerve cells! In a cold-acclimated herring gull, for instance, a nerve in the tibial portion of the leg showed blockage of conduction at temperatures of 11.7 to 14 degrees centigrade, while the metatarsal region remained active until temperature fell to between 2.8 and 3.9 degrees centigrade. Although it is not known yet what temperature-dependent biochemical property is responsible for these differences, this adaptation of the gull implies a remarkable distributional control within one cytoplasmic mass.

All of these adaptations may ultimately be found to result from changed enzymatic activities (i.e., the enzymes may be altered, different enzymes may be produced, and so on). As an example, hemoglobin provides a clear demonstration of how the activity of a protein is affected by amino acid substitutions. The hemoglobin of each vertebrate shows optimal oxygen-carrying capacity near normal body temperatures; differences in hemoglobins between animals result from different primary protein structures of globins. All hemoglobins respond in the same basic way to altered temperature: a lowered affinity for oxygen when temperature rises, and an increased affinity as it falls (this response is an adaptation, since temperature can fall in the lung capillaries, where oxygen loading takes place). The changing affinity is probably caused by altered folding of globin in response to temperature; the effect is great if one compares hemoglobin from vertebrates well separated by evolution. For example, if a frog's body temperature has been raised to mammalian body temperature, the hemoglobin has such low affinity for oxygen that it cannot load; conversely, human hemoglobin chilled to temperatures common for amphibia cannot unload its oxygen. In a given species the effect may provide a physiological limitation on behavior. Thus, as a lizard's body and blood temperature rise above 40 degrees centigrade, hemoglobin can no longer load adequately and metabolism necessarily falls; clearly, the possibility of death is strong under such circumstances because effective behavior to counteract the high temperature might be precluded by the relative lack of oxygen.

The gross anatomy of homeotherms exhibits a number of adaptations that can be traced to temperature regulation. Body size of terrestrial mammals tends to be larger, and the limbs shorter, in temperate or cool latitudes than in tropical ones. Both properties obviously result from the relationship of the body mass, which is the source of heat, to the surface area, from which heat is lost. Although there are many exceptions to generalizations like these, it is correct to say that the small animal in a cold habitat must have extraordinary physiological or behavioral adaptations to survive. Two other generalizations that are more difficult to dispute are these: (1) the thickness and quality of insulation is greater in colder climates; (2) extremities show modifications designed to permit tolerance of low temperatures and continuing physiological functioning under conditions in which central body organs would be inoperative (an example of this type of modification is the nerve conduction discussed above).

We have mentioned several specializations of the extremities that permit survival in cold environments. In warm environments, the extremities, as sites of controlled heat loss, are equally important. The hairless tail of a muskrat, the horns of a goat, the tail of a beaver, the flippers of seals, the legs of birds, and the huge ears of a jackrabbit all function in this way. In these organs, insulation tends to be sparse, vasoconstriction and rete mirabili nets are well controlled, and biochemical specializations are present. A bird's body lacks sweat glands, and little water leaks through the skin.

Figure 2. Responses of a stork to altering environmental temperature. As room temperature (indicated by solid circles) rises, the respiratory rate (indicated by open circles) rises to increase evaporative cooling. In addition, the stork begins to urinate on its legs (see the bars at the top) so that evaporation from these uninsulated regions can aid the cooling process.
[After Kahl, M. P., Jr., *Physiol. Zool.* **36**, 1963.]

Hyperventilation and air sac evaporation, and radiation from the feather-less legs are the ways in which birds lower their body heat. Interestingly, an overheated wood stork will urinate on its long legs as often as once a minute, using evaporation from the warm legs as a means of lowering body heat.

The final article in this section provides a good view of how extreme temperatures affect the lives of mammals. After generalizing about physiology or morphology, it is often most instructive to return to specific examples of wild animals and to examine as many parameters of their biology as possible, for only in this way can perspective on laboratory results be gained. "Desert Ground Squirrels" by George Bartholomew and Jack Hudson is concerned with two kinds of ground squirrels living in a desert environment. The details of the temperature regulation and the water-balance physiology of these creatures are a remarkable lesson about mammalian evolution, and they show how a given habitat can be shared by species that do not really compete with each other.

Despite the many vertebrate adaptations to life in cold and hot environments, some animals simply avoid extremes of temperature by performing complex behavior. The best-known examples are those in response to incipient cold weather: namely, migration to warmer climates, or hibernation.

Hibernation of mammals, large or small, is the suspension of maintenance of high body temperature. It necessitates a long preparative period during which stores of body fat are built up. The endocrine system has a central function in coordinating the process. During hibernation, temperature regulation occurs about a new low "set point," usually near 5 degrees centigrade, and as little as 2 percent of normal body heat is produced. The basal metabolic rate may drop to 1 percent of the normal rate, and, as a result, physiological adjustments commensurate with low temperature and low metabolism operate. Although heart rate slows (in a ground squirrel, for example, from 200 beats per minute to 10 beats per minute), the organ continues to function normally as a pump. Clotting could result from the slow blood flow, but it does not, because of the altered clotting capacity of the plasma. Severe peripheral vasoconstriction is maintained, and it keeps central blood pressure high despite the low rate of pumping by the heart. Nerves continue to conduct impulses when the body temperature falls far below the normal blockage temperature for impulses. Neither the heart nor the brain of a nonhibernator can function at such low temperatures. Low rates of metabolism demand much less oxygen: this permits breathing in the ground squirrel to slow from 100 breaths per minute to 4 breaths. Awakening and rewarming at the normal termination of hibernation is a complex process in itself, and necessitates great energy expenditure; the squirrel can increase its body heat from 4 degrees centigrade to 35 degrees in only 4 hours.

Emergency control mechanisms operate during hibernation to awaken a mammal if the body temperature falls toward lethal cold. Shivering starts, the body warms, and behavior to avoid the danger can be initiated. This kind of response consumes large quantities of the animal's stored fat; this may make survival through the long winter period impossible, but, since stored food would be of little use to a frozen animal, the hibernator awakens!

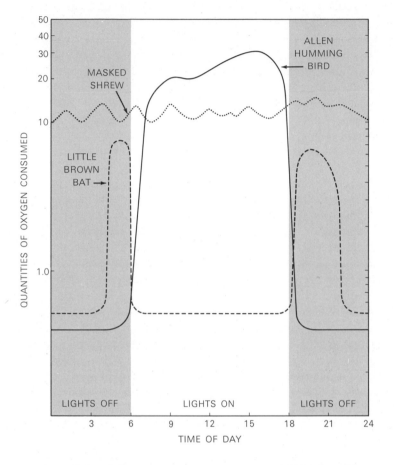

Figure 3. The pattern of metabolism (as reflected in quantities of oxygen consumed) of three small homeotherms (each weighs from 3 to 6 grams and so might be expected to have similar heat-balance problems). The animals were kept on a regular schedule of light and dark periods. The shrew maintains its high metabolic rate at all times. The hummingbird enters the state of torpor soon after the lights go off. The bat shows two activity periods, one in the "evening," soon after the lights are extinguished, and the other in the early "morning," just before they come on again. Note that the oxygen consumed is expressed on a logarithmic scale, and that the hummingbird's consumption falls more than thirtyfold during torpor.
[After Bartholomew, G.; in M. S. Gordon, ed., *Animal Function: Principles and Adaptations*, Macmillan, 1968.]

A parallel to hibernation is seen in many small birds and mammals that suspend high temperature maintenance each night and become torpid. This torpor is necessitated by the large relative surface areas of these animals and the resultant heat loss during periods of inactivity. Bats and hummingbirds become poikilotherms, and they show the same basic regulatory phenomena and awakening sequence, including repeated muscle flection, as is seen in hibernators. The amount of energy saved by torpor is significant: for a hummingbird, 10.3 kilocalories per 24 hours would be lost if sleeping took place at normal body temperatures, but only 7.6 kilocalories are lost in 24 hours if the torpid state is entered at night. If hummingbirds did not lower their nighttime temperature they would be unable to survive unless they awoke and fed during the night. This, of course, would require an additional set of special adaptations for navigation and food gathering in the dark. Such additional adaptations and continual activity at high metabolic rates would seem to be of little value for survival to reproduce; instead, small birds and mammals utilize torpidity and limited times of activity.

22

How Reptiles Regulate Their Body Temperature

CHARLES M. BOGERT · April 1959

More than 50 years ago Sir Charles Martin, a distinguished British physiologist, compared the regulation of body temperature in a number of mammals with that of a lizard. He showed that the mammals were able to maintain their temperatures within a fairly narrow range during wide variations in the temperature of the laboratory environment. The temperature of the lizard, on the other hand, rose and fell almost as rapidly as that of the environment. Observations of this sort long ago established the textbook aphorism to the effect that "reptiles have the temperature of the surrounding atmosphere."

It is true that reptiles are "cold-blooded" animals and have no mechanism of temperature regulation such as that of mammals. The laboratory observations correctly reflect what happens to a lizard's body temperature when the laboratory temperature is changed. But the conclusion drawn from these observations holds true only for the lizard in the laboratory. In their natural habitats during the day, lizards forage, mate, defend territories and flee at body temperatures that may be even higher than our own, and they maintain their temperatures within narrow limits despite wide variation in air temperature. The greater earless lizard (*Holbrookia texana*), an inhabitant of the foothills of the U. S. Southwest, has a mean temperature of 101.3 degrees Fahrenheit (38.5 degrees centigrade), slightly above our own, and while the lizard is active its temperature is within 3.3 de-

grees of this level 75 per cent of the time. At 14,600 feet in the Peruvian Andes, with the temperature of the thin air at the freezing point, Oliver P. Pearson of the University of California found that the lizard *Liolaemus multiformis* had a body temperature of 87.8 degrees F. (31 degrees C.); at temperatures as much as eight degrees below freezing he found other lizards abroad, a trifle sluggish, with body temperatures of 58 degrees (14.4 degrees C.), or 34 degrees above the temperature of the air. In my own studies over the past 14 years I have measured the temperatures of lizards of many different North American species. I have found that members of the same or closely related species show the same high and constant temperature in widely different

CHUCKWALLA (*Sauromalus obesus*) is found in deserts of the southwestern states. When this lizard cannot take shelter from the sun, it pants to cool itself by the evaporation of moisture from its lungs and places itself parallel to the sun's rays in order to expose a minimum of body surface to the radiant heat. This animal was photographed at three o'clock in the afternoon on a clear day.

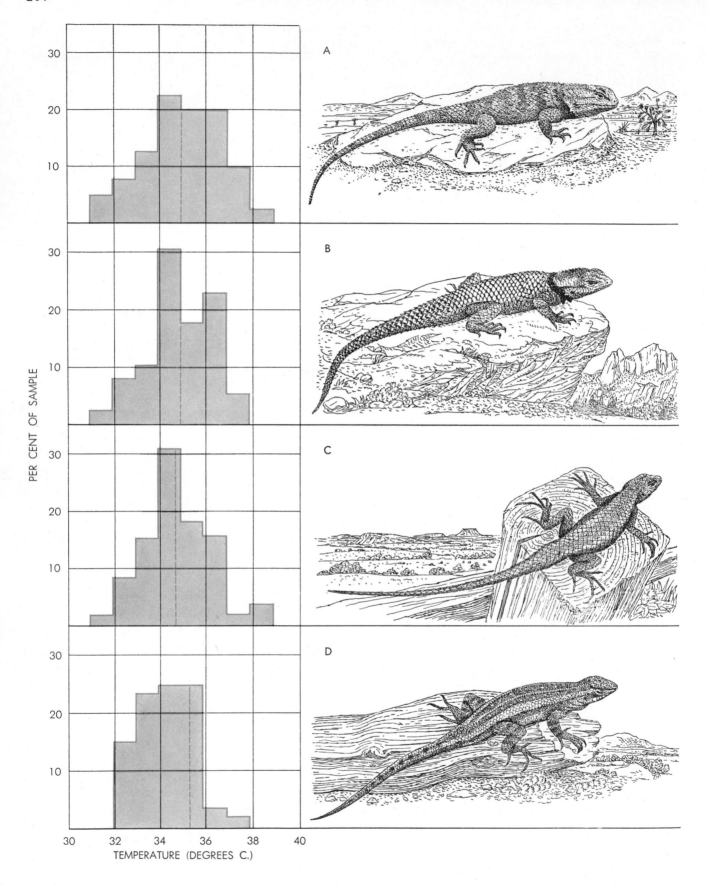

TEMPERATURES OF SPINY LIZARDS of four species were tested by the author, who sampled 39 or more active animals of each kind in their native habitats. In each species the average temperature (*broken line*) fell close to 35 degrees C. (95 degrees F.). The lizards tested were *Sceloporus magister* (A), *Sceloporus jarrovi* (B), *Sceloporus undulatus* (C), *Sceloporus variabilis* (D).

environments, although members of distantly related species maintain distinctly different mean temperatures in the same environment.

Why were the laboratory observations so misleading? For much the same reason that a man with a heavy iron ball chained to one leg cannot demonstrate how fast he can run! The analogy is to the point, because lizards regulate their temperatures to a large degree by their behavior. Many of these creatures are "heliotherms," deriving the heat they need to energize their body chemistry directly from the sun. In consequence of this dependence they have developed basking to a fine art. Lizards do not merely crawl out of their nocturnal shelter and rest in the sunlight. When their temperatures are below the threshold for normal activity, they orient their bodies at right angles to the sun's rays in order to maximize their exposure and even seek inclined surfaces to achieve such orientation with respect to the slanting rays of the morning sun. In the desert, where the ground becomes warmer than the air, lizards often press their bodies close to the surface, shifting slowly from side to side in the loose sand to secure better conduction of heat. On a rocky mountainside that warms up more slowly, they do their basking on mats of dead grass that insulate them from the cold ground. When a lizard's temperature approaches the upper limit of tolerance, on the other hand, it faces the sun, exposing the least possible surface, or returns to cooler temperatures in the shade or underground.

The size and shape of their bodies and the pigmentation of their skins play a part in determining and regulating the rate at which lizards absorb heat from their surroundings. But the decisive factor is behavior. In the artificial situation of the laboratory the lizard could not show what it can do.

When our department at the American Museum of Natural History and R. B. Cowles of the University of California at Los Angeles undertook to study heat regulation in reptiles, we had a general understanding of the factors involved. We expected to find, however, that temperature tolerances played an important part in determining the distribution of species and that the various species would show different optimal body temperatures in their various environments. In framing these assumptions, it turned out, we underestimated the efficiency of our subjects' heat-regulating behavior and equipment.

We chose the spiny lizards as our subjects, because their 50 species are abundant all over North America, from coast to coast and from southern Canada to Panama. Few groups of lizards have penetrated more environments. As many as five species may occur in a single locality, each in its own ecological niche. Some live on the ground, others on trees or shrubs; they variously frequent rocky hillsides, canyon walls, sand dunes, grassy plains and even human habitations. We sought them out in coastal areas, foothills, plateaus and mountains; in arid regions with little vegetation; in pine barrens, short-tree forests, pine forests and high-altitude cloud forests. We made our measurements in habitats ranging from sea level to near the timber line at 12,500 feet on the Nevado de Toluca in Mexico.

In all of this diversity of habitat, to our surprise, measurements indicate that spiny lizards go about their active lives at a mean body temperature of about 93 degrees (34 degrees C.). This approximates the average for all species, but does not imply that spiny lizards

have no leeway in temperature. They function at apparently full efficiency with body temperatures between 86 and 104 degrees (30 and 40 degrees C.). In their natural environments, however, these extremes are exceptional. Once their basking has brought them to the temperature threshold at which activity begins, spiny lizards maintain their body temperatures within 4.5 degrees of the 93-degree mean for about 80 per cent of the time and over the entire range of environmental temperature to which they voluntarily subject themselves during their daily routine.

These lizards regulate their heat intake largely by exposing themselves to direct sunlight, prolonging their forays by suitably orienting their bodies to the sun much as they do when basking, or by retreating from the sunlight when their temperatures run high. Comparisons of the temperature curves of various spiny lizards reveal only minor differences between species. Most of the peaks fall near the 93-degree average for the group. For species living in the tropical lowlands of Mexico and Honduras,

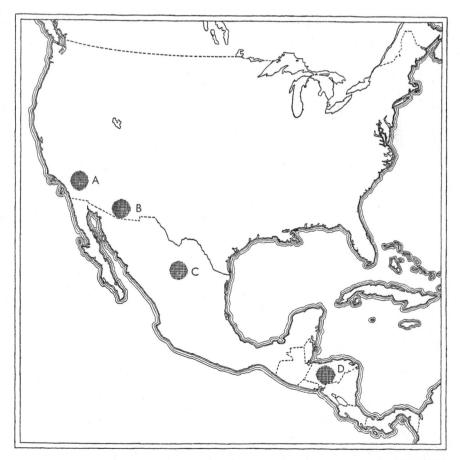

HABITATS of the lizards shown on the opposite page are marked with the corresponding letters on this map. They are (A) the Mojave Desert of California, elevation 3,000 to 4,000 feet; (B) the Chiricahua Mountains of Arizona, elevation 5,000 to 9,000 feet; (C) La Goma, Durango, Mexico, elevation 4,000 feet; (D) El Zamorano, Honduras, 2,600 to 3,000 feet.

REGAL HORNED LIZARDS (*Phrynosoma solare*) **weighing respectively 12.4 grams (A), 29.4 grams (B) and 85.5 grams (C) were exposed to the midday sun while their body temperatures were** continuously measured by means of wires from the cloaca of each to a recording potentiometer. The colors of the lizards were nearly the same at start but then changed, smallest lizard becoming palest.

the curves shift scarcely three or four degrees toward the warmer end of the scale. For those in higher mountains, the shift is two or three degrees toward the lower end of the scale.

We do not know whether such slight differences result from variations in the physiological adaptation of the animals or from the limitations of behavioral regulation. We sometimes lose sight of the fact that temperature refers to the amount of heat per unit of mass, or the degree of heat concentration, as measured on one scale or another. Optimum heat concentrations for biological processes, however, lie not at points but within zones on the scale. The "normal temperature" of human beings is actually an average for a zone between limits set roughly at 98 to 99.5 degrees (37 to 37.5 degrees C.). Hence the differences observed between the mean temperatures of the spiny lizard in different environments may still lie within the zone of optimum temperature for their biological activity.

In the Arizona desert the air temperatures recorded at sites of capture averaged 90 degrees (32.2 degrees C.); the temperature of the spiny lizards averaged 95 degrees (35 degrees C.). In contrast, the average body temperature of cloud-forest lizards is 91 degrees (32.8 degrees C.) when the air around them averages 66 degrees. The greater differential between air and body temperature in the case of the cloud-forest lizard should accelerate the loss of heat to the air. Nevertheless the lizards absorb enough solar heat to compensate for these losses and thus keep their body temperature within the zone permitting them to be active.

So, we learned, spiny lizards do not have different body temperatures reflecting different physiological adaptation to different environmental temperatures. Instead these reptiles restrict the fluctuation of their body temperature to a relatively narrow zone suitable to the similar physiological needs of all species. Probably the optimum zone for activity in spiny lizards is an ancestral trait. If so, their physiological adaptation became stabilized for a narrow zone centering around 93 degrees early in the evolution of the stock. The subsequent diversification and dispersal of the stock is largely a history of changes in such characteristics as size, shape, pigmentation and basking behavior, as species after species became adapted for survival under various combinations of environmental conditions.

From one standpoint the evolution of the spiny lizard, as a minor current in the broad stream of evolution, followed the course of least resistance. Once the delicate equilibrium of its physiological processes had been established in a particular zone of temperature, any adaptation to lower internal temperatures would have entailed revision of the whole complex system. The lizard's behavior, on the other hand, provided the necessary leeway to permit it to invade different environments successfully. There, under the pressure of selection, the various species developed adaptations in pigmentation and other physical characteristics associated with the regulation of body heat.

Spiny lizards are not the only lizards whose normal physiological activity is restricted to a narrow zone of temperature characteristic of the group as a whole. Other groups exhibit a similar identity. The whip-tailed lizards (*Cnemidophorus*), with species widely distributed in North, Central and South America, are active at body temperatures in a zone higher on the scale. They maintain a mean temperature close to 104 or 106 degrees (40 or 41 degrees C.), with no significant difference between the temperatures of populations in climates and landscapes as widely different as Arizona, Florida and Honduras.

Whip-tailed and spiny lizards often occur side by side in the same habitat. Invariably they show an average difference of 10 or 12 degrees between the means of their respective ranges in temperature, even though the identical sources of external heat are available to both. This alone is evidence of the effectiveness of behavioral control of heat intake and dissipation, augmented by pigmentation and enhanced by adaptation in structure.

This interaction of structure and behavior makes it difficult to design experiments testing one or another of the reptile's temperature-regulating at-

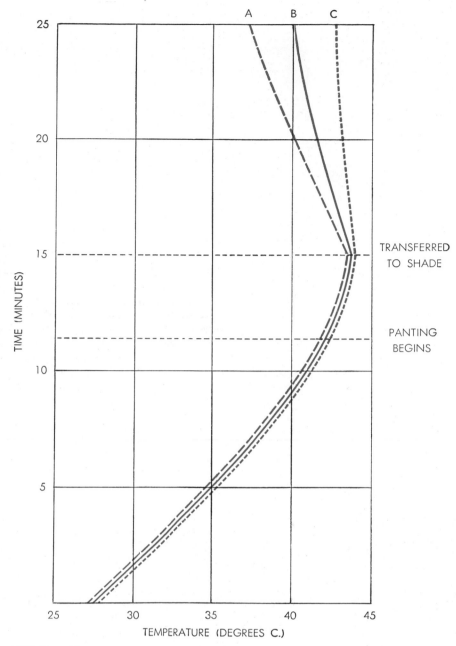

TEMPERATURE CURVES of the three lizards in the experiment depicted on page 108 were virtually identical as the animals absorbed heat. The smaller animals lightened in color, which aided the absorption of heat and compensated for their smaller ratio of surface to mass. Actually the lines on the chart were nearly superimposed. They were separated by transferring the smallest lizard (A) to the shade, while the next largest lizard (B) had only its head in the sun and the largest lizard (C) had its head and half its body in the sun.

tributes. Unquestionably size is subject to adaptive changes. Whenever we compare adequate samples from various portions of the range of a widely distributed reptile, we nearly always find that the average size of adults in one area is larger than that of adults in another area. Often the trend in size parallels the trend in climate, with the larger animals restricted to warmer areas or to regions with longer growing-seasons. Such correlations are suggestive, but without experimental evidence we cannot be certain that heat and size are directly re-

lated. The length or bulk of a reptile may be governed by such other variables as the food supply or gene combinations.

The problem of evaluating the adaptive significance of size is not simplified by the existence of adults and young of the same species in the same environments at the same time. In the desert-dwelling whip-tailed lizard (*Cnemidophorus tigris*) we found that juveniles of the species, weighing two or three grams, keep their bodies at mean temperatures identical with those of

TEXAS HORNED LIZARD, like the regal horned lizard, has the ability to change the color of its skin. When its body temperature is low, the animal is quite dark (*left*), but the same animal becomes paler (*right*) after it has been exposed to higher temperatures.

adults weighing up to 16 grams. However, we found a difference between adults and juveniles when we recorded the daily variation of their temperatures. The smaller lizards restrict their temperature fluctuations to a narrow zone of five or six degrees, while the activity zones in adults range over 10 or 11 degrees, from 99 to 110 degrees (37.2 to 43.3 degrees C.). The juveniles may be more responsive to heat and so may adjust their exposure more sensitively, or their body temperature may adjust more quickly by virtue of their smaller bulk.

Other things being equal, the temperature of a smaller lizard should rise or fall faster because it has more surface in proportion to its mass. In the first rough experiment we performed to test the validity of this generalization from the physics of inanimate objects, however, we discovered how important "other things" can be if they are not equal. Our subjects were adult specimens of two species of spiny lizard. The larger of the two was a green spiny lizard (*Sceloporus formosus*), a species restricted to open areas in moist forests of broad-leaved trees at elevations above 5,000 feet in central Honduras; its green

skin is marked with black pigment sparsely distributed in a reticulated pattern of lines and smaller blotches. The other was a much smaller, slate-colored spiny lizard (*Sceloporus variabilis*) that lives at elevations up to 3,000 feet in the arid valleys below the cloud forests on the mountain summits. In their very different environments the two species keep nearly the same average body temperature.

Though our two specimens had roughly the same bodily proportions, the greenish one, weighing 27.8 grams, had four times the bulk of the other, which weighed only 6.9 grams. The temperature of both lizards was 77 degrees (25 degrees C.) when they were placed in full sunlight with the air temperature at about 90 degrees. Temperatures were recorded at intervals of three minutes. During the first nine minutes the body temperature of the larger lizard lagged less than a degree behind that of the smaller lizard. But after 12 minutes the temperature of the larger lizard rose slightly above that of the smaller. At the conclusion of the experiment, after 18 minutes, the temperature of the larger lizard was 109 degrees (43 degrees C.),

and that of the smaller was 108.7 degrees (42.6 degrees C.). If the two lizards had absorbed heat at rates predicated solely on their weight, the heavier should have required approximately 10 more minutes to reach the temperature attained by the smaller animal in 18 minutes. Though inexact, the results of our simple experiment suggest that the cloud-forest lizard is better equipped, figuratively, "to make hay while the sun shines." Because the pigments in its skin absorb heat so rapidly, it can attain its threshold temperature quickly enough and often enough during the year to permit it to forage and fuel itself.

We suspected that the outcome of this experiment may have been influenced by changes in the pigmentation of one or the other reptile in the course of the experiment. To find out how important such changes are in regulating the absorption of heat we performed an experiment with individuals of different weights but belonging to the same species. This time we used regal horned lizards (*Phrynosoma solare*) weighing respectively 12.4, 29.4 and 85.5 grams. The experiment was conducted in

August on a clear day, with no wind, in the foothills of the Chiricahua Mountains in Arizona. The body temperature of each lizard was 80 degrees (27 degrees C.) at the start of the experiment; within 15 minutes their temperatures simultaneously reached 109 degrees (43 degrees C.), with the curves on the recording instrument indicating that they had risen at a virtually identical rate. About halfway through the experiment the temperature of the smallest lizard ran a degree ahead of the others, but shifted back to the curves being plotted for the other two, as though some mechanism were regulating the rate of heat absorption. This proved to be the case. Although the three lizards were not conspicuously different in color at the beginning of the experiment, we could discern distinct differences at the conclusion. The largest lizard was the darkest of the three, and the smallest lizard the palest.

While their broadly flattened bodies are adapted for the rapid absorption of heat, it is apparent that horned lizards are equally well equipped by pigmenta-tion to regulate the rate at which they absorb heat. The black-pigmented cells, or melanophores, of their skin expand laterally when the animal is cold, thus darkening the body and increasing the rate at which it absorbs radiant energy. When the body is warm, the same cells contract, thereby exposing light pigments in adjacent cells that reflect infra-red radiation. To match such efficiency we would need a mechanism that automatically exchanged our dark winter clothing for white linens with the advent of hot weather.

There appears to be an upper limit of bulk beyond which behavioral and physiological adaptations can no longer secure adequate regulation of a reptile's internal body heat. At the Archbold Biological Station in Florida, E. H. Colbert, R. B. Cowles and I conducted a suggestive experiment with a five-foot, 30-pound alligator as the subject. We found that it took the summer sun 7.5 minutes to increase the animal's temperature by two degrees. To see what this signifies for large reptiles, let us consider the plight of a 10-ton dinosaur under the same circumstances. This creature would have to bask in a blazing sun for more than an hour to elevate its body temperature to the same extent. Suppose our hypothetical dinosaur were active in daytime, and subject to cooling at night, as it would be in any desert region today. If its temperature dropped even four or five degrees below its threshold for activity, the dinosaur would have to bask for a large part of the following day in order to regain the threshold temperature of activity. The odds favor the deduction that dinosaurs, at least the larger ones, lived under fairly constant environmental temperatures. This is an important piece of evidence favoring the conclusion that the earth's climate was once quite uniformly tropical, for the distribution of fossils shows that the large dinosaurs roamed the earth far beyond the borders of the modern tropics.

All the truly large reptiles still abroad in the world today—pythons in Asia as long as 33 feet, anacondas in South America as long as 28 feet, monitor liz-

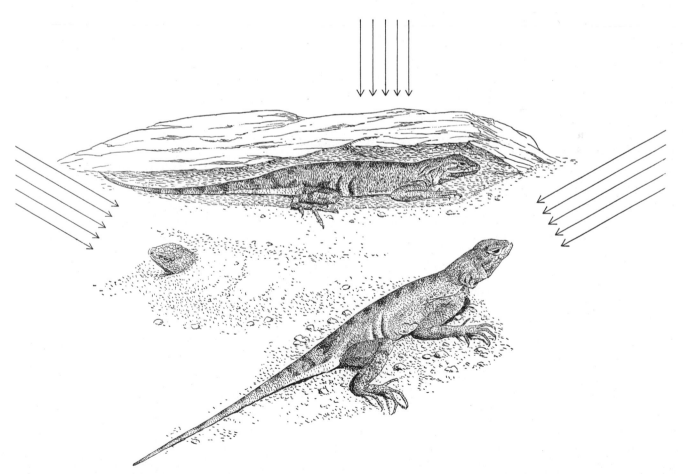

EARLESS LIZARD of the Southwest regulates its temperature within narrow limits by means of its behavior. The morning sun (*arrows at left*) warms the blood in the animal's head while the rest of it remains hidden in the sand until it is warm enough to be active. At noon (*top*) the lizard seeks shelter from the hot sun, but later it emerges and lies parallel to the sun's rays (*bottom*).

ards in Indonesia as long as 10 feet, crocodilians in the Americas as long as 23 feet and tortoises in the Galápagos Islands weighing more than 500 pounds—are residents of the tropics. The only exception is the enormous leatherback turtle *Dermochelys*, which is known to reach and possibly to exceed 1,500 pounds and is perhaps the largest living reptile. But this creature is protected by the constant warmth of its oceanic environment. The occasional specimen that turns up on the coast of Nova Scotia is probably carried there by the Gulf Stream.

In general the tropics afford stable temperatures that fluctuate in the narrow and comfortable range from 68 to 86 degrees year in and year out. The hottest places on earth are found not in the tropics but in the desert regions of the zones so inappropriately called "temperate." In winter these same deserts may be bitterly cold, and the daily fluctuation in temperature throughout the year far exceeds any encountered in the tropics. The night temperature of a tropical forest may drop only a few degrees below that of the day. Thus none of the large reptiles is ever exposed to either the freezing or the high temperatures encountered by reptiles in the middle-latitude deserts.

The green iguana (*Iguana iguana*), the largest lizard found on the American continent, illustrates the dependence of large reptiles on the constancy of the tropical temperature-environment. This animal, widely distributed in the lowlands of Latin America, reaches a length of at least 5.5 feet and a weight of 13 pounds. In a population we studied on the west coast of Mexico we found that the body temperature of the green iguana fluctuates much more than smaller lizards living in the same area or in the deserts 700 miles to the north. Green iguanas spend virtually all of their time high up in the crowns of large trees, feeding on leaves, buds or fruits during the day, and sleeping at night with only branches or foliage to conceal them from predators and to protect them from heat loss. They evidently do some basking; we found that the temperatures of nearly 50 iguanas were 10 to 15 degrees above the level of the air. But it is doubtful that there has ever been sufficient stress from heat fluctuations in the environment of the green iguana to induce adaptive changes in its behavior.

We had an opportunity to test this supposition by exposing several green iguanas to summer conditions in the desert. Instead of fleeing from the heat of direct sunlight, as any reptile native to the desert would have done, they literally sat in the sun until they died. The increase in their body temperatures was slowed a little by respiratory cooling when their breathing turned to panting, but this merely prolonged their discomfiture before breathing stopped. Green iguanas are equally unprepared for exposure to low temperatures. One specimen at the San Diego Zoo had to be moved indoors overnight because it showed no disposition to seek shelter of its own accord. However, one evening preceding a cold snap the creature chanced to be overlooked. Next morning it was found in a state of cold narcosis,

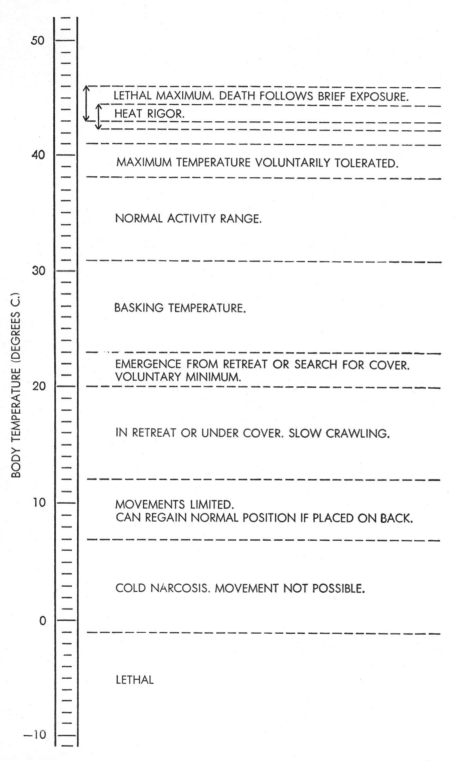

SIGNIFICANCE OF BODY TEMPERATURE to the behavior of reptiles is indicated by this chart giving the approximate temperatures for various activities of spiny lizards. The effects of exposure to heat levels near the extremes depend on duration. Even temperatures near the upper limit for the lizards' normal activity become lethal if exposure is prolonged.

suspended by a single claw accidentally hooked to a twig.

Considering that all reptiles would be just about equally vulnerable to cold and heat were it not for their behavioral adaptations, it is remarkable that so many lizard species are established in the temperate zone. It should be noted that snakes and turtles also have adapted themselves by much the same means to survive in rigorous climates. Snakes in particular have gotten around the surface-to-mass limitation by the lengthening of their bodies, which exposes more surface per unit of mass to absorb solar energy. In Canada snakes outnumber lizards and turtles combined, and in Europe one viper (*Vipera berus*) has penetrated to regions within the Arctic Circle. However, one European lizard (*Lacerta vivipara*) ranges even farther to the north, farther from the Equator than any other living reptile.

In common with the majority of reptiles near the northern limit of their distribution, both the snake and the lizard give birth to living young. Some snakes and lizards transfer nutrients and oxygen from maternal blood to the developing embryo by means of mammal-like placental structures. Most of these live-bearing reptiles, however, incubate the eggs within the body of the female, where behavioral regulation of temperatures keeps the eggs at heat levels within the optimum zone for development. Such modification of the reproductive pattern, peculiar to lizards and snakes, gives them a leeway in dispersal not open to turtles and crocodilians. Snakes and lizards are accordingly the most widely distributed reptiles, with lizards having a slight edge in number of species. Of the two groups it is the lizard that best exemplifies the complexity of adaptations involving the coordination of structure, physiology and behavior in response to the interplay of selective forces in the environment.

Perhaps the most amazing behavioral adaptation is that of the earless lizard, which is almost never found abroad with its body temperature below 96 degrees. We exposed its secret only by observing what it did in a laboratory cage provided with sources of radiant heat. From its overnight retreat, submerged in the sand, the earless lizard first thrusts its inconspicuous head above the surface; there it waits until the blood coursing through a large sinus in its head has absorbed enough heat from the sunlight to raise the temperature of its entire body. When its temperature is well above the threshold for efficient activity, this wary reptile emerges from the sand, preheated and ready to take off at top speed.

23

Adaptations to Cold

LAURENCE IRVING · January 1966

All living organisms abhor cold. For many susceptible forms of life a temperature difference of a few degrees means the difference between life and death. Everyone knows how critical temperature is for the growth of plants. Insects and fishes are similarly sensitive; a drop of two degrees in temperature when the sun goes behind a cloud, for instance, can convert a fly from a swift flier to a slow walker. In view of the general hostility of cold to life and activity, the ability of mammals and birds to survive and flourish in all climates is altogether remarkable.

It is not that these animals are basically more tolerant of cold. We know from our own reactions how sensitive the human body is to chilling. A naked, inactive human being soon becomes miserable in air colder than 28 degrees centigrade (about 82 degrees Fahrenheit), only 10 degrees C. below his body temperature. Even in the Tropics the coolness of night can make a person uncomfortable. The discomfort of cold is one of the most vivid of experiences; it stands out as a persistent memory in a soldier's recollections of the unpleasantness of his episodes in the field. The coming of winter in temperate climates has a profound effect on human wellbeing and activity. Cold weather, or cold living quarters, compounds the misery of illness or poverty. Over the entire planet a large proportion of man's efforts, culture and economy is devoted to the simple necessity of protection against cold.

Yet strangely enough neither man nor other mammals have consistently avoided cold climates. Indeed, the venturesome human species often goes out of its way to seek a cold environment, for sport or for the adventure of living in a challenging situation. One of the

marvels of man's history is the endurance and stability of the human settlements that have been established in arctic latitudes.

The Norse colonists who settled in Greenland 1,000 years ago found Eskimos already living there. Archaeologists today are finding many sites and relics of earlier ancestors of the Eskimos who occupied arctic North America as long as 6,000 years ago. In the middens left by these ancient inhabitants are bones and hunting implements that indicate man was accompanied in the cold north by many other warm-blooded animals: caribou, moose, bison, bears, hares, seals, walruses and whales. All the species, including man, seem to have been well adapted to arctic life for thousands of years.

It is therefore a matter of more than idle interest to look closely into how mammals adapt to cold. In all climates and everywhere on the earth mammals maintain a body temperature of about 38 degrees C. It looks as if evolution has settled on this temperature as an optimum for the mammalian class. (In birds the standard body temperature is a few degrees higher.) To keep their internal temperature at a viable level the mammals must be capable of adjusting to a wide range of environmental temperatures. In tropical air at 30 degrees C. (86 degrees F.), for example, the environment is only eight degrees cooler than the body temperature; in arctic air at −50 degrees C. it is 88 degrees colder. A man or other mammal in the Arctic must adjust to both extremes as seasons change.

The mechanisms available for making the adjustments are (1) the generation of body heat by the metabolic burning of food as fuel and (2) the use

of insulation and other devices to retain body heat. The requirements can be expressed quantitatively in a Newtonian formula concerning the cooling of warm bodies. A calculation based on the formula shows that to maintain the necessary warmth of its body a mammal must generate 10 times more heat in the Arctic than in the Tropics or clothe itself in 10 times more effective insulation or employ some intermediate combination of the two mechanisms.

We need not dwell on the metabolic requirement; it is rarely a major factor. An animal can increase its food intake and generation of heat to only a very modest degree. Moreover, even if metabolic capacity and the food supply were unlimited, no animal could spend all its time eating. Like man, nearly all other mammals spend a great deal of time in curious exploration of their surroundings, in play and in family and social activities. In the arctic winter a herd of caribou often rests and ruminates while the young engage in aimless play. I have seen caribou resting calmly with wolves lying asleep in the snow in plain view only a few hundred yards away. There is a common impression that life in the cold climates is more active than in the Tropics, but the fact is that for the natural populations of mammals, including man, life goes on at the same leisurely pace in the Arctic as it does in warmer regions; in all climates there is the same requirement of rest and social activities.

The decisive difference in resisting cold, then, lies in the mechanisms for conserving body heat. In the Institute of Arctic Biology at the University of Alaska we are continuing studies that have been in progress there and elsewhere for 18 years to compare the

ARCTIC ZONE (20 TO −60 DEGREES C.)

TEMPERATE ZONE (20 TO −20 DEGREES C.)

TROPICAL ZONE (35 TO 25 DEGREES C.)

RANGE OF TEMPERATURES to which warm-blooded animals must adapt is indicated. All the animals shown have a body temperature close to 100 degrees Fahrenheit, yet they survive at outside temperatures that, for the arctic animals, can be more than 100 degrees cooler. Insulation by fur is a major means of adaptation to cold. Man is insulated by clothing; some other relatively hairless animals, by fat. Some animals have a mechanism for conserving heat internally so that it is not dissipated at the extremities.

AIR (0 DEGREES C.)

WATER (0 DEGREES C.)

TEMPERATURE GRADIENTS in the outer parts of the body of a pig (*left*) and of a seal (*right*) result from two effects: the insulation provided by fat and the exchange of heat between arterial and venous blood, which produces lower temperatures near the surface.

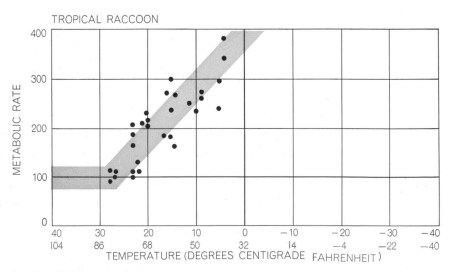

RATE OF METABOLISM provides a limited means of adaptation to cold. The effect of declining temperatures on the metabolic rate is shown for an Eskimo dog (*top*), an arctic lemming (*middle*) and a tropical raccoon (*bottom*). Animals in warmer climates tend to increase metabolism more rapidly than arctic animals do when the temperature declines.

mechanisms for conservation of heat in arctic and tropical animals. The investigations have covered a wide variety of mammals and birds and have yielded conclusions of general physiological interest.

The studies began with an examination of body insulation. The fur of arctic animals is considerably thicker, of course, than that of tropical animals. Actual measurements showed that its insulating power is many times greater. An arctic fox clothed in its winter fur can rest comfortably at a temperature of −50 degrees C. without increasing its resting rate of metabolism. On the other hand, a tropical animal of the same size (a coati, related to the raccoon) must increase its metabolic effort when the temperature drops to 20 degrees C. That is to say, the fox's insulation is so far superior that the animal can withstand air 88 degrees C. colder than its body at resting metabolism, whereas the coati can withstand a difference of only 18 degrees C. Naked man is less well protected by natural insulation than the coati; if unclothed, he begins shivering and raising his metabolic rate when the air temperature falls to 28 degrees C.

Obviously as animals decrease in size they become less able to carry a thick fur. The arctic hare is about the smallest mammal with enough fur to enable it to endure continual exposure to winter cold. The smaller animals take shelter under the snow in winter. Weasels, for example, venture out of their burrows only for short periods; mice spend the winter in nests and sheltered runways under the snow and rarely come to the surface.

No animal, large or small, can cover all of its body with insulating fur. Organs such as the feet, legs and nose must be left unencumbered if they are to be functional. Yet if these extremities allowed the escape of body heat, neither mammals nor birds could survive in cold climates. A gull or duck swimming in icy water would lose heat through its webbed feet faster than the bird could generate it. Warm feet standing on snow or ice would melt it and soon be frozen solidly to the place where they stood. For the unprotected extremities, therefore, nature has evolved a simple but effective mechanism to reduce the loss of heat: the warm outgoing blood in the arteries heats the cool blood returning in the veins from the extremities. This exchange occurs in the *rete mirabile* (wonderful net), a network of small arteries and veins near the junction between the trunk of the animal and the extremity [see "'The Wonderful Net,'" by P. F. Scholander, beginning on page 125 in this book]. Hence the extremities can become much colder than the body without either draining off body heat or losing their ability to function.

This mechanism serves a dual purpose. When necessary, the thickly furred animals can use their bare extremities to release excess heat from the body. A heavily insulated animal would soon be overheated by running or other active exercise were it not for these outlets. The generation of heat by exercise turns on the flow of blood to the extremities so that they radiate heat. The large, bare flippers of a resting fur seal are normally cold, but we have found that when these animals on the Pribilof Islands are driven overland at their laborious gait, the flippers become warm. In contrast to the warm flippers, the rest of the fur seal's body surface feels cold, because very little heat escapes through the animal's dense fur. Heat can also be dissipated by evaporation from the mouth and tongue. Thus a dog or a caribou begins to pant, as a means of evaporative cooling, as soon as it starts to run.

In the pig the adaptation to cold by means of a variable circulation of heat in the blood achieves a high degree of refinement. The pig, with its skin only thinly covered with bristles, is as naked as a man. Yet it does well in the Alaskan winter without clothing. We can read the animal's response to cold by its expressions of comfort or discomfort, and we have measured its physiological reactions. In cold air the circulation of heat in the blood of swine is shunted away from the entire body surface, so that the surface becomes an effective insulator against loss of body heat. The pig can withstand considerable cooling of its body surface. Although a man is highly uncomfortable when his skin is cooled to 7 degrees C. below the internal temperature, a pig can be comfortable with its skin 30 degrees C. colder than the interior, that is, at a temperature of 8 degrees C. (about 46 degrees F.). Not until the air temperature drops below the freezing point (0 degrees C.) does the pig increase its rate of metabolism; in contrast a man, as I have mentioned, must do so at an air temperature of 28 degrees C.

With thermocouples in the form of needles we have probed the tissues of pigs below the skin surface. (Some pigs, like some people, will accept a little

AIR −30 DEGREES C.

AIR −31 DEGREES C.

AIR −16 DEGREES C.

TEMPERATURES AT EXTREMITIES of arctic animals are far lower than the internal body temperature of about 38 degrees centigrade, as shown by measurements made on Eskimo dogs, caribou and sea gulls. Some extremities approach the outside temperature.

pain to win a reward.) We found that with the air temperature at −12 degrees C. the cooling of the pig's tissues extended as deep as 100 millimeters (about four inches) into its body. In warmer air the thermal gradient through the tissues was shorter and less steep. In short, the insulating mechanism of the hog involves a considerable depth of the animal's fatty mantle.

Even more striking examples of this kind of mechanism are to be found in whales, walruses and hair seals that dwell in the icy arctic seas. The whale and the walrus are completely bare; the hair seal is covered only with thin, short hair that provides almost no insulation when it is sleeked down in the water. Yet these animals remain comfortable in water around the freezing point although water, with a much greater heat capacity than air, can extract a great deal more heat from a warm body.

Examining hair seals from cold waters of the North Atlantic, we found that even in ice water these animals did not raise their rate of metabolism. Their skin was only one degree or so warmer than the water, and the cooling effect extended deep into the tissues—as much as a quarter of the distance through the thick part of the body. Hour after hour the animal's flippers all the way through would remain only a few degrees above freezing without the seals' showing any sign of discomfort. When the seals were moved into warmer water, their outer tissues rapidly warmed up. They would accept a transfer from warm water to ice water with equanimity and with no diminution of their characteristic liveliness.

How are the chilled tissues of all these animals able to function normally at temperatures close to freezing? There is first of all the puzzle of the response of fatty tissue. Animal fat usually becomes hard and brittle when it is cooled to low temperatures. This is true even of the land mammals of the Arctic, as far as their internal fats are concerned. If it were also true of extremities such as their feet, however, in cold weather their feet would become too inflexible to be useful. Actually it turns out that the fats in these organs behave differently from those in the warm internal tissues. Farmers have known for a long time that neat's-foot oil, extracted from the feet of cattle, can be used to keep leather boots and harness flexible in cold weather. By laboratory examination we have found that the fats in the bones of the lower leg and foot of the caribou remain soft even at 0 degrees C. The melting point of the fats in the leg steadily goes up in the higher portions of the leg. Eskimos have long been aware that fat from a caribou's foot will serve as a fluid lubricant in the cold, whereas the marrow fat from the upper leg is a solid food even at room temperature.

About the nonfatty substances in tissues we have little information; I have seen no reports by biochemists on the effects of temperature on their properties. It is known, however, that many of the organic substances of animal tissues are highly sensitive to temperature. We must therefore wonder how the tissues can maintain their serviceability over the very wide range of temperatures that the body surface experiences in the arctic climate.

We have approached this question by studies of the behavior of tissues at various temperatures. Nature offers many illustrations of the slowing of tissue functions by cold. Fishes, frogs and water insects are noticeably slowed down by cool water. Cooling by 10 degrees

AIR (0 DEGREES C.)

HOT PLATE
(37 DEGREES C.)

FUR

FUR

INSULATION BY FUR was tested in this apparatus, shown in a front view at left and a side view at right. The battery-operated heating unit provided the equivalent of body temperature on one side of the fur; outdoor temperatures were approximated on the other side.

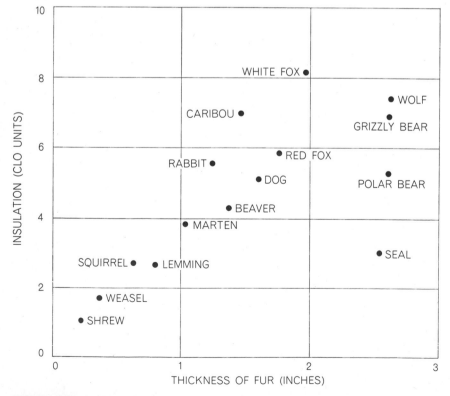

INSULATING CAPACITY of fur is compared for various animals. A "clo unit" equals the amount of insulation provided by the clothing a man usually wears at room temperature.

C. will immobilize most insects. A grasshopper in the warm noonday sun can be caught only by a swift bird, but in the chill of early morning it is so sluggish that anyone can seize it. I had a vivid demonstration of the temperature effect one summer day when I went hunting on the arctic tundra near Point Barrow for flies to use in experiments. When the sun was behind clouds, I had no trouble picking up the flies as they crawled about in the sparse vegetation, but as soon as the sun came out the flies took off and were uncatchable. Measuring the temperature of flies on the ground, I ascertained that the difference between the flying and the slow-crawling state was a matter of only 2 degrees C.

Sea gulls walking barefoot on the ice in the Arctic are just as nimble as gulls on the warm beaches of California. We know from our own sensations that our fingers and hands are numbed by cold. I have used a simple test to measure the amount of this desensitization. After cooling the skin on my fingertips to about 20 degrees C. (68 degrees F.) by keeping them on ice-filled bags, I tested their sensitivity by dropping a light ball (weighing about one milligram) on them from a measured height. The weight multiplied by the distance of fall gave me a measure of the impact on the skin. I found that the skin at a temperature of 20 degrees C. was only a sixth as sensitive as at 35 degrees C. (95 degrees F.); that is, the impact had to be six times greater to be felt.

We know that even the human body surface has some adaptability to cold. Men who make their living by fishing can handle their nets and fish with wet hands in cold that other people cannot endure. The hands of fishermen, Eskimos and Indians have been found to be capable of maintaining an exceptionally vigorous blood circulation in the cold. This is possible, however, only at the cost of a higher metabolic production of body heat, and the production in any case has a limit. What must arouse our wonder is the extraordinary adaptability of an animal such as the hair seal. It swims in icy waters with its flippers and the skin over its body at close to the freezing temperature, and yet under the ice in the dark arctic sea it remains sensitive enough to capture moving prey and find its way to breathing holes.

Here lies an inviting challenge for all biologists. By what devices is an animal able to preserve nervous sensitivity in tissues cooled to low temperatures? Beyond this is a more universal and more

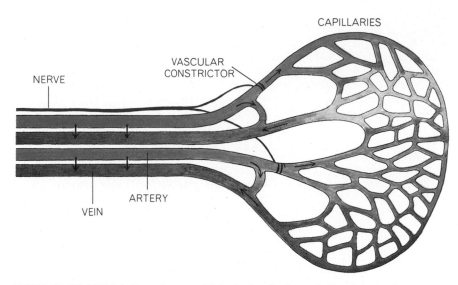

ROLE OF BLOOD in adaptation to cold is depicted schematically. One mechanism, indicated by the vertical arrows, is an exchange of heat between arterial and venous blood. The cold venous blood returning from an extremity acquires heat from an arterial network. The outgoing arterial blood is thus cooled. Hence the exchange helps to keep heat in the body and away from the extremities when the extremities are exposed to low temperatures. The effect is enhanced by the fact that blood vessels near the surface constrict in cold.

interesting question: How do the warm-blooded animals preserve their overall stability in the varying environments to which they are exposed? Adjustment to changes in temperature requires them to make a variety of adaptations in the various tissues of the body. Yet these changes must be harmonized to maintain the integration of the organism as a whole. I predict that further studies of the mechanisms involved in adaptation to cold will yield exciting new insights into the processes that sustain the integrity of warm-blooded animals.

FINGER EXPERIMENT performed by the author showed that the more a finger was chilled, the farther a one-milligram ball had to be dropped for its impact to be felt on the finger. The vertical scale is arbitrary but reflects the relative increase in the force of impact.

24

The Human Thermostat

T. H. BENZINGER · January 1961

Fever is usually the first symptom to arouse concern in illness. The rise in body temperature is not great in the absolute sense. On the contrary, the attention it attracts is a measure of the constancy with which the body temperature is normally maintained. Compared to the daily and seasonal variation in the temperature of "cold-blooded" animals, whose internal temperature depends upon that of the environment, a fever represents a tiny variation in temperature. Yet it is many times greater than the normal variation in the regulated temperature of the healthy body. In spite of large differences in environmental temperature—from the arctic tundra and windswept highlands to fiery deserts and steaming jungles, from season to season and from day to night—the body temperature departs little from the norm of 37 degrees centigrade (98.6 degrees Fahrenheit). Life in the cells continues undisturbed, although the metabolic processes are irrevocably linked to temperature by the laws of thermodynamics and the kinetics of chemical reactions.

Heat is a by-product of these processes. With the body at rest, the heat of basal metabolism easily supplies the necessary interior warmth when external conditions are comfortably cool. Only under extreme conditions does the system fail; as when, in a hot environment, physical effort fans the flame of the metabolic furnace beyond control by the regulatory system; or when, in a very cold environment, the loss of heat by radiation, conduction and convection overbalances the metabolic production of heat and reduces body temperature to a fatal degree. Man of course shares this vital capacity with other mammals and with birds. Favored in consequence with nervous systems maintained at optimal working temperatures under all environmental conditions, the "warm-blooded" animals have become masters of the living world on our planet.

The question of how the body keeps its temperature constant within such narrow limits has engaged the efforts of an astonishing number of investigators. It is only recently, however, that one of the two parts of the regulating mechanism—defense against overheating—has been clarified. Max Rubner of Berlin had recognized in 1900 that sweating and the dilation of the peripheral blood vessels constitute the effector mechanisms for the dissipation of excess heat from the body. E. Aronsohn and J. Sachs, two medical students at the University of Berlin, came upon the center of control in the brain as long ago as 1884, when they damaged in animals an area "adjacent to the corpus striatum toward the midline." A few months earlier Charles Richet of Paris had also produced excessive body temperature by puncturing the forebrain. It now seems certain that in both cases the investigators damaged the hypothalamus, an area at the base of the brain stem just above the crossing of the optic nerves.

But how does the body sense and measure its temperature and bring the control center into action? The investigation of this question was confused for a long time by the conspicuous part that the temperature-sensitive nerve endings in the skin play in the feeling of warmth and cold. In recent years, however, a new approach to the problem has been made possible by the development of a new principle of measurement called gradient calorimetry and of the instrumentation to go with it. Experiments employing this instrumentation have now located the sensory end-organ at which the body "takes" its own temperature when it becomes too warm. The discovery is an unusual one at this late date in the history of physiology. The body's "thermostat" must now be included in the short list of major sensory organs adapted to the primary reception and measurement of physical or chemical quantities. Moreover, it now becomes possible to measure the characteristic responses of the thermostat and perhaps to produce or to suppress those responses artificially. Such investigation will lead to a better understanding not only of the aberration of fever but also of the precise regulation of internal temperature that is so important to the vital function of the body, particularly to the function of the delicate nervous system. With the thermostat identified, it has also become possible to explain

TEMPERATURE AT THERMOSTAT in the brain is measured by thermocouples

placed at forward wall of ethmoid sinus ("a" *in diagram at left*), deep in rear wall of nasopharyngeal cavity (c) and at eardrum (d). Thermostat itself is in hypothalamus behind sphenoid sinus (b), at which temperature has also been measured by thermocouple.

HEAT CONTROL CENTER is located in forward part of hypothalamus (*a*), shown in cross section (*left*) and from below (*right*). Hypothalamus, centrally located under great hemispheres of brain, rests on the Circle of Willis (*e*), an arterial ring through which

the effects of such mundane factors as a hot meal, a cold drink, a hot bath and a cold shower.

When one encounters a physical or chemical quantity in technology or in a living organism that is maintained at a constant level against disturbances from outside, one looks for a "servomechanism." Pressure, rate of flow, chemical composition or temperature are automatically controlled by such mechanisms in the realm of engineering. The servomechanisms of the body control the same kinds of variable. In manmade devices the chain of control begins with a "sensory" instrument, perhaps a thermometer, which measures the variable in question. The measurement is relayed to a "controller" which compares it with a set point to which the variable is to be held. Whenever the need arises,

the controller sends instruction to an "effector" mechanism, perhaps to the heating system, which brings the temperature into accord with the set point in the controller [see "Feedback," by Arnold Tustin; SCIENTIFIC AMERICAN, September, 1952].

The corresponding elements in biological servomechanisms and the nervous and chemical pathways that interconnect the sites of stimulus and response constitute systems of far greater complexity. They are nonetheless put together in a similar way. A servomechanism in the human body may be considered to be clarified when the sensory organ, the controller and the effector mechanism are known, and when a reproducible, inseparable and quantitative relation has been established between the magnitudes of the stimuli and of the responses they induce. The net

effect of the response must be the restoration of "homeostatic" equilibrium; that is, the variable in question must return to the optimum, stable level essential to the life of the cells.

In the control circuit that prevents overheating of the body, classical physiology had identified the effector and the controller mechanism, but not the sensory organ. In a hot environment, as Rubner showed, the effector is the dilation of the blood vessels in the skin, which increases the transport of heat from the interior of the body to the surface; and sweating, which increases the rate of total heat loss from the surface to the environment as energy is absorbed in evaporation. In a cold environment the corresponding mechanism is increased metabolic heat-production.

The location of the controller in the hypothalamus by Aronsohn and Sachs blood supply to the brain flows from carotid arteries (*c and c'*) and basilar artery (*d*). Hypothalamus, optic nerves (*b and b'*) and ret- ina derive from same tissue matrix. Bulb of pituitary gland attached to hypothalamus appears at left, but is cut away at right.

was confirmed by later investigators. Some of them applied the stimulus of temperature directly to the site. In 1904 Richard Hans Kahn of the German University in Prague found that heating the head arteries of a dog lowered its body temperature. In 1912 Henry Gray Barbour, a young American physician working in Vienna, carrying out an experiment designed by the pharmacologist H. Meyer, applied warm and cold probes to the general area of the hypothalamus. He observed the expected thermoregulatory responses. In 1938 Horace W. Magoun, now at the University of California at Los Angeles, discovered that this function is mediated by a circumscribed area in the forward part of the hypothalamus. Bengt Andersson of the Royal Swedish Veterinary Institute in 1956 delineated the organ with unprecedented precision in goats. In 1950 Curt

von Euler of the Nobel Neurophysiological Institute in Stockholm even succeeded in recording, in parallel with temperature changes, slow electrical "action potentials" from this area of the hypothalamus of cats.

But the body is also equipped with an elaborate system of millions of tiny sensitive nerve endings, distributed throughout the skin, which produce conscious sensations of warmth. The scientific literature tended to support the view that the skin and not the hypothalamus furnishes the primary temperature measurements to the control center for sweating and the dilation of the arteries. Some investigators held that both systems were involved; a rise in the temperature of the "heat center" in the hypothalamus supposedly made it more responsive to incoming impulses from the temperature-sensing organs of the skin. The

question, in this view, was one of determining the relative importance of the two sites. It was also possible, as some believed, that the body possessed a third area sensitive to temperature or heat flow, and that neither the skin nor the brain was involved.

It was not easy to design a conclusive experiment. In experimental animals one might destroy the nervous pathways from the thermoreceptors in the skin to the heat center. But the results of such an experiment would not exclude the possibility that the temperature of these centers played a role in heat regulation under normal conditions. It would still be necessary to carry out the reverse experiment and destroy the heat-sensitive part of the hypothalamus. Since this structure is intimately involved with the temperature-control center itself, it seems impossible to secure the final evidence by surgical procedures alone.

To observe the operation of sensory receptors in the skin and in the brain independently of each other in the intact organism presented comparable difficulties. No one, apparently, had succeeded in keeping one of the two sites at a constant temperature while observing the effects brought about by a temperature change in the other. This approach called for techniques to measure temperature in the human body at the two sites of presumed temperature-reception—the skin and the hypothalamus—and some way to record, rapidly and continuously, the effector responses of vasodilation and sweating.

The gradient calorimeter has satisfied the second of these two requirements. This rapidly responding and continuously recording successor to the classical calorimeter makes it possible to record for the first time the total output of the effector mechanisms. It measures separately the heat that is carried from the body by radiation and convection and the heat that is dissipated by the evaporation of sweat. From working models made and tested by Charlotte Kitzinger at the Naval Medical Research Institute in Bethesda, Md., the first full-scale human gradient calorimeter was constructed under the direction of Richard G. Huebscher at the laboratory of the American Society of Heating and Ventilating Engineers in Cleveland. Similar units have now been constructed at other laboratories. The gradient calorimeter now operated at Bethesda is a chamber large enough to hold a man stretched out at full length [see illustration below]. The subject is suspended in an open-weave sling, out of contact with the floor or walls of the chamber, and is free to go through the motions of prescribed exercise when the experiment calls for such exertion.

The new and essential feature of gradient calorimetry is the "gradient layer," a thin foil of material with a uniform resistance to heat flow which lines the entire inner surface of the chamber. Some thousands of thermoelectric junctions interlace the foil in a regular pattern and measure the local difference in temperature (and hence the local heat flow) at as many points across the foil. The junctions are wired in series; their readings are thus recorded in a single potential at the terminals of the circuit. That potential measures the total energetic output from the subject's skin, independent of his position with respect to the surfaces of the gradient layer lining the chamber. The rate of blood flow through the skin can be derived by computing this measurement against the temperature of the outgoing blood (measured internally) and the temperature of the returning blood (measured on the skin), since the observed transfer of heat per unit time at any given difference between internal and external temperature can be effected by only one calculable rate of blood flow. The energy dissipated by evaporation from the subject's skin is also measured by gradient layers which line heat-exchange meters at the inlet and outlet of the air circuit of the calorimeter. Measurements taken for control make it possible to maintain the same temperature and humidity in the air at these two points, so that the air neither gains nor loses energy as it passes through the system. The unbalanced output from the additional gradient layers thus precisely measures the heat loss by evaporation and hence the sweat-gland activity. Heat loss through the lungs is measured separately and subtracted from the total.

With the help of the gradient calorimeter our group at Bethesda set out to establish the correlations obtaining, on the one hand, between the performance of the effector mechanisms and the temperature of the skin and, on the other hand, between the performance of the effector mechanisms and the internal temperature of the body. In these first experiments it was assumed that rectal temperature provided an adequate index of internal temperature as measured at the internal temperature-sensing organ, wherever that might be located. But no correlation could be found, in either resting or "working" subjects, between rectal temperature and the observed rates of sweating. Measurement of skin temperature against the same heat-dissipation variable yielded equally meaningless plots. For a time it seemed that all the effort that had gone into the design of the gradient calorimeter had been wasted. The results made sense only in terms of the classical notion that the thermostat in the interior of the body and the temperature-sensing nerve endings in the skin have indissolubly interlaced effects upon the vasodilation and sweating responses.

Then we found a way to measure the internal temperature of the body at a site near the center of temperature regulation in the brain. We introduced a thermocouple through the outer ear canal and held it against the eardrum membrane under slight pressure. The eardrum is near the hypothalamus and shares a common blood supply with it from the internal carotid artery. At the

HUMAN GRADIENT CALORIMETER makes it possible to correlate body temperature with dissipation of heat by radiation and convection from skin and by evaporation of sweat. Lining of chamber is interlaced with thermoelectric junctions which measure heat loss from skin; loss by sweating is measured by temperature and humidity control system of calorimeter.

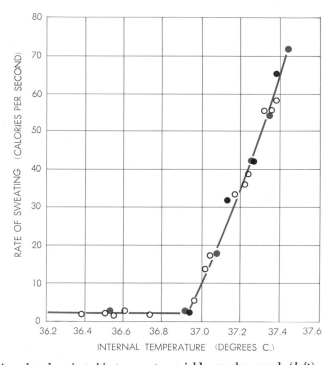

○ REST
● WORK (6 CALORIES PER SECOND)
● WORK (12 CALORIES PER SECOND)

HEAT DISSIPATION by sweating plotted against skin temperature yields senseless graph (*left*) when natural correlation between skin and internal temperature is broken by internal heating through exercise. When the same measurements of sweating are plotted instead against internal head temperature (*right*), an inseparable and always reproducible relation appears between the stimulus of temperature and the response of the sweat glands, whether the subject is sweating or not.

very first attempt we observed temperature changes associated with the eating of ice or the drinking of hot fluids, and we soon found we could detect variations caused by immersion of the limbs in warm water. Parallel rectal measurement did not show these variations at all. To make sure that the entire region of the head supplied by the carotid arteries can be expected to show the same temperature variations as the eardrum, we tried other sites. With the help of local anesthesia H. W. Taylor, a surgeon at the Naval Hospital in Bethesda, placed thermocouples in our heads: at the main trunk of the internal carotid in the rear of the nasopharyngeal cavity, in the nasal cavity below the forebrain and at the forward wall of the sphenoid sinus only one inch away from the hypothalamus [*see illustration on pages 228 and 229*]. Continuous measurements of temperature at these points showed large discrepancies with internal temperature as measured at the rectum.

The discrepancies appeared before and after the subject exerted himself by physical exercise, after internal cooling by the eating of ice, after warming the arms or legs in warm water and cooling them in cold water and after immersing the whole body in warm or cold water. These were precisely the situations in which earlier experimenters had found the same absence of correlation between

rectal temperature and the heat-dissipating responses of vasodilation and sweating. It was clear that the temperature at the rectum could under no circumstances be trusted as reflecting the temperature at the internal temperature-sensing organ. The hypothalamus was plainly the place to look for correlation between changes of internal temperature and the responses that regulate it. Since the eardrum is by all odds the most accessible of the four sites thus measured in the head, it was adopted in the experiments that followed. Readings could be taken here with an error of .01 degree centigrade against a standard of temperature maintained with an error of .002 degree C.

The subjects now spent time in the calorimeter on many different days at different environmental temperatures ranging from almost intolerably cold for the nude body at rest to almost intolerably hot for the subject undergoing exertion. Between these two extremes, measurements were made for all the intermediate levels at five-degree temperature intervals and with the subject at rest and at work. Under each set of circumstances the instruments kept a continuous record as the state of homeostasis was reached and maintained for one hour. This arduous series of experiments, extended over two months, made it possi-

ble to plot for the first time the heat-dissipating responses of vasodilation and sweating independently against skin temperature and against internal head temperature. The volunteer subject for this series, Lawrence R. Neff, was observed with a cool skin and cool interior (resting in a cold environment), with a cool skin and warm interior (working in a cold environment), with a hot skin and a relatively cool interior (resting in a hot environment) and with a hot skin and warm interior (working in a hot environment).

The records showed the familiar disordered relationship between the heat-dissipating responses and skin temperature. But the plot of the responses against eardrum temperature showed an almost perfect undisturbed relation. Whatever the temperature of the skin, one certain specific rate of sweating and no other invariably showed up in association with a given internal temperature measured at the eardrum. A reproducible, inseparable and quantitative relation between the stimulus of temperature and one of the heat-dissipating responses had at last been observed. It exhibited a sharply defined breakoff at 36.9 degrees C. (98.4 degrees F.). This was no doubt the set point of the human thermostat in this subject at the time of the experiment. The response proved to be so forceful that a mere .01-degree-C.

rise in temperature was sufficient to increase the dissipation of heat through sweating by one calorie per second and to raise the blood flow through the skin by 15 milliliters per minute.

The success of this series of experiments in distinguishing between the variations in skin and brain temperature was confirmed in many other experiments that subjected the body to quite different sets of extremes. In one of them the skin and the interior of the body were warmed as the subject accommodated himself in the calorimeter to an environmental temperature of 45 degrees C. (113 degrees F.). With homeostasis attained, the subject gulped down large measured helpings of sherbet three times at suitable intervals. On each occasion, as the melting ice withdrew heat from the internal organs and the circulating blood, the brain temperature declined. No less impressively, the skin temperature was observed to rise. The curve

RECTAL TEMPERATURE is shown in this graph to have an uncertain relationship to the hypothalamic temperature measured at the forward wall of the sphenoid sinus. The sphenoid temperature rises sharply as an experimental subject enters a warm bath and falls off sharply when the subject leaves the bath. The rectal temperature reaches a peak only after the subject has left the bath.

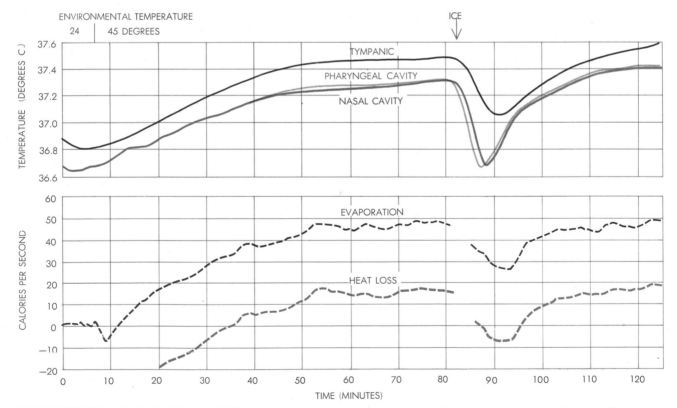

MEASUREMENTS OF HEAD TEMPERATURE at three points near the hypothalamus—at eardrum (tympanic), at ethmoid sinus (nasal cavity) and in rear wall of pharyngeal cavity—show close correspondence with one another and with the heat dissipation by evaporation of sweat and heat loss by vasodilation. Location of these points is shown in the illustration on pages 228 and 229.

drawn by sweat-gland activity now showed unequivocally which temperature-sensing system controls the heat-dissipating responses: the rate of sweating fell off and rose in perfect parallel with the decline and rise in internal head temperature. It was the consequent drying of the skin that caused the skin to be heated by radiation and conduction in the hot environment. But the sensory reception of heat in the skin brought no response from the heat-dissipating mechanism.

These observations accord well with the familiar constancy of the body temperature. It is difficult to see how it could be maintained within the same narrow range, year in and year out, if the heat-controlling responses were not always triggered at the same set point. As these experiments show, moreover, the responses always closely match the

magnitude of the stimulus. Such precise regulation of temperature could not be achieved by measurement of skin temperature. As in all feedback systems, the quantity which is controlled must itself be measured. An architect who wants to control the temperature of a house does not distribute thousands of thermometers over the outside walls. One thermostat in the living room suffices. It responds not only to warming and chilling from out-of-doors but to overheating from within. The thermostat in the hypothalamus similarly monitors the internal temperature of the body from the inside and thereby maintains its constancy.

This is not to say that the warm-sensitive nerve endings of the skin have no function in the regulation of body temperature. They are the sensory organs for another system which operates via the centers of consciousness in the cortex, bypassing the unconscious control

center in the hypothalamus. To sensations of heat or cold reported by the skin the body reacts by using the muscles as effector organs. Under the stimulus of discomfort from the extremes of both heat and cold, man seeks a cooler or a warmer environment or takes the measures necessary to make his environment comfortably cool or warm. But for all the mastery of external circumstances that follows from this linkage in the body's temperature-sensing equipment, the skin thermoreceptors cannot regulate internal temperature with any degree of precision. They can contribute directly to the regulation of skin temperature alone. The automatic system of hypothalamic temperature regulation takes over from there and achieves the final adjustment with almost unbelievable sensitivity and precision.

In the regulation of internal temperature, therefore, the hypothalamus can

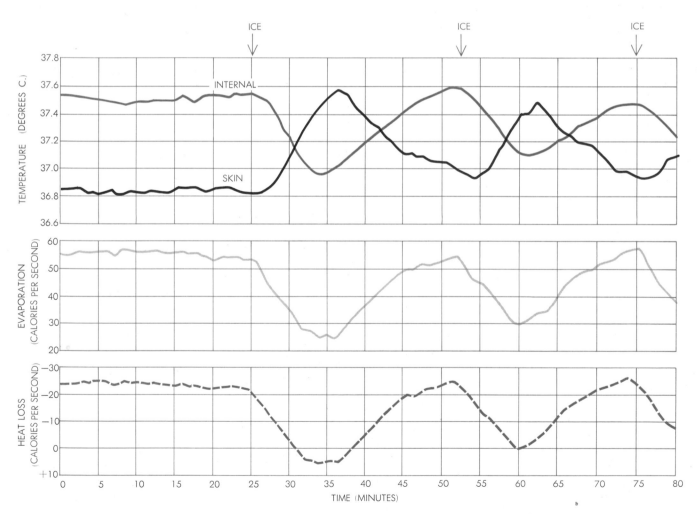

CONCLUSIVE EXPERIMENT establishing hypothalamic temperature as key to control of body temperature is charted. At left in top chart the subject's hypothalamic (internal) temperature is stabilized at the "normal" 37 degrees C. in an environment of 45 degrees C. (113 degrees F.). Upon ingestion of ice at half-hour intervals, internal temperature drops sharply and skin temperature ascends. In middle chart rate of sweating falls and rises in close correlation with hypothalamic temperature; shutdown of sweating accounts for rise in skin temperature. In bottom chart heat loss from skin shows same correlation with hypothalamic temperature.

no longer be regarded simply as a controller which converts incoming sensory stimuli into outgoing impulses to the effector system. It is itself the site of a receptor end-organ, an "eye" for temperature comparable to the retina—the receptor organ for light. This analogy between the temperature eye and the optical eye has, in fact, a sound anatomical basis. Both are derived from the same matrix: the bottom of the third ventricle of the brain. These are two parts of the brain that have a proved sensory receptor function. In the course of evolution the optical eye moved outward to connect with a dioptric apparatus partly derived from the skin, and thereby gained a view of the external world. The temperature eye in the hypothalamus is located in the interior of the head, where it properly belongs. It measures as well as regulates the temperature of the blood which bathes its cells and the rest of the brain, the vital function of which requires a closely maintained optimal temperature.

The feedback system that dissipates heat and thus keeps the body from overheating under normal conditions has thus been elucidated. The same cannot be said, however, of the regulatory system that steps up metabolic heat production and keeps the body temperature from falling below the optimum level. It appears that the two systems operate quite differently and that in the metabolic warming-up of the body the temperature-eye performs its task by inhibition of sensory impulses originating elsewhere.

On the other hand, the sure location of the thermostat in experiments on the "warm side" now makes it possible to renew the study of many interesting questions. Temperature measurements at sites that reliably reflect hypothalamic temperature should replace rectal observations of temperature in all these studies and even in some clinical situations. How bacterial toxins produce fever and how drugs act to reduce it can now be redefined in terms of shifts in the set point of the thermostat and may be made the subject of quantitative investigation. The same direct attack may also be made upon individual or group tolerances and the adaptability of human temperature regulation. These are important objectives in connection with hypothermia (the reduction of the body temperature to low levels) in surgical operations, and with the conquest of new spaces for the life of the human species.

25

The Production
of Heat by Fat

MICHAEL J. R. DAWKINS AND DAVID HULL · August 1965

When a warm-blooded animal is exposed to cold, it increases its production of body heat by shivering. Mammals face a cool environment for the first time at birth, however, and many newborn mammals (including human infants) do not shiver. Yet they somehow manage to generate heat in response to a cool environment. The mystery of how this is done has only recently been cleared up. It turns out that the young of many species (and adults of hibernating species as well) are fortified with a special tissue that is exceptionally efficient in producing heat. The tissue in question, long a puzzle to investigators, has become a highly interesting object of physiological and

chemical study within the past few years.

Our own interest in it was aroused in 1963 by a chance observation at the Nuffield Institute for Medical Research of the University of Oxford, where we were working in a group studying physiological problems of the newborn. Examining newborn rabbits, we noticed that they had striking pads of brown adipose tissue around the neck and between the shoulder blades. Adipose tissue is a salient feature of all warm-blooded animals. It constitutes the layer of fat underlying the skin over most of the body, and it is known to serve not only as an insulating blanket but also as a storehouse of food and en-

ergy. In the adult animal the adipose tissue is almost entirely of the white variety. The large deposits of adipose tissue we saw in the newborn rabbits were in the brown form, and this was a phenomenon that called for explanation.

Looking back through the literature, we found that the brown adipose tissue had mystified investigators for hundreds of years. It was noted as early as 1551 by the Swiss naturalist Konrad von Gesner, who was impressed by the mass of this tissue he observed between the shoulder blades of a marmot. Some observers confused the tissue with the thymus gland, another mysterious structure that had been found to be particularly prominent in newborn ani-

 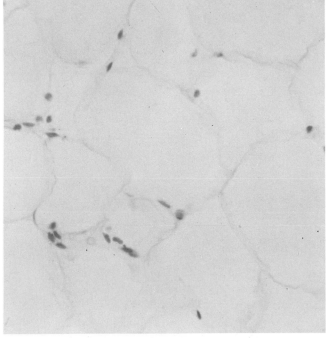

ADIPOSE TISSUE is enlarged 425 diameters in these photomicrographs made by the authors. Brown fat cells (*left*) from between the shoulder blades of a newborn rabbit have numerous small drop- lets of fat suspended in the stained cytoplasm. White fat cells (*right*) from an adult rabbit have large droplets of fat surrounded by narrow rims of cytoplasm. The stain was hematoxylin and eosin.

mals. Other zoologists, noting that a brown adipose mass was typical of hibernating animals, called it the hibernation gland. In this century more modern theories were advanced. Some physiologists suggested that brown adipose tissue had something to do with the formation of blood cells; others, that it was an endocrine gland. It does, in fact, contain hormones similar to those secreted by the adrenal cortex, but experiments in administering extracts from the tissue failed to show any consistent evidence of hormonal effects.

In 1961 two physiologists independently suggested a more plausible hypothesis. George F. Cahill, Jr., of the Harvard Medical School, noting that adipose tissue has an active metabolism that must generate heat as a by-product, proposed that the layer of white fat clothing the body should be regarded "not merely as a simple insulating blanket but perhaps as an electric blanket." And Robert E. Smith of the University of California School of Medicine at Los Angeles specifically called attention to the high heat-producing potentiality of brown adipose tissue, whose oxidative metabolism he had found to be much more active than that of white adipose tissue.

The cells of adipose tissue are characterized by droplets of fat in the cytoplasm (the part of the cell that lies outside the nucleus). In the white adipose cell there is a single large droplet, surrounded by a small amount of cytoplasm. The brown adipose cell, on the other hand, has many small droplets of fat, suspended in a considerably larger amount of cytoplasm. With the electron microscope one can see that the brown fat cells contain many mitochondria, whereas the white fat cells have comparatively few. Mitochondria, the small bodies sometimes called the powerhouses of cells, carry the enzymes needed for oxidative metabolism. What gives the brown fat cells their color is a high concentration of iron-containing cytochrome pigments—an essential part of the oxidizing enzyme apparatus—in the mitochondria.

It is easy to show by experiment that brown fat cells, loaded as they are with mitochondria, have a large capacity for generating energy through oxidation of substrates. Tested, for example, on succinic acid, an intermediate product in the Krebs energy-producing cycle, the brown fat cells of rabbits prove to have a capacity for oxidizing this substance that is 20 times greater than the oxidative capacity of white fat cells

BROWN FAT accounts for 5 or 6 percent of the body weight of the newborn rabbit. It is concentrated, as shown in sections, around the neck and between the shoulder blades.

HUMAN INFANT at birth has a thin sheet of brown adipose tissue between the shoulder blades and around the neck, and small deposits behind the breastbone and along the spine.

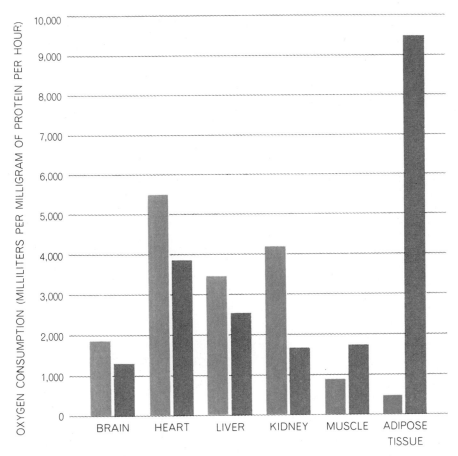

OXIDATIVE CAPACITY of various tissues is compared by measuring their ability to oxidize succinic acid. The colored bars are for adult rabbit tissues, the grey bars for tissues from newborn rabbits. Newborn brown fat (*right*) is the most active oxidizer by far.

and is even greater than that of the hardworking cells of the heart muscle.

To explore the role of the brown adipose tissue in newborn rabbits we began by measuring the animals' total heat production. An indirect measure of this production is the animal's consumption of oxygen: each milliliter of oxygen consumed is equivalent to about five calories of heat in the body. We found that at an environmental temperature of 35 degrees centigrade (95 degrees Fahrenheit) newborn rabbits produced heat at a minimal rate. When their environment was cooled to 25 degrees C. (77 degrees F.), they trebled their heat output. At 20 degrees C. (68 degrees F.) their heat production reached a peak: 400 calories per kilogram of body weight per minute. If newborn rabbits were as fully protected against heat loss and as large as adults are, this rate of production would be sufficient to maintain their internal body temperature at a normal level even in a cold environment as low as 30 degrees below zero C. A newborn rabbit, however, has little or no fur and a large surface area in relation to its body mass;

hence its deep-body temperature falls when the animal is only mildly chilled by the outside air.

The next step was to determine whether or not heat production was concentrated in the brown adipose tissue. In a newborn rabbit this tissue makes up 5 to 6 percent of the total body weight and is localized, as we have noted, around the neck and between the shoulder blades. We inserted a fine thermocouple under the skin next to the brown adipose tissue to measure any change in the temperature of that tissue, and for comparison we inserted a second thermocouple in back-muscle tissue at the same distance from the skin and a third in the colon to record the deep-body temperature. At the neutral environmental temperature of 35 degrees C. the temperatures at all three sites in the body were the same. When the environmental temperature was lowered to 25 degrees C., differences developed: the temperature at the brown adipose tissue then was 2.5 degrees higher than that in muscle tissue in the back and 1.3 degrees higher than the deep-body temperature [*see illustra-*

tion on the next page]. The temperature difference persisted for many hours, until the fat stored in the brown tissue was almost completely exhausted.

This clear indication that the brown adipose tissue produced heat was strengthened by an experiment in which the newborn animals were deprived of oxygen, the oxygen content of the air in the experimental chamber being reduced from the normal 21 percent to 5 percent. Deprived of the oxygen required for oxidative metabolism, the brown adipose tissue promptly cooled to the same low temperature as the muscle tissue. When the oxygen concentration in the air was restored to the normal 21 percent, the brown adipose tissue immediately warmed up again, with the muscle tissue and deep-body temperature trailing after it in recovery.

Is the brown adipose tissue solely responsible for the newborn animal's increase in heat production in response to cold? We examined this question in a series of experiments with Malcolm M. Segall collaborating. The experiments consisted simply in observing the effect of excising most of the brown adipose tissue (amounting to a few grams) from newborn rabbits. When 80 percent of this tissue was removed (by surgery under anesthesia), the animals no longer increased their heat production in response to exposure to cold. In short, removal of the few grams of this specific tissue practically abolished the newborn rabbit's ability to multiply its oxygen consumption threefold and step up its heat production correspondingly. Evidently, then, the brown adipose tissue was entirely, or almost entirely, responsible for this ability.

Our results did not necessarily mean that all the metabolic heat in response to cold was produced within the brown fat cells themselves. Those cells might release fat in some form into the bloodstream for transport to other tissues, where it might be oxidized. Fortunately this question too could be investigated experimentally.

The fat in the droplets in adipose cells is in the form of triglyceride molecules. A triglyceride consists of a glycerol molecule with three long-chain fatty acids attached [*see middle illustration on page 241*]. Before the triglyceride can be oxidized it must be split into smaller, more soluble units—that is, into glycerol and free fatty acids. Glycerol cannot be used for metabolism in a fat cell, because that type of cell does not contain the necessary enzymes. Consequently all the glycerol molecules freed by the splitting of triglycerides in fat cells are discharged into the bloodstream. The glycerol level in the blood therefore provides an index of the rate of breakdown of triglycerides in fat cells. Now, if the level of free fatty acids in the blood corresponds to the glycerol level, we can assume that fatty acids also are released from these cells in substantial amounts for distribution to other tissues.

We examined the blood of newborn rabbits from this point of view. To begin with, at the neutral incubation temperature of 35 degrees C. the level of free fatty acids in the blood was slightly higher than that of glycerol. When the environmental temperature was lowered to 20 degrees, the glycerol level in the blood increased threefold. The concentration of free fatty acids in the blood, however, rose only a little. This showed that most of the fatty acid molecules freed by the splitting of triglycerides in fat cells must have remained in the cells and been metabolized there. Studies of adipose tissue in the test tube indeed demonstrated that less than 10 percent of the freed fatty acid is released from the cell. We can conclude that the brown fat cells are the main site of cold-stimulated heat production.

How is the heat produced? Brown fat cells are admirably suited, by virtue of their abundance of mitochondria, for generating heat by means of the oxidation of fatty acids. In this process a key role is played by adenosine triphosphate (ATP), the packaged chemical energy that powers all forms of biological work, from the contraction of muscle to the light of the firefly. The probable cycle of reactions that turns chemical energy into heat in adipose tissue cells is shown in the illustration on page 242.

Triggered by the stimulus of cold, the brown fat cell splits triglyceride molecules into glycerol and fatty acids. The glycerol and a small proportion of the free fatty acids are released into the bloodstream for metabolism by other tissues (probably liver and muscle). More than 90 percent of the fatty acid molecules remain, however, in the fat cell. They combine with coenzyme A, the energy for this combination being donated by ATP. Since the donation involves the splitting of high-energy bonds in ATP, with its consequent hydrolysis to adenosine monophosphate (AMP), the cell has to regenerate ATP.

This is accomplished by oxidative phosphorylation: the addition of inorganic phosphate to AMP with the simultaneous oxidation of a substrate.

Now, some molecules of the fatty acid–coenzyme A compound formed with the help of ATP are oxidized to provide energy for the regeneration of ATP. But most of this complex is reconverted, by combination with alphaglycerol phosphate, to the original triglyceride. In short, there is an apparently purposeless cycle that breaks triglyceride down to fatty acids only

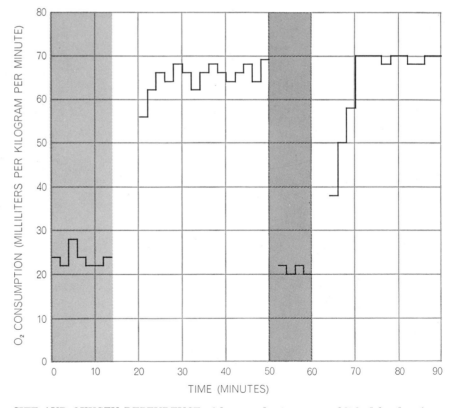

SITE AND OXYGEN DEPENDENCE of heat production are established by data from newborn rabbits subjected to cold and temporarily deprived of oxygen. The top curves are for body temperature measured near brown fat (*solid black line*), in muscle (*broken gray*) and in the colon (*broken black*). The bottom curves trace metabolic activity. In the period covered by the colored band the environmental temperature was 35 degrees centigrade; thereafter it was 25 degrees. The gray band marks a period during which the oxygen concentration was cut from 21 percent to 5 percent. Apparently brown-fat metabolism in the presence of adequate oxygen accounts for a rabbit's ability to respond to a drop in temperature.

REMOVAL OF BROWN FAT by surgery sharply curtails the response to cold. The two bars at the left show the oxygen consumption in intact newborn rabbits at two temperatures. The bars at the right are for rabbits that have had 80 percent of their brown fat removed: metabolism at 35 degrees is unchanged but there is virtually no increase at 20 degrees.

METABOLISM OF BROWN FAT begins with the hydrolysis of the triglyceride molecule (*left*), yielding one molecule of glycerol (*center*) and three of free fatty acid (*right*).

GLYCEROL CONCENTRATION (*broken line*) in the blood of a newborn rabbit rises sharply when the environmental temperature drops from 35 degrees centigrade (*colored area*) to 20 degrees (*white area*). The concentration of fatty acids in the blood rises only slightly, however (*solid line*). Apparently fatty acids are largely metabolized in the cell.

to resynthesize the latter back to triglyceride. Although the cycle seems pointless in chemical terms, it is clearly significant in terms of work. The cycle is, in fact, a device for turning the chemical-bond energy of fatty acids into heat. The energy driving the cycle comes fundamentally from the oxidation of the fatty acids, and the fact that the cycle is exceptionally active in brown adipose tissue is demonstrated by that tissue's high consumption of oxygen. Judging from the proportion of free fatty acids retained by the cells of brown adipose tissue, and from the effects of surgical removal, this tissue accounts for more than 80 percent of the increased body heat produced by a newborn rabbit in the cold.

The heat must of course be distributed to the rest of the body by the bloodstream. The newborn animal's brown adipose tissue has an extremely rich blood supply. During exposure to cold the blood flow through this tissue may increase to several times its normal rate, and indirect calculations suggest that as much as a third of the total cardiac output is directed through the tissue.

How does cold stimulate the brown adipose tissue to generate heat? There are two possible means by which the body's sensation of cold may be communicated to the tissue: by nerve impulses and by hormones, the chemical "messengers" of the body. We found that the hormone noradrenaline has a specific stimulating effect on the brown adipose tissue. An intravenous infusion of noradrenaline in a newborn rabbit will bring about a large increase in the animal's oxygen consumption and heat production in its brown fat. If the brown fat is removed, the hormone no longer produces any increase in the body's oxygen consumption. The question remains: Is the hormone delivered to the intact tissue by way of the bloodstream or by release at sympathetic nerve endings, which are known to secrete noradrenaline close to cells? Several clues suggest that the nerve endings, rather than the bloodstream, are the agent of delivery. For one thing, the adipose tissue's rapid response to cold indicates that the message travels via the nerves. Second, experiments show that drugs that block the action of noradrenaline circulating in the blood do not block the tissue's response to cold. Third and conclusively, direct electrical stimulation of the sympathetic nerves going to the tissue will cause the brown adipose tissue to produce heat, whereas when the sympathetic nerves are cut, the tissue can no longer burn its fat when the animal is exposed to cold.

Various findings indicate that the overall system controlling the production of heat by brown adipose tissue is probably as follows: The temperature receptors in the skin, on sensing cold, send nerve impulses to the brain. The brain's temperature-regulating center then relays impulses along the sympathetic nerves to the brown adipose tissue, where the nerve endings release noradrenaline. The hormone activates an enzyme that splits triglyceride molecules into glycerol and free fatty acids and thereby triggers the heat-producing cycle. Thus the rate of heat production is controlled by the sympathetic nervous system.

Among the animals that have brown adipose tissue at birth, the amount varies considerably from species to species. As in the rabbit, there are large deposits between the shoulder blades in the newborn guinea pig and the coypu (a water rodent). In the cat, dog and sheep at birth there are sheets of brown adipose tissue between the muscles of the trunk and around the kidneys. The human infant has well-marked deposits of such tissue [see bottom illustration on page 238], and recent studies indicate that this tissue is a source of heat for a baby as it is for other newborn animals. When a baby is exposed to cold, its blood shows a small but definite rise in the glycerol level with no significant change in the level of fatty acids; on prolonged exposure to cold the fat in its brown adipose tissue is used up.

In most species of animals born with brown adipose tissue the tissue appears to be largely converted to the white form by the time the animal has reached adulthood. Certain animals retain at least some tissue in the brown form, however. The adult rat, for example, has small amounts of brown adipose tissue in the shoulder blade region and elsewhere. The rat's venous system indicates that there is a rich flow of blood from this region to the plexus of veins around the spinal cord; this suggests that the brown adipose tissue in the adult rat may serve particularly to warm vital structures in the animal's body core during exposure to cold. When a laboratory rat is kept in a cold environment, it develops additional brown adipose tissue and an increased ability to produce heat without shivering.

For hibernating animals brown adipose tissue is an all-important necessity throughout life. These animals possess large amounts of the tissue, and direct studies have now shown that the brown adipose tissue is responsible for the animals' rapid warming and awakening from the torpid hibernating state.

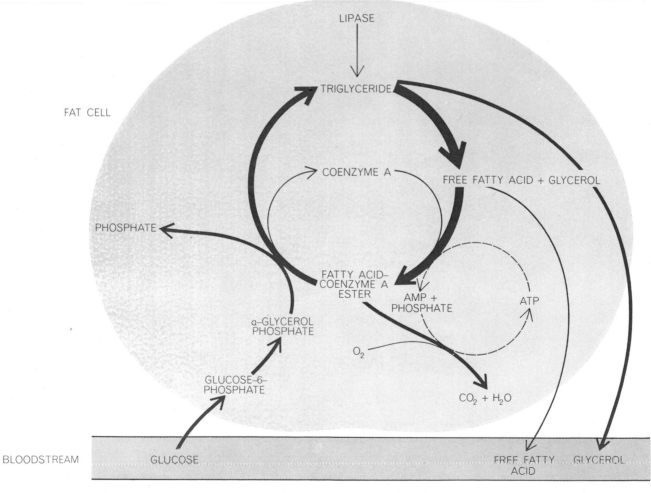

HEAT IS PRODUCED in brown fat cells by the oxidation of fatty acids. In response to cold an enzyme, lipase, splits triglyceride. The glycerol leaves the cell. The fatty acid forms an ester with coenzyme A, the reaction acquiring energy from the splitting of adenosine triphosphate (ATP) into adenosine monophosphate (AMP) and inorganic phosphate. Some of the ester is oxidized to regenerate ATP; the rest goes to resynthesize triglyceride. The effect of the cycle, then, is to turn chemical-bond energy into heat energy.

26

Desert Ground Squirrels

GEORGE A. BARTHOLOMEW AND JACK W. HUDSON · November 1961

Among the handful of animals that inhabit the hot, dry and sparsely vegetated Mohave Desert of California are two species of ground squirrel: the antelope ground squirrel and the mohave ground squirrel. Both species live in burrows, both are active and aboveground during the day and both feed on the small amount of plant life that is available.

This is an uncommon situation in nature. Species as closely related as these two, and as much alike in their food and habitat requirements, seldom live together even in more favorable environments. In his *Origin of Species* Charles Darwin suggested the reason. "As the species of the same genus usually have ...much similarity in habits and constitution, and always in structure," he wrote, "the struggle will generally be more severe between them, if they come into competition with each other, than between the species of distinct genera." Implicit in Darwin's statement is a concept now fundamental to biology. It is known as the principle of competitive exclusion and it says, in brief, that two noninterbreeding populations that stand in precisely the same relationship to their environment cannot occupy the same territory indefinitely. They cannot, in other words, live in "sympatry" forever. Sooner or later one will displace the other.

Such a displacement could be under way in the Mohave Desert right now. The mohave ground squirrel may well be a species in the process of extinction. Not only does it have a smaller total population and a narrower geographical distribution than the antelope ground squirrel (which is one of the commonest ground squirrels of the southwestern U.S.); it also appears to be less numerous in the small section of the Mohave Desert to which it is restricted. But since no historical information is available on the population trends of the two animals, there is no way of knowing exactly what the present difference in their number portends.

In any case the mohave ground squirrel is not as yet extinct. This raises a number of intriguing questions. Do the two species have the same way of life and the same relationship to their environment? If so, the competition between them must be severe. Or are there differences in their adaptation to their common environment? If there are, do these differences reduce competition between them sufficiently to permit them, at least temporarily, a period of peaceful coexistence?

These questions become more intriguing when one considers the nature of the desert environment. Aridity and heat make particularly severe demands on animals, and animals that live in deserts must be equipped with special physiological and behavioral adaptations to meet these demands. The camel, for example, withstands aridity because it can tolerate a high degree of dehydration, can restore its body fluids quickly and can travel long distances in search of water and succulent vegetation. It withstands heat through its tolerance of a wide range of body temperatures and

ANTELOPE GROUND SQUIRREL is found in the Mohave Desert and throughout the southwestern U.S. It is active during the day all year round, in spite of extremes of heat and aridity. Both of these photographs were made in the laboratory by Jack W. Hudson.

MOHAVE GROUND SQUIRREL is found only in one corner of the Mohave Desert. It is active during the day from March to August but remains in its burrow the rest of the year. Before retiring underground it becomes very fat, as this photograph shows.

ACTIVITY OF ANTELOPE GROUND SQUIRREL on a typical summer day is charted. On emerging from its burrow animal runs to feeding area. Then it suns and grooms itself. When its body temperature rises too high, it goes to a special retreat burrow to cool

BODY TEMPERATURE
ENVIRONMENTAL TEMPERATURE
LEVEL OF ACTIVITY

through the insulating qualities of its coat [see "The Physiology of the Camel," by Knut Schmidt-Nielsen, beginning on page 192 in this book]. The desert rat of the U.S. Southwest has adapted equally well but in quite different ways. To combat aridity it conserves its body water; the desert rat's kidney is so efficient that it uses only about a fourth of the amount of water that the human kidney requires to excrete the same amount of urea. This adaptation enables the animal to meet a substantial fraction of

its water needs by the oxidation of foodstuff, as opposed to drinking. The desert rat deals with heat by avoiding it: the animal remains in its burrow during the daylight hours, emerging only at night, when the air and soil are cool [see "The Desert Rat," by Knut and Bodil Schmidt-Nielsen; SCIENTIFIC AMERICAN, July, 1953].

Like the desert rat, most small, burrowing desert rodents are nocturnal. But both the mohave ground squirrel and the antelope ground squirrel are diurnal.

They emerge from their burrows near sunrise and forage outdoors throughout the day. They do so even in summer, when the air temperature may reach 110 degrees Fahrenheit or higher, and when the surface temperature of the soil may rise above 150 degrees F. Since the desert is as arid as it is hot, they must sustain their exposure to heat with a minimum loss of water for evaporative cooling.

In appearance and temperament the antelope ground squirrel resembles the

RETREAT BURROW OF ANTELOPE GROUND SQUIRREL is shown at right in this drawing. It is usually dug in soft soil close

to desert vegetation and is about one foot deep and 12 to 15 feet long. The animal seems to use this burrow to unload body heat off. In early afternoon it stays in the shade. Before retiring to its home burrow it returns to feeding area, and at any time may catch insects or feed on dead animals. On the graph, dip in body tem- perature is shown only at noon. But dips occur often, whenever animal goes underground to unload heat. At all other times its temperature is a few degrees above the environmental temperature.

chipmunk. Its body is about six inches long; its weight is about 90 grams. It has two white stripes down its grayish-brown back. It carries its tail high, exposing a white rump; this suggests the appear- ance of the pronghorn antelope, for which it is named. An extraordinarily active and high-strung animal, the ante- lope ground squirrel is constantly in motion, dashing from place to place, often traveling hundreds of feet from its home burrow. That it can maintain such hyperactivity even in soaring tempera-

tures is in itself evidence of unusual adaptive mechanisms.

For every animal the ability to adapt to external temperatures depends on two internal factors: the range of body temperatures in which it can function effectively and the rate at which it can produce body heat. Below a lower critical environmental temperature the body loses so much heat that internal tempera- ture can be maintained only if the ani- mal can step up its production of body heat sufficiently. Above an upper critical

environmental temperature the body re- tains so much metabolic heat that inter- nal temperature can be held within the required range only if the animal can get rid of heat, in most cases by evaporative cooling; that is, by sweating or panting at a sufficient rate. Between the upper and lower critical temperatures—in the thermal neutral zone—an animal can maintain its optimum body temperature without having either to increase its metabolic rate or to lose body water. Such stratagems as contracting or dilat-

and to store food, but not as a living place; the dens in the burrow contain neither nests nor fecal matter. The antelope ground squir- rel's living burrows have not been excavated. They are probably dug under rocky buttes, like that seen at left side of drawing.

BODY TEMPERATURE
ENVIRONMENTAL TEMPERATURE

ACTIVITY OF MOHAVE GROUND SQUIRREL for six months is shown here. Animal emerges from burrow in March. In April young are born. From May through July it fattens on desert vegetation and in August returns underground for seven months. Broken line

ing cutaneous blood vessels and depressing or raising hair or feathers allow the animal to function at a minimum cost of energy for temperature maintenance.

In terms of this analysis of the adjustment of body temperature to environmental temperature, the adaptation of the antelope ground squirrel is admirable. It has a broad thermal neutral zone and one that accommodates to high environmental temperatures. Between environmental temperatures of 90 and

107 degrees F. its metabolic rate remains virtually constant. No other nonsweating mammal has a thermal neutral zone extending so high [see illustration on page 248].

Unlike man, the antelope ground squirrel can tolerate a high body temperature; in other words, it can "run a fever" without debility. It can therefore permit its temperature to rise with the temperature of the environment. Like the camel, it can store heat, and it does not have to dispose of heat until its body

temperature reaches an extreme point. The antelope ground squirrel shows no serious discomfort even when its body temperature goes above 110 degrees. Throughout the thermal neutral zone it runs a temperature a few degrees above that of the environment [see top illustration on pages 244 and 245]. Instead of expending energy to cool itself and thereby adding to its heat load—as man must do—this animal actually disposes of a portion of its metabolic heat to the lower-temperature environment by

LIVING BURROW OF MOHAVE GROUND SQUIRREL is seen here at various stages and times of year. Burrow is dug in soft sand near the desert plants the animal eats. It is about 18 feet long and three feet deep. First panel shows burrow in early spring, on graph is desert air temperature when animal is in burrow. Gray line under it is burrow temperature then. Rise and fall of animal's temperature in August corresponds to its periods of wakefulness and torpor. Body temperature is always higher than environmental temperature, although when animal is active its temperature fluctuates sharply. A mean body temperature is shown here.

conduction, convection and radiation.

But environmental temperatures in the desert are commonly far higher than tissues can tolerate, and small animals heat up rapidly. The antelope ground squirrel must therefore unload some of its accumulated body heat at intervals during the day. It does this either by flattening itself against the soil in a shaded area or by retreating underground to its burrow. When its body temperature gets dangerously high, it has only to return to the relative coolness of its burrow and remain quiet for a few minutes until its fever has subsided. In our laboratory at the University of California at Los Angeles, antelope ground squirrels have lowered their body temperature from above 107 degrees to about 100 degrees within three minutes after being transferred from an environmental temperature of 104 degrees to one of 77 degrees.

The antelope ground squirrel contends with heat in still another way. Under protracted heat stress it will begin to drool. The animal then systematically spreads the saliva over its cheeks and head with its forepaws as though it were grooming itself. On very hot days, when it has had to tolerate air temperatures of 104 degrees or more for several hours, the antelope ground squirrel may be soaking wet around the head.

Drooling, with its high cost in water losses, is a last resort. But even when the temperature is not extreme, the antelope ground squirrel loses a considerable amount of body water. At 100

when animal emerges. Second shows animal digging new burrow. Third shows it closing burrow in August before retiring underground. In last panel it is winter and animal is torpid. Periods of torpor probably last longer in winter months than in summer.

degrees, long before it has begun to drool, this hyperactive animal gives up water equal to 10 per cent of its body weight in respiration and evaporation through its skin in the course of a day. This is 15 per cent of its total body water. Fortunately the animal withstands dehydration well. Although it gives up three times more water every day than it can extract from its food by oxidation, it can survive from three to five weeks on a completely dry diet. If the antelope ground squirrel is to maintain itself in a healthy state, however, it must find sources of preformed water. It is therefore hardly surprising that the animal is omnivorous, eating insects as well as desert vegetation. When it is seen on the highways, as it often is, it is probably feeding on the corpse of some animal, perhaps another of its species that has been hit by a car.

The antelope ground squirrel is able to stretch its scanty water supply because, like the desert rat, it loses a minimal amount of water in the excretion of nitrogenous wastes. On a dry diet this animal can produce urine with a mean concentration of 3,700 milliosmols (the

maximum concentration of human urine is about 1,300 milliosmols). The urine of the desert rat is somewhat more concentrated. But the antelope ground squirrel's urine is still 10 times more concentrated than its body fluids. Its ability to turn salty water to physiological use is even more impressive. The desert rat can maintain itself on sea water; the antelope ground squirrel can drink water approximately 1.4 times saltier than sea water and still remain in good health. No other mammal can process water of such high salinity. This capacity is important in the desert, where the little surface water that is available is usually highly mineralized.

The structure of the animal's kidney explains its efficient use of water. As in several other desert mammals, the renal papilla—that part of the kidney which contains the ascending and descending kidney tubules—of the antelope ground squirrel is extremely large, extending as far down as the ureter [see illustration on page 249]. In the formation of urine the kidney first extracts a filtrate containing all the constituents of blood except proteins and blood cells. This filtrate

is then converted to urine by the selective reabsorption of water and essential solutes in the kidney tubules. The longer the tubules, the greater the amount of water they can absorb and the greater the amount the body retains. As the antelope ground squirrel's tolerance for high body temperatures constitutes its major physiological adaptation to heat, so the efficiency of its kidney embodies its major adaptation to aridity.

Considering the success with which the antelope ground squirrel occupies its narrow desert niche, how does the mohave ground squirrel manage to find a place beside it? The question cannot be fully answered, because less is known about the life history of the mohave ground squirrel. This in itself is significant, because it appears that the mohave ground squirrel manages to persist largely by staying out of the way of the antelope ground squirrel.

Of the two animals the mohave ground squirrel is the bigger and fatter, and it has the temperament that goes with its more generous proportions. Its body length is about six and a half

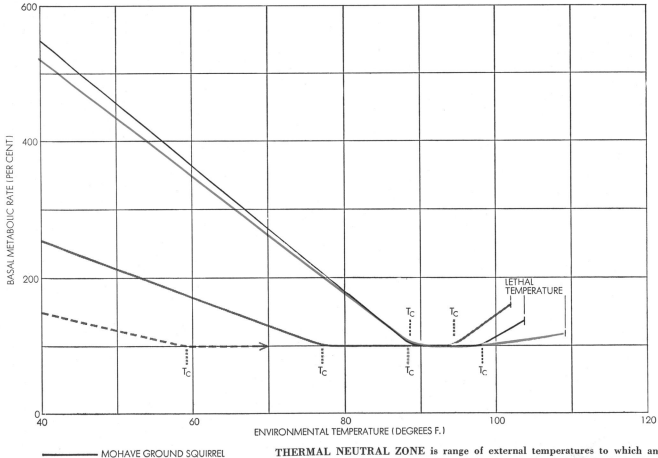

THERMAL NEUTRAL ZONE is range of external temperatures to which an animal is best adjusted. In it body temperature and metabolism can be held at optimum levels. At critical temperatures (T_C) metabolic rate begins to rise. Lemming is an arctic rodent. Kangaroo rat and ground squirrels are desert dwellers.

———————— MOHAVE GROUND SQUIRREL
———————— ANTELOPE GROUND SQUIRREL
———————— MERRIAM'S KANGAROO RAT
= = = = = = LEMMING

inches; its weight in its natural habitat, about 150 grams. In temperament it is placid, docile and sedentary. This little brown animal seldom wanders far from its home burrow, which it digs in loose sand, generally in the shade of the desert plants that provide it with its food. For more than half the year, from August to March, it remains in its burrow. During the spring months, when the desert vegetation is at its annual peak, the mohave ground squirrel emerges to reproduce and to fatten itself in preparation for its return underground.

The major proportion of the mohave ground squirrel's life is therefore normally concealed from observation. Fortunately it seems to show a comparable pattern of behavior in the laboratory. Here, as in its natural habitat, the animal is active throughout the day from March to August. During the remainder of the year, however, even at room temperature, and in spite of the continuous availability of food and water, it is intermittently torpid for periods lasting from several hours to several days. If food and water are at hand, it will eat and drink in its periods of wakefulness. If they are not, it does not seem to be disturbed. We do not know whether or not in its natural habitat it stores food in its burrow. We do know that it is usually thin in early spring, when it emerges from its burrow, and that it can add as much as 100 grams to its body weight in the period before its retirement underground. We also know that in the laboratory, where the animal becomes exceedingly fat, it loses an appreciable amount of weight during its period of dormancy only if no food and water have been made available to it.

Since this pattern of intermittent dormancy extends from late summer to early spring, it involves what would normally be considered two separate processes—hibernation and the summer dormancy called estivation. Our studies indicate, however, that in the mohave ground squirrel the two processes are merely aspects of the same physiological phenomenon. From early August to the end of February, whether the temperature in the laboratory is one that would normally be associated with estivation or whether it is one at which hibernation would be expected to occur, the same events take place. As the animal becomes torpid, its oxygen consumption and its body temperature drop sharply. Then both level off, and the body temperature stabilizes at the environmental temperature or very slightly above it. During the time the animal is dormant its torpor is more pronounced than

deep sleep, its breathing is suspended for long periods and its heart rate is profoundly reduced. On arousal it restores its body temperature to normal through increases in breathing movements, acceleration of heartbeat, shivering (which releases heat) and increased oxygen consumption. In the laboratory arousal may come about spontaneously or it may be induced by a touch or a sound. In either event it is extremely rapid. Although the animal can take as long as six hours to enter torpor, it can wake in less than one hour. Oxygen consumption can reach its peak in 15 to 20 minutes, and body temperature can rise from 68 to 86 degrees in 20 to 35 minutes.

Such rapid alterations in temperature do not occur during the five-month period in which the mohave ground squirrel is active. Even then, however, its body temperature is remarkably variable and fluctuates over a broad range. We have measured a deep-body temper-

ature as low as 88 degrees in individual animals engaged in normal activity, and yet the animal does not seem to suffer any ill effects from body temperatures as high as 107 degrees. Its thermal neutral zone does not, however, extend as high as that of the antelope ground squirrel. The metabolism of the mohave ground squirrel begins to rise at an environmental temperature of about 98 degrees. Its tolerance for high body temperatures is of major adaptive value in June and July, when the desert is particularly hot.

Obviously the mohave ground squirrel's dormancy serves the function traditionally associated with hibernation: it conserves energy. At an environmental temperature of 68 degrees the oxygen consumption of a dormant mohave ground squirrel is only about a tenth that of the same animal active at the same temperature. Fat is undoubtedly the major energy source. Since the oxidation

SECTION OF KIDNEY of antelope ground squirrel is magnified 20 times in this micrograph by Hudson. Mass outlined in white is papilla, containing renal tubules. In this species it is very large. This permits reabsorption of much water and production of concentrated urine.

of one gram of fat requires two liters of oxygen, a simple calculation shows that a torpid squirrel, weighing 300 grams and consuming oxygen at a rate of .08 cubic centimeter per gram per hour, will burn .29 gram of fat a day. Some 50 grams of fat would therefore supply it with all its energy requirements for 172 days; this is just half the fat supply it usually accumulates in the active months of the year. According to this calculation a mohave ground squirrel should be able to remain torpid for a whole year if it did not arouse at all. We do not know, of course, how much its energy requirements are increased by periods of arousal during the months of dormancy. Not being able to observe the animals in their burrows, we do not know how long these periods last. But from laboratory evidence we deduce that the cycles of torpor and wakefulness are repeated every week, with three to five days spent in torpor. The mohave ground squirrel should therefore be able to get along on its accumulated fat.

Energy conservation is not the only function that dormancy serves. Like the antelope ground squirrel, the mohave ground squirrel loses considerable body water in evaporative cooling and, like the antelope ground squirrel, it must have preformed water in its food. The sedentary mohave ground squirrel does not go in search of water; it gets its water almost entirely from the desert plants it eats. During the period the animal is underground this vegetation is in decline and the desert is at its driest. Thus dormancy is an important adaptation to seasonal aridity.

The mohave ground squirrel's seven months of estivation and hibernation serves still another function: it minimizes competition with the more active and abundant antelope ground squirrel. During the time the mohave ground squirrel is aboveground the food and water available are probably adequate to sustain both animals. But during its months of dormancy both food and water are in short supply.

The two animals have adapted well to desert life—the antelope ground squirrel by its tolerance for high body temperatures and the efficiency of its kidney, and the mohave ground squirrel by its avoidance underground of the most rigorous months of the year. One may conclude that these adaptations are sufficiently different to permit the two animals to live in sympatry in spite of Darwin's stern injunction.

Orientation
and Navigation

It is clearly obvious that fishes possess a sense of smell, as they are not all attracted by the same food, and they smell a thing before they seize it…indeed the stench of a ship's bilge makes them flee far away, but most of all the blood of fishes.

Pliny
NATURAL HISTORY, X, xc.

VI

Orientation and Navigation

INTRODUCTION

In this section we will study the ways in which vertebrates orient to their environment. Homing and electric location by fishes, sonar navigation by bats, and sun navigation by birds are the topics of the articles that are included. They involve the senses of smell, electric field measurement, hearing, and sight. In this introduction we will discuss these senses in general and how they are used by some vertebrates other than those described in the accompanying articles.

A convenient means of distinguishing "tasting" from "smelling" in vertebrates and in other animals is as follows: taste is the response to quite high concentrations of chemicals present in the mouth, with the result being acceptance or rejection of material as food; smell is the response to low concentrations of chemicals in the nasal passage, with the result being locomotion or complicated behavioral responses. Smell can be thought of as a long-distance orienting sense; and taste, a short-distance feeding sense. There is some overlap: for example, in human beings odor can help to assign a characteristic "taste" to food; as a consequence, during illnesses that reduce smell sensitivity, food tastes "flat" and abnormal. The reason is that smell complements taste in man. Nevertheless, the basic distinction between the two is generally obvious in terrestrial vertebrates, but less so in aquatic vertebrates. The hypothesis is supported strongly by the fact that sensory cells for the two processes differ morphologically in all vertebrates.

Smell is initiated by excitation of bipolar nerve cells, of which one end is exposed to the environment and the other is connected to the dendrites of an associational neuron that transmits nerve impulses toward the central nervous system. The outer receptor process of the nasal bipolar cell extends between epithelial cells of the nasal organ so that its outer end is exposed directly to the nasal cavity. Only a layer of liquid or mucus covers the outer plasma membrane of the cell, where foreign odoriferous substances initially make contact.

The taste sensation is initiated on modified columnar epithelial cells. The outer ends of many of these cells are hair-like processes; the inner ends contact dendrites of nerve cells. In land vertebrates, these taste cells are found only in the mouth, whereas, in fishes, the same kinds of taste receptors may also be scattered over portions of the outer surface. Obviously this fact complicates our semantic separation of taste from smell in fish, for in a sense these "taste" receptors are sampling fluid-borne chemicals outside of the mouth, much as smell receptors function in land vertebrates.

To be complete we must mention the most primitive class of chemo-receptors of all: they are nerve endings that are unspecialized morphologically, but that respond to specific chemical conditions by changing the pattern of their nerve impulses. Such endings in the aortic bodies of vertebrates are stimulated by alterations in pH or in carbon dioxide and so influence the control of breathing. It seems reasonable to guess that smell receptors, at least, are specialized hypersensitive forms of these basic chemoreceptors.

All substances that can be smelled are volatile at normal environmental temperatures, and most are of reasonably large molecular size. Various "classes" of odors have been proposed to categorize the thousands of chemicals that can be detected by olfaction. It seems clear that certain molecular arrangements evoke the sensation of a "smell"; considerable variation in molecular detail can occur, but as long as a specific grouping is present a given "name" of the smell will usually be assigned. As was pointed out by A. J. Haagen-Smit ("Smell and Taste," *Scientific American*, March, 1952; Offprint 404), however, as small a difference as the replacement of a hydrogen atom by a methyl group changes the odor from "mint" to "camphor." It seems likely that there are different kinds of receptor molecules on the outer surface of odor-sensing cells, and that the steric fit between air-borne agent and receptor determines whether association between the molecules will occur. We do not know how the combination of receptor with foreign molecule is transduced into altered cell metabolism and so to depolarization and impulse initiation. Nor is it clear what happens to the molecular complex so that the ability to continue to respond to a particular substance is possible.

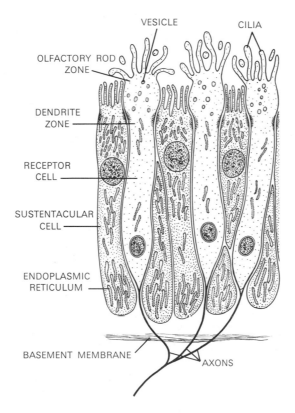

VESICLE CILIA

OLFACTORY ROD
ZONE

DENDRITE
ZONE

RECEPTOR
CELL

SUSTENTACULAR
CELL

ENDOPLASMIC
RETICULUM

BASEMENT MEMBRANE

AXONS

Figure 1. A typical portion of the nasal epithelium. The sensory cells extend from the outer surface—where their ends are exposed to foreign molecules—through the epithelium, and then continue as nerve axons toward the olfactory bulb of the brain. Note that there is no discrete localization of these sensory cells, as there is of taste cells in "buds." The sustentacular cells are thought to "insulate" receptor cells, that is, to isolate them from each other. [From DeLorenzo, A. J. D.; in Y. Zotterman, *Wenner-Gren Center International Symposium Series*, Vol. 1, Macmillan, 1963.]

Other phenomena of odor detection are equally inexplicable: we do not understand, for example, why certain substances, in small quantity, will dominate large quantities of others, so that only the small quantities are "smelled;" also confusing is the fact that some substances smell differently when present in large or small amount. Whether phenomena such as these occur in the receptors or in the subsequent neural pathways has not been established.

Neurophysiologists have recorded electrical activity from single smell receptors and have established that different cells are sensitive to different classes of molecules. No unique pattern of response has been observed, however: the rate of impulse initiation in a given cell may go up or down, or it can be turned on or off in response to an agent. What seems to be important in evoking the sensation of a particular smell, is the distribution of many cells responding in different degrees to a foreign molecule: in a sense, then, the organization of the sensory epithelium is a critical feature of the system, because that organization determines which of the thousands of olfactory nerve axons will initiate a new pattern of impulses and so send information to the brain. Other studies show that the terminations of nerve tracts leading from the olfactory epithelium to the olfactory bulb of the brain are distributed nonrandomly. On the olfactory bulb is a topographical representation of the nasal epithelium: that is, the spatial relationship between points on the epithelium is reflected on the bulb. Interestingly, cells that detect water-soluble chemicals tend to be located at one end of the bulb, and those that sense oil-soluble molecules are localized at the other end.

Most substances that can be tasted are soluble in water. They must be present at about 3,000 times the minimal concentration required for smell to operate. Taste is simpler than smell in that four discrete groups—salt, sour, sweet, and bitter—are known. Variation in sensation occurs within some of the groups. In the absence of smell, for instance, all acids (H^+ ions) taste alike—sour; but many substances that taste "sweet" can be distinguished from each other, as indicated by conditioning experiments or verbal description by human subjects.

Like the olfactory cells, individual taste receptor cells respond to specific sets of molecules. *One cell,* for instance, may cause nerve impulse discharge when sodium chloride or potassium chloride ("salt"), or hydrochloric acid ("sour") are present, but not when sucrose ("sweet") or quinine ("bitter") are applied; another will respond only to sour and bitter; others, to different sets. Thus, there is no correspondence between these classes of receptor cells and the four basic types of tastes. Like smell, the ultimate taste sensation recorded in higher centers of the brain may be dependent on the pattern of impulses from many taste-sensitive cells. Again, the spatial distribution of the receptor cells that respond to various combinations of tastable substances and their balance of activity (whether impulse initiation speeds or slows, etc.) seem to be the important features of the ability to taste. This would suggest that the gustatory sensory apparatus may be a simpler version of the olfactory one, a not unexpected conclusion if the terrestrial olfactory system evolved from the taste receptors of fish.

Chemoreception has many functions in the lives of fishes. In parasitic lampreys, it leads the fish to a host. Even young lampreys fresh from metamorphosis respond to the odor of a potential host fish by oriented swimming behavior. Since these fish had not been exposed to the odor of any other fish during larval life, this is a good example of a behavioral pattern that is built into the nervous system during development and maturation. It is innate behavior, which does not depend upon learning or conditioning. The substances that cause the reaction have been extracted from trout: they are amines. The same lamprey species (*Petromyzon marinus*) that displays this orienting behavior uses a pulsating electric field to locate prey within 15 to 20 centimeters; the chemical sensing is used for long-distance orientation.

Other examples of odor-elicited behavior in fishes are the fright reaction, and homing in order to reproduce. Particularly in a number of small schooling fishes, substances that cause an immediate fear reaction of the school are present in the skin cells. When the skin of one fish is injured, the chemical is released into the water, causing rapid escape swimming and dispersion of the clustered fishes. This substance is a warning device that helps others of the same species avoid imminent danger of predation.

Arthur Hasler and James Larsen review the homing of salmon in their article, "The Homing Salmon." A variety of experiments conducted since the article was published confirm and elaborate on the hypotheses presented by these authors. Although it has not been proved, it seems reasonable to suppose that a salmon far out in the Pacific finds its way back to the general area of its river system by use of celestial navigation. This process, which is the orientation in relation to the sun or stars, is described in greater detail toward the end of this introduction. A number of experiments have established that fishes, like birds, show oriented swimming under clear skies but not under cloudy ones. Once the fishes are near the home river system, the senses of smell (and perhaps taste) can be assumed to lead the fish back to the stream where it grew up.

Consistent with this hypothesis is the finding that "home" water perfused into the nasal epithelium of a salmon elicits a burst of nerve impulse firing in the olfactory bulb. Water from nearby regions draining similar geological areas fails to alter the basic electroencephalogram firing pattern. Interestingly, the rate of the electrical activity in the olfactory bulb is high in young fish—at a time when they may be in the process of learning to recognize home water—but it is lower during adult life when the eyes are said to be the dominant sense. Finally, electrical activity increases again at the time of homing when smell apparently leads the fish to its spawning site.

Young salmon may be trained in the laboratory with a given type of water, and they will return to it from the sea years later. Apparently they are imprinted with certain odorous substances of the home stream, so that these substances alone lead to a successful homing reaction. It is not known yet whether a single organic molecular type functions to mark the home territory, or whether groups of molecules combine to give a characteristic smell to each portion of each breeding stream.

Although fishes can employ smell for long-distance orientation, they can use electric locationing only for short distances. As pointed out by H. W. Lissmann in "Electric Location By Fishes," the sense is used under conditions of low visibility, due either to darkness or to abundant suspended material in the water. The two families of fresh-water fishes in which the ability is found are quite distinct morphologically and only distantly related. Nevertheless, they have arrived at the same solution to problems of orientation in a difficult environment. In fact, we can assume that the only way such fishes can survive today is to be active at night, when nonelectric bony fishes are at rest in the water. This is because the mode of swimming of electric fishes—with a stiff body axis and propulsion by the fins—does not allow the quick movement needed for evasion of predators that is possible in typical sine-wave swimming.

Organs used to detect electric fields are probably modifications of the ordinary lateral line organs found on all vertebrate fishes. Each lateral line organ includes a structure that can be displaced by water currents; as a result of this displacement, sensory hairs are moved, and altered patterns of nerve impulses ensue. Thus, disturbances in the water pattern caused by objects near the fishes are detectable. In acting this way, the lateral line serves as an extension of the sense of touch.

Variations of the lateral line organ are found in sharks and their relatives and in electric fishes. In the electric fishes, the sensory epithelium is beneath the surface of the skin. In some electric receptors the canal leading from the sensory area to the surface is filled with jelly; this jelly has remarkable electrical conductivity (85 to 90 percent of that of sea water, compared to 45 percent in body fluids). In another type of electro-receptor, thin covering cells lie on top of the sensory cells. Neither these nor the cells under the jelly show any hint of ciliary derivation, a common feature of the lateral line neuromasts, as described above. The electric sensing cells are always found in close proximity to nerve endings (presumed to be sensory in nature). Even chemical coupling, like that in the main vertebrate nervous system, seems to exist between some of these sensory cells and nerve endings; for example, vesicles thought to contain a transmitter substance are found in the sensory cell cytoplasm, in the intercellular space, and in the nerve ending cytoplasm.

Electric organs can detect weak potential changes in the water—such as those caused by another fish or even by a bare metal wire—or they may be used to measure alterations in the electric field generated by the same organism. The remarkable feature of the electric organs is their great sensitivity; responses to currents as small as 2×10^{-5} microamperes per square centimeter have been observed. It seems clear that, in the course of the evolution of these various fishes, the basic mechanoreceptor properties of the lateral line have been modified to permit detection of electrical signals in the environment. The absence of any hint of cilia on the electric sensing cells emphasizes the change in sensory modality that has occurred in this evolutionary transition.

Another mechanism is used by some marine vertebrates for orientation in the water as well as by terrestrial vertebrates for orientation in the air: it is echolocation. This capacity to use sound pulses and their echoes has evolved several times in the vertebrates. The oil birds of the caves in Venezuela, the dolphins and their relatives, the bats, and some insectivores employ the mechanism. In each group the process is employed under conditions of low visibility, and, in each, rapid movement is made so that appropriate analysis of the environment by means of smell or taste is impossible. Both the bats and the cetaceans (dolphins, whales, and their relatives) are reasonably close relatives of the insectivores, the ancestral group of modern mammals. Bats, of course, have retained the nocturnal habits of insectivores and many of them have adopted the echolocation method of orientation.

As described by Donald R. Griffin in "More about Bat 'Radar,'" the process depends upon the emission of pulses of high frequency sound from the mouth or the nose, and the detection of objects by distinguishing sound echoes with a hypersensitive auditory system. Except for a few kinds of bats, the length of time during which an individual pulse is emitted is quite short. Therefore, the pulse of sound energy traveling through the air is short also. This distinguishes such bat sounds from most sounds that we produce when speaking—common words are trains of sound waves in the air that may be hundreds of feet in length. Since the bat may have reduced sensitivity of hearing while it is emitting each high-energy pulse from the throat, it is obviously advantageous to have short sound pulses. Short pulses of sound are particularly important for hunting insects: first, when the bat is searching for the insects, it is listening for faint echoes that may come from long distances; second, when the bat is homing-in rapidly, immediately before seizing the prey, echoes return to the ear after very short periods of time. In both situations, the auditory system might not function optimally if echoes were returning from objects while a long sound pulse was still being emitted.

Sound pulses are produced by specialized vibrating sheets of tissue in the larynx (the voice box). These sheets are only 8 microns thick, and they are stretched tautly across shallow depressions in the lateral walls of the larynx. Extraordinarily large cricothyroid muscles stretch the membranes tightly, and vary the tension during pulse emission in order to alter the frequency of emitted sound. It is still not known how the pulses are turned on and off with such rapidity, or how emission of sound is coordinated with muscle contractions in the ear. The actual intensity of each ultrasonic pulse generated by the larynx is amazingly high. Two to three inches in front of the bat's mouth the intensity may be six times the intensity of a subway train roaring through a station (60 versus 10 dynes per square centimeter). One might guess that these sounds are very loud to other organisms whose hearing abilities range from 20 to 80 kilohertz.

A variety of adaptations coordinate activity in the larynx with that in the ear. For instance, the large stapedius muscles in the ears contract and pull on the ear bones to reduce sensitivity of the hearing apparatus. As might be expected, the muscles normally contract just before the larynx begins to produce a pulse of sound; muscle relaxation starts during the pulse emission so the ear is returned to full sensitivity for at least the last part of the interval between sound pulses. But, as a flying insect is approached, the muscles in some bats remain contracted constantly; this apparently permits the higher pulse emission rate and prevents damage to the ear. How the faint echo is detected above the high frequency outgoing pulses when the ear is in a state of reduced sensitivity is a mystery.

A final interesting aspect of echolocation is the method of detecting directionality. Some species of bats emit narrow cones of sound directly in front of their head, whereas others send out a wide arc of sound. In part the structure of the nostrils determines which pattern is used and whether the sounds are amplified after emission from the larynx. The ears also function in directional sensing. Many bats have exceedingly large ears.

The rhinolophids can move the ears back and forth as pulses are emitted from the nose. During flight, the ears move a distance of 8 millimeters about 50 times per second. If the movement is stopped by denervating the muscles that move the ears, the bats can no longer echolocate effectively. Other bats may determine the direction of an object by the difference in intensity of an echo at each ear, or by the difference in the length of time it takes for an echo from one source to arrive at each ear.

To add even further to the incredulity that these echolocating adaptations evoke, think of the problem of discrimination between echoes. How can the echoes from a moth be distinguished from those rebounding from tree trunks, twigs, leaves, other bats, or even rain drops? With many other bats flying about, the noise level must be intense. One possibility is that this discrimination is based upon a special programming, or preconditioning, that occurs in the auditory system as each sound pulse is emitted. Thus, the neurons receiving information from the ear may be made especially sensitive to sound patterns with the same characteristics as those of the pulse that had just been emitted. In this way an ordered and predictable pattern could be distinguished from the din of echoes and pulses in the environment.

As an addendum to Griffin's article, it is now known how fish-eating bats detect their prey. Roderick A. Suthers, an associate of Griffin, found that the pulses of sound from these bats are reflected off minute waves in the surface of the water or from fins or tiny objects protruding through the surface film (even as small an object as a 1-millimeter length of wire, 0.21 millimeters in diameter, reflected sound). Fish that are swimming or hovering just beneath the surface are thought to set up irregularities in the water surface, and the swooping bat responds by dipping its feet into the water as it skims along in order to snatch up the unsuspecting fish. These bats have been seen occasionally to "trawl" with their hooked claws dragging in the water as they swoop along. How they avoid alligators or gars is a mystery!

The use of sound by cetaceans is of particular interest, because some of these animals have the most complex brain of any mammal other than man. Dolphins emit two types of sound: high-frequency pulses that sound like "clicks" to us, and whistling noises reminiscent of canary "chirps." The sounds are generated by passing air from one nasal sac to the other through specially constructed valves. No air is lost from the body in the process. The clicks are the echolocating pulses, and just as a bat increases the pulse repetition rate when a flying insect is detected, so a dolphin increases its rate of pulsing when a fish is thrown into the water in front of it. Here the rate may rise from five to several hundred pulses per second. The frequency of sound (20 to 100 kilohertz) emitted with each pulse is complex, and it seems likely that low frequencies (sometimes coupled with high intensity and long duration) are used for long-range general assessment of the environment, whereas brief, high-frequency ultrasonic pulses are of use in short-range discrimination.

The purpose of dolphin whistles is not as well defined. Each emission of sound lasts for longer periods (for as much as half a second, versus milliseconds for a click), and the frequency of sound rises from 7,000 to 15,000 hertz as the whistle continues. Winthrop N. Kellogg has proposed that such sounds may be used as a form of frequency-modulated echolocation, in contrast to the pulse-modulation of clicking. The constantly changing emission of the whistle would produce echoes of constantly changing frequency, so that any one echo would be of a frequency different from that of the sound being emitted. Thus the echoes could be heard even though sound was still being generated. Because their frequency is lower than that of clicks, whistles would attenuate less in water and so would be of greater use in long-range assessment of the environment. Whether they are actually employed for such purposes or for communication is yet unknown.

Directionality in echolocation has not yet been studied extensively, but two interesting mechanisms are known. Some dolphins can emit highly directional clicks, with most of the sound energy being directed in a narrow cone directly in front of the animal. The other form of behavior is seen in the bottlenose dolphin as it swims toward a small target in the water: the animal's head moves back and forth in the water once every 2 to 3 seconds (the head moves about 5 degrees on each side of the axis of swimming movement). These head oscillations are obviously a form of auditory scanning, with the ears being moved back and forth to establish the source of the echo. As the echoes reach one ear and then the other, phase differences, intensity differences, and time differences can be detected by moving the head in this manner. Thus, the bottlenose dolphin has arrived at the same basic solution to locating its target in space as have rhinolophid bats.

The ear of cetaceans is truly remarkable. Because the ear is necessarily streamlined into the head, there is no external ear. Sound waves reaching the side of the marine mammal are transmitted down the ear canal and also through the body tissues toward the ear drum. This might suggest that the head oscillations described above would be of little use since sound approaches both ears from all directions. The secret of directional hearing lies in the fact that the middle and inner ears are encased in special massive bones called the tympanopetromastoids. In contrast to the structures in most terrestrial mammals, these bones are not attached directly to the skull or to other body skeletal parts. Consequently, they do not vibrate when the rest of the skeleton does. In addition, the bones are so massive that they probably do not vibrate in response to sound waves over

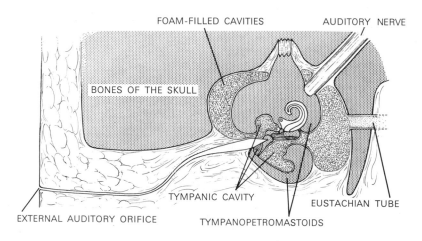

FOAM-FILLED CAVITIES   AUDITORY NERVE

BONES OF THE SKULL

TYMPANIC CAVITY

EXTERNAL AUDITORY ORIFICE   TYMPANOPETROMASTOIDS   EUSTACHIAN TUBE

Figure 2. A diagrammatic section through the ear region of a dolphin. The internal ear parts are located in the tympanic cavity enclosed by the ear bones. "Foamy" material insulates the bones from the skull. Sound vibrations travel down the ear canal toward the ear drum.
[After deHaan, Reysenbach, *Acta Oto-Laryngologica,* Supplementum 134, 1957.]

150 hertz. Finally, a gelatinous "foam" insulates the internal ear parts from the ear bones themselves; this air-filled foam probably reflects and absorbs most of the sound energy that succeeds in passing through the ear bones. The result of all of these structural adaptations is to insulate the ear effectively from vibrations in all directions but one—from the ear canal to the ear drum. This means that sound can be detected only on the two sides of the body, and directional hearing is the result. This is why auditory scanning developed in the bottlenose dolphin, and why other cetaceans can echolocate objects in the water.

In cetaceans, the auditory nerve leading from the cochlea of the ear to the brain is very large, and the lateral lobes of the cerebral cortex are huge. This is a major reason why the large complex brain of a dolphin has a width greater than its length. In man, for whom sight is dominant, or in a dog, for whom smell is so important, expansion of the frontal or olfactory centers causes the brain to be lengthened in the anterior-posterior direction. The brain of the bottlenose dolphin is an example of the opposite extreme, for the olfactory lobes and tracts are missing altogether, and the brain is short and wide.

How else, aside from catching food, do cetaceans use their echolocation abilities? One example is observed in whales during annual migrations. As gray whales migrate from the Arctic Ocean to Baja California each year, they tend to travel fairly close to the shore. Many other whales also remain above continental shelves for portions of their long migrations. Typical echolocation signals have been recorded for most of them, and it is supposed that in regions of shallow water they use their sound system as a

Figure 3. The main migratory routes of humpback whales in the southern hemisphere. Note the prevalence of coastal routes for long portions of the journeys. Many whales spend winter in the tropics where they breed. They migrate to the Antarctic and its abundant food supply for the summer and then return to the tropics where the young are born (often in shallow coastal waters). The young are weaned the summer following the return journey to the Antarctic. [After Slijper, E. J., *Whales,* Basic Books, 1962.]

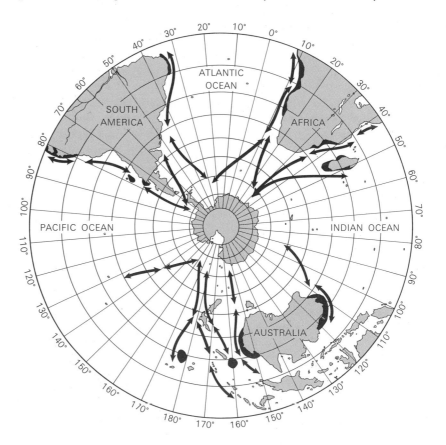

fathometer, or depth-gauging device. In regions of deep oceanic trenches, it is common to see whales surfacing repeatedly, coming high out of the water, almost to the level of their fins. The biologist Kenneth Norris has proposed that they use eyesight at such times to guide them across the deep water to areas where depth detection is once more possible. Since in the course of most whale migrations extended periods of deep-water cruising take place, it seems likely that celestial navigation or some other undefined orienting device may be used. In effect, we can assume that the sensory system best suited for particular circumstances will be employed, and that echolocation is utilized in shallow-water swimming.

Cetaceans use sound also for communication. A captured animal detained next to a ship emits characteristic whistles or click patterns; others of the school respond behaviorally and emit sounds in return. The clearest demonstration of such communication comes from an experiment in which two bottlenose dolphins were placed in separate tanks connected only by an acoustic link. Six types of whistles were exchanged between the two animals, as well as occasional trains of clicks. Evidence implies that certain of the whistles may be a call or recognition signal, whereas several of the others are much less stereotyped and so may have more variable information content. As might be expected from the complexity of the cetacean brain, communication behavior depends on age, sex, and emotional state of the animal. Innumerable historical accounts relate instances in which the observed behavior of the animals seems to have been dependent upon sound communication.

Another fascinating use of echolocation is found in blind human beings. It has been known for many years that the blind have "facial vision," that is, an ability to detect objects in their vicinity, presumably by sensing differences in air pressure on the face. In fact, this ability is dependent upon the sense of hearing, so that plugging the ears causes disorientation of the subject. When blind people were allowed to select noises that they found most effective at producing echoes (i.e., "awareness" of objects in the environment), all chose forms of "hissing" or tongue "clicking." The skill in detecting objects in the environment varies from person to person; a typical subject identified a 7.1-centimeter target, located 61 centimeters from his face, 100 percent of the time, and a 30.5-centimeter target, 274 centimeters away, 95 percent of the time. The frequency of correct identification diminishes with decreasing target size, no matter what the distance is.

The sounds emitted by these subjects varied in frequency from 170 hertz to 16 kilohertz and even the clicks were of relatively long duration (0.025 seconds). This meant that echoes were returning before the sound production and emission were completed. Clearly, this learned adaptation of atypical human beings does not equal the highly evolved system of a bat.

Do these human subjects have good directional sensing ability? The experiments showed that some people could emit clicks and localize targets with the use of only one ear. With both ears uncovered and sound directed from the mouth straight in front of the face, these subjects could detect targets as much as 90 degrees to the right or the left and point them out with good accuracy. All of these results attest to the adaptability of the human organism in employing substitute sensory mechanisms when normal primary orientation by vision is not possible.

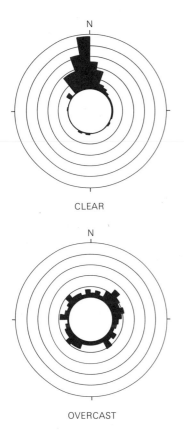

CLEAR

OVERCAST

Figure 4. Flight directions taken by mallard ducks that had been displaced prior to release. Under clear skies, most flew north, but if the skies were cloudy, flight orientation was incorrect. Equivalent data were obtained when mallards were released on clear or overcast nights.
[After Bellrose, F. C.; in R. M. Storm, ed., *Animal Orientation and Navigation: Oregon State University Biology Colloquium, 1966*, Oregon State University Press, 1967.]

The last type of vertebrate orientation that we will discuss—celestial navigation—is one of the most fascinating aspects of vertebrate biology. Birds, of course, provide the most widely quoted cases of long-range navigation, with flights of thousands of miles often occurring twice each year for many species. As pointed out by the late German behaviorist Gustav Kramer, true navigation requires that the organism have at least three pieces of information: (1) knowledge of its current position on the earth; (2) knowledge of the position (latitude and longitude) of the target of navigation; (3) knowledge of the direction from site one to site two. The basic question is whether birds or other animals are truly capable of such navigation, or whether compass direction alone is the parameter employed during oriented movement. Because it does seem likely that many animals use land marks extensively in initiating and terminating migration, compass direction might be the crucial information for them if navigation normally starts and ends only in known regions.

Sun navigation of birds has been investigated by many research workers since Kramer demonstrated "fluttering" orientation of starlings. Owing to altering day lengths, hormonal changes occur in a bird that bring it into a migratory condition. When caged, such birds become hyperactive and hop and flutter in the direction that they would fly if free to migrate. This oriented behavior occurs *only when the sun is visible,* and the direction of fluttering shifts a predictable number of degrees when the image of the sun is displaced a known amount by mirrors. This finding demonstrates that direction is determined in response to the sun; it does not prove true navigational ability, which demands, in addition, at least assessment of latitude. One of the best cases of measurement of the height of the sun (so that latitude can be determined) comes from fishes that give clear evidence of compensation in orientation when the sun's altitude in the sky is raised with mirrors or by other means. If this capacity is present also in birds, then the idea that they are true navigators becomes more acceptable.

If the sun or the stars are to be used as guides in navigation, the organism must possess an internal biological "clock." As the sun moves across the sky, the bird is able to maintain a straight migratory course over the surface of the earth only if it can compensate for movement of the sun; thus, with the aid of its clock, the bird continually alters the angle between the sun and the axis of migration. The presence of the clock may be demonstrated by two types of experiments: In the first, a bird is displaced a long distance east or west. Despite the displacement in longitude the bird's clock still runs on the original "local" time, and, as shown in Figure 5, the bird orients as it normally would at home. A bird makes the same error in the second experiment, in which its clock has been "reset" by a gradual altering of the day-night cycle with artificial lighting. Afterward, even when it is exposed to sunlight in its home environment, it acts according to the new time and orients in the wrong direction. As discussed in "The Navigation of Penguins" by John T. Emlen and Richard L. Penney, exposure to sunlight in the new longitude for several weeks will allow the clock to become gradually reset to the new local time.

All of these physiological and navigational abilities also operate at night, the time when most birds migrate. Directional fluttering, similar to that seen during the day, can be observed under a clear, starry sky but

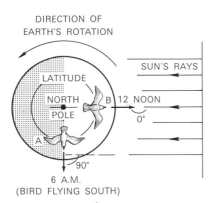

DIRECTION OF
EARTH'S ROTATION

LATITUDE
NORTH
POLE

SUN'S RAYS

B 12 NOON
0°

A

90°
6 A.M.
(BIRD FLYING SOUTH)

a. BEHAVIOR OF BIRD
IN NATIVE LONGITUDE

6-HOUR WESTWARD
LONGITUDINAL DISPLACEMENT
BIRD'S "CLOCK" READS 6 A.M.
WHEN TRUE LOCAL TIME IS MIDNIGHT

A

B

0°

BIRD'S "CLOCK" READS 12 NOON
WHEN THE LOCAL TIME IS 6 A.M.

BEHAVIOR OF BIRD WHEN
b. DISPLACED 6 HOURS LONGITUDINALLY
TO WEST OF NATIVE LONGITUDE,
SAME LATITUDE

Figure 5. Results of longitude displacement on bird orientation. Imagine that you are in space directly above the North Pole and the earth is rotating counterclockwise beneath you. In Figure *a* the bird flies directly away from the North Pole toward the south. If it begins its journey at 6:00 A.M., it displaces its angle of flight 90° with respect to the rays of the sun (position A). Six hours later, the earth has rotated on its axis, and now in order to fly "south," the bird has a 0° angle between flight path and sun's rays. In fact, all day long he compensates for the continually shifting sun and so maintains a constant course on the earth's surface.

In *b* the bird is displaced to the west. As shown in the illustration, when its clock reads 6:00 A.M. the bird is perched on a branch in darkness. During the ensuing 6 hours, the earth rotates and the bird's clock advances. Then the sun appears. It is 6:00 A.M. local time, but the bird's clock reads 12 noon. He orients just as he did at position B of Figure *a* at noon; that is, he flies directly toward the sun. Thus, instead of flying south on the earth's surface, he flies eastward.

not on a cloudy night. Equivalent behavior was observed when birds were exposed to a normal autumn sky in a planetarium, and, interestingly, compensatory shifts in orientation were made when the sky was "advanced" or "retarded" from 1 to 6 hours.

Although many statistical problems make strict interpretation of some of these experiments difficult, the results, in general, concur with what is known of normal field behavior. In one of the most important sets of observations to date, A. C. Perdeck displaced a large number of marked adult and young migrating starlings from Holland several hundred kilometers southeast to Switzerland. The adults that were released after such displacement compensated, and they were recovered in their normal wintering area on the northwestern coast of France. They must have "navigated" to get there since they had to go in an abnormal *direction* to complete the trip. The young birds did not go northwest but instead flew to southwestern France and even to Spain and Portugal independently of the old birds, on a route parallel to the normal migratory route from Holland. Furthermore, some of the young birds kept flying farther than they would have on the normal route; they did not stop at a specific longitude. The next spring, both the young and the old birds returned to the original nesting grounds in Holland. Then, the following autumn, the younger birds again went their separate way back to the first year's wintering ground in the southwest of France and in Spain. Related observations indicate that "early" migrants that are captured and displaced to a region in Spain suitable for wintering, continue to migrate. But "late" migrants displaced to the same region soon search for nesting sites. Analogous results have been observed in other contexts, and it seems correct to conclude that the early migrant must migrate for a minimum time before it can enter a behavioral stage of site selection. These experiments demonstrate that untrained young birds have an innate migratory direction that they follow, and that they fly an approximate distance (or time). Obviously learning, too, occurs since the site of hatching and upbringing continued to be the home breeding ground, and the first-year wintering ground was equally permanent.

27

The Homing Salmon

ARTHUR D. HASLER AND JAMES A. LARSEN · August 1955

A learned naturalist once remarked that among the many riddles of nature, not the least mysterious is the migration of fishes. The homing of salmon is a particularly dramatic example. The Chinook salmon of the U. S. Northwest is born in a small stream, migrates downriver to the Pacific Ocean as a young smolt and, after living in the sea for as long as five years, swims back unerringly to the stream of its birth to spawn. Its determination to return to its birthplace is legendary. No one who has seen a 100-pound Chinook salmon fling itself into the air again and again until it is exhausted in a vain effort to sur-

mount a waterfall can fail to marvel at the strength of the instinct that draws the salmon upriver to the stream where it was born.

How do salmon remember their birthplace, and how do they find their way back, sometimes from 800 or 900 miles away? This enigma, which has fascinated naturalists for many years, is the subject of the research to be reported here. The question has an economic as well as a scientific interest, because new dams which stand in the salmon's way have cut heavily into salmon fishing along the Pacific Coast. Before long nearly every stream of any appreciable size in the

West will be blocked by dams. It is true that the dams have fish lifts and ladders designed to help salmon to hurdle them. Unfortunately, and for reasons which are different for nearly every dam so far designed, salmon are lost in tremendous numbers.

There are six common species of salmon. One, called the Atlantic salmon, is of the same genus as the steelhead trout. These two fish go to sea and come back upstream to spawn year after year. The other five salmon species, all on the Pacific Coast, are the Chinook (also called the king salmon), the sockeye, the silver, the humpback and the chum. The

TWO COMMON SPECIES of salmon are (*top*) the Atlantic salmon (*Salmo salar*) and (*bottom*) the silver salmon (*Oncorhynchus kisutch*). The Atlantic salmon goes upstream to spawn year after year; the silver salmon, like other Pacific species, spawns only once.

ODOR
RELEASER

DEAERATION
FUNNEL

SIPHON

ODOR
JETS

FEEDING
TROUGH

ELECTRODES

AIR INLET

EXPERIMENTAL TANK was built in the Wisconsin Lake Laboratory to train fish to discriminate between two odors. In this isometric drawing the vessel at the left above the tank contains water of one odor. The vessel at the right contains water of another odor. When the valve below one of the vessels was opened, the water in it was mixed with water siphoned out of the tank. The mixed water was then pumped into the tank by air. When the fish (minnows or salmon) moved toward one of the odors, they were rewarded with food. When they moved toward the other odor, they were punished with a mild electric shock from the electrodes mounted inside the tank. Each of the fish was blinded to make sure that it would not associate reward and punishment with the movements of the experimenters.

Pacific salmon home only once: after spawning they die.

A young salmon first sees the light of day when it hatches and wriggles up through the pebbles of the stream where the egg was laid and fertilized. For a few weeks the fingerling feeds on insects and small aquatic animals. Then it answers its first migratory call and swims downstream to the sea. It must survive many hazards to mature: an estimated 15 per cent of the young salmon are lost at every large dam, such as Bonneville, on the downstream trip; others die in polluted streams; many are swallowed up by bigger fish in the ocean. When, after several years in the sea, the salmon is ready to spawn, it responds to the second great migratory call. It finds the mouth of the river by which it entered the ocean and then swims steadily upstream, unerringly choosing the correct turn at each tributary fork, until it arrives at the stream where it was hatched. Generation after generation, families of salmon return to the same rivulet so consistently that populations in streams not far apart follow distinctly separate lines of evolution.

The homing behavior of the salmon

has been convincingly documented by many studies since the turn of the century. One of the most elaborate was made by Andrew L. Pritchard, Wilbert A. Clemens and Russell E. Foerster in Canada. They marked 469,326 young sockeye salmon born in a tributary of the Fraser River, and they recovered nearly 11,000 of these in the same parent stream after the fishes' migration to the ocean and back. What is more, not one of the marked fish was ever found to have strayed to another stream. This remarkable demonstration of the salmon's precision in homing has presented an exciting challenge to investigators.

At the Wisconsin Lake Laboratory during the past decade we have been studying the sense of smell in fish, beginning with minnows and going on to salmon. Our findings suggest that the salmon identifies the stream of its birth by odor and literally smells its way home from the sea.

Fish have an extremely sensitive sense of smell. This has often been observed by students of fish behavior. Karl von Frisch showed that odors from the injured skin of a fish produce a fright reaction among its schoolmates. He once noticed that when a bird dropped an injured fish in the water, the school of fish from which it had been seized quickly dispersed and later avoided the area. It is well known that sharks and tuna are drawn to a vessel by the odor of bait in the water. Indeed, the time-honored custom of spitting on bait may be founded on something more than superstition; laboratory studies have proved that human saliva is quite stimulating to the taste buds of a bullhead. The sense of taste of course is closely allied to the sense of smell. The bullhead has taste buds all over the surface of its body; they are especially numerous on its whiskers. It will quickly grab for a piece of meat that touches any part of its skin. But it becomes insensitive to taste and will not respond in this way if a nerve serving the skin buds is cut.

The smelling organs of fish have evolved in a great variety of forms. In the bony fishes the nose pits have two separate openings. The fish takes water into the front opening as it swims or breathes (sometimes assisting the intake with cilia), and then the water passes out through the second opening, which may be opened and closed rhythmically by the fish's breathing. Any odorous substances in the water stimulate the nasal receptors chemically, perhaps by an effect on enzyme reactions, and the re-

FOUR RUNWAYS are used to test the reaction of untrained salmon fingerlings to various odors. Water is introduced at the outer end of each runway and flows down a series of steps into a central compartment, where it drains. In the runway at the lower left the water cascades down to the central compartment in a series of miniature waterfalls; in the other runways the water is omitted to show the construction of the apparatus. Odors may be introduced into the apparatus from the vessels suspended above the runways. In an experiment salmon fingerlings are placed in the central compartment and an odor is introduced into one of the runways. When the four doors to the central compartment are opened, the fingerlings tend to enter the arms, proceeding upstream by jumping the waterfalls. Whether an odor attracts them, repels or has no effect is judged by the observed distribution of the fish in the runways.

sulting electrical impulses are relayed to the central nervous system by the olfactory nerve.

The human nose, and that of other land vertebrates, can smell a substance only if it is volatile and soluble in fat solvents. But in the final analysis smell is always aquatic, for a substance is not smelled until it passes into solution in the mucous film of the nasal passages. For fishes, of course, the odors are already in solution in their watery environment. Like any other animal, they can follow an odor to its source, as a hunting dog follows the scent of an animal. The quality or effect of a scent changes as the concentration changes; everyone knows that an odor may be pleasant at one concentration and unpleasant at another.

When we began our experiments, we first undertook to find out whether fish could distinguish the odors of different water plants. We used a specially developed aquarium with jets which could inject odors into the water. For responding to one odor (by moving toward the jet), the fish were rewarded with food; for responding to another odor, they were punished with a mild electric shock. After the fish were trained to make choices between odors, they were tested on dilute rinses from 14 different aquatic plants. They proved able to distinguish the odors of all these plants from one another.

Plants must play an important role in the life of many freshwater fish. Their odors may guide fish to feeding grounds when visibility is poor, as in muddy water or at night, and they may hold young fish from straying from protective cover. Odors may also warn fish away from poisons. In fact, we discovered that fish could be put to use to assay industrial pollutants: our trained minnows were able to detect phenol, a common pollutant, at concentrations far below those detectable by man.

All this suggested a clear-cut working hypothesis for investigating the mystery of the homing of salmon. We can suppose that every little stream has its own characteristic odor, which stays the same year after year; that young salmon become conditioned to this odor before they go to sea; that they remember the odor as they grow to maturity, and that they are able to find it and follow it to its source when they come back upstream to spawn.

Plainly there are quite a few ifs in this theory. The first one we tested was the question: Does each stream have its own odor? We took water from two creeks in Wisconsin and investigated whether fish could learn to discriminate between them. Our subjects, first minnows and then salmon, were indeed able to detect a difference. If, however, we destroyed a fish's nose tissue, it was no longer able to distinguish between the two water samples.

Chemical analysis indicated that the only major difference between the two waters lay in the organic material. By testing the fish with various fractions of the water separated by distillation, we confirmed that the identifying material was some volatile organic substance.

The idea that fish are guided by odors in their migrations was further supported by a field test. From each of two different branches of the Issaquah River in the State of Washington we took a number of sexually ripe silver salmon which had come home to spawn. We then plugged with cotton the noses of half the fish in each group and placed all the salmon in the river below the fork to make the upstream run again. Most of the fish with unplugged noses swam back to the stream they had selected the first time. But the "odor-blinded" fish migrated back in random fashion, picking the wrong stream as often as the right one.

In 1949 eggs from salmon of the Horsefly River in British Columbia were hatched and reared in a hatchery in a tributary called the Little Horsefly. Then they were flown a considerable distance and released in the main Horsefly River, from which they migrated to the sea. Three years later 13 of them had returned to their rearing place in the Little Horsefly, according to the report of the Canadian experimenters.

In our own laboratory experiments we tested the memory of fish for odors and found that they retained the ability to differentiate between odors for a long period after their training. Young fish remembered odors better than the old. That animals "remember" conditioning to which they have been exposed in their youth, and act accordingly, has been demonstrated in other fields. For instance, there is a fly which normally lays its eggs on the larvae of the flour moth, where the fly larvae then hatch and develop. But if larvae of this fly are raised on another host, the beeswax moth, when the flies mature they will seek out beeswax moth larvae on which to lay their eggs, in preference to the traditional host.

With respect to the homing of salmon we have shown, then, that different streams have different odors, that salmon respond to these odors and that they remember odors to which they have been conditioned. The next question is: Is a salmon's homeward migration guided solely by its sense of smell? If we could decoy homing salmon to a stream other than their birthplace, by means of an odor to which they were conditioned artificially, we might have not only a solution to the riddle that has puzzled scientists but also a practical means of saving the salmon—guiding them to breeding streams not obstructed by dams.

We set out to find a suitable substance to which salmon could be conditioned. A student, W. J. Wisby, and I [Arthur Hasler] designed an apparatus to test the reactions of salmon to various organic odors. It consists of a compartment from which radiate four runways, each with several steps which the fish must jump to climb the runway. Water cascades down each of the arms. An odorous substance is introduced into one of the arms, and its effect on the fish is judged by whether the odor appears to attract fish into that arm, to repel them or to be indifferent to them.

We needed a substance which initially would not be either attractive or repellent to salmon but to which they could be conditioned so that it would attract them. After testing several score organic odors, we found that dilute solutions of morpholine neither attracted nor repelled salmon but were detectable by them in extremely low concentrations—as low as one part per million. It appears that morpholine fits the requirements for the substance needed: it is soluble in water; it is detectable in extremely low concentrations; it is chemically stable under stream conditions. It is neither an attractant nor a repellent to unconditioned salmon, and would have meaning only to those conditioned to it.

Federal collaborators of ours are now conducting field tests on the Pacific Coast to learn whether salmon fry and fingerlings which have been conditioned to morpholine can be decoyed to a stream other than that of their birth when they return from the sea to spawn. Unfortunately this type of experiment may not be decisive. If the salmon are not decoyed to the new stream, it may simply mean that they cannot be drawn by a single substance but will react only to a combination of subtle odors in their parent stream. Perhaps adding morpholine to the water is like adding the whistle of a freight train to the quiet strains of a violin, cello and flute. The salmon may still seek out the subtle harmonies of an odor combination to which they have been reacting by instinct for centuries. But there is still hope that they may respond to the call of the whistle.

28

Electric Location by Fishes

H. W. LISSMANN · March 1963

Study of the ingenious adaptations displayed in the anatomy, physiology and behavior of animals leads to the familiar conclusion that each has evolved to suit life in its particular corner of the world. It is well to bear in mind, however, that each animal also inhabits a private subjective world that is not accessible to direct observation. This world is made up of information communicated to the creature from the outside in the form of messages picked up by its sense organs. No adaptation is more crucial to survival; the environment changes from place to place and from moment to moment, and the animal must respond appropriately in every place and at every moment. The sense organs transform energy of various kinds—heat and light, mechanical energy and chemical energy—into nerve impulses. Because the human organism is sensitive to the same kinds of energy, man can to some extent visualize the world as it appears to other living things. It helps in considering the behavior of a dog, for example, to realize that it can see less well than a man but can hear and smell better. There are limits to this procedure; ultimately the dog's sensory messages are projected onto its brain and are there evaluated differently.

Some animals present more serious obstacles to understanding. As I sit writing at my desk I face a large aquarium that contains an elegant fish about 20 inches long. It has no popular name but is known to science as *Gymnarchus niloticus*. This same fish has been facing me for the past 12 years, ever since I brought it from Africa. By observation and experiment I have tried to understand its behavior in response to stimuli from its environment. I am now convinced that *Gymnarchus* lives in a world totally alien to man: its most important sense is an electric one, different from any we possess.

From time to time over the past century investigators have examined and dissected this curious animal. The literature describes its locomotive apparatus, central nervous system, skin and electric organs, its habitat and its family relation to the "elephant-trunk fishes," or mormyrids, of Africa. But the parts have not been fitted together into a functional pattern, comprehending the design of the animal as a whole and the history of its development. In this line of biological research one must resist the temptation to be deflected by details, to follow the fashion of putting the pieces too early under the electron microscope. The magnitude of a scientific revelation is not always paralleled by the degree of magnification employed. It is easier to select the points on which attention should be concentrated once the plan is understood. In the case of *Gymnarchus,* I think, this can now be attempted.

A casual observer is at once impressed by the grace with which *Gymnarchus* swims. It does not lash its tail from side to side, as most other fishes do, but keeps its spine straight. A beautiful undulating fin along its back propels its body through the water—forward or backward with equal ease. *Gymnarchus* can maintain its rigid posture even when turning, with complex wave forms running hither and thither over different regions of the dorsal fin at one and the same time.

Closer observation leaves no doubt that the movements are executed with great precision. When *Gymnarchus* darts after the small fish on which it feeds, it never bumps into the walls of its tank, and it clearly takes evasive action at some distance from obstacles placed in its aquarium. Such maneuvers are not surprising in a fish swimming forward, but *Gymnarchus* performs them equally well swimming backward. As a matter of fact it should be handicapped even when it is moving forward: its rather degenerate eyes seem to react only to excessively bright light.

Still another unusual aspect of this fish and, it turns out, the key to all the puzzles it poses, is its tail, a slender, pointed process bare of any fin ("gymnarchus" means "naked tail"). The tail was first dissected by Michael Pius Erdl of the University of Munich in 1847. He found tissue resembling a small electric organ, consisting of four thin spindles running up each side to somewhere beyond the middle of the body. Electric organs constructed rather differently, once thought to be "pseudoelectric," are also found at the hind end of the related mormyrids.

Such small electric organs have been an enigma for a long time. Like the powerful electric organs of electric eels and some other fishes, they are derived from muscle tissue. Apparently in the course of evolution the tissue lost its power to contract and became specialized in various ways to produce electric discharges [see "Electric Fishes," by Harry Grundfest; SCIENTIFIC AMERICAN, October, 1960]. In the strongly electric fishes this adaptation serves to deter predators and to paralyze prey. But the powerful electric organs must have evolved from weak ones. The original swimming muscles would therefore seem to have possessed or have acquired at some stage a subsidiary electric function that had survival value. Until recently no one had found a function for weak electric organs. This was one of the questions on my mind when I began to study *Gymnarchus*.

I noticed quite early, when I placed a

ELECTRIC FISH *Gymnarchus niloticus*, from Africa, generates weak discharges that enable it to detect objects. In this sequence the fish catches a smaller fish. *Gymnarchus* takes its name, which means "naked tail," from the fact that its pointed tail has no fin.

new object in the aquarium of a well-established *Gymnarchus*, that the fish would approach it with some caution, making what appeared to be exploratory movements with the tip of its tail. It occurred to me that the supposed electric organ in the tail might be a detecting mechanism. Accordingly I put into the water a pair of electrodes, connected to an amplifier and an oscilloscope. The result was a surprise. I had expected to find sporadic discharges co-ordinated with the swimming or exploratory motions of the animal. Instead the apparatus recorded a continuous stream of electric discharges at a constant frequency of about 300 per second, waxing and waning in amplitude as the fish changed position in relation to the stationary electrodes. Even when the fish was completely motionless, the electric activity remained unchanged.

This was the first electric fish found to behave in such a manner. After a brief search I discovered two other kinds that emit an uninterrupted stream of weak discharges. One is a mormyrid relative of *Gymnarchus;* the other is a gymnotid, a small, fresh-water South American relative of the electric eel, belonging to a group of fish rather far removed from *Gymnarchus* and the mormyrids.

It had been known for some time that the electric eel generates not only strong discharges but also irregular series of weaker discharges. Various functions had been ascribed to these weak discharges of the eel. Christopher W. Coates, director of the New York Aquarium, had suggested that they might serve in navigation, postulating that the eel somehow measured the time delay between the output of a pulse and its reflection from an object. This idea was untenable on physical as well as physiological grounds. The eel does not, in the first place, produce electromagnetic waves; if it did, they would travel too fast to be timed at the close range at which such a mechanism might be useful, and in any case they would hardly penetrate water. Electric current, which the eel does produce, is not reflected from objects in the surrounding environment.

Observation of *Gymnarchus* suggested another mechanism. During each discharge the tip of its tail becomes momentarily negative with respect to the head. The electric current may thus be pictured as spreading out into the surrounding water in the pattern of lines that describes a dipole field [*see illustration on the next page*]. The exact configuration of this electric field depends on the conductivity of the water and on the distortions introduced in the field by objects with electrical conductivity different from that of the water. In a large volume of water containing no objects the field is symmetrical. When objects are present, the lines of current will converge on those that have better conductivity and diverge from the poor conductors [*see top illustration on page 273*]. Such objects alter the distribution of electric potential over the surface of the fish. If the fish could register these changes, it would have a means of detecting the objects.

Calculations showed that *Gymnarchus* would have to be much more sensitive electrically than any fish was known to be if this mechanism were to work. I had observed, however, that *Gymnarchus* was sensitive to extremely small external electrical disturbances. It responded violently when a small magnet or an electrified insulator (such as a comb that had just been drawn through a person's hair) was moved near the aquarium. The electric fields produced in the water by such objects must be very small indeed, in the range of fractions of a millionth of one volt per centimeter. This crude observation was enough to justify a series of experiments under more stringent conditions.

In the most significant of these experiments Kenneth E. Machin and I trained the fish to distinguish between objects that could be recognized only by an electric sense. These were enclosed in porous ceramic pots or tubes with thick walls. When they were soaked in water, the ceramic material alone had little effect on the shape of the electric field. The pots excluded the possibility of discrimination by vision or, because each test lasted only a short time, by a chemical sense such as taste or smell.

The fish quickly learned to choose between two pots when one contained aquarium water or tap water and the other paraffin wax (a nonconductor). After training, the fish came regularly to pick a piece of food from a thread suspended behind a pot filled with aquarium or tap water and ignored the pot filled with wax [*see bottom illustration on page 273*]. Without further conditioning it also avoided pots filled with air, with distilled water, with a close-fitting glass tube or with another nonconductor. On the other hand, when the electrical conductivity of the distilled water was matched to that of tap or aquarium water by the addition of salts or acids, the fish would go to the pot for food.

A more prolonged series of trials showed that *Gymnarchus* could distinguish mixtures in different proportions of tap water and distilled water and perform other remarkable feats of discrimination. The limits of this performance can best be illustrated by the fact that the fish could detect the presence of a glass rod two millimeters in diameter and would fail to respond to a glass rod .8 millimeter in diameter, each hidden in a

UNUSUAL FINS characterize *Gymnarchus* (*top*), a gymnotid from South America (*middle*) and sea-dwelling skate (*bottom*). All swim with spine rigid, probably in order to keep electric generating and detecting organs aligned. *Gymnarchus* is propelled by undulating dorsal fin, gymnotid by similar fin underneath and skate by lateral fins resembling wings.

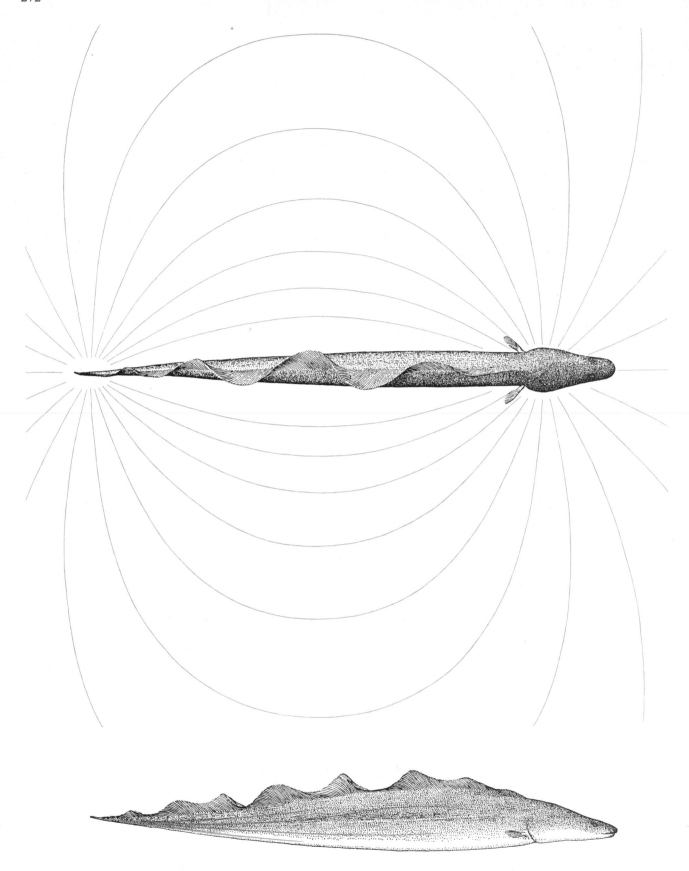

ELECTRIC FIELD of *Gymnarchus* and location of electric generating organs are diagramed. Each electric discharge from organs in rear portion of body (*color in side view*) makes tail negative with respect to head. Most of the electric sensory pores or organs are in head region. Undisturbed electric field resembles a dipole field, as shown, but is more complex. The fish responds to changes in the distribution of electric potential over the surface of its body. The conductivity of objects affects distribution of potential.

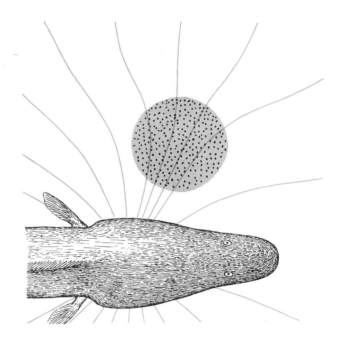

OBJECTS IN ELECTRIC FIELD of *Gymnarchus* distort the lines of current flow. The lines diverge from a poor conductor (*left*) and converge toward a good conductor (*right*). Sensory pores in the head region detect the effect and inform the fish about the object.

pot of the same dimensions. The threshold of its electric sense must lie somewhere between these two values.

These experiments seemed to establish beyond reasonable doubt that *Gymnarchus* detects objects by an electrical mechanism. The next step was to seek the possible channels through which the electrical information may reach the brain. It is generally accepted that the tissues and fluids of a fresh-water fish are relatively good electrical conductors enclosed in a skin that conducts poorly. The skin of *Gymnarchus* and of many mormyrids is exceptionally thick, with layers of platelike cells sometimes arrayed in a remarkable hexagonal pattern [*see · top illustration on page 276*]. It can therefore be assumed that natural selection has provided these fishes with better-than-average exterior insulation.

In some places, particularly on and around the head, the skin is closely perforated. The pores lead into tubes often filled with a jelly-like substance or a loose aggregation of cells. If this jelly is a good electrical conductor, the arrangement would suggest that the lines of electric current from the water into the body of the fish are made to converge at these pores, as if focused by a lens. Each jelly-filled tube widens at the base into

EXPERIMENTAL ARRANGEMENT for conditioned-reflex training of *Gymnarchus* includes two porous pots or tubes and recording mechanism. The fish learns to discriminate between objects of different electrical conductivity placed in the pots and to seek bait tied to string behind the pot holding the object that conducts best. *Gymnarchus* displays a remarkable ability to discriminate.

a small round capsule that contains a group of cells long known to histologists by such names as "multicellular glands," "mormyromasts" and "snout organs." These, I believe, are the electric sense organs.

The supporting evidence appears fairly strong: The structures in the capsule at the base of a tube receive sensory nerve fibers that unite to form the stoutest of all the nerves leading into the brain. Electrical recording of the impulse traffic in such nerves has shown that they lead away from organs highly sensitive to electric stimuli. The brain centers into which these nerves run are remarkably large and complex in *Gymnarchus,* and in some mormyrids they completely cover the remaining portions of the brain [*see illustration on next page*].

If this evidence for the plan as well as the existence of an electric sense does not seem sufficiently persuasive, corroboration is supplied by other weakly electric fishes. Except for the electric eel, all species of gymnotids investigated so far emit continuous electric pulses. They are also highly sensitive to electric fields. Dissection of these fishes reveals the expected histological counterparts of the structures found in the mormyrids: similar sense organs embedded in a similar skin, and the corresponding regions of the brain much enlarged.

Skates also have a weak electric organ in the tail. They are cartilaginous fishes, not bony fishes, or teleosts, as are the mormyrids and gymnotids. This means that they are far removed on the family line. Moreover, they live in the sea, which conducts electricity much better than fresh water does. It is almost too much to expect structural resemblances to the fresh-water bony fishes, or an electrical mechanism operating along similar lines. Yet skates possess sense organs, known as the ampullae of Lorenzini, that consist of long jelly-filled tubes opening to the water at one end and terminating in a sensory vesicle at the other. Recently Richard W. Murray of the University of Birmingham has found that these organs respond to very delicate electrical stimulation. Unfortunately, either skates are rather uncooperative animals or we have not mastered the trick of training them; we have been unable to repeat with them the experiments in discrimination in which *Gymnarchus* performs so well.

Gymnarchus, the gymnotids and skates all share one obvious feature: they swim in an unusual way. *Gymnarchus* swims with the aid of a fin on its back; the gymnotids have a similar fin on their

ELECTRIC DISCHARGES of *Gymnarchus* show reversal of polarity when detecting electrodes are rotated 180 degrees (*enlarged records at top*). The discharges, at rate of 300 per second, are remarkably regular even when fish is resting, as seen in lower records.

DISCHARGE RATES DIFFER in different species of gymnotids. *Sternopygus macrurus* (*upper record*) has rate of 55 per second; *Eigenmannia virescens* (*lower*), 300 per second.

VARIABLE DISCHARGE RATE is seen in some species. Tap on tank (*white line in upper record*) caused mormyrid to increase rate. Tap on fish (*lower record*) had greater effect.

underside; skates swim with pectoral fins stuck out sideways like wings [*see illustration on page 271*]. They all keep the spine rigid as they move. It would be rash to suggest that such deviations from the basic fish plan could be attributed to an accident of nature. In biology it always seems safer to assume that any redesign has arisen for some reason, even if the reason obstinately eludes the investigator. Since few fishes swim in this way or have electric organs, and since the fishes that combine these features are not related, a mere coincidence would appear most unlikely.

A good reason for the rigid swimming posture emerged when we built a model to simulate the discharge mecha-

nism and the sensory-perception system. We placed a pair of electrodes in a large tank of water; to represent the electric organ they were made to emit repetitive electric pulses. A second pair of electrodes, representing the electric sense organ, was placed some distance away to pick up the pulses. We rotated the second pair of electrodes until they were on a line of equipotential, where they ceased to record signals from the sending electrodes. With all the electrodes clamped in this position, we showed that the introduction of either a conductor or a nonconductor into the electric field could cause sufficient distortion of the field for the signals to reappear in the detectors.

In a prolonged series of readings the

slightest displacement of either pair of electrodes would produce great variations in the received signal. These could be smoothed to some extent by recording not the change of potential but the change in the potential gradient over the "surface" of our model fish. It is probable that the real fish uses this principle, but to make it work the electrode system must be kept more or less constantly aligned. Even though a few cubic centimeters of fish brain may in some respects put many electronic computers in the shade, the fish brain might be unable to obtain any sensible information if the fish's electrodes were to be misaligned by the tail-thrashing that propels an ordinary fish. A mode of swimming that keeps the electric field symmetrical with respect to the body most of the time would therefore offer obvious advantages. It seems logical to assume that *Gymnarchus,* or its ancestors, acquired the rigid mode of swimming along with the electric sensory apparatus and subsequently lost the broad, oarlike tail fin.

Our experiments with models also showed that objects could be detected only at a relatively short distance, in spite of high amplification in the receiving system. As an object was moved farther and farther away, a point was soon reached where the signals arriving at the oscilloscope became submerged in the general "noise" inherent in every detector system. Now, it is known that minute amounts of energy can stimulate a sense organ: one quantum of light registers on a visual sense cell; vibrations of subatomic dimensions excite the ear; a single molecule in a chemical sense organ can produce a sensation, and so on. Just how such small external signals can be picked out from the general noise in and around a metabolizing cell represents one of the central questions of sensory physiology. Considered in connection with the electric sense of fishes, this question is complicated further by the high frequency of the discharges from the electric organ that excite the sensory apparatus.

In general, a stimulus from the environment acting on a sense organ produces a sequence of repetitive impulses in the sensory nerve. A decrease in the strength of the stimulus causes a lower frequency of impulses in the nerve. Conversely, as the stimulus grows stronger, the frequency of impulses rises, up to a certain limit. This limit may vary from one sense organ to another, but 500 impulses per second is a common upper limit, although 1,000 per second have been recorded over brief intervals.

In the case of the electric sense organ of a fish the stimulus energy is provided by the discharges of the animal's electric organ. *Gymnarchus* discharges at the rate of 300 pulses per second. A change in the amplitude—not the rate—of these pulses, caused by the presence of an object in the field, constitutes the effective stimulus at the sense organ. Assuming that the reception of a single discharge of small amplitude excites one impulse in a sensory nerve, a discharge of larger amplitude that excited two impulses would probably reach and exceed the upper limit at which the nerve can generate impulses, since the nerve would now be firing 600 times a second (twice the rate of discharge of the electric organ). This would leave no room

BRAIN AND NERVE ADAPTATIONS of electric fish are readily apparent. Brain of typical nonelectric fish (*top*) has prominent cerebellum (*gray*). Regions associated with electric sense (*color*) are quite large in *Gymnarchus* (*middle*) and even larger in the mormyrid (*bottom*). Lateral-line nerves of electric fishes are larger, nerves of nose and eyes smaller.

to convey information about gradual changes in the amplitude of incoming stimuli. Moreover, the electric organs of some gymnotids discharge at a much higher rate; 1,600 impulses per second have been recorded. It therefore appears unlikely that each individual discharge is communicated to the sense organs as a discrete stimulus.

We also hit on the alternative idea that the frequency of impulses from the sensory nerve might be determined by the mean value of electric current transmitted to the sense organ over a unit of time; in other words, that the significant messages from the environment are averaged out and so discriminated from the background of noise. We tested this idea on *Gymnarchus* by applying trains of rectangular electric pulses of varying voltage, duration and frequency across the aquarium. Again using the conditioned-reflex technique, we determined the threshold of perception for the different pulse trains. We found that the fish is in fact as sensitive to high-frequency pulses of short duration as it is to low-frequency pulses of identical voltage but correspondingly longer duration. For any given pulse train, reduction in voltage could be compensated either by an increase in frequency of stimulus or an increase in the duration of the pulse. Conversely, reduction in the frequency required an increase in the voltage or in the duration of the pulse to reach the threshold. The threshold would therefore appear to be determined by the product of voltage times duration times frequency.

Since the frequency and the duration of discharges are fixed by the output of the electric organ, the critical variable at the sensory organ is voltage. Threshold determinations of the fish's response to single pulses, compared with quantitative data on its response to trains of pulses, made it possible to calculate the time over which the fish averages out the necessarily blurred information carried within a single discharge of its own. This time proved to be 25 milliseconds, sufficient for the electric organ to emit seven or eight discharges.

The averaging out of information in this manner is a familiar technique for improving the signal-to-noise ratio; it has been found useful in various branches of technology for dealing with barely perceptible signals. In view of the very low signal energy that *Gymnarchus* can detect, such refinements in information processing, including the ability to average out information picked up by a large number of separate sense organs,

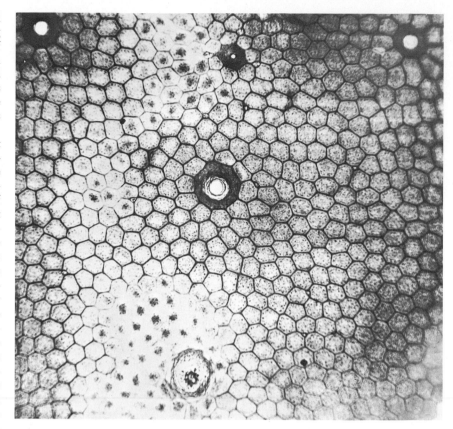

SKIN OF MORMYRID is made up of many layers of platelike cells having remarkable hexagonal structure. The pores contain tubes leading to electric sense organs. This photomicrograph by the author shows a horizontal section through the skin, enlarged 100 diameters.

MEETING POINT of electric sensory cell (*left*) and its nerve (*right*) is enlarged 120,000 diameters in this electron micrograph by the author and Ann M. Mullinger. Bulge of sensory cell into nerve ending displays the characteristic dense streak surrounded by vesicles.

appear to be essential. We have found that *Gymnarchus* can respond to a continuous direct-current electric stimulus of about .15 microvolt per centimeter, a value that agrees reasonably well with the calculated sensitivity required to recognize a glass rod two millimeters in diameter. This means that an individual sense organ should be able to convey information about a current change as small as .003 micromicroampere. Extended over the integration time of 25 milliseconds, this tiny current corresponds to a movement of some 1,000 univalent, or singly charged, ions.

The intimate mechanism of the single sensory cell of these organs is still a complete mystery. In structure the sense organs differ somewhat from species to species and different types are also found

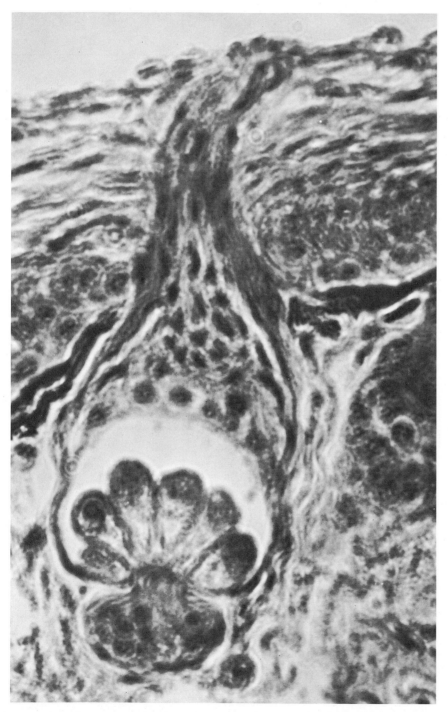

VERTICAL SECTION through skin and electric sense organ of a gymnotid shows tube containing jelly-like substance widening at base into a capsule, known as multicellular gland, that holds a group of special cells. Enlargement of this photomicrograph is 1,000 diameters.

in an individual fish. The fine structure of the sensory cells, their nerves and associated elements, which Ann M. Mullinger and I have studied with both the light microscope and the electron microscope, shows many interesting details. Along specialized areas of the boundary between the sensory cell and the nerve fiber there are sites of intimate contact where the sensory cell bulges into the fiber. A dense streak extends from the cell into this bulge, and the vesicles alongside it seem to penetrate the intercellular space. The integrating system of the sensory cell may be here.

These findings, however, apply only to *Gymnarchus* and to about half of the species of gymnotids investigated to date. The electric organs of these fishes emit pulses of constant frequency. In the other gymnotids and all the mormyrids the discharge frequency changes with the state of excitation of the fish. There is therefore no constant mean value of current transmitted in a unit of time; the integration of information in these species may perhaps be carried out in the brain. Nevertheless, it is interesting that both types of sensory system should have evolved independently in the two different families, one in Africa and one in South America.

The experiments with *Gymnarchus,* which indicate that no information is carried by the pulse nature of the discharges, leave us with a still unsolved problem. If the pulses are "smoothed out," it is difficult to see how any one fish can receive information in its own frequency range without interference from its neighbors. In this connection Akira Watanabe and Kimihisa Takeda at the University of Tokyo have made the potentially significant finding that the gymnotids respond to electric oscillations close in frequency to their own by shifting their frequency away from the applied frequency. Two fish might thus react to each other's presence.

For reasons that are perhaps associated with the evolutionary origin of their electric sense, the electric fishes are elusive subjects for study in the field. I have visited Africa and South America in order to observe them in their natural habitat. Although some respectable specimens were caught, it was only on rare occasions that I actually saw a *Gymnarchus*, a mormyrid or a gymnotid in the turbid waters in which they live. While such waters must have favored the evolution of an electric sense, it could not have been the only factor. The same waters contain a large number of other fishes that apparently have no electric organs.

Although electric fishes cannot be seen in their natural habitat, it is still possible to detect and follow them by picking up their discharges from the water. In South America I have found that the gymnotids are all active during the night. Darkness and the turbidity of the water offer good protection to these fishes, which rely on their eyes only for the knowledge that it is day or night. At night most of the predatory fishes, which have well-developed eyes, sleep on the bottom of rivers, ponds and lakes. Early in the morning, before the predators wake up, the gymnotids return from their nightly excursions and occupy inaccessible hiding places, where they often collect in vast numbers. In the rocks and vegetation along the shore the ticking, rattling, humming and whistling can be heard in bewildering profusion when the electrodes are connected to a loudspeaker. With a little practice one can begin to distinguish the various species by these sounds.

When one observes life in this highly competitive environment, it becomes clear what advantages the electric sense confers on these fishes and why they have evolved their curiously specialized sense organs, skin, brain, electric organs and peculiar mode of swimming. Such well-established specialists must have originated, however, from ordinary fishes in which the characteristics of the specialists are found in their primitive state: the electric organs as locomotive muscles and the sense organs as mechanoreceptors along the lateral line of the body that signal displacement of water. Somewhere there must be intermediate forms in which the contraction of a muscle, with its accompanying change in electric potential, interacts with these sense organs. For survival it may be important to be able to distinguish water movements caused by animate or inanimate objects. This may have started the evolutionary trend toward an electric sense.

Already we know some supposedly nonelectric fishes from which, nevertheless, we can pick up signals having many characteristics of the discharges of electric fishes. We know of sense organs that appear to be structurally intermediate between ordinary lateral-line receptors and electroreceptors. Furthermore, fishes that have both of these characteristics are also electrically very sensitive. We may hope one day to piece the whole evolutionary line together and express, at least in physical terms, what it is like to live in an electric world.

STATION 1   STATION 2

3:00 A.M.
4:00 A.M.
1:00 P.M.
5:45 P.M.
5:59 P.M.
6:02 P.M.
6:05 P.M.
7:00 P.M.
9:00 P.M.
11:00 P.M.

TRACKING ELECTRIC FISH in nature involves placing electrodes in water they inhabit. Records at left were made in South American stream near daytime hiding place of gymnotids, those at right out in main channel of stream, where they seek food at night.

AFRICAN CATFISH, supposedly nonelectric, produced the discharges shown here. Normal action potentials of muscles are seen, along with odd regular blips and still other oscillations of higher frequency. Such fish may be evolving an electric sense or may already have one.

29

More about Bat "Radar"

DONALD R. GRIFFIN · July 1958

In these days of technological triumphs it is well to remind ourselves from time to time that living mechanisms are often incomparably more efficient than their artificial imitations. There is no better illustration of this rule than the sonar system of bats. Ounce for ounce and watt for watt, it is billions of times more efficient and more sensitive than the radars and sonars contrived by man [*see table at bottom of page 281*].

Of course the bats have had some 50 million years of evolution to refine their sonar. Their physiological mechanisms for echolocation, based on all this accumulated experience, should therefore repay our thorough study and analysis.

To appreciate the precision of the bats' echolocation we must first consider the degree of their reliance upon it. Thanks to sonar, an insect-eating bat can get along perfectly well without eyesight. This was brilliantly demonstrated by an experiment performed in the late 18th century by the Italian naturalist Lazaro Spallanzani. He caught some bats in a bell tower, blinded them and released them outdoors. Four of these blind bats were recaptured after they had found their way back to the bell tower, and on examining their stomach contents Spallanzani found that they had been able to capture and gorge themselves with flying insects in the field. We know from experiments that bats easily find insects in the dark of night, even when the insects emit no sound that can be heard by human ears. A bat will catch hundreds of soft-bodied, silent-flying moths or gnats in a single hour. It will even detect and chase pebbles or cotton spitballs tossed into the air.

In our studies of bats engaged in insect-hunting in the field we use an apparatus which translates the bats' high-pitched, inaudible sonar signals into audible clicks. When the big brown bat (*Eptesicus fuscus*) cruises past at 40 or 50 feet above the ground, the clicks sound like the slow put-put of an old marine engine. As the bat swoops toward a moth, the sounds speed up to the tempo of an idling outboard motor, and

OBSTACLES in the form of thin vertical wires are avoided by a bat despite the presence of interfering noise. The noise comes from banks of loudspeakers to left and right of the four sets of wires. Man at right holds microphone which picks up bat's signals.

when the chase grows really hot they are like the buzz of a model-airplane gasoline engine. It seems almost certain that these adjustments of the pulses are made in order to enable the bat to home on its insect prey.

At the cruising tempo each pulse is about 10 to 15 thousandths of a second long; during the buzz the pulses are shortened to less than a thousandth of a second and are emitted at rates as high as 200 per second. These sound patterns can be visualized by means of a sound spectrogram [*see charts on page 282*]. Within each individual pulse of sound the frequency drops as much as a whole octave (from about 50,000 to 25,000 cycles per second). As the pitch changes, the wavelength rises from about six to 12 millimeters. This is just the size range of most insects upon which the bat feeds. The bat's sound pulse may sweep the whole octave, because its target varies in size as the insect turns its body and flutters its wings.

The largest bats, such as the flying foxes or Old World fruit bats [see "Bats," by William A. Wimsatt; SCIENTIFIC AMERICAN, November, 1957], have no sonar. As their prominent eyes suggest, they depend on vision; if forced to fly in the dark, they are as helpless as an ordinary bird. One genus of bat uses echolocation in dark caves but flies by vision and emits no sounds in the light. Its orientation sounds are sharp clicks audible to the human ear, like those of the cave-dwelling oil bird of South America [see "Bird Sonar," by Donald R. Griffin; SCIENTIFIC AMERICAN, March, 1954].

On the other hand, all of the small bats (suborder *Microchiroptera*) rely largely on echolocation, to the best of our present knowledge. Certain families of bats in tropical America use only a single wavelength or a mixture of harmonically related frequencies, instead of varying the frequency systematically in each pulse. Those that live on fruit, and the vampire bats that feed on the blood of animals, employ faint pulses of this type.

Another highly specialized group, the horseshoe bats of the Old World, have elaborate nose leaves which act as horns to focus their orientation sounds in a sharp beam; they sweep the beam back and forth to scan their surroundings. The most surprising of all the specialized bats are the species that feed on fish. These bats, like the brown bat and many other species, have a well-developed system of frequency-modulated ("FM") sonar, but since sound loses much of its energy in passing from air into water and *vice*

BATS shown in these drawings all use some type of echolocation system except for the fruit bat *Rousettus*, which appears at bottom right. The other species represented are the small brown bat *Myotis lucifugus* (*top*), the long-eared bat *Plecotus* (*left center*), the large brown bat *Eptesicus* (*right center*) and the horseshoe bat *Rhinolophus* (*bottom left*).

versa, the big puzzle is: How can the bats locate fish under water by means of this system?

Echolocation by bats is still such a new discovery that we have not yet grasped all its refinements. The common impression is that it is merely a crude collision warning device. But the bats' use of their system to hunt insects shows that it must be very sharp and precise, and we have verified this by experiments in the laboratory. Small bats are put through their maneuvers in a room full of standardized arrays of rods or fine wire. Flying in a room with quarter-inch rods spaced about twice their wingspan apart, the bats usually dodge the rods successfully, touching the rods only a small percentage of the time. As the diameter of the rods or wires is reduced, the percentage of success falls off. When the thickness of the wire is considerably less than one tenth the wavelength of the bat's sounds, the animal's sonar becomes ineffective. For example, the little brown bat (*Myotis lucifugus*), whose shortest sound wavelength is about three millimeters, can detect a wire less than two tenths of a millimeter in diameter, but its sonar system fails on wires less than one tenth of a millimeter in diameter.

When obstacles (including insect prey) loom up in the bat's path, it speeds up its emission of sound pulses to help in location. We have made use of this fact to measure the little brown bat's range of detection. Motion pictures, accompanied by a sound track, showed that the bat detects a three-millimeter wire at a distance of about seven feet, on the average, and its range for the finest wires it can avoid at all is about three feet. Considering the size of the bat and of the target, these are truly remarkable distances.

Do the echoes tell the bat anything about the detected object? Some years ago Sven Dijkgraaf at the University of Utrecht in the Netherlands trained some bats to distinguish between two targets which had the form of a circle and a cross respectively. The animals learned to select and land on the target where they had been trained to expect food. Bats can tell whether bars in their path are horizontal or vertical, and they will attempt to get through a much tighter spacing of horizontal bars than of vertical bars. In gliding through a closely spaced horizontal array the bat must decide just how to time its wingbeats so that its wings are level, rather than at the top or bottom of the stroke, at the moment of passage. All in all, we can say that bats obtain a fairly detailed acoustic "picture" of their surroundings by means of echolocation.

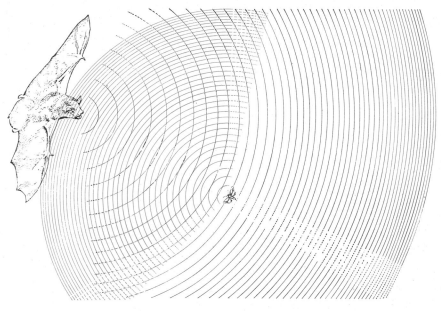

INSECT IS LOCATED by means of reflected sound waves (*colored curves*). Variation in the spacing of the curves represents changing wavelength and frequency of the bat's cry.

	BAT	RADARS		SONAR
	EPTESICUS	SCR-268	AN/APS-10	QCS/T
RANGE OF DETECTION (METERS)	2	150,000	80,000	2,500
WEIGHT OF SYSTEM (KILOGRAMS)	.012	12,000	90	450
PEAK POWER OUTPUT (WATTS)	.00001	75,000	10,000	600
DIAMETER OF TARGET (METERS)	.01	5	3	5
ECHOLOCATION EFFICIENCY INDEX	2×10^9	6×10^{-5}	3×10^{-2}	2×10^{-3}
RELATIVE FIGURE OF MERIT	1	3×10^{-14}	1.5×10^{-11}	10^{-12}

COMPARISON of the efficiency of the bat's echolocation system with that of man-made devices shows that nature knows tricks which engineers have not yet learned. "Echolocation efficiency index" is range divided by the product of weight times power times target diameter. "Relative figure of merit" compares the echolocation efficiency indexes with the bat as 1.

Probably the most impressive aspect of the bats' echolocation performance is their ability to detect their targets in spite of loud "noise" or jamming. They have a truly remarkable "discriminator," as a radio engineer would say. Bats are highly gregarious animals, and hundreds fly in and out of the same cave within range of one another's sounds. Yet in spite of all the confusion of signals in the same frequency band, each bat is

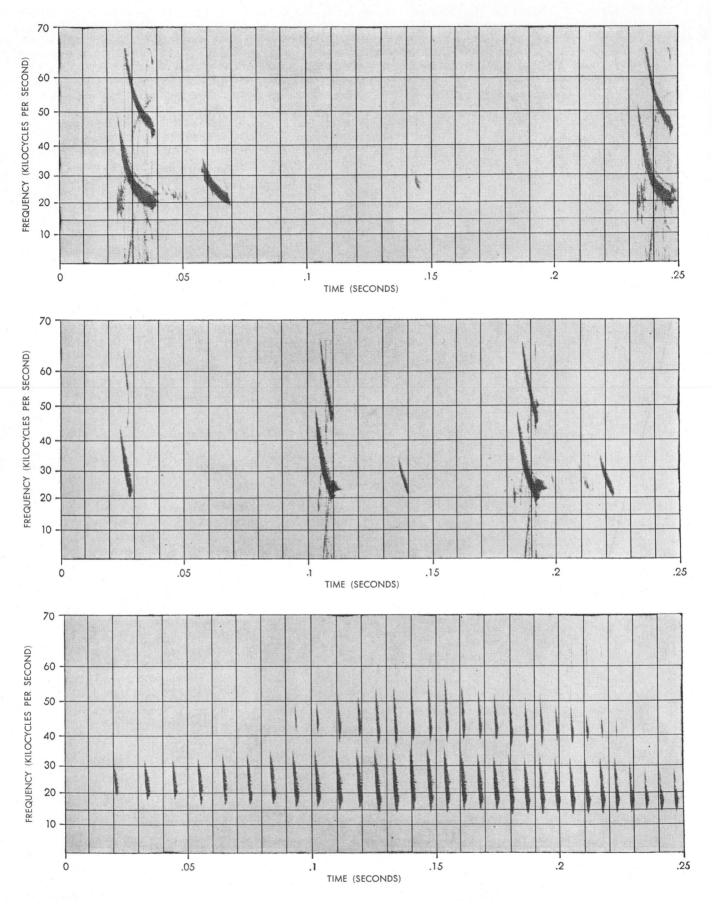

ORIENTATION SOUNDS of the large brown bat were recorded as slanting traces in these spectrograms while the animal was cruising (*top*), beginning pursuit of an insect (*middle*) and closing in on its prey (*bottom*). The traces appearing at .06 seconds in the top spectrogram and at .14 and .22 seconds in the middle spectrogram are echoes, which probably come from nearby buildings.

able to guide itself by the echoes of its own signals. Bats learned long ago how to distinguish the critically important echoes from other distracting sounds having similar properties.

We have recently tested the bats' discriminatory powers by means of special loudspeakers which can generate intense sound pulses. We found that a continuous broad-band noise which all but drowned out the bats' cries did not disorient them. They could still evade an insect net with which one tried to catch them; they were able to dodge wires about one millimeter in diameter; they landed wherever they chose.

In some experiments A. D. Grinnell and I did succeed in jamming certain FM bats, but it was not easy, and the effect was only slight. We worked on a species of lump-nosed bat (*Plecotus rafinesquii*) which emits comparatively weak signals. With two banks of loudspeakers we filled the flight room with a noise field of about the same intensity as the bats' echolocation signals. The more skillful individual bats were still able to thread their way through an array of one-millimeter wires spaced 18 inches apart. Only when we reduced the wires to well below half a millimeter in diameter (less than one tenth the wavelength of the bats' sounds) did the bats fail to detect the wires.

To appreciate the bats' feats of auditory discrimination, we must remember that the echoes are very much fainter than the sounds they emit—in fact, fainter by a factor of 2,000. And they must pick out these echoes in a field which is as loud as their emitted sounds. The situation is dramatically illustrated when we play back the recordings at a reduced speed which brings the sounds into the range of human hearing. The bat's outgoing pulses can just barely be heard amid the random noise; the echoes are quite inaudible. Yet the bat is distinguishing and using these signals, some 2,000 times fainter than the background noise!

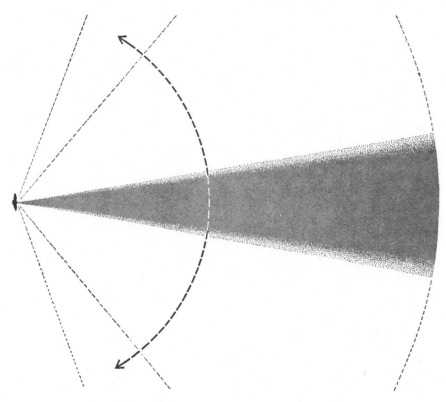

NARROW BEAM which sweeps back and forth is emitted by horseshoe bat in hunting insects. Beam is about 20 degrees wide, has a constant frequency and a pulse length of 50 feet.

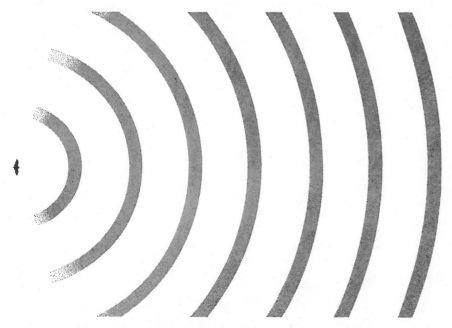

WIDE BEAM of short, frequency-modulated pulses is emitted by most bats while hunting. Each pulse (*gray curves*) is about 1.5 feet long. Beam is fixed with respect to bat's head.

Much of the modern study of communication systems centers on this problem of discriminating information-carrying signals from competing noise. Engineers must find ways to "reach down into the noise" to detect and identify faint signals not discernible by ordinary methods. Perhaps we can learn something from the bats, which have solved the problem with surprising success. They have achieved their signal-to-noise discrimination with an auditory system that weighs only a fraction of a gram, while we rely on computing machines which seem grossly cumbersome by comparison.

When I watch bats darting about in pursuit of insects, dodging wires in the midst of the nastiest noise that I can generate, and indeed employing their gift of echolocation in a vast variety of ways, I cannot escape the conviction that new and enlightening surprises still wait upon the appropriate experiments. It would be wise to learn as much as we possibly can from the long and successful experience of these little animals with problems so closely analogous to those that rightly command the urgent attention of physicists and engineers.

30

The Navigation of Penguins

JOHN T. EMLEN AND RICHARD L. PENNEY · October 1966

It has long been known that the domesticated pigeon can find its way home after having been transported to a strange location, and experiments conducted in recent years have shown that a number of wild bird species possess the same ability. A series of experiments conducted recently in Antarctica has demonstrated that one wild bird's ability to travel almost straight across hundreds of miles of featureless antarctic landscape depends on a "clock" and a "compass" working in combination. The experiments were conducted with a flightless bird, the Adélie penguin (*Pygoscelis adeliae*). Their results may help to answer the question that inevitably arises in discussions of bird navigation: How do the animals do it? In this article we shall relate why both

an unusual field area and an unusual bird were selected for the experiments, relate the outcome of our studies and conclude with a summary of the questions concerning bird navigation to which there now appear to be complete or partial answers.

Early in the nesting season of 1959 five adult male Adélie penguins were captured and banded at an Adélie rookery near Wilkes Station in Antarctica and flown 1,200 miles to McMurdo Sound. The birds were then released; in effect they were being asked if they could find their way home. The majority answer was yes: when the Wilkes rookery penguin population assembled the following spring, three of the five kidnapped males waddled up the beach from the sea to establish their claim at the very nesting sites from which they had been so abruptly taken 10 months earlier. By what route they had traveled home no one knows, but their performance added the Adélie penguin to the lengthening list of bird species able to navigate over long distances. The achievement has an extra dimension; most bird navigators fly, but the penguins had walked, tobogganed on their bellies or swum the entire way.

The observation that migratory birds return to the same nesting sites year after year almost always raises questions that are phrased in terms of how the migrants find their home. The late Gustav Kramer's discovery that captive birds could orient themselves by means of the sun was hailed as a major research breakthrough at the time of his first experiments in Germany 15 years ago. Here was a new insight into a compass-like mechanism that might explain birds' navigational abilities. As Kramer and others pointed out, however, neither bird nor man nor any

other animal is able to find the way home from a strange place with the aid of a compass alone. A man who undertakes true bicoordinate navigation needs both a compass and the equivalent of a map on which both his present position and his destination are located; at the very least a bird needs some kind of information about its position with respect to home at some point during its journey. Nonetheless, many investigators who are attempting to discover the cues that may tell navigating birds the direction of home have begun to wonder if the birds have access to such information after all.

One of the more troublesome problems connected with studies of bird navigation gave us a reason for selecting Antarctica as an experimental site. This is the difficulty involved in keeping track of experimental birds and recording their performance. If a bird is placed in a circular cage during its migrating season, it will provide information on some aspects of orientation. But if the bird is released from the cage in the hope of obtaining more information, control of the experiment flies out the window with the bird. Although free-flight experiments making use of birds fitted with telemetering devices that radio their position are currently yielding interesting results, at the time our antarctic experiments were undertaken the advantages offered by a flightless bird that travels overland in an environment free of obstacles and disturbances were compelling.

In addition to being a slow enough traveler on land to be followed easily, the Adélie penguin has a number of other assets as an experimental animal. First, it is a migratory bird with a demonstrated homing ability; each spring

PENGUIN ROOKERY at Cape Crozier in Antarctica has a summer population of some 300,000 Adélie penguins. The aerial photograph on the opposite page shows a part of the rookery; each of the black dots is the shadow of single or paired birds. The area indicated in color is shown enlarged above. Most of the birds used in the authors' studies of penguin navigation were adult or juvenile inhabitants of the rookery at Cape Crozier.

and fall Adélies travel hundreds of miles between the outer fringe of the antarctic pack ice and their rookeries on the coast of the continent. Second, it thrives in subzero weather and shuns all food for weeks on end during the nesting season. Third, it is abundant and easily captured at its rookeries. Fourth, because its normal range is along the coastal fringe of the continent, individual birds are not likely to be familiar with any landmarks in inland areas. Finally, the Adélie's back is broad, black and conspicuous in the polar snowscape,

and on most snow surfaces its tracks can be followed and charted in detail [*see illustration on page 291*].

The experimental advantages of Antarctica itself, in addition to its vast stretches of generally featureless interior, include 24-hour daylight during the summer season. Furthermore, the meridians of longitude come closer and closer together until they meet at the South Pole; therefore a comparatively short journey east or west along the coast may cover dozens of degrees of longitude. With the excellent facilities

provided by the Navy and the scientific-support arm of the Antarctic Research Program, it was possible to move captured penguins readily to locales many miles and many degrees of longitude distant from their home.

The subjects in most of our tests came from a thriving Adélie rookery at Cape Crozier, where some 300,000 birds gather each nesting season. We netted and moved the penguins 20 at a time to our test areas. There they were banded (on the wing) and housed

ANTARCTICA was selected as a location for the authors' studies both because Adélie penguins are hardy and accomplished migrants and because moving captive birds a comparatively short distance to the east or west placed them in a completely novel environment that contained a minimum of familiar navigation cues. Each fall the birds travel from any one of a number of coastal rookeries such as Cape Crozier north to the open water along the edge of the pack ice. When spring comes, they return to their home rookeries.

in pits excavated in the snow until it was their turn to be tested. Our principal test site was located in the middle of the 150,000-square-mile Ross Ice Shelf, some 180 miles southeast of Cape Crozier, at a point where the 180th meridian and the 80th parallel of south latitude intersect. Here a featureless white landscape stretches northward 105 miles to the Ross Sea and extends unchanged even farther southward and eastward. Only to the west is the flat terrain eventually broken by glacier-crowned mountain ranges, and these were out of sight 180 miles from our camp. Although the snow surface close at hand is wrinkled by irregular wind furrows, the distant line where sky and land meet is monotonously level.

In order to record the direction in which the penguins traveled when they were released we set up three tall tripods so that they formed the points of an equilateral triangle 200 meters on a side. A surveyor's transit was placed at the top of each tripod. At the midpoint of the triangular area we dug a small release pit with a cover that could be pulled clear with a tug on a length of cord that extended to an inconspicuous white shelter some distance away. When all was in readiness, we would remove a bird from its storage pit, put it in the release pit and set the cover in place. We then retired to our shelter and pulled the cord; the bird promptly jumped up to the surface, ready either to travel or, as sometimes happened, to lie down and go to sleep.

Usually the newly freed bird would make a few short dashes in various directions and then stand and peer at the limited scenery: the three transit tripods, our shelter and the antarctic sun. After a few minutes the bird would set off again, this time in a definite direction from which it rarely veered. Every five minutes two observers would take simultaneous azimuth readings, using the two transits that were best situated for the purpose. These readings enabled us to plot the bird's course over a distance of one to three miles and usually for 20 to 40 minutes, by which time our subject would have disappeared over the horizon [see top illustration at right]. Sometimes we extended the record by following a bird's tracks for as many as 16 miles from the release site. We also fitted a few penguins with radio transmitters and recorded their direction of travel for 50 miles or so. The bulk of our most useful data, however, was obtained by visually tracking 174 penguins during the first one to three miles of their journey. Most of our subjects

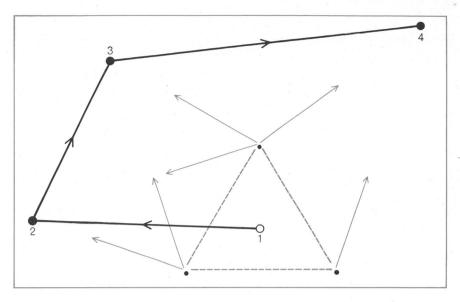

TRACKING SYSTEM required visual checks on the position of each bird at five-minute intervals after it was released from a pit located at the midpoint of an equilateral triangle with sides 200 meters long (*1*). A transit was located at each point of the triangle; readings from the two best-situated instruments (*arrows*) allowed the bird's position to be recorded until it vanished over the horizon. Some birds were subsequently tracked as far as 16 miles across the snow. A few birds fitted with radio transmitters were monitored up to 50 miles.

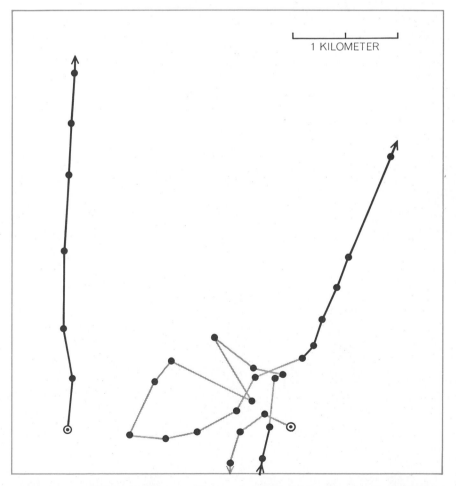

CLEAR AND CLOUDY SKIES caused the tracks illustrated in this diagram. Each dot represents the position of an Adélie penguin at five-minute intervals following its release (*bull's-eye*). In sunlight one bird (*left*) started on and held to a straight course until out of sight. Released under a cloudy sky, a second bird (*right*) headed the opposite way (*gray line*) but reappeared (*black*) when the sky cleared. More clouds left the bird moving at random until sunlight again headed it on much the same course as the first bird's.

CLEAR SUN   VEILED SUN   OBSCURED SUN

DEPENDENCE ON THE SUN as a compass was demonstrated by recording the penguins' movements in varying weather conditions. Each dot near the edges of the three circles represents the direction in which one bird left the test area; the arrows (*left and center*) show the mean heading. Thin clouds that veiled the sun (*center*) reduced the penguins' ability to orient themselves. When the sun was obscured (*right*), they were totally disoriented.

were birds from Cape Crozier released at the test site on the Ross Ice Shelf, but we also released birds at this site that had been captured at a rookery near Mirny Station, the Russian antarctic headquarters on the Queen Maud Coast. We also shifted release sites, liberating some Cape Crozier penguins on Marie Byrd Land (at 120 degrees west longitude), on the Victoria Land plateau (at 155 degrees east longitude), at a camp on the pack ice offshore from Cape Crozier and even at the South Pole.

One of the first things we learned

was that under clear skies our penguins characteristically selected and followed a straight line of travel for as long as we could see them. They often took small jogs right or left of the line, but these slight deviations were usually corrected in two seconds or so. When we plotted each bird's path as observed at five-minute intervals and compared the length of the plotted path with that of a straight line connecting the starting point and the last observed position, we found that the paths actually traveled by 62 penguins were only 1.025 times longer than the straight-line distances. In fact, nearly 90 percent of the birds achieved a "straightness index" of better than 1.009.

The importance of a clear sky and a good image of the sun to penguin orientation was soon demonstrated. When the sun was veiled by thin clouds (even though we could judge its position in the sky to within a few degrees), the performance of the departing penguins became erratic. When heavy clouds obscured the sun, the birds were completely disoriented and their selection of departure directions became random [*see top illustration at left*]. A dramatic demonstration of the birds' dependence on the sun was provided by one penguin whose movements we were able to follow for a four-hour interval that included two periods of overcast and two of clear sky. Heavy clouds covered the sun when the bird was released; it soon moved off in a direction exactly opposite to that taken by most birds under a clear sky and was lost from view about a mile away. Half an hour later it reappeared on the horizon, where there was now a patch of sunshine. As the sky cleared above us the bird continued to toboggan in our direction, approaching and passing our observation post. When it had traveled less than half a mile beyond us, clouds covered the sun again; it stopped and after a considerable pause set off at a right angle to its previous heading. It wandered irregularly and sometimes hesitantly for the next two hours, which remained cloudy. Then, as the sun broke through again, the bird resumed its interrupted direction of travel and passed out of sight over the horizon.

Navigation that uses the sun as a guide is by no means as simple as it may seem at first. The sun does more than rise in the east and set in the west. Its daily journey across the sky is complicated by an azimuthal motion that continuously alters its position with respect to landmarks on the horizon. In the

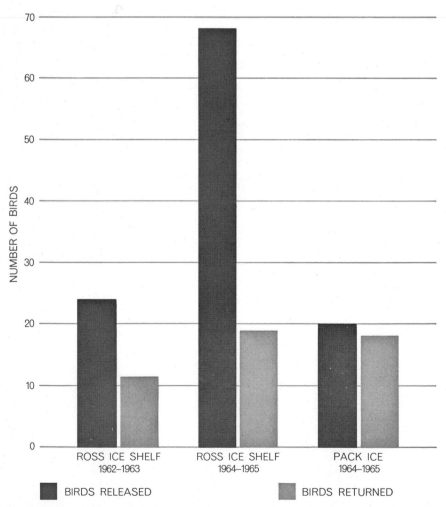

HOMING ABILITY of Adélie penguins is attested not only by their annual migrations but also by the eventual return to Cape Crozier of many of the birds that were transported to areas as far as 200 miles away. Use of the sun as a compass, although it enabled the penguins to orient consistently in unfamiliar territory, is not enough to explain their homing skill.

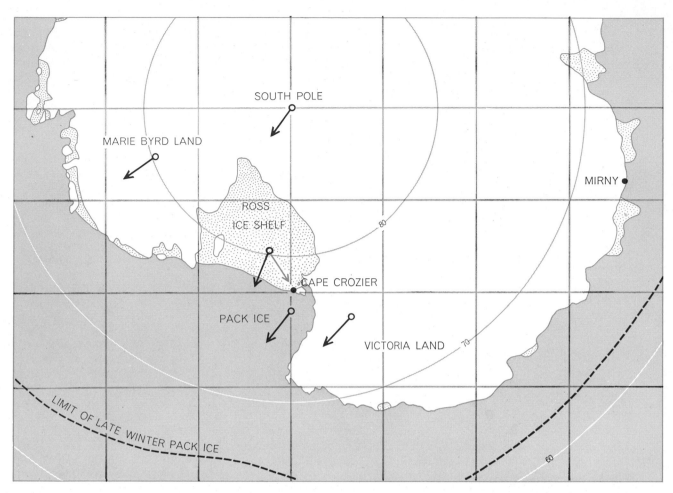

FIVE RELEASE POINTS, situated to the east, west, north and south of Cape Crozier, were used by the authors for their tests. Regardless of where they were released, birds from Cape Crozier all chose escape routes that were roughly parallel and approximately north-northeast with respect to a north-south line passing through Cape Crozier (*black arrows and gray grid*). When birds from the Russian antarctic station of Mirny were transported to the Ross Ice Shelf and released, they first chose escape routes almost perpendicular to those of Cape Crozier birds (*colored arrow*). When plotted with respect to a north-south line passing through Mirny, this heading also proved to be north-northeast. Other penguins from Mirny, kept on the Ross Ice Shelf for a few weeks, readjusted their "biological clock." When released, they chose the same general escape direction taken by the birds from the Cape Crozier rookery.

polar summer, when the sun neither rises nor sets, almost all its motion is azimuthal. To hold a constant course while one's "sun compass" swings around the horizon calls for continuous access to information on the passage of time, yet we found that the penguins were not affected by the sun's shifting azimuth. Birds that were released early in the morning set off northward, even though at that time a northerly heading was about 90 degrees to the left of the sun; at noon their northward departure was straight toward the sun; in the afternoon they still headed north, although by then such a heading was about 90 degrees to the right of the sun. Moreover, once the birds selected a course, they showed no tendency to fix on and follow the sun in its inexorable counterclockwise march along the horizon. This ability to be guided by the sun and yet to compensate for changes in its azimuthal position with the passage of

time is the strongest kind of evidence that the Adélie penguins possess the timing mechanism commonly called a "biological clock."

Although the penguins' general heading after release was northward, it could more accurately be described as north-northeasterly rather than due north. Some considerations of polar geography are a necessary preliminary to discussion of this point. When one is standing on the South Pole, all true compass directions are north. In polar areas, therefore, it is useful to forget about true compass headings and instead to calculate directions on the basis of a rectangular grid. Such grids take the meridian on which the user is located as their central vertical line. In the illustration above, for example, the grid is oriented to the meridian that runs from the South Pole through the Cape Crozier rookery. Analyzing the penguins' travel directions in terms of this grid,

we found that no matter where birds from Cape Crozier were set free they all set off in much the same north-northeast direction. This meant, of course, that they seldom headed for "home" at all. When Cape Crozier penguins were released on the Ross Ice Shelf or at Byrd Station, which are to the east of Cape Crozier, their heading pointed them far to the right of a homing course; when released in Victoria Land, to the west, their heading was about 90 degrees to the left of home. As for the penguins we released on the pack ice some 125 miles offshore, they set off on a north-northeast heading that took them directly away from the Cape Crozier rookery.

The fact that all the Cape Crozier birds, wherever they were released, pursued essentially parallel courses regardless of the actual direction of their home rookery is further evidence that the cue that guided all the birds was far more

POSITION READING is taken by a member of the authors' party, who stands atop a step-ladder in the middle of the Ross Ice Shelf. The escape paths pursued by 54 penguins released during clear weather varied from a straight line by a factor of less than 1 percent.

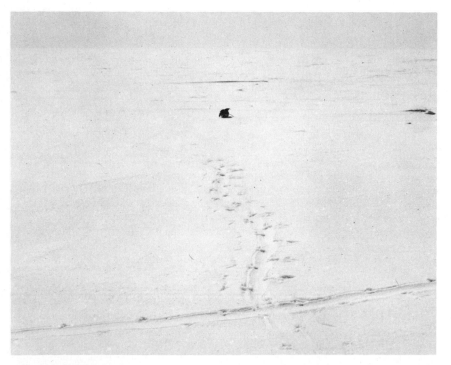

ESCAPING PENGUIN ignores another bird's path as it heads across the Ross Ice Shelf. Adélie penguins travel two to three miles per hour; the fastest did eight miles per hour.

remote than anything connected with their home or, for that matter, with any localized terrestrial cue. The sun, some 93 million miles away, was their compass, and they could use it unerringly because their biological clocks served to correct for its azimuthal changes. At the same time, it was clear that the Cape Crozier penguins did not head for home. Their movements were oriented in terms of a common direction of escape rather than an approach toward a common goal.

The cooperation of our Russian colleagues at Mirny, 2,000 miles and 90 degrees of longitude away, enabled us to make a further test of our conclusion. Forty Adélie penguins were captured at Mirny and flown to the Ross Ice Shelf. When we released 20 of them, the birds set off north-northeast, but north-northeast only with respect to a grid centered on their home meridian at Mirny. Their actual course with respect to the local grid was northwest, so that their route lay almost at right angles to that of the Cape Crozier penguins.

What functional explanation can be found, in terms of survival value, for the generally northward escape route taken by the Adélie penguins we captured at various rookeries? Northward, to be sure, is always seaward in Antarctica; an attractively simple explanation is that movement northward would carry a lost penguin along the shortest route to the sea—the species' only source of food. There is also another consideration. For migratory birds such as the Adélie penguin a sun compass "set" to a home meridian would tend to reduce lateral dispersal of any one rookery's population and ensure that the same group of penguins returned from the fringes of the pack ice to the same stretch of coast each year. Indeed, the home meridian—regarded as a reasonably broad corridor with one end in the coastal rookery and the other in the food-rich waters at the edge of the pack ice—may be what "home" is to an Adélie penguin. The bird's annual movements inward or outward along the corridor could be the result of physiologically controlled negative or positive responses to the same basic orientation cue or cues.

What accounts for the slight but unmistakable easterly vector that turns the outward journey from true north to north-northeast? At the end of our first season's work in Antarctica we were prepared to dismiss it as a chance variation. Further and stronger evidence of the easterly vector gathered in 1964

PENGUIN'S PROGRESS on land can vary from a brisk waddle (*left*), in which the bird's oscillating tail leaves a serpentine track in the snow, to a swift tobogganing, sometimes propelled by the feet alone (*center*) and sometimes assisted by wing strokes (*right*).

made it impossible to ignore. One possible answer suggests itself at present: The coastal currents in both the Cape Crozier and the Mirny areas are westerly. A penguin adrift on the offshore pack ice would be slowly carried westward out of its home zone unless it compensated by moving to the east from time to time. Similarly, a bird moving from the coast to the outer fringe of the pack ice would be borne toward the west if its line of march were true north instead of north-northeast. One observation that lends weight to our suggestion that the easterly vector is a compensation for westerly coastal currents is that the Mirny birds released on the Ross Ice Shelf showed a stronger easterly bias than the Cape Crozier birds released there. The westerly currents off the Mirny coast are known to run strong.

The contrast between the escape headings chosen by Cape Crozier and Mirny birds immediately raises two questions. It seems safe to assume that a penguin's ability to select an escape direction when transferred to a strange environment is something innate. But what about the specific direction selected? Is this innately determined or is it a function of the environment in which the bird was raised? And can external influences alter the setting of the bird's compass?

We decided to see what information the escape behavior of two-month-old, inexperienced penguins might provide concerning the first of these questions. We captured a number of Cape Crozier chicks, some near the nests where they had been hatched and others on the beach that borders the rookery. When they were released on the Ross Ice Shelf, all of them headed off generally north-northeast on a straight course, although they showed somewhat greater variations in their selection of departure directions than did the adult Adélies.

The chicks' possession of a directional preference cannot, however, be taken as proof that the response is innate in the species. From the day they emerge from their eggs the Adélie penguins at Cape Crozier look down a steep slope that faces the Ross Sea to the northeast. Below, adult penguins are constantly entering and leaving the water, returning with food for the ravenous chicks (who, when their hunger is unsatisfied, will often pursue a parent part of the way back to the water). The same north-easterly direction is the one in which the chicks themselves will move once they become independent of the nesting area. North-northeast thus becomes a significant direction to the birds as they mature. It seems plausible that such an upbringing, in which the topographic cues that come to mean "seaward" are constantly associated with the celestial cues that represent north-northeast, might allow the celestial cues to persist and function in situations where the topographic ones are no longer available.

As for the second question, we would have found it surprising if our birds had proved impervious to the environmental influences that are known to reset the biological clocks of many Temperate Zone animals within a period of a week or so. Yet, compared with the day-and-night cycle of the Temperate Zone, the cues available in the continuous daylight of the antarctic summer are notably weak ones. To put the matter to a test we kept the remaining 20 of the 40 birds from Mirny penned under the open sky on the Ross Ice Shelf for periods that ranged from 18 to 27 days. These birds had arrived with their clock synchronized to a time zone some 88 degrees to the west (equivalent to the six-hour time difference between London and New Orleans). At the end of their three- to four-week detention the 20 Mirny birds selected local north-northeast as their departure direction. Their clock—and thus their compass—had been reset; the resetting turned them 55 degrees to the right and pointed them in the same general escape direction as the one selected by the "local" Cape Crozier birds.

This finding leaves us in something of a dilemma. If all the Adélie penguins in the Antarctic can reset their clock as easily as the 20 birds from Mirny did, our earlier speculation that a constant local escape orientation would be useful in maintaining population-specific coastal zones may not be warranted. Any birds that wandered toward the lateral boundary of their population's corridor would be in danger of adapting to the new conditions there. The unifying interrelation of breeding grounds and feeding area that is provided by a common compass setting would therefore be lost to them. For the moment we can only suggest that unconfined birds may not reset their clock as readily as birds that are artificially detained do.

We have seen that the Adélie pen-guin can navigate with the sun as a directional cue and with an inherent timing mechanism as compensation for the sun's position changes from hour to hour. We have also seen that the consistent escape direction chosen by released birds is a northerly one that under normal circumstances would possess considerable survival value by leading a lost bird to the nearest feeding ground at sea. Unfortunately these two observations tell us little about the question that faced us at the outset: How do the birds find their way home? The fact that so many of our experimental subjects did reach their home rookeries indicates that Adélie penguins possess something by way of navigational equipment in addition to the sun-compass orientation they demonstrated during the release experiments. Cape Crozier birds released on the Ross Ice Shelf consistently headed far to the right of their true homeward direction, but at least half of them were back at Cape Crozier within 25 days. Of the 20 Cape Crozier birds we turned loose on the pack ice many miles offshore, 15 were back home within two weeks even though all had started off in exactly the opposite direction. How did the three birds from Wilkes Station and at least two of the birds from Mirny find their way home over thousands of intervening miles in time for the next nesting season? For that matter, how do millions of Adélie penguins do much the same thing in their annual migrations?

We can only speculate that a homing bird must receive new information at some point on its long trek. We suspect that the birds receive this new information when they reach the point at which open water enables them to swim and feed after a long period of deprivation. What a homing bird does and what cues it uses at this or any other critical point in its travels, however, are unknown. A simple 180-degree reversal in direction of travel, still depending on the sun compass, would be a maneuver useful to a penguin that had finally penetrated to the seaward fringe of the pack ice. Birds within 75 miles or so of the coast might also make use of visual cues such as the 13,000-foot peak of Mount Erebus on Ross Island. But at this stage in our investigations it is fruitless to speculate further.

To sum up, we have shown that the Adélie penguin uses a sun compass for orientation when released in a strange environment. We surmise that the same sun compass may guide the birds back from the open water to their breeding grounds after some other as yet undetermined cue or cues have reversed their direction of travel. A number of questions remain to be answered. We may, however, already have the answer to one of them. The antarctic winter is the season during which Adélie penguins spend their time away from land; when they leave the polar ocean at all, they perch on the ceaselessly shifting and drifting floes of the offshore pack ice. The antarctic winter is also a time of nearly total darkness, just as summer is a time of 24-hour-long daylight. How do these competent little navigators keep track of their position during the long dark period? We suspect that in the Adélie penguins' winter habitat the sun's brief appearance low on the horizon each noon is a strong enough cue to keep the birds' sun compass correctly set throughout the long polar night.

VII

Hormones and
Internal Regulation

There is another remarkable fact about song-birds; they usually change their colour and note with the season, and suddenly become different—which among the larger class of birds only cranes do, for these grow black in old age. The blackbird changes from black to red; and it sings in the summer, and chirps in winter, but at midsummer is silent; also the beak of yearling blackbirds, at all events the cocks, is turned to ivory colour. Thrushes are of a speckled colour round the neck in summer but self-coloured in winter.

Pliny
NATURAL HISTORY, X, XLI.

VII

Hormones and
Internal Regulation

INTRODUCTION

The article "Hormones" by Solly Zuckerman provides a broad introduction to the subject of hormones and control of body functions by the endocrine system. Work of the past decade has demonstrated the central role of the hypothalamus in the control of endocrine activities. There are two groups of neurosecretory cells in the hypothalamus. Those of the first group have cell bodies at various points in that portion of the brain and neurosecretory endings in the median eminence or stalk region near the anterior pituitary gland (the adenohypophysis). The other neurosecretory cells have axonal terminations in the posterior pituitary gland (the neurohypophysis).

The first group of cells produces, stores, and releases specific molecules (all of which may be polypeptides) that act as releasing agents for anterior pituitary hormones: growth hormone, leuteinizing hormone, corticotropin (ACTH), follicle-stimulating hormone, and thyrotropin are all released by these agents. Neuronal discharge in the hypothalamus apparently stimulates appropriate neurosecretory discharge of the agents, which then travel by special portal blood vessels to the adenohypophysis where they cause secretion of the hormones. Interestingly, the secretion of prolactin and probably of melanocyte-stimulating hormone (MSH) is inhibited by their hypothalamic substances.

The second group of neurosecretory cells, extending into the posterior pituitary, produces, stores, and releases vasopressin (ADH or antidiuretic hormone) and oxytocin. Within the cells, both of these peptides are apparently bound to a protein called neurophysin, so that discharge of the hormones requires dissociation from this complex. When nerve impulses reach the secretory endings, calcium ions (Ca^{++}) enter the cells and somehow participate in the release of the hormones.

The steps leading to release of the neurohypophyseal hormones are simpler than those causing discharge of adenohypophyseal hormones. Thus, nerve discharge in the hypothalamus causes the release of the neurohypophyseal hormone ADH, which acts directly on the target organs, the kidney tubules, to produce physiological effects. In contrast, when hypothalamic activity stimulates the production of the ACTH-releasing agent, that chemical must go to the adenohypophysis to cause discharge of ACTH, which in turn passes to the adrenal gland to evoke increased secretion of such compounds as cortisol (one of the adrenal steriods). The cortisol then acts on the target organ to produce a physiological response; the response may then affect in some way the hypothalamus, and so complete the loop. Thus, three agents and three cell types are involved in the complete process from nerve discharge to target-organ response. Other adenohypophyseal hormones involve only two agents and cell types in their loops.

It is not certain which of the two types of secretory control is more primitive. Although the neurohypophyseal system appears to be simpler, it is difficult to assign specific and consistent functions to ADH or to oxytocin in the fishes. ADH, for instance, seems to affect ion (particularly sodium) balance in fishes, influencing water balance too only in terrestrial vertebrates. The endocrinologists Aubrey Gorbman and Howard A. Bern have suggested that, in the earliest vertebrate endocrine system, hypothalamic neurosecretion may have acted on the adenohypophysis. Then, hypothalamic cell secretions began acting directly elsewhere in the body. The cells producing these neurosecretions (ADH, oxytocin) could next have acquired a more efficient means of secreting directly into the systemic circulation; thus, the discrete anatomical area, the neurohypophysis (pars nervosa) and its blood supply appeared.

Further studies have shown that there are close chemical relationships between endocrine agents performing quite different functions. Thus, ADH is very similar to the ACTH-releasing polypeptide that originates in the median eminence near the adenohypophysis. In fact, injected ADH can cause release of ACTH from the adenohypophysis (it is not absolutely certain here whether the ADH acts directly upon the ACTH, or indirectly by causing release of ACTH-releasing factor). Mammalian oxytocin differs from vasopressin in only two of its eight amino acids; and, mammalian vasopressin differs from the vasopressin of other terrestrial vertebrates (arginine "vasotocin") by a single amino acid substitution (see the following paragraph for details). Still another similarity in structure is that between MSH and ACTH: the amino acid sequence of the first compound is found in the longer peptide chain of the second. Finally, the whole family of steroids produced by the adrenal glands (aldosterone, cortisol, and so on) are built around a single basic chemical backbone. We could list other examples of this phenomenon, but these should make it clear that at all levels in the endocrine system the same basic molecules are adapted for different purposes. This, of course, is one reason why different hormones may cause similar effects: for example, an ACTH injection will

Figure 1. Representations of the pituitary gland of a bird (left) and of that of a mammal (right). The median eminence is the source of the various "releasing factors." In a bird, none of the neurosecretory cells originating in the hypothalamus end in the median eminence; instead, blood vessels course near the axons of the neurosecretory cells and then carry the blood and releasing factors downward to the adenohypophysis. In contrast, in a mammal, some neurosecretory cells actually terminate near the capillary loops that pick up the releasing factor peptides. Note that the blood supply of the neural lobe of the neurohypophysis is separate from that of the adenohypophysis in both kinds of organisms. This separate circulatory system, and the region it drains in the neurohypophysis, are not found in fishes; hence the presence of these structures is correlated with life on land and with the ready release of vasopressin and oxytocin.

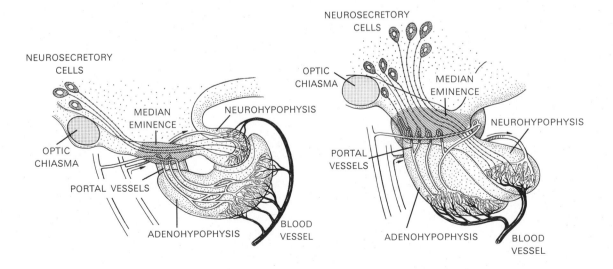

cause pigment cells to darken; recall its structural similarity to MSH, the hormone that normally controls this process. If in fact the same molecules are used in many ways, then it is obvious that the critical variable in the endocrine system is the sensitivity and specificity of target organs. Thus, some anterior pituitary cells respond to a particular hypothalamic peptide by secreting a hormone, and certain kidney tubular cells respond to a very closely related hypothalamic peptide by becoming permeable to water; the difference is due to the target organ, and appropriately so, for that is where the physiologically useful response occurs. In summary, two properties are critical to the development of the endocrine system: (1) the production of specific chemicals by hypothalamic cells; (2) the ability of different cell types to respond physiologically, in different ways, to such chemicals. Evolutionary changes in the endocrine system have centered on variations in molecular hormone structures, and on alterations in sensitivity and selectivity among different potential target cell types.

A good example of the mechanisms of evolutionary change has been provided by analyses of the amino acid sequences of the posterior pituitary hormones in various vertebrates. Professor R. Archer of the University of Paris has recently summarized the data. It seems very likely that the gene coding for the ancestral molecule was duplicated and that each copy subsequently evolved separately by modifications in the amino acids located at positions 3, 4 and 8 of the peptide. Thus, an oxytocin "line" and a vasopressin "line" can be traced through the vertebrates (neither hormone has been detected yet in cyclostomes). The table shows the amino acid variations in the posterior pituitary hormones of several classes of vertebrate animals (the numbers in superscript refer to the positions in the peptide chains). Examine the amino acids in the three variable positions and note how single substitutions are the bases for difference among the various animals. The invariability of the other amino acids suggests their critical nature in the shape of the molecules, whereas the substitutions at positions 3, 4 and 8 are obviously sources of difference in physiological action.

position	1	2	3	4	5	6	7	8	9
amino acid	cystine—	tyrosine—	☐ —	☐ —	asparagine—	cystine—	proline—	☐ —	glycine

	OXYTOCIN LINE		VASOPRESSIN LINE	
bony fish	*isotocin*	serine[4], isoleucine[8]	*vasotocin*	isoleucine[3], arginine[8]
amphibians	*mesotocin*	glutamine[4], isoleucine[8]	*vasotocin*	isoleucine[3], arginine[8]
mammals	*oxytocin*	glutamine[4], leucine[8]	*vasopressin*	phenylalanine[3], arginine[8]
pig	*oxytocin*	glutamine[4], leucine[8]	*vasopressin*	phenylalanine[3], lysine[8]

Because a number of discoveries about the endocrine system have been made since the articles in this section were published, modifications of the discussions presented by the authors are necessary.

First, we have learned that the control of MSH release is complicated by the role of melatonin. When the pineal discharges melatonin (see "The

Pineal Gland" by Richard J. Wurtman and Julius Axelrod), MSH stores in the adenohypophysis are depleted. Therefore, both the hypothalamic releasing agent and melatonin can control MSH levels in the blood.

The mechanism of feedback inhibition by sex steroids like estrogen or progesterone is dependent on the hypothalamus. It is now thought that these chemicals do not work directly upon the secretory cells of the adenohypophysis, but act instead in the hypothalamus to control the discharge of the releasing factors for luteinizing hormone or follicle-stimulating hormone. In other examples of feedback inhibition by hormones, or of direct effects by normal body chemicals on release of adenohypophyseal hormones, it is not yet known whether such action must always be routed through the hypothalamus.

The pineal organ, which is usually assumed to participate in control of pigmentation or cyclical biological activities, may also affect responses to altered ion balance and osmotic pressure. When abnormally low body fluid volumes, or high extracellular potassium ion (K^+) concentration is present, a substance called glomerulotropin is apparently released from the pineal gland. This hormone acts on the adrenal gland to adjust aldosterone levels and so bring about sodium retention and potassium excretion. Evidence that such a hormone exists comes from experiments in which pineal extracts were injected into operated animals.

Analogous experiments have recently been performed on rats, and they demonstrate that the pituitary gland has a role in aldosterone secretion. If its pituitary gland is missing, a rat fails to respond to sodium depletion by releasing aldosterone. Injection of whole frozen pituitaries restores this ability, but injection of various known pituitary hormones (such as ACTH and the growth hormone, STH) does not. Perhaps a heretofore unidentified hormone is involved in the reaction.

If they are corroborated, these results will imply that the renin-aldosterone regulatory system of the kidney can be influenced by central nervous system tissues (the pineal and the hypothalamus-pituitary tissues), just as other peripheral endocrine systems can.

Our knowledge of the intricate workings of calcium and phosphate regulation, as stated in "The Parathyroid Hormone" by Howard Rasmussen, has now been complicated further by the discovery of thyrocalcitonin. This polypeptide hormone (with a molecular weight of 3600) is thought to be produced by the parafollicular cells of the thyroid gland. It acts in a manner opposite that of parathormone (called "parathyroid hormone" by Rasmussen), the agent that causes calcium levels to rise: that is, thyrocalcitonin acts when calcium levels are too high, and inhibits bone resorption (the degradation process that goes on normally and by which calcium is continually being freed into the blood fluid). Other products of bone resorption, such as degraded collagen, the main fibrous protein in the matrix of bone, also cease to appear in the blood and be excreted when thyrocalcitonin is released. Because thyrocalcitonin inhibits bone resorption, and because it also increases phosphate excretion by kidney tubules, it causes the levels of blood calcium to fall rapidly. Some experiments suggest that a thyrocalcitonin-releasing factor comes from the parathyroid gland to act upon the thyroid and cause discharge of the active hormone; if so, this relationship is like that between the hypothalamus and the anterior pituitary cells. In summary, calcium regulation results from a balance of positive (parathormone) and negative (thyrocalcitonin) hormones acting concordantly with vitamin D.

One of the main obstacles to our understanding of this regulatory complex is its high variability among different vertebrates. A dog or a pigeon is in immediate distress after the parathyroids are removed, but a rat or a rooster is hardly affected. Different amphibia are equally variable, and no parathyroids are known in fishes. In fishes, however, another derivative of the anterior embryonic gut is present and may be a source of a calcium-regulating hormone. This tissue is called the ultimobranchial body, and it arises as a pouch, as do the thyroid and parathyroid glands. In terrestrial vertebrates the ultimobranchial body may regress (in birds), or it may persist (in mammals) and become a part of the region in which thyrocalcitonin-secreting cells are found. Thyrocalcitonin has been isolated from several birds, a reptile, and a dogfish shark. The presence of a discrete ultimobranchial body in lower vertebrates, and the probable positive correlation between its presence and the production of thyrocalcitonin, suggest that the negative regulation by thyrocalcitonin may be the primitive means of controlling calcium levels in vertebrates, and that the parathyroid gland and parathormone came later in terrestrial forms as a refinement in control. Verification of this hypothesis must wait until thyrocalcitonin has been identified in various types of bony fishes.

An interesting sidelight on vitamin D action in man has been suggested by W. Farnsworth Loomis of Brandeis University. Vitamin D can, in fact, be manufactured in vertebrate skin when ultraviolet light of the correct wavelength and intensity strikes the body; thus, the compound might be called a "hormone," since it is produced by one cell type and acts on another. The amounts of vitamin D in the human diet vary, being generally very low in winter time. Consequently, the sunlight-induced conversion of 7-dehydrocholesterol into vitamin D is the sole source of the agent if dietary supplementation is not employed. Normal amounts of Vitamin D within the body are essential: rickets and "softening" of the adult bones result from a deficiency in the vitamin; abnormal calcifications and kidney stones may be caused by an overabundance.

Loomis proposes that the quantities of vitamin D synthesized in skin are controlled by the amounts of melanin pigmentation (browns, blacks) or of keratinization (yellows) in the outer cell layers of the epidermis. Among human populations, such pigmentation varies with latitudes, the lighter, unpigmented skins being common in northern latitudes, where the intensity of ultraviolet light is very low for portions of the year. But in the latitudes near the equator, where the intensity of sunlight is high, darker skins that produce relatively less vitamin D are found. As might be expected, in the populations of the northern latitudes reversible pigmentation—suntanning—can occur to prevent excess production of vitamin D during the summer when the sun is high in the sky. Perhaps it is no coincidence that the melanization and the keratinization that constitute suntanning are elicited by the same wavelengths of light that produce vitamin D. Data show that the amount of ultraviolet radiation transmitted by the skin of an albino African negro is close to that transmitted by the skin of caucasian northern Europeans, and it is about three times the amount transmitted by normal negro skin (i.e., 53 percent of incident ultraviolet is passed through the skin of an albino African negro; 18 percent, through the skin of a normal negro).

Some of the implications of these relations are borne out by medical data: negroes tend to be particularly susceptible to rickets, particularly in high latitudes. Although less information is available, it also seems likely that white northerners may be disposed to have kidney stones when living in tropic regions. Evolutionary implications are equally obvious: presumably the early hominids of Africa were hairy and pigmented and had no problem of too much Vitamin D. But some of their descendants migrated north, and those early men became subject to Vitamin D deficiency and, to counteract this, depigmentation may have resulted. The only northern people having reasonably heavy pigmentation are the Eskimos, and their diet is heavily supplemented with fish oils containing Vitamin D.

Although Loomis' arguments are controversial, they offer a logical and cohesive explanation of pigmentation differences among men. They also suggest an answer to the long-standing enigma of pigmentation and heat absorption. It has never been clear why darkly pigmented skin, which absorbs heat so well, should be found in the tropics, while white skin, which tends to reflect heat rather than absorbing it, should be found in cooler climates. Just the opposite might be expected. However, if ultraviolet absorption and regulation of vitamin D synthesis is more critical than problems of heat balance, then an explanation is available.

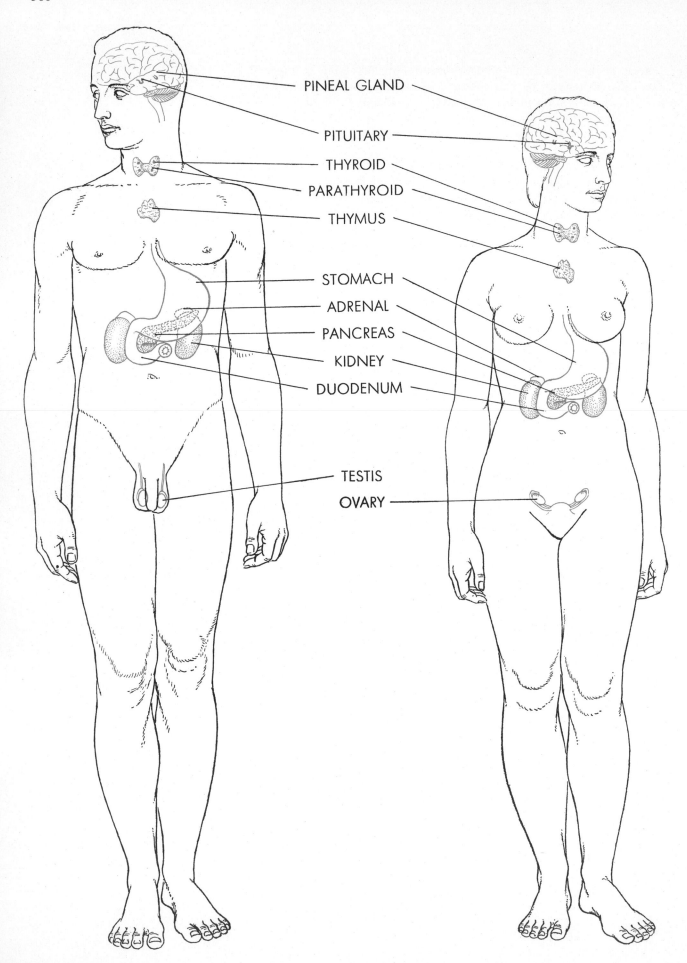

PINEAL GLAND

PITUITARY

THYROID

PARATHYROID

THYMUS

STOMACH

ADRENAL

PANCREAS

KIDNEY

DUODENUM

TESTIS

OVARY

31

Hormones

SIR SOLLY ZUCKERMAN · March 1957

When a cockerel is castrated, it fails to develop into a rooster. Normal development of the secondary sexual characters that mark a male fowl depends upon a chemical substance which is secreted by the testes and transported by the bloodstream to all parts of the body, including the germ buds of the feathers and the region of the comb and wattles. The maleness and femaleness of most animals is determined in this chemical way.

The idea that something of this kind happens in the body came early in man's speculation about his physiological workings. Aristotle made observations about the effects of castration, and so did many after him. John Hunter, the distinguished 18th-century English anatomist, went a step further and experimented on transplanting the testes. When they were regrafted to another part of the abdominal cavity, the animal developed normally. This implied that the mechanism of their effects must be chemical rather than nervous, for the original nerve connections of the testes to the body were cut by the operation. But it was not until 1849 that A. A. Berthold, a young German zoologist, made a detailed study of the effects of removal and replacement of testicular tissue and so discovered the principle of what is now called endocrine action. His short paper on the subject provides the essential foundation of the modern study of hormones.

Soon afterward the observation by Claude Bernard, the famous French physiologist, that the liver "secretes" sugar into the blood led to the general understanding that there are special endocrine glands which pour their secretions directly into the bloodstream. The whole concept was given a specific meaning when, in 1904, the English physiologists Ernest Starling and William Bayliss conceived the endocrine system as a complex of chemical messengers which coordinate the functions of different tissues of the body. Starling observed that these "hormones," as he named them, "have to be carried from the organ where they are produced to the organ which they affect, by means of the bloodstream, and the continually recurring physiological needs of the organism must determine their repeated production and circulation through the body."

Modern endocrinology, in spite of all the attention it has received, remains essentially an empirical science, for we have only a vague understanding of the fundamental mechanisms of endocrine action. We observe the physiological effects of hormones, but we know little about how they act upon cells. We have nothing like a full list of the hormones themselves, or of the organs that produce them. The usual method of identifying a hormone is to remove the organ suspected of secreting a chemical messenger, analyze the effects of its removal and then try to extract the active agent. But obviously these methods are inapplicable to an organ such as the lungs, whose removal would mean immediate death. We have no present means of determining with certainty whether or not such organs secrete hormones, although they may well do so.

Of the established endocrine organs, the most important is the pituitary gland, attached to the base of the brain. It has two lobes. The posterior lobe secretes hormones which stimulate the contractions of the uterus during childbirth and also the release of milk from the mammary gland. Posterior lobe secretions also control the amount of fluid filtered by the kidneys. Hormones of the pituitary's anterior lobe control the functioning of most of the other endocrine organs of the body. They include the thyrotrophic hormone (TSH), which acts upon the thyroid gland; the adrenocorticotrophic hormone (ACTH), which stimulates the cortex (outer part) of the adrenal glands, and the gonadotrophic hormones (FSH and LH), which control the secretion of sex hormones by the ovaries and the testes, respectively. In addition, the anterior lobe produces a growth hormone, somatotrophin (STH), which acts on the whole body.

Other endocrine organs are the pancreas, which secretes insulin; the parathyroids, four beads of tissue embedded in the back of the thyroid; the adrenal medulla, the core of the adrenal glands; certain cells lining the first part of the gut; the pineal gland, attached to the brain, and the thymus gland, behind the breastplate.

Effects on Growth

We know that hormones are concerned in almost every living process, including every phase of the growth of the body. If an immature animal is deprived of the anterior lobe of its pituitary gland, it ceases to grow or mature. To grow it must be supplied with the growth hormone (STH), and for sexual maturation it requires the gonad-stimulating hormones (FSH and LH). The growth of the body as a whole is also influenced by the male sex hormones produced by the testes. This is shown by the fact that about the time of puberty

HORMONE-SECRETING ORGANS of man are outlined in color in the figures on the opposite page. Except for the gonads, the organs are the same in the male and female.

GONAD

MESONEPHROS

BLADDER

CLOACA

OVARY

UTERUS

UTERINE TUBE

BLADDER

VAGINA

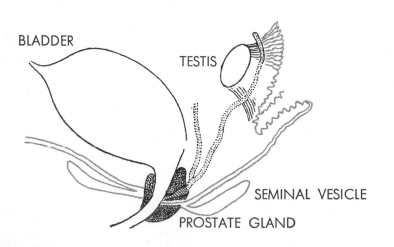

BLADDER

TESTIS

SEMINAL VESICLE

PROSTATE GLAND

the male begins to grow bigger than the female. Indeed, it is through hormones that the animal's sex itself is determined. In the early stages the embryo is sexually neutral, possessing tissues out of which either female or male reproductive organs can be formed. If the embryo is a genetic male, its embryonic gonad produces hormone which promotes the development of masculine organs and suppresses the feminine.

The development of the body is also profoundly affected by the hormones of the thyroid gland (thyroxine and triiodothyronine). Removal of this gland from a young animal will inhibit growth, delay bone formation and prevent proper development of the reproductive system. These disturbances of growth combine to produce cretinism. The physical basis of the retardation of mental development in cretins has recently been clarified by experiments on rats. In an animal deprived of thyroid hormone there is a reduction in development of the network of dendrites, the tendril-like processes which act as contacts between nerve cells, and also in growth of the nerve axon, down which impulses are fired from one nerve cell to the next. As a result the animal's reflex responses are considerably slower than normal. The nerve cells of such an animal can be stimulated to resume normal growth by giving it thyroxine, if the hormone is supplied before it is too late. The treatment restores some, but not all, of its adaptive behavior.

The parathyroid glands also influence growth, by their control over calcium and phosphorus metabolism, and of course so too does the adrenal cortex; when it ceases to pour its secretions in normal fashion into the bloodstream, not only growth but life itself must stop.

Effects on Metabolism

Hormones regulate metabolism in the body in intricate and far-reaching ways. Consider the metabolism of sugar. For good health the supply or level of sugar

GONADAL SYSTEM of vertebrates is sexually neutral in the early embryo (*schematic drawing at top*). The mesonephros, an excretory organ, retains its function even after birth. If the embryo develops into a female (*center*), the outer tubes (*color*) regress while the uterine tube, uterus and vagina form from the inner ones. In the male (*bottom*), the inner tubes practically disappear while the outer ones (*color*) form the seminal vesicles and ducts from testes.

MALE HORMONE TESTOSTERONE was injected into the 18-day-old chick at left by Hans Selye of the University of Montreal.

The injection resulted in male characteristics. The normal chick at right, which is the same age, lacks precocious comb and wattles.

in the blood must be held fairly constant. Four factors enter here: (1) the rate of use of sugar for energy by the tissues; (2) the rate of absorption of sugar by the blood from the intestines and of reabsorption from the fluid filtered by the kidneys; (3) the release of sugar from the carbohydrate-storing tissues (*e.g.*, the liver and muscle), and (4) the formation of sugar from fats and proteins. In all these processes hormones play a part. Insulin, produced in the pancreas, speeds up the rate at which the tissues use sugar. If the body is deprived of this hormone, by removal or poor functioning of the pancreas (as in the disease diabetes mellitus), the level of sugar in the blood rises considerably. This can lead to death, unless insulin is given to depress the blood-sugar level. On the other hand, if the anterior lobe of the pituitary gland, as well as the pancreas, is removed from an animal, it may survive for months, in spite of the lack of insulin. Evidently the anterior pituitary normally has something to do with supplying sugar to the blood, and its removal therefore reduces the sugar level.

The pituitary apparently acts indirectly to promote both the formation of sugar and its release into the bloodstream. For example, the pituitary hormone ACTH stimulates the adrenal cortex to secrete hormones which in turn stimulate the tissues to synthesize glycogen (animal starch) from proteins. Again, the anterior pituitary causes the thyroid to release a hormone which speeds up the oxidation of sugar by the tissues and also affects the rate at which sugar is absorbed into the bloodstream through the gut.

The metabolism of proteins likewise is considerably influenced by hormonal reactions. So too is the retention or shift of water between and within cells, which is determined mainly by the movement of sodium and potassium ions across cell membranes. One of the hormones involved in water metabolism is aldosterone, produced by the adrenal cortex: it promotes the retention of sodium and chloride in the tissues and stimulates the excretion of potassium. Other hormones that affect the body's retention of water are the hormone serotonin (found in brain tissue and in certain cells of the gut) and an antidiuretic hormone of the posterior pituitary. The sex hormones also influence water metabolism to some extent.

Controls

These examples illustrate that hormones play a vital part in the orderly development and functioning of the body, in general metabolic processes and in specific bodily adaptations such as the cyclic changes in the female reproductive organs. How are all these mechanisms organized into an orderly pattern of operation?

The pattern of control seems to be made up of sets of reciprocal interactions between the endocrine organs. For example, the anterior pituitary and the adrenal cortex are parts of a feedback system. The pituitary hormone ACTH stimulates the adrenal cortex to secrete its steroid hormones. If one adrenal gland is removed, the ACTH stimulation causes the cortex of the remaining adrenal to increase in size. If, on the other hand, the anterior pituitary lobe is removed, the resultant lack of ACTH leads to a considerable atrophy of the cortex of both adrenal glands. If ACTH is then injected, the adrenals return to their usual size. It appears that under normal conditions the concentration of adrenal cortex hormones in the bloodstream controls the secretion of stimulating ACTH by the pituitary: when this concentration is high, less ACTH is released; when it is low, the release of ACTH increases. The same sort of "push-and-pull" mechanism is believed to operate in other cases of hormones stimulating a specific target organ. The secretion of sex hormones by the ovaries and testes is subject to a similar feedback control, and the various sex hormones in turn interact with each other. Thus the effects of estrogen, one of the two hormones produced by the ovaries, may be neutralized by an extra output of progesterone, the other ovarian hormone.

There is considerable ignorance about how all these sets of interactions are organized into a pattern. One possibility is that a chain reaction involving several endocrine organs may be called forth by a general metabolic condition or need of the body. For example, during exercise the muscles require more sugar. This single need may call a number of hormonal processes into play. Insulin stimulates the transformation of glycogen in the liver and muscle into glucose. The release and conversion of this glycogen is also promoted by adrenalin from the adrenal medulla, which is activated by nerve impulses during exercise or stress. In addition, the secretion of adrenalin apparently stimulates the anterior pituitary to secrete ACTH, which in turn causes the adrenal cortex to release hormones that promote the synthesis of glycogen from protein. Adrenalin may also stimulate the anterior pituitary to produce ACTH indirectly by way of its effects on the hypothalamus, to which the posterior part of the pituitary is connected. Finally, it has been suggested that a low level of sugar in the blood itself directly stimulates the secretion of ACTH. These various possibilities indicate the complex interplay of events that must be involved even in a single metabolic process.

The problems become still more complex in responses in which the nervous system plays a part. An example is the seasonal reproductive behavior of animals whose breeding is conditioned by the length of the day, or exposure to light. A female ferret, which is sexually dormant during the autumn and winter, can be brought into heat at that time by keeping it in artificial light for a few hours after sunset each day. But it will not respond if it is blind or if its pituitary gland or its ovaries are removed. The chain of reactions clearly follows the sequence: stimulation of the retina by light, transmission of impulses along the optic nerves to the brain, stimulation of the anterior pituitary to secrete the gonadotrophic hormone, which stimulates the ovaries to secrete estrogen which in turn produces sexual heat, marked by swelling of the genital organs. The main gap in our knowledge here is: How do the nervous impulses reaching the brain via the optic nerves trigger the secretion of gonadotrophic hormone by the anterior pituitary?

The hypothalamus, at the base of the brain, is connected to the pituitary by a stalk of nerve fibers. These are known to pass to the posterior lobe, but whether any reach the anterior lobe of the pituitary, which produces the gonadotrophic hormone, is still unsettled, in spite of considerable study. If they do, one might suppose that nerve impulses directly activate the anterior pituitary to release the hormone; if not, we might assume that the hypothalamus sends a chemical messenger to the anterior pituitary by way of the bloodstream. But unfortunately the whole problem is made completely mysterious by the experimental finding that the anterior pituitary can secrete the gonadotrophic hormone even when its nerve and blood-vessel connections to the hypothalamus are completely severed!

Hormones from Nerve Cells

There is considerable evidence, however, that the hypothalamus itself does produce hormones—hormones previously supposed to be secreted by the posterior pituitary. The hormones in question include oxytocin, which triggers labor contractions of the uterus and the release of milk by the mammary glands, and vasopressin, which raises blood pressure and reduces the excretion of urine.

Some years ago the anatomist Ernst A. Scharrer (now at the Albert Einstein College of Medicine) drew attention to the fact that certain nerve cells in the hypothalamus contained what looked like secretory granules. He therefore argued that the hypothalamus, in addition to being a primitive motor center of the brain, was also in effect a secretory organ. Similar granules were later found also within the nerve fibers of the pituitary stalk. When the stalk was tied or cut, secretory material collected in the fibers immediately above the knot, and the part of the posterior pituitary below the ligature rapidly became depleted of such material. Other experiments showed that extracts of the hypothalamus have the properties of the hormones that had been thought to be produced by the posterior pituitary. It is now believed that the hypothalamus is the source of the hormones and the posterior lobe of the pituitary is essentially a storehouse for them, although very likely it also modifies them chemically.

Action in the Cell

The concept of nerve cells secreting hormones immediately raises some provocative questions. For example, can the same cell generate a nerve impulse and secrete a hormone? However, the whole subject of the way hormonal mechanisms operate at the cell level is clouded by ignorance. It is tempting to suppose that hormones act in the cell by regulating enzyme reactions, which are involved in all metabolic transformations (e.g., the

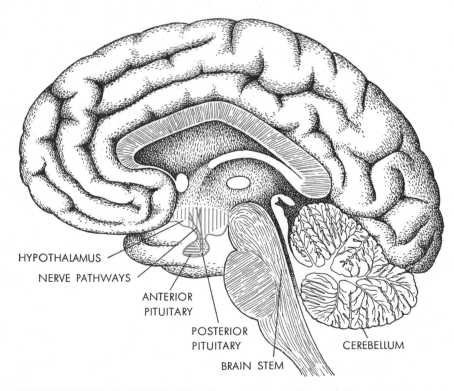

SECTION OF THE HUMAN BRAIN indicates the close relationship between the pituitary and the hypothalamus. The two structures are connected by a stalk of nerve fibers. It is not clear, however, whether the hypothalamus stimulates the secretions of the pituitary.

HYPOTHALAMUS

NERVE PATHWAYS

ANTERIOR PITUITARY

POSTERIOR PITUITARY

BRAIN STEM

CEREBELLUM

SECONDARY CHARACTERISTICS of male and female animals are brought out by hormones acting in concert with hereditary factors. Estrogen produces the plumage of the female pheasant (*top right*). Testosterone causes the development of comb and spurs in the white leghorn rooster (*right center*), the antlers of the white-tailed deer (*left center*) and probably the mane of the lion (*bottom*).

1 TESTOSTERONE

2 19-NOR-TESTOSTERONE

3 PROGESTERONE

ANDROGENS and related compounds have the molecular structures depicted in these diagrams, in which carbon rings are abbreviated. The arrows in the diagrams emphasize significant differences in structure. Male characteristics are induced by compounds 1

1 DESOXYCORTICOSTERONE

2 HYDROCORTISONE

3 PREDNISOLONE

ADRENOCORTICAL STEROIDS and related compounds are important in the treatment of certain diseases. Compounds 1 and 4 are associated with retention of sodium and water, while 2 is associated with excretion of sodium and water and with carbohydrate-

1 ESTRADIOL

2 DIETHYLSTILBESTROL

3 DIMETHYLSTILBESTROL

ESTROGENS and related compounds do not all have the configuration of four joined rings characteristic of the steroid hormones. Estradiol (1) is the natural female hormone. Synthetic compounds 2 and 3 are closely related but only 2 has estrogenic properties.

4

21-FLUORO-PROGESTERONE

5

AMPHENONE-B

and 2, but 1 is considerably more potent. Progesterone (3) is produced by the ovary. Compounds 4 and 5 have properties similar to 3, even though the structure of 5 is unrelated.

4

ALDOSTERONE

forming properties. Both 2 and 3 may be made synthetically; 3 is the more potent.

4

GENISTEIN

Genistein is extracted from subterranean clover, a spreading species of clover genus.

conversion of liver glycogen to glucose). If so, they must act in a great variety of ways, because the hormones are chemically very diverse: those secreted by the adrenal cortex and the gonads are steroids; insulin is a protein; the gonadotrophins are glycoproteins; the posterior pituitary hormones are polypeptides; thyroxine is an amino acid combined with iodine; adrenalin is an amine derivative. A further indication of the hormones' chemical versatility is the fact that a single hormone may act upon various enzymes: estrogen is apparently able to influence at least six enzyme reactions.

Yet all the enzyme systems with which we are acquainted appear to be able to function without the intervention of any hormone, and it has not yet been possible to trace the physiological action of hormones to their chemical action. According to some authorities, it is even possible that hormones exercise their effects not by modulating the action of particular enzymes but by influencing energy transfers. For example, it has been suggested that estrogens increase the availability of energy to the cell by altering the physical state of a part of the cell where glucose is formed. By so doing they provide energy for the synthetic processes which underlie cellular division. In addition, estrogens possibly regulate the permeability of tissues to water, partly by altering the ground substance in which the cells of the body are embedded.

Hormones which apparently differ only slightly in molecular structure sometimes have vastly different effects. In some cases, on the other hand, compounds of very different structure produce the same effect [see formulas in bottom row at the left]. There is no obvious explanation for such facts, but in the case of the natural estrogen estradiol and the synthetic estrogen stilbestrol, the similarity of their biological effects may be due to a correspondence of interatomic distance between the two hydroxylic groups of the molecule.

Among the difficulties which prevent any real understanding of the relation of chemical structure to hormonal action is the fact that the experimentalist can rarely be certain that an isolated hormone is chemically identical with its form in the body. There is always a danger that the extracted, "chemically pure" hormone has lost some of the activities which it normally exercises in the body. It frequently turns out, too, that several pure substances are isolated from extracts of an endocrine organ and it is difficult to decide which of them is the natural hormone. For example, several clearly defined estrogens have been isolated from the ovaries. Are they all normal secretions, or are some laboratory artifacts? And in view of the chemical transformations that natural estrogens undergo in the body, can we be certain which of its natural forms is the one that acts on estrogen-sensitive tissues? Again, of some 30 different steroids isolated from the adrenal cortex, only a few are biologically active. Which of them is the important hormone? We still do not know how many active steroids the adrenal cortex produces under normal conditions, and what their respective effects are on the metabolism of carbohydrates, proteins and minerals. Studies with radioactive tracers may soon answer some of these questions, however. Such studies have already helped greatly in elucidating stages in the chemical breakdown of hormones before their excretion from the body.

One of the remarkable features of the endocrine glands is the capacity of the same cell to produce a number of different hormones. We have just seen that the cells of the adrenal cortex make several different biologically active steroids. From just a few types of cells in the anterior pituitary come diverse secretions which stimulate the thyroid, the gonads, the adrenal cortex, the mammary glands and other organs, not to speak of body growth in general. In the testes the same cells can produce male and female hormones. In fact a stallion gives forth more estrogen than a mare does, except during a brief period of the mare's gestation!

Most hormones are produced only by a specific organ and effect a specific reaction. In some cases the target is a reaction that takes place throughout the body: for instance, the adrenal hormone aldosterone affects the water balance of all tissues. In others the target is a specific organ: the pituitary gonadotrophin acts basically on the testes or ovaries. Yet, to add to the complexity of the hormonal system, there are deviations even from this fundamental concept of specificity. The adrenal cortex can produce sex hormones; the gonads, conversely, can secrete substances with the properties of adrenocortical hormones. Some specialized reactions may be triggered by several types of stimulation: for example, menstrual bleeding, normally brought on by cessation of stimulation by ovarian hormone, can also be induced experimentally by certain adrenocortical steroids.

Hormones and Disease

In view of the complex, interlocking character of the endocrine system, it is not surprising that a derangement of the functioning of an endocrine gland produces far-reaching effects. A marked deficiency of secretion by the adrenal cortex results in Addison's disease, which manifests a variety of symptoms—extreme weakness, wasting, gastro-intestinal disturbances, a pronounced darkening of the skin—and was almost invariably fatal until the recent development of hormonal treatment. On the other hand, overactivity of the adrenal cortex may lead to various disorders: among other things, it may cause women to develop masculine characteristics, because it produces steroids with the properties of the male sex hormone. When the anterior pituitary gland functions poorly, growth of the body is impaired and puberty is delayed; development of the reproductive organs may even fail altogether. Conversely, overactivity of the pituitary leads to gigantism or, in an adult, to overgrowth of the head, hands and feet—the condition known as acromegaly. In the case of the thyroid gland, under-

NERVE CELL of the hypothalamus secretes the dark-staining material which fills the cell body (top) and most of its long, thin axon. The material exudes from the end of the axon. This preparation was made from a dog's hypothalamus by Walther Hild of the University of Texas School of Medicine in Galveston. It is magnified 1,100 diameters.

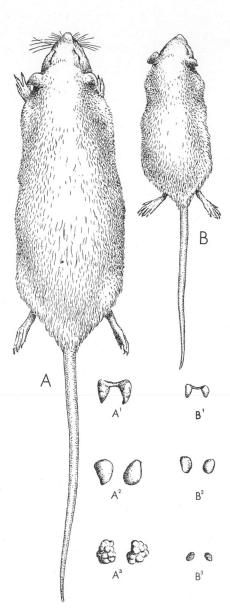

EFFECT OF PITUITARY HORMONE on growth may be demonstrated in the rat. The pituitary was removed from one of two littermates 36 days after birth, at which time both rats had the same weight. After several months the normal animal (left) had tripled its weight and had matured while the other (right) had gained little weight and was maturing much more slowly. At left are the thyroids (A1), adrenals (A2), and ovaries (A3) of the normal rat, and at right are glands (B1, B2, B3) of operated rat.

functioning in childhood produces cretinism, and in adulthood it leads to a strange thickening of the skin, loss of hair, great lethargy and mental slowness. Overactivity of the thyroid (called Graves' disease) results in the familiar symptoms of a high rate of metabolism, great excitability and protruding eyes. And of course everyone knows that a deficiency of secretion of insulin by the pancreas is responsible for diabetes.

The results of derangement of the endocrine system are so pervasive that it is natural to suspect it of complicity in various systemic diseases. The estrogenic hormones are chemically related to some of the hydrocarbons that induce cancer when applied to the skin of rats and mice. These hormones stimulate the growth of cells in the reproductive organs of women, including the breast. Could they initiate malignant growth in those organs? So far all that has been proved is that estrogenic stimulation does play a part in the triggering of cancer in strains of mice genetically susceptible to the disease. Paradoxically, estrogen can be used as a treatment for certain forms of cancer—for example, cancer of the prostate.

Hans Selye of Montreal has grouped together arthritis, hypertension and kidney disease as a set of disorders resulting from derangement of the pituitary-adrenal system. The basic idea is that when the body is subjected to some general stress (such as extreme cold or shock), the adrenal cortex immediately releases and becomes temporarily depleted of its steroid hormones. If the stress continues, the anterior pituitary secretes so much ACTH as to overstimulate the adrenal cortex. This leads to pathological results, including rheumatoid arthritis. Popular interest in the idea was excited when it was found that ACTH and cortisone had an almost miraculous effect in relieving the symptoms of rheumatoid arthritis. However, the relief lasts only so long as the hormones are being administered, and if administered too long, they frequently have dangerous side effects.

The "adaptation syndrome" has been hailed as a "unified concept of disease." This seems too sweeping and overambitious a view. Nevertheless it is difficult to exaggerate the importance of the study of endocrinology. The past 10 years have seen the development of the concept of secretions by nerve cells, the synthesis of the hormones of the pituitary posterior lobe, the discovery of such potent adrenal hormones as aldosterone and hydrocortisone and the complete working out of the structure of the insulin molecule. They have also brought to light the possible roles of hormones in immunological reactions, in the genesis of cancer and in the control of fertility—a subject which may have enormous importance for the future welfare of the world. Other vast fields of endocrine action have been found in invertebrate animals and in plants. Hormones are no longer regarded merely as chemical messengers in the bloodstream. They play a part in almost every, if not every, living process.

32

The Pineal Gland

RICHARD J. WURTMAN AND JULIUS AXELROD · July 1965

Buried nearly in the center of the brain in any mammal is a small white structure, shaped somewhat like a pinecone, called the pineal body. In man this organ is roughly a quarter of an inch long and weighs about a tenth of a gram. The function of the pineal body has never been clearly understood. Now that the role of the thymus gland in establishing the body's immunological defenses has been demonstrated, the pineal has become perhaps the last great mystery in the physiology of mammalian organs. This mystery may be nearing a solution: studies conducted within the past few years indicate that the pineal is an intricate and sensitive "biological clock," converting cyclic nervous activity generated by light in the environment into endocrine—that is, hormonal—information. It is not yet certain what physiological processes depend on the pineal clock for cues, but the evidence at hand suggests that the pineal participates in some way in the regulation of the gonads, or sex glands.

A Fourth Neuroendocrine Transducer

Until quite recently most investigators thought that the mammalian pineal was simply a vestige of a primitive light-sensing organ: the "third eye" found in certain cold-blooded vertebrates such as the frog. Other workers, noting the precocious sexual development of some young boys with pineal tumors, had proposed that in mammals the pineal was a gland. When the standard endocrine tests were applied to determine the possible glandular function of the pineal, however, the results varied so much from experiment to experiment that few positive conclusions seemed justified. Removal of the pin-

eal in young female rats was frequently followed by an enlargement of the ovaries, but the microscopic appearance of the ovaries did not change consistently, and replacement of the extirpated pineal by transplantation seemed to have little or no physiological effect. Most experimental animals could survive the loss of the pineal body with no major change in appearance or function.

In retrospect much of the difficulty early workers had in exploring and defining the glandular function of the pineal arose from limitations in the traditional concept of an endocrine organ. Glands were once thought to be entirely dependent on substances in the bloodstream both for their own control and for their effects on the rest of the body: glands secreted hormones into the blood and were themselves regulated by other hormones, which were delivered to them by the circulation. The secretory activity of a gland was thought to be maintained at a fairly constant level by homeostatic mechanisms: as the level of a particular hormone in the bloodstream rose, the gland invariably responded by decreasing its secretion of that hormone; when the level of the hormone fell, the gland increased its secretion.

In the past two decades this concept of how the endocrine system works has proved inadequate to explain several kinds of glandular response, including changes in hormone secretion brought about by changes in the external environment and also regular cyclic changes in the secretion of certain hormones (for example, the hormones responsible for the menstrual cycle and the steroid hormones that are produced on a daily cycle by the adrenal gland). Out of the realization that these and other endocrine responses must depend

in some way on interactions between the glands and the nervous system the new discipline of neuroendocrinology has developed.

In recent years much attention has centered on the problem of locating the nervous structures that participate in the control of glandular function. It has been known for some time that special types of organs would be needed to "transduce" neural information into endocrine information. Nervous tissue is specialized to receive and transmit information directly from cell to cell; according to the traditional view, glands are controlled by substances in the bloodstream and dispatch their messages to target organs by the secretion of hormones into the bloodstream. In order to transmit information from the nervous system to an endocrine organ a hypothetical "neuroendocrine transducer" would require some of the special characteristics of both neural and endocrine tissue. It should respond to substances (called neurohumors) released locally from nerve endings, and it should contain the biochemical machinery necessary for synthesizing a hormone and releasing it into the bloodstream. Three such neurosecretory systems have so far been identified. They are (1) the hypothalamus–posterior-pituitary system, which secretes the antidiuretic hormone and oxytocin, a hormone that causes the uterus to contract during labor; (2) the pituitary-releasing-factor system, also located in the hypothalamus, which secretes polypeptides that control the function of the pituitary gland, and (3) the adrenal medulla, whose cells respond to a nervous input by releasing adrenaline into the bloodstream.

The advent of neuroendocrinology has provided a conceptual framework

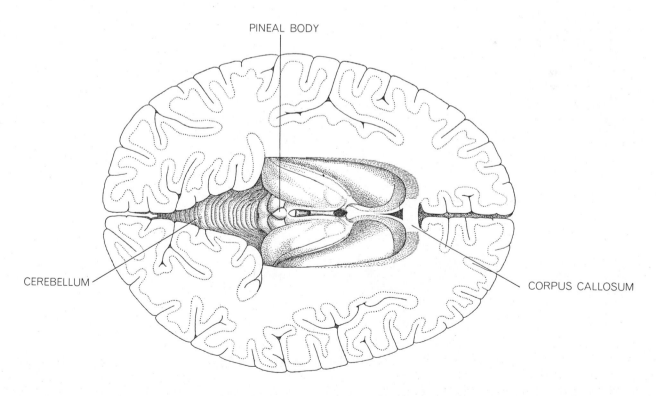

TWO VIEWS of the human brain reveal the central position of the pineal body. Section at top is cut in the median sagittal plane and is viewed from the side. Section at bottom is cut in a horizontal plane and is viewed from above; an additional excision has been made in this view to reveal the region immediately surrounding the pineal. In mammals the pineal is the only unpaired midline organ in the brain. The name "pineal" comes from the organ's resemblance to a pinecone, the Latin equivalent of which is *pinea*.

that has been most helpful in characterizing the role of the pineal gland. On the basis of recent studies conducted by the authors and their colleagues at the National Institute of Mental Health, as well as by investigators at other institutions, it now appears that the pineal is not a gland in the traditional sense but is a fourth neuroendocrine transducer; it is a gland that converts a nervous input into a hormonal output.

A Prophetic Formulation

The existence of the pineal body has been known for at least 2,000 years. Galen, writing in the second century A.D., quoted studies of earlier Greek anatomists who were impressed with the fact that the pineal was perched atop the aqueduct of the cerebrum and was a single structure rather than a paired one; he concluded that it served as a valve to regulate the flow of thought out of its "storage bin" in the lateral ventricles of the brain. In the 17th century René Descartes embellished this notion; he believed that the pineal housed the seat of the rational soul. In his formulation the eyes perceived the events of the real world and transmitted what they saw to the pineal by way of "strings" in the brain [see illustration below]. The pineal responded by allowing humors to pass down hollow tubes to the muscles, where they produced the appropriate responses. With the hindsight of 300 years of scientific development, we can admire this prophetic formulation of the pineal as a neuroendocrine transducer!

In the late 19th and early 20th centuries the pineal fell from its exalted metaphysical state. In 1898 Otto Heubner, a German physician, published a case report of a young boy who had shown precocious puberty and was also found to have a pineal tumor. In the course of the next 50 years many other children with pineal tumors and precocious sexual development were described, as well as a smaller number of patients whose pineal tumors were associated with delayed sexual development. Inexplicably almost all the cases of precocious puberty were observed in boys.

In a review of the literature on pineal tumors published in 1954 Julian I. Kitay, then a fellow in endocrinology at the Harvard Medical School, found that most of the tumors associated with precocious puberty were not really pineal in origin but either were tumors of supporting tissues or were teratomas (primitive tumors containing many types of cells). The tumors associated with delayed puberty, however, were in most cases true pineal tumors. He concluded that the cases of precocious puberty resulted from reduced pineal function due to disease of the surrounding tissue, whereas delayed sexual development in children with true pineal tumors was a consequence of increased pineal activity.

The association of pineal tumors and sexual malfunction gave rise to hundreds of research projects designed to test the hypothesis that the pineal was a gland whose function was to inhibit the gonads. Little appears to have resulted from these early efforts. Later in 1954 Kitay and Mark D. Altschule, director of internal medicine at McLean Hospital in Waverly, Mass., reviewed the entire world literature on the pineal: some 1,800 references, about half of which dealt with the pineal-gonad question. They concluded that of all the studies published only two or three had used enough experimental animals and adequate controls for their data to be analyzed statistically. These few papers suggested a relation between the pineal and the gonads but did little to characterize it. After puberty the human pineal is hardened by calcification; this change in the appearance of the pineal led many investigators to assume that the organ was without function and further served to discourage research in the field. (Actually calcification appears to be unrelated to the pineal functions we have measured.)

As long ago as 1918 Nils Holmgren, a Swedish anatomist, had examined the pineal region of the frog and the dogfish with a light microscope. He was surprised to find that the pineal contained distinct sensory cells; they bore a marked resemblance to the cone cells of the retina and were in contact with nerve cells. On the basis of these obser-

SEAT OF THE RATIONAL SOUL was the function assigned to the human pineal (H) by René Descartes in his mechanistic theory of perception. According to Descartes, the eyes perceived the events of the real world and transmitted what they saw to the pineal by way of "strings" in the brain. The pineal responded by allowing animal humors to pass down hollow tubes to the muscles, where they produced the appropriate responses. The size of the pineal has been exaggerated in this wood engraving, which first appeared in 1677.

vations he suggested that the pineal might function as a photoreceptor, or "third eye," in cold-blooded vertebrates. In the past five years this hypothesis has finally been confirmed by electrophysiological studies: Eberhardt Dodt and his colleagues in Germany have shown that the frog pineal is a wavelength discriminator: it converts light energy of certain wavelengths into nervous impulses. In 1927 Carey P. McCord and Floyd P. Allen, working at Johns Hopkins University, observed that if they made extracts of cattle pineals and added them to the media in which tadpoles were swimming, the tadpoles' skin blanched, that is, became lighter in color.

Such was the state of knowledge about the pineal as late as five or six years ago. It appeared to be a photoreceptor in the frog, had something to do with sexual function in rats and in humans (at least those with pineal tumors) and contained a factor (at least in cattle) that blanched pigment cells in tadpoles.

The Discovery of Melatonin

Then in 1958 Aaron B. Lerner and his co-workers at the Yale University School of Medicine identified a unique compound, melatonin, in the pineal gland of cattle [see "Hormones and Skin Color," by Aaron B. Lerner; SCIENTIFIC AMERICAN, July, 1961]. During the next four years at least half a dozen other major discoveries were made about the pineal by investigators representing many different disciplines and institutions. Lerner, a dermatologist and biochemist, was interested in identifying the substance in cattle pineal extracts that blanched frog skin. He and his colleagues prepared and purified extracts from more than 200,000 cattle pineals and tested the ability of the extracts to alter the reflectivity of light by pieces of excised frog skin. After four years of effort they succeeded in isolating and identifying the blanching agent and found that it was a new kind of biological compound: a methoxylated indole, whose biological activity requires a methyl group (CH_3) attached to an oxygen atom [see illustration on next two pages].

Methoxylation had been noted previously in mammalian tissue, but the products of this reaction had always appeared to lose their biological activity as a result. The new compound, named melatonin for its effect on cells containing the pigment melanin, appeared to lighten the amphibian skin by causing

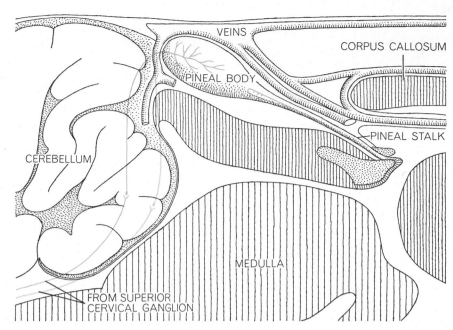

INNERVATION OF RAT PINEAL was the subject of a meticulous study by the Dutch neuroanatomist Johannes Ariëns Kappers in 1961. He demonstrated that the pineal of the adult rat is extensively innervated by nerves from the sympathetic nervous system. The sympathetic nerves to the pineal originate in the neck in the superior cervical ganglion, enter the skull along the blood vessels and eventually penetrate the pineal at its blunt end (top). Aberrant neurons from the central nervous system sometimes run up the pineal stalk from its base, but these generally turn and run back down the stalk again without synapsing. The pineal is surrounded by a network of great veins, into which its secretions probably pass. According to Ariëns Kappers, the innervation of the human pineal is quite similar.

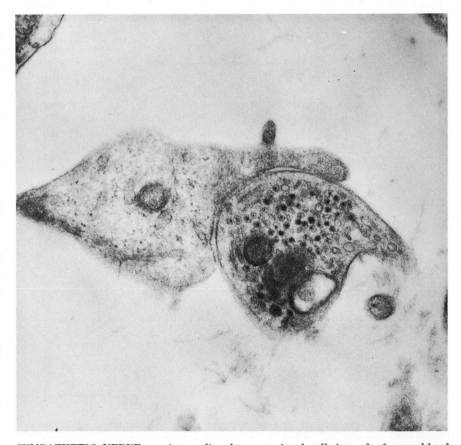

SYMPATHETIC NERVE terminates directly on a pineal cell, instead of on a blood vessel or smooth muscle cell, in this electron micrograph of a portion of a rat pineal made by David Wolfe of the Harvard Medical School. The nerve ending is characterized by dark vesicles, or sacs, that contain neurohumors. Magnification is about 12,500 diameters.

5-HYDROXYTRYPTOPHAN

DECARBOXYLATING
ENZYME

SEROTONIN

ACETYLATING
ENZYME

SYNTHESIS OF MELATONIN in the rat pineal begins with the removal of a carboxyl (COOH) group from the amino acid 5-hydroxytryptophan by the enzyme 5-hydroxytryptophan decarboxylase. Serotonin, the product of this reaction, is then enzymatically

the aggregation of melanin granules within the cells. It was effective in a concentration of only a trillionth of a gram per cubic centimeter of medium. No influence of melatonin could be demonstrated on mammalian pigmentation, nor could the substance actually be identified in amphibians, in which it exerted such a striking effect. It remained a biological enigma that the mammalian pineal should produce a substance that appeared to have no biological activity in mammals but was a potent skin-lightening agent in amphibians, which were unable to produce it!

Both aspects of the foregoing enigma have now been resolved. Subsequent research has shown that melatonin does in fact have a biological effect in mammals and can be produced by amphibians. Spurred by Lerner's discovery of this new indole in the cattle pineal, Nicholas J. Giarman, a pharmacologist at the Yale School of Medicine, analyzed pineal extracts for their content of other biologically active compounds. He found that both cattle and human pineals contained comparatively high levels of sero-

tonin, an amine whose molecular structure is similar to melatonin and whose function in nervous tissue is largely unknown. Studies by other investigators subsequently showed that the rat pineal contains the highest concentration of serotonin yet recorded in any tissue of any species.

A year before the discovery of melatonin one of the authors (Axelrod) and his co-workers had identified a methoxylating enzyme (catechol-O-methyl transferase) in a number of tissues. This enzyme acted on a variety of catechols (compounds with two adjacent hydroxyl, or OH, groups on a benzene ring) but showed essentially no activity with respect to single-hydroxyl compounds such as serotonin, the most likely precursor of melatonin. In 1959 Axelrod and Herbert Weissbach studied cattle pineal tissue to see if it might have the special enzymatic capacity to methoxylate hydroxyindoles. They incubated N-acetylserotonin (melatonin without the methoxyl group) with pineal tissue and a suitable methyl donor and observed that melatonin was indeed formed. Sub-

sequently they found that all mammalian pineals shared this biochemical property but that no tissue other than pineal could make melatonin. Extensive studies of a variety of mammalian species have confirmed this original observation that only the pineal appears to have the ability to synthesize melatonin. (In amphibians and some birds small amounts of melatonin are also manufactured by the brain and the eye.) Other investigators have found that the pineal contains all the biochemical machinery needed to make melatonin from an amino acid precursor, 5-hydroxytryptophan, which it obtains from the bloodstream. It was also found that circulating melatonin is rapidly metabolized in the liver to form 6-hydroxymelatonin.

Anatomy of the Pineal

While these investigations of the biochemical properties of the pineal were in progress, important advances were being made in the anatomy of the pineal by the Dutch neuroanatomist Johannes Ariëns Kappers and by several

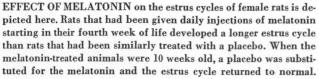

EFFECT OF MELATONIN on the estrus cycles of female rats is depicted here. Rats that had been given daily injections of melatonin starting in their fourth week of life developed a longer estrus cycle than rats that had been similarly treated with a placebo. When the melatonin-treated animals were 10 weeks old, a placebo was substituted for the melatonin and the estrus cycle returned to normal.

EFFECTS OF LIGHTING on the estrus cycles of three groups of female rats are shown in the graphs on these two pages. The groups, each consisting of about 20 rats, were subjected respectively to a sham operation (*left*), removal of their superior cervical ganglion (*middle*) and removal of their eyes (*right*). Each group was then further subdivided, with about half being placed in constant light

N-ACETYLSEROTONIN   → METHOXYLATING ENZYME →   MELATONIN

acetylated to form N-acetylserotonin. This compound in turn is methoxylated by the enzyme hydroxyindole-O-methyl transferase

(HIOMT) to yield melatonin. In mammals HIOMT is found only in the pineal. Changes in basic molecule are indicated by color.

American electron microscopists, including Douglas E. Kelly of the University of Washington, Aaron Milofsky of the Yale School of Medicine and David Wolfe, then at the National Institute of Neurologic Diseases and Blindness. In 1961 Ariëns Kappers published a meticulous study of the nerve connections in the rat pineal. He demonstrated clearly that although this organ originates in the brain in the development of the embryo, it loses all nerve connections with the brain soon after birth. There is thus no anatomical basis for invoking "tracts from the brain" as the pathway by which neural information is delivered to the pineal.

Ariëns Kappers showed that instead the pineal of the adult rat is extensively penetrated by nerves from the sympathetic portion of the autonomic nervous system. The sympathetic nervous system is involuntary and is concerned with adapting to rapid changes in the internal and external environments; the sympathetic nerves to the pineal originate in the superior cervical ganglion in the neck, enter the skull along the

blood vessels and eventually penetrate the pineal [see top illustration on page 313]. Electron microscope studies later showed that within the pineal many sympathetic nerve endings actually terminate directly on the pineal cells, instead of on blood vessels or smooth-muscle cells, as in most other organs [see bottom illustration on page 313]. Among endocrine structures the organization of nerves in the mammalian pineal appeared to be most analogous to that of the adrenal medulla, one of the three demonstrated neuroendocrine transducers.

Meanwhile electron microscope studies by other workers on the pineal regions of frogs had confirmed many of Holmgren's speculations. It was found that the pineal cells of amphibians contained light-sensitive elements that were practically indistinguishable from those found in the cone cells of the retina, but that the pineal cells of mammals did not contain such elements. By 1962 it could be stated with some assurance that the mammalian pineal was not simply a vestige of the frog "third eye,"

since the "vestige" had undergone profound anatomical changes with evolution.

The Melatonin Hypothesis

Even though the mammalian pineal no longer seemed to respond directly to light, there now appeared good evidence that its function continued to be related somehow to environmental light. In 1961 Virginia Fiske, working at Wellesley College, reported that the exposure of rats to continuous environmental illumination for several weeks brought about a decrease in the weight of their pineals. She had been interested in studying the mechanisms by which the exposure of rats to light for long periods induces changes in the function of their gonads. (For example, continous light increased the weight of the ovaries and accelerated the estrus cycle). At the same time one of the authors (Wurtman, then at the Harvard Medical School), in collaboration with Altschule and Willard Roth, was studying the conditions under which the administration

and the other half in constant darkness beginning one day after their respective operations. Daily vaginal smears were taken on the first day and on the sixth through the 30th days after the operations. Results were plotted as the percentage of all the smears in a treatment group showing estrus phases each day. In general it was found that interference with the transmission of light information

to the pineal gland (either by blinding or by cutting the sympathetic nerves) also abolished most of the gonadal response to light. These findings supported the authors' melatonin hypothesis, which holds that one mechanism whereby light is able to accelerate the estrus cycle in normal animals is by inhibiting the synthesis in the pineal of melatonin, a compound that in turn inhibits estrus.

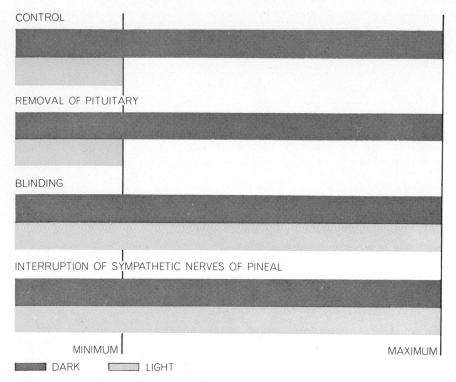

CONTROL

REMOVAL OF PITUITARY

BLINDING

INTERRUPTION OF SYMPATHETIC NERVES OF PINEAL

MINIMUM   MAXIMUM

■ DARK   ■ LIGHT

RESPONSE OF MELATONIN-FORMING ENZYME hydroxyindole-O-methyl transferase (HIOMT) to continuous light or darkness is shown under four different circumstances. In the control, or normal, animal continuous darkness induces an increase in HIOMT activity, whereas exposing the animal to continuous light has the opposite effect. The ability of the pineal gland to respond to environmental lighting is unaffected by the removal of the pituitary gland but is abolished following blinding or sympathetic denervation of the pineal.

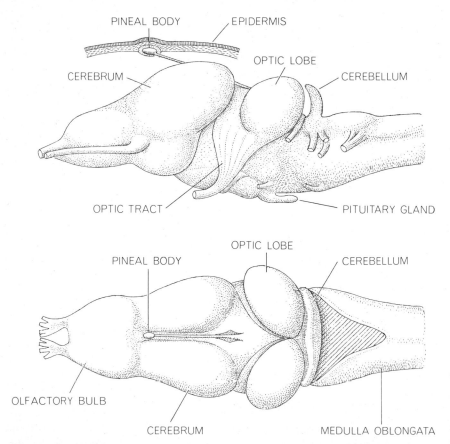

PINEAL EYE is a primitive photoreceptive organ found in certain cold-blooded vertebrates such as the frog. Frog's brain is shown from the side (*top*) and from above (*bottom*).

of cattle pineal extracts decreased ovary weight and slowed the estrus cycle.

We soon confirmed Mrs. Fiske's findings, and we were also able to show that the exposure of female rats to continuous light or the removal of their pineals had similar, but not additive, effects on the weight of their ovaries. These experiments suggested that perhaps one way in which light stimulates ovary function in rats is by inhibiting the action of an inhibitor found in pineal extracts. It now became crucial to identify the gonad-inhibiting substance in pineal extracts and to see if its synthesis or its actions were modified by environmental lighting.

In 1962 we began to work together on isolating the anti-gonadal substance present in pineal extracts. Our plan was to subject extracts of cattle pineal glands to successive purification steps and test the purified material for its ability to block the induction by light of an accelerated estrus cycle in the rat. Before undertaking the complicated and time-consuming procedure of isolating the active substance in the pineal glands of cattle, we first tested a mixture of all the constituents that had already been identified in this tissue. The mixture was found to block the effects of light on the estrus cycle.

Next we tested melatonin alone, since it was apparently the only compound produced uniquely by the pineal. To our good fortune we found that when rats were given tiny doses (one to 10 micrograms per day) of melatonin by injection, starting before puberty and continuing for a month thereafter, the estrus cycle was slowed and the ovaries lost weight—just as though the animals had been treated with pineal extracts. In later studies we found that this effect of melatonin was chemically specific: it was simulated by neither N-acetylserotonin, the immediate precursor of melatonin, nor 6-hydroxymelatonin, the major product of its metabolism. Moreover, it was possible to accelerate the estrus cycle by removal of the pineal and to block this response by the injection of melatonin.

On the basis of these studies, performed in collaboration with Elizabeth Chu of the National Cancer Institute, we postulated that melatonin was a mammalian hormone, since it is produced uniquely by a single gland (the pineal), is secreted into the bloodstream and has an effect on a distant target organ (the vagina and possibly also the ovaries). We were not able to identify the precise site of action of melatonin in affecting the gonads. The slowing of the estrus cycle could be produced by actions at any of several sites in the neuroendocrine apparatus, including the brain, the pituitary, the ovaries or the vagina itself. When melatonin was labeled with radioactive atoms and injected into cats, it was taken up by all these organs and was selectively concentrated by the ovaries.

William M. McIsaac and his colleagues at the Cleveland Clinic have confirmed the effects of melatonin on the estrus cycle and have identified another pineal methoxyindole—methoxytryptophol—that has similar effects. It appears likely that pineal extracts contain a family of hormones: the methoxyindoles, all of which have in common the fact that they can be synthesized by the methoxylating enzyme found only in the mammalian pineal.

We next set out to determine whether or not these effects of injected melatonin were physiological. Could the rat pineal synthesize melatonin and, if so, in what quantities? When rat pineal glands were examined for their ability to make melatonin, we were disappointed to find that the activity of the melatonin-forming enzyme (hydroxyindole-O-methyl transferase, or HIOMT) in the rat was much lower than in most other species; the maximum amount of melatonin that the rat could make was probably on the order of one microgram per day. Our disappointment was soon relieved, however, when we realized that the low activity of this enzyme made it likely that it was controlling the rate-limiting step in melatonin synthesis in the intact animal. Knowing that continuous exposure to light decreased pineal weight, as well as the amount of ribonucleic acid (RNA) and protein in the pineal, we next explored what effect illumination might have on HIOMT activity and thus on melatonin synthesis.

Since the rat pineal gland was so small (about a milligram in weight) and had so little enzymatic activity, it was necessary to devise extremely sensitive techniques to measure this activity. When rats were subjected to constant light for as short a period as a day or two, the rate of melatonin synthesis in their pineals fell to as little as a fifth that of animals kept in continuous darkness. Since this effect of illumination or its absence could be blocked by agents that interfered with protein synthesis, it appeared that light was actually influencing the rate of formation of the enzyme protein itself.

How was information about the state of lighting being transmitted to the rat pineal? Three possible routes suggested

RETINAL CONE CELL from the eye of an adult frog is shown in this electron micrograph made by Douglas E. Kelly of the University of Washington. The photoreceptive outer segment of the cell (*top center*) consists of a densely lamellated membrane. Parts of two larger rod photoreceptors can be seen on each side of cone. Magnification is about 13,000 diameters.

PINEAL CONE CELL from the pineal eye of an adult frog is shown in this electron micrograph made by Kelly at approximately the same magnification as the micrograph at top. The lamellated outer segment of the pineal cell is practically indistinguishable from that of the retinal photoreceptor. Part of the membrane has torn away from the cell (*top left*).

themselves. The first was that light penetrated the skull and acted directly on the pineal; W. F. Ganong and his colleagues at the University of California at Berkeley had already shown that significant quantities of light do penetrate the skulls of mammals. This hypothesis was ruled out, however, by demonstrating that blinded rats completely lost the capacity to respond to light with changed HIOMT activity; hence light had to be perceived first by the retina and was not acting directly on the pineal.

The second possibility was that light altered the level of a circulating hormone, perhaps by affecting the pituitary gland, and that this hormone secondarily influenced enzyme activity in the pineal gland. This hypothesis was also ruled out by demonstrating that the removal of various endocrine organs, including the pituitary and the ovaries, did not interfere with the response of pineal HIOMT to light.

The third possibility was that information about lighting was transmitted to the pineal by nerves. Fortunately Ariëns Kappers had just identified the nerve connections of the rat pineal as coming from the sympathetic nervous system. We found that if the sympathetic pathway to the pineal was interrupted by the removal of the superior cervical ganglion, the ability of melatonin-forming activity to be altered by light was completely lost. Thus it appeared that light was stimulating the retina and then information about this light was being transmitted to the pineal via sympathetic nerves. Within the pineal the sympathetic nerves probably released neurohumors (noradrenaline or serotonin), which acted on pineal cells to induce (or block the induction of) HIOMT; this enzyme in turn regulated the synthesis of melatonin.

Since one way light influences the gonads is by changing the amount of melatonin secreted from the pineal, we reasoned that the effects of light on the gonads might be blocked if the transmission of information about light to the pineal were interrupted. This could be accomplished by cutting the sympathetic nerves to the pineal—a procedure much less traumatic than the removal of the pineal itself. To test this hypothesis we placed groups of rats whose pineals had been denervated along with blinded and untreated animals in continuous light or darkness for a month. Vaginal smears were checked daily for evidence of changes in the estrus cycle, and pineals were tested for melatonin-synthesizing ability at the end of the experiment. It was found that interrupting the transmission of light information to the pineal (by cutting its sympathetic nerves—a procedure that does not interfere with the visual response to light) also abolished most of the gonadal response to light.

Incidentally, the observation that sympathetic nerves control enzyme synthesis in the pineal has provided, and should continue to provide, a useful tool for studies in a number of other biological disciplines. For example, studying the changes in brain enzymes produced by environmental factors offers a useful method for tracing the anatomy

SUGGESTED PATHWAY by which light influences the estrus cycle in the rat is depicted in this schematic diagram. Light stimuli impinge on the retinas and cause a change in the neural output of the superior cervical ganglion by way of an unknown route. This information is then carried by sympathetic nerves to the pineal gland, where it causes a decrease in the activity of HIOMT and in the synthesis and release of melatonin. This decrease in turn lessens the inhibiting effect of the circulating melatonin on the rate of the estrus cycle. The precise site of action of melatonin in influencing the gonads is unknown; the slowing of the estrus cycle could be produced by actions at any one of several sites in the neuroendocrine apparatus, including the brain, the pituitary, the ovaries and the vagina.

of the nerve tracts involved. The observation that the activity of at least one part of the sympathetic nervous system (the superior cervical ganglion) is affected by environmental lighting raises the possibility that other regions of this neural apparatus are affected similarly. If so, physiological studies of the effects of light on other sympathetically innervated structures (for example the kidneys and fat tissue) may be profitable.

We have also found that light influences the serotonin-forming enzyme in the pineal gland but not in other organs. In contrast to HIOMT, the activity of this enzyme increases when rats are kept in constant light and decreases in darkness. When rats are blinded or when the sympathetic nerves to the pineal are cut, the effect of light and darkness on the serotonin-forming enzyme is also extinguished. Furthermore, certain drugs that block the transmission of sympathetic nervous impulses also abolish the effect of illumination on this enzyme. The fact that lighting influences pineal weight and at least two enzyme systems in this organ suggests that it may regulate many additional, undiscovered biochemical events in the pineal, via the sympathetic nervous system.

Diurnal and Circadian Rhythms

The pineal had been shown to respond and function under quite unusual conditions; for example, when an experimental animal was exposed to continuous light or darkness for several days. In nature, of course, animals that live in the temperate and tropical zones are rarely subjected to such conditions. It became important to determine if the pineal could also respond to naturally occurring changes in the environment.

In nature the level of light exposure changes with both diurnal and annual cycles. Except in polar regions every 24-hour day includes a period of sunlight and a period of darkness; the ratio of day to night varies with an annual rhythm that reaches its nadir at the winter solstice and its zenith on the first day of summer. Lighting cycles have been shown to be important in regulating several types of endocrine function: the increase in sunlight during the winter and spring triggers the annual gonadal growth and breeding cycles in many birds and some mammals that breed yearly, and the daily rhythm of day and night synchronizes a variety of roughly daily rhythms in mammals, such as the cycle of adrenal-steroid secretion. Such rhythms are called circadian, from the Latin phrase meaning "about one day." Could the pineal respond to natural diurnal lighting shifts? If so, it might function to synchronize the endocrine apparatus with these shifts.

In order to determine if normal lighting rhythms influenced the pineal, we kept a large population of rats under controlled lighting conditions (lights on from 7:00 A.M. to 7:00 P.M.) for several weeks and then tested their pineals for melatonin-forming ability at 6:00 A.M., noon, 6:00 P.M. and midnight. In the five hours after the onset of darkness (that is, by midnight) this enzymatic capacity increased between two and three times. Moreover, pineal weight also changed significantly during this period, again indicating that light was affecting many more compounds in the pineal than the single enzyme we were measuring.

All circadian rhythms studied up to this stage had in common the ability to persist for some weeks after animals were deprived of environmental lighting cues (by blinding or being placed in darkness). These rhythms no longer showed a period of precisely 24 hours, but they did fall in a range between 22 and 26 hours and hence were thought to be regulated by some internal mechanism not dependent on, but usually synchronized with, environmental lighting. Such endogenous, or internally regulated, circadian rhythms in rodents include motor activity and rectal temperature, as well as the rhythm in adrenal-steroid secretion. When we blinded rats or placed them in continuous light or darkness, the pineal rhythm in melatonin-forming activity was rapidly extinguished. If instead of turning off the lights at 7:00 P.M. illumination was

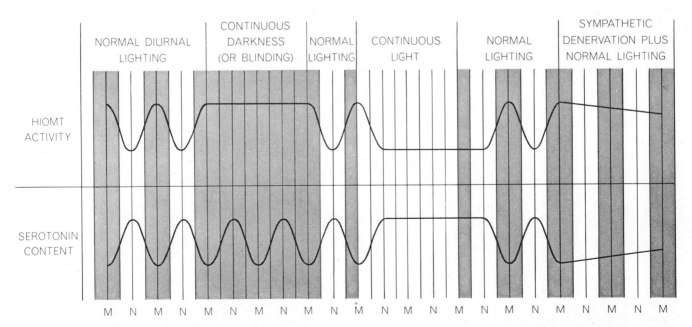

BIOCHEMICAL RHYTHMS in the pineal gland of the rat were recorded under various lighting and other conditions. Normally both the content of serotonin and the activity of the melatonin-forming enzyme (HIOMT) vary with a 24-hour cycle. The serotonin content is greatest at noon (N), whereas the HIOMT activity is greatest at midnight (M). The HIOMT cycle is completely dependent on environmental lighting conditions: it disappears when animals are kept in continuous light or darkness, or when they are blinded. The serotonin cycle persists in continuous darkness or after blinding but can be abolished by keeping the rats in continuous light. Both cycles are depressed when the sympathetic nerves to the pineal gland are cut (extreme right). Gray areas signify darkness.

continued for an additional five hours and pineals were examined as usual at midnight, the expected rise in melatonin-forming activity was completely blocked. This pineal rhythm in HIOMT activity thus appears to be truly exogenous, or externally regulated, and is entirely dependent on shifts in environmental lighting. Hence this enzyme rhythm may be more important in carrying information about light to the glands than other circadian rhythms that do not depend on light for their existence.

Recently Wilbur Quay of the University of California at Berkeley has found that the content of serotonin in the rat pineal also undergoes marked circadian rhythms. The highest levels of this amine are found in pineals at noon and the lowest levels at midnight. Serotonin content falls rapidly just at the time that melatonin-forming activity is rising.

In collaboration with Solomon Snyder we studied the mechanism of the serotonin cycle. When rats are kept in continuous light, the serotonin cycle is extinguished. To our surprise, however, when rats are kept continuously in darkness or blinded, this rhythm persists, unlike the rhythm in the melatonin-forming ezyme. When the sympathetic nerves to the pineal are cut, the serotonin and HIOMT cycles are both suppressed. When the nerves from the central nervous system to the superior cervical ganglion are interrupted, the serotonin rhythm is also abolished [*see illustration on previous page*]. Hence the serotonin rhythm in the pineal gland is similar to most other circadian rhythms (and differs from the HIOMT cycle) in that it is endogenous and depends on environmental light only as an external synchronizer. The mechanism that controls the serotonin rhythm appears to reside within the central nervous system. The pineal gland thus contains at least two distinct biological clocks, one totally dependent on environmental lighting and the other originating within the brain but cued by changes in lighting.

At present little is known about what organs are dependent on the pineal clock for cues. The ability of melatonin to modify gonadal function suggests, but does not prove, that its secretion may have something to do with the timing of the estrus and menstrual cycles—two phenomena about whose mechanisms of control very little is known. One is tempted to argue teleologically that any control mechanism as complicated and sensitive as that found in the mammalian pineal gland must have some place in the economy of the body.

33

The Parathyroid Hormone

HOWARD RASMUSSEN · April 1961

There are eight well-defined endocrine glands in the human body, and together they secrete into the bloodstream at least 20 different kinds of hormone. These hormones fall into two main groups: the steroid hormones from the adrenal glands and sex organs, and the protein and peptide hormones of the pituitary gland, pancreas, thyroid and parathyroid glands. With the development of new techniques for separating complex protein mixtures, many of the second group have now been obtained in pure form. The most recently isolated is the parathyroid hormone. Only when the pure hormone is available for study can its properties and function be rigorously established. The availability of the pure parathyroid hormone has enabled physiologists to clear up basic controversies as to its function, and physiological studies have underscored the subtlety of its action.

Hormones are appropriately called chemical messengers; the word "hormone" means "I arouse to activity." The arousal ability of such hormones as those produced by the adrenal glands is well known. There is, however, another class of hormones, of which the parathyroid hormone is a member, that operates silently, so to speak, but no less profoundly. These hormones are concerned primarily with maintaining the constancy of the *milieu intérieur*. This is the felicitous term proposed nearly a century ago by the French physiologist Claude Bernard, who used it to emphasize that the cells of the body are insulated from the erratic, and frequently harsh, external environment by a carefully regulated internal environment composed of the circulating fluids—blood plasma and extracellular fluid—that bathe them. In the 1920's Walter B. Cannon of the Harvard Medical School introduced the term "homeostasis" to describe the varied physiological processes that endow the *milieu intérieur* with its remarkable stability.

One of the most important constituents of the internal environment is the calcium ion, which is released when calcium compounds go into solution and dissociate. An optimum calcium-ion concentration is necessary for the normal transmission of nerve impulses, the contraction of muscles, the coagulation of blood, the fertilization of eggs and the formation of bone. A precise endocrine control system has evolved to ensure a stable concentration of this essential ion in the *milieu intérieur*. The two hormones of major importance in this system are vitamin D and the parathyroid hormone.

Vitamin D can be classified as a hormone because it is manufactured in the skin (which is an organ) when the skin is exposed to sunlight. The vitamin is important in the prevention of rickets, a wasting disease of bone. Because man no longer goes around seminude, a substance that was once adequately supplied by internal synthesis (a hormone) has become an essential factor in the diet (a vitamin).

The parathyroid hormone is a protein secreted by the parathyroid glands: four tiny organs located in the neck adjacent to, or embedded in, the thyroid gland [*see illustration on the next page*]. Amphibia and all higher animals have parathyroid glands. In man the glands are reddish-brown and resemble slightly flattened garden peas. They are composed of cords of secretory epithelial cells, separated by a small number of fat cells. Notwithstanding their name, they are distinct from the thyroid gland both in structure and in function. The parathyroids were first described over 100 years ago by the British anatomist Richard Owen, who found them while dissecting an Indian rhinoceros. Owen's discovery went unnoticed, but the glands were rediscovered by a number of investigators. Among them was the Swedish anatomist Ivor Sandström, who gave them their name in 1880.

Some 16 years later, G. Vassale and F. Generali of Italy removed the parathyroids from experimental animals and observed that before the animals died their muscles twitched, went into spasms and finally became rigid. In 1909 W. G. MacCallum and Carl Voegtlin of Johns Hopkins University attributed these muscle symptoms to a calcium deficiency; they had found that removal of the parathyroids was followed by a decrease in the amount of calcium in the blood. A few years later Isidor Greenwald of Roosevelt Hospital in New York observed that the decrease in calcium was accompanied by an increase in blood phosphate. In 1925 J. B. Collip and his co-workers at the University of Alberta prepared the first stable acid extract of beef parathyroid glands; when injected into experimental animals or humans, it increased the calcium content and decreased the phosphate content of the blood plasma. Shortly thereafter the conditions of hyperparathyroidism (overactivity of the parathyroids and hypoparathyroidism (underactivity) were recognized as causes of human disease.

At about the same time vitamin D was identified chemically and was shown to be an essential dietary factor, important in the regulation of calcium and phosphate metabolism. Because vitamin D and the parathyroid hormone overlap in function and to some extent act synergistically (reinforce each other's activity), it is only very recently that their physiological roles have been satisfactorily disentangled. The work proceeded along two general lines: biochemists sought to isolate in pure form and to identify chemically the parathyroid hormone; physiologists sought to clarify the mechanisms by which vitamin D and the parathyroid hormone control the metabolism of calcium and phosphate.

Last year Lyman C. Craig and I, working at the Rockefeller Institute in New York, finished purifying the parathyroid hormone and established that it was a protein. The task took five years. To obtain one milligram of pure parathyroid hormone we had to process 200,-000 milligrams of fresh beef parathyroid tissue, representing the glands from 300 animals. In starting such a job, the first step is to find a reliable method for detecting hormonal activity in crude extracts. We adopted a method that had been developed by A. H. Gordon and his associates in England and Paul Munson and his colleagues at Harvard University. They injected crude extracts of parathyroid hormone into rats whose parathyroid glands had been removed and then measured the concentration of calcium in the rats' blood plasma. Changes in the concentration are directly related to the amount of hormonal activity in the crude extract. Using this assay we began separating the hormone from the many nonhormonal constituents of the glands.

We tried several methods of extracting the hormone before settling on a method devised by Gerald Aurbach of Tufts University. He had found that a concentrated phenol solution would extract most of the hormone. Unfortunately phenol also extracts many other proteins. When Aurbach tried to purify his crude extracts by making the hormone precipitate out of solution preferentially, he had only limited success. We as well as Aurbach began looking for a better separation method. After experimenting with various techniques, including electrophoresis, chromatography and ultra-centrifugation, we concluded (as did Aurbach independently) that the separation method known as countercurrent distribution was the most promising.

This technique exploits the fact that when proteins are shaken together with two nonmiscible liquids, both of which will dissolve proteins, each protein will be distributed between the two liquids in a unique manner. After repeated extractions of this sort, proteins that prefer one solvent can be separated with high purity from proteins that prefer a second solvent. The actual separation is carried out in long rows of interconnected tubes, which permit the process to be fully automatic [see illustrations on next two pages]. The mixture of proteins, dissolved in the proper solvents, is placed in the first few tubes of the train; after the machine has carried out 100 or more separate transfers by rocking back and forth, the various tubes are analyzed for their protein content.

The distribution pattern illustrated

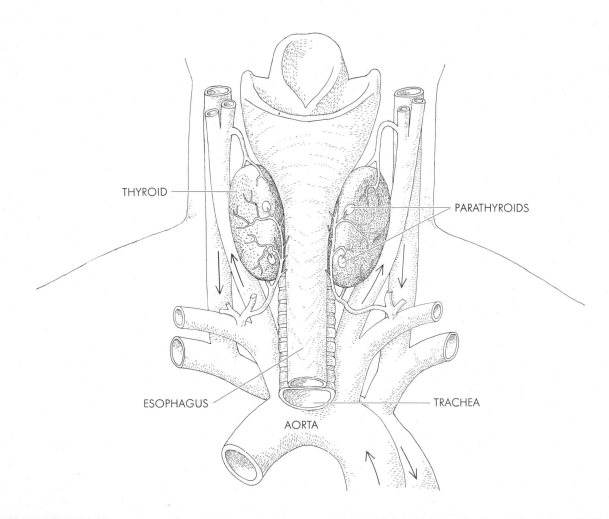

THYROID

PARATHYROIDS

ESOPHAGUS

TRACHEA

AORTA

PARATHYROID GLANDS are four small reddish-brown bodies embedded in the rear of the thyroid gland. They are structurally and functionally distinct from the larger gland. Here the thyroid, the parathyroids and nearby structures are viewed from the back.

on page 325 was obtained when a crude parathyroid extract was run for 250 transfers in a two-phase system composed of pyridine, butanol, acetic acid and water. At this point we knew only that proteins had concentrated in certain tubes; we still knew nothing about their hormonal activity. By evaporation and freeze-drying we removed the solvents from samples representing the different protein peaks. For assay purposes the dry protein powder recovered from each peak was suspended in sterile oil and injected under the skin of each of six rats. Six hours later a sample of blood was taken from each rat. After the removal of red blood cells, each sample of clear plasma was analyzed chemically for its calcium content. Another group of rats served as a control and received no hormone; still others received graded doses of a standard crude hormone preparation. By comparing the responses of the various groups it was found that only the second peak [*labeled "A" in the illustration on page 325*] showed hormonal ac-

tivity. Its specific activity was about 10 times that of the crude starting material. The one small peak, containing less than 10 per cent of the protein estimated to be in the crude extract, contained over 85 per cent of the hormonal activity.

The partially purified material was returned to the countercurrent distribution machine and subjected to another 2,600 transfers. This time the parathyroid hormone was separated completely from the other proteins. The molecule of the hormone was found to be rather small as protein molecules go: it has a molecular weight of 9,500 (9,500 times the weight of the hydrogen atom). It is larger, however, than the molecule of the hormone insulin, which has a molecular weight of 5,733. The molecule of the parathyroid hormone is made up of a chain of 83 separate amino acid residues of 17 different amino acids. The exact sequence in which these are assembled has not been established, but we know that only 33 of them are required for the protein to exert its characteristic effects.

The other 50 amino acid residues apparently help to stabilize the essential 33. The determination of the sequence of the 83 amino acids is now being undertaken with the methods used to establish the amino acid sequence of insulin and other proteins [see "The Chemical Structure of Proteins," by William H. Stein and Stanford Moore, SCIENTIFIC AMERICAN Offprint 80].

With the isolation of the pure parathyroid hormone it became possible to reinvestigate its mode of action. It had been known, of course, that when a crude parathyroid extract is administered to an experimental animal or to a human subject, it increases the amount of calcium and decreases the amount of phosphate in the internal environment, it increases the excretion of phosphate in the urine and at first it decreases the excretion of calcium. If, however, the amount of calcium in the internal environment becomes excessive, there is a rise in the calcium excreted. All these

COUNTERCURRENT DISTRIBUTION MACHINE provided the means for separating the parathyroid hormone from the mixture of proteins present in a crude extract obtained from hundreds of beef parathyroid glands. The machine operates on the principle of differential extraction. If a mixture of proteins is shaken together with two immiscible liquids, both of them protein solvents, each type of protein will distribute itself between the two liquid phases in a unique way. The machine, by rocking back and forth, subjects a mixture of proteins to repeated extractions. As a result different proteins concentrate in different regions of the machine.

changes are the result of changes in the function of the various organs concerned with maintaining a constant calcium content in the internal environment. There has been considerable controversy as to how the hormone alters their function. Some physiologists contended that the primary hormonal action was to increase the excretion of phosphate in the urine and that all the other effects followed as a consequence. Others proposed that the hormone's only significant effect was to bring about the release of calcium stored in so-called nonexchangeable bone: the relatively old bone, which normally does not enter into chemical transactions with body fluids. (As we shall see, the newly formed bone is called exchangeable bone because it remains in equilibrium with surrounding fluids.) Still other physiologists suggested that there might be two hormones; one acting on the kidney, the other on the bone. It has now been shown that our purified parathyroid protein acts on both the kidneys and bone.

A DETAIL VIEW of countercurrent distribution machine showing how the glass tubes are interconnected so that they permit the two liquid phases to move in opposite directions. The machine was designed by Lyman C. Craig of the Rockefeller Institute.

A direct action on bone has been demonstrated by Pieter Gaillard of the University of Leiden in the Netherlands in an ingenious series of experiments using the recently developed techniques of tissue- and organ-culture. In one set of culture tubes he grew thin sections of bone from the skulls of newborn mice; in another set of tubes he grew small bits of fetal parathyroid tissue. When both the bone and the parathyroid tissue were growing well separately, he put them together. Before long he could see changes in the bone indicating increased activity of the bone-destroying cells called osteoclasts. It is these cells that release calcium from storage and make it available elsewhere. Gaillard then took just the fluid from the parathyroid cultures and placed it in the cultures of bone. Again he observed the same changes in the bone, suggesting that the cells of the parathyroid tissue growing outside the body were secreting a hormone into the tissue-culture fluid. Finally he took our purified parathyroid hormone and placed it in the bone cultures. Once again he observed the destruction of the bone and all the other histological changes associated with hyperparathyroidism [*see middle illustration on page 327*].

While this work was going on, Ray Lavender and Theodore Pullman of the University of Chicago, working in collaboration with the author, unequivocally demonstrated that the hormone had a direct effect on the kidneys. They infused solutions of pure parathyroid hormone into the artery of one kidney of a dog, and measured the amount of phosphate in the urine collected separately from each kidney. They found a marked increase in the amount of phosphate in the urine from the infused side and little or no change in the phosphate content of the urine from the other kidney.

Earlier investigators concentrated almost exclusively upon the bone and kidney as possible sites of action of the parathyroid hormone. More recent studies indicate that the hormone also influences the rate of exchange of calcium in the lactating mammary gland and in the gastrointestinal tract. In the past two years we have established that the parathyroid hormone acts in the gastrointestinal tract to promote the absorption of calcium into the bloodstream.

It is now possible to present with some confidence a unified picture of how the parathyroid glands control the concentration of the calcium in the internal environment [*see illustration on page 326*]. Many other endocrine systems are under the control of secretions from the anterior part of the pituitary gland, but this is not true of the parathyroid glands. The secretory activity of the parathyroids is controlled by the concentration of a simple substance in the circulating blood: the calcium ion itself. When the concentration of this ion falls, the glands are stimulated to secrete more hormone, much as a thermostatically controlled furnace increases its heat output as the temperature falls. Instead of a thermostat there is a "calciostat" in the cells of the parathyroid glands. Once the hormone is released into the bloodstream it is carried to the parts of the body in which its action takes place. It acts on the intestinal cells to increase the absorption of calcium; it acts on the cells of the kidney tubules to increase the reabsorption of calcium from the filtered urine; and it acts upon the bone cells to convert them to osteoclastic cells, which break down the nonexchangeable bone and release the stored calcium. All these effects lead to an increase in the concentration of calcium in the internal environment. The hormone has the additional effect on the cells of the kidney tubules of making them excrete more phosphate into the urine, thereby diminishing the amount of phosphate in the internal environment. This more than offsets the increased phosphate released by the breakdown of bone. The final result is an increase in the amount of calcium and a decrease in the amount of phosphate in the blood plasma and extracellular fluid. Once the calcium-ion concentration has been restored to normal, the fact is perceived by the calciostat, which thereupon decreases the output of the hormone. In many respects this system is analogous to a servomechanism employing the principle of negative feedback.

It may seem puzzling that such an elaborate system is required. Why couldn't either the bone or the kidneys, under parathyroid control, maintain the calcium content of the *milieu intérieur?* Actually, there are striking differences in the capacity and rapidity with which the various organs respond to the hormone. The responses of the kidneys and gastrointestinal tract are rapid, sensitive to small changes in hormone concentration and of limited capacity. The response of bone is slow, insensitive and of nearly unlimited capacity. By integrating these two types of response, the organism is able to achieve a wider range and finer degree of control than would be possible by utilizing either response alone.

Before describing the role played by vitamin D in calcium-phosphate metabolism it is necessary to digress for a moment to discuss bone, its nature and its relationship to the calcium and phosphate ions in the internal environment. Until recently bone was considered an inert tissue, but studies made with the radioactive isotopes of calcium and phosphorous have shown the bone is being remodeled constantly. Bone contains more than 98 per cent of the body's

calcium and about 66 per cent of its phosphate. These are deposited as a complex salt, hydroxyapatite, in a framework of protein fibers called collagen. Specific cells, the osteoblasts, manufacture these fibers and align them to form the bone template. When sufficient concentrations of calcium and phosphate ions are circulating in the internal environment, they interact with specific

sites on the collagen fibers to form small hydroxyapatite crystals, which then slowly grow. While small and growing they constitute exchangeable bone, able quickly to return calcium and phosphate ions to the internal environment. As the crystals keep growing they exclude more and more water until they become nonexchangeable bone—a solid, inert, diffusion-locked mass that does not release its ions readily. In the adult organism more than 99 per cent of the bone is in this condition. Eventually all the bone would assume this state if it were not being remodeled constantly, even deep in the interior of bones. By means of a radioactive isotope of calcium it is possible to estimate that in a normal adult human enough old bone is broken down each day to release approximately half a gram of calcium into the internal environment. This breakdown, or reabsorption, of bone is brought about by the action of the osteoclasts, which not only dissolve the bone mineral but also destroy the bone collagen. The dissolved old bone is normally replaced by an equivalent amount of new bone.

To simplify slightly, one may regard the ions in the circulating fluids as being in simple equilibrium with those in the exchangeable bone. This implies that ions will leave the exchangeable bone when the amount of either phosphate or calcium falls in the plasma and extracellular fluid. Calcium and phosphate will enter the exchangeable bone if their concentrations increase in the body fluids. Consequently the exchangeable bone, acting as a buffer, is the first line of defense in controlling the concentration of these ions in the internal environment of the body.

PROTEIN DISTRIBUTION CURVE shows by tube number where parathyroid proteins were concentrated by countercurrent separation. Animal assay found hormone in peak A.

This leads us back to the role of vitamin D. Unless the total amount of calcium and phosphate ions in the internal environment is kept at a certain critical level, bone formation stops. The maintenance of this level appears to be the primary function of vitamin D. Under normal conditions calcium is excreted primarily in the feces; phosphate, primarily in the urine. Vitamin D reduces the excretion of each by promoting their retention in the body. When vitamin D is lacking, there is a decline in the total amount of calcium and phosphate in the internal environment; bone collagen no longer becomes calcified and eventually the bones stop growing, bend and break. This is the condition known as rickets. It is obvious that vitamin D cannot correct a lack of calcium in the diet. It can, however, promote maximum retention of whatever calcium is avail-

ANIMAL ASSAY CURVE shows how calcium-ion level in blood plasma is raised by injection of graded doses of parathyroid extract. Test animals lacked parathyroid glands.

ACTION OF PARATHYROID GLANDS is symbolized in this sequence of three diagrams. In *a* the calcium-ion concentration of the extracellular fluid is at a normal level and is in equilibrium with the calcium ions deposited in exchangeable bone (*gray tone in two boxes at left*). Calcium-ion level is also normal in blood reaching the parathyroid glands (*horizontal black arrow*), resulting in a normal output of hormone. At the three sites of calcium regulation the hormone sees to it that the proper amount of calcium is retained and the proper amount is excreted to maintain optimum calcium level in the extracellular fluid. In *b* a drop in this level causes an immediate drop in the calcium stored in exchangeable bone. The drop is also signaled to the parathyroids by the decreased calcium in the blood plasma. A rise in hormone output follows, which promotes retention of calcium by gastrointestinal tract and kidneys and causes withdrawal of calcium from nonexchangeable bone. The result is a reduction in calcium excretion and an increased supply to the extracellular fluid. In *c* an oversupply of calcium in the extracellular fluid causes a reversal of the whole process.

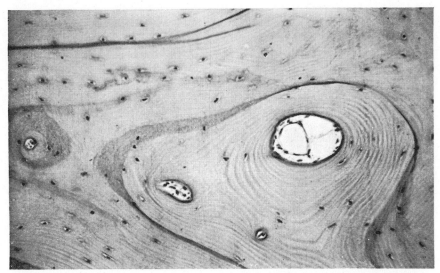

NORMAL BONE has the appearance of a contour map. This magnified section through a canal shows how layers of new bone grow into the canal and narrow it. This micrograph and the one below were made by H. R. Dudley of the Massachusetts General Hospital.

HYPERPARATHYROID BONE shows fibrous tissue filling a canal (*entire central area*). The parathyroid hormone has stimulated formation of special cells called osteoclasts, which destroy the bone and return its calcium and phosphate to the blood and extracellular fluid.

EXCHANGEABLE BONE is formed when crystals of hydroxyapatite (*small black spots*) are deposited along collagen fibers. As crystals grow they fuse into nonexchangeable bone. Micrograph was made by Melvin J. Glimcher of the Massachusetts General Hospital.

able. And it can do more. By promoting retention of phosphate it can often maintain the product of the two ion concentrations (calcium times phosphate) above the critical level. So long as this level is maintained, bone calcification will take place regardless of the absolute level of calcium ion.

Nerve and muscle cells, however, are critically dependent on the proper concentration of calcium ions for optimum functioning. Maintenance of this concentration is the task of the parathyroid glands. Vitamin D and parathyroid hormone, acting in concert, control both the total amount and the ratio of the calcium and phosphate in the internal environment. Their relationship is such that adequate amounts of vitamin D must be available for the hormone to exert its characteristic effects. The converse, however, does not hold true; vitamin D can act in the complete absence of the parathyroid hormone and can, in large doses, overcome the effects of parathyroid deficiency. When both are present in proper amounts, the regulation of the calcium and phosphate content of the internal environment is brought about as shown in the illustration on the next page.

Although vitamin D and parathyroid hormone are the two most important endocrine agents in this regulatory system, other hormones play a role. The steroid hormones of the cortex of the adrenal glands, the growth hormone of the pituitary gland, insulin from the pancreas, the thyroid hormone and the sex hormones all influence one or more of the processes of bone growth and reabsorption, or the metabolism of calcium and phosphate. Ultimately they can also influence the activity of the parathyroid glands.

It is evident, therefore, that a variety of diseases, particularly those affecting the bones, kidneys and gastrointestinal tract, can lead to alterations in calcium and phosphate metabolism and consequently to changes in parathyroid gland activity. Conversely, diseases of the parathyroid glands can upset the functioning of many organs. Hyperparathyroidism usually results from benign tumors of these glands and is characterized by changes in the function of the kidneys, nervous system, bones and gastrointestinal tract. Removal of the tumors usually effects a complete cure. Hypoparathyroidism, or underactivity of the glands, may have no apparent cause in some cases; in other cases it results from inadvertent removal of the parathyroid glands during surgical operations on the neck, particularly those on the thyroid gland. Its most striking manifestation is increased neuromuscular activity. The logical therapeutic agent for this condition is parathyroid hormone. Since the hormone is not yet available commercially, the present treatment is to increase the calcium content and decrease the phosphate content of the diet, and to administer large doses of vitamin D.

Although we have a general understanding of what the parathyroid hormone is, where it acts and what diseases result from too little or too much of it, we still have no knowledge of the specific biochemical reactions it controls within the various cells to bring about changes in their function. Now that the pure hormone is available for biochemical studies, our knowledge in this area should increase rapidly.

CALCIUM ION, REGULATED FLOW

CALCIUM ION, UNREGULATED FLOW

PHOSPHATE ION, REGULATED FLOW

PHOSPHATE ION, UNREGULATED FLOW

FLOW INCREASED BY VITAMIN D

CALCIUM AND PHOSPHATE REGULATION is accomplished jointly by parathyroid hormone and vitamin D. When the extracellular fluid is low in calcium (*top*), the hormone acts upon nonexchangeable bone, kidney and gastrointestinal tract to increase the supply. It also increases excretion of phosphate from the kidney to eliminate phosphate produced by reabsorption of bone. Vitamin D acts synergistically with the hormone except in the kidneys, where the vitamin causes phosphate retention. When extracellular fluid contains an excess of calcium (*bottom*), the supply of parathyroid hormone drops. Flow of calcium from nonexchangeable bone and gastrointestinal tract is much reduced; excretion of calcium by the kidneys is increased and excretion of phosphate decreased. Integrated action of the hormone and vitamin D is the predominant means of controlling both total amount and ratio of calcium and phosphate ions in the internal environment.

Communication Between Vertebrates

Nightingales pour out a ceaseless gush of song for fifteen days and nights on end when the buds of the leaves are swelling—a bird not in the lowest rank remarkable. In the first place there is so loud a voice and so persistent a supply of breath in such a tiny body; then there is consummate knowledge of music in a single bird: the sound is given out with modulations, and now is drawn out into a long note with one continuous breath, now varied by managing the breath, now made staccato by checking it, or linked together by prolonging it, or carried on by holding it back; or it is suddenly lowered, and at times sinks into a mere murmur, loud, low, bass, treble, with trills, with long notes, modulated when this seems good—soprano, mezzo, baritone; and briefly all the devices in that tiny throat which human science has devised with all the elaborate mechanisms of the flute, so that there can be no doubt that this sweetness was foretold by a convincing omen when it made music on the lips of the infant Stesichorus. And that no one may doubt its being a matter of science, the birds have several songs each, and not all the same but every bird songs of its own. They compete with one another, and there is clearly an animated rivalry between them; the loser often ends her life by dying, her breath giving out before her song. Often younger birds practise their music, and are given verses to imitate; the pupil listens with close attention and repeats the phrase, and the two keep silence by turns: we notice improvement in the one under instruction and a sort of criticism on the part of the instructress.

Pliny
NATURAL HISTORY, X, XLIII.

VIII

Communication Between Vertebrates

INTRODUCTION

In this short section we will consider two means of communication by vertebrates: rabbit odors and bird songs. Communication within a species or between species depends, of course, on sensory cues, and it may elicit a variety of behavioral responses. Danger signals, feeding calls, and territorial warning devices are but a few of the many kinds of communication that animals employ. The complexity of the signal, the response, and the mode of communication (visual, odorous, vocal, or other) are highly variable and are appropriate for the circumstances of the situation and the environment. Thus the signals of night monkeys perched high in the branches of a tree in the dark are stereotyped relatively simple vocal calls, whereas equivalent signals among diurnal monkeys or apes in the daylight might include visual clues and more complex sound patterns. For these animals, visual signals and sound are appropriate vehicles of information exchange, whereas odors, electrical signals, and so on, which might function well for other animals in other types of environments, are less efficient and so are not used.

Territoriality provides good examples of simple communication. Territories may be feeding ranges, mating grounds, nest sites, and the like. It may be the exclusive area of one male who excludes all other males of the same species, it may be an area more loosely defended so that occasional intruders are tolerated, or it may be a region shared among one group of the species from which all other individuals of the same species are repelled. Nesting territories of birds are maintained by singing: the male repeats the song over and over as he flies from one part of the territory to another. As a result, other members of the species are made aware of the claim to the site. Birds, then, employ primarily sound and sometimes visual display for conveying their territorial information. In contrast, rabbits produce and distribute odorous chemicals that warn other rabbits to stay away from a territory. Because the fecal pellets retain their odor for a long time, "communication" can continue while the animal that left the pellets is active elsewhere.

The response of a rabbit coming upon pellets that carry the odor of a foreign territory is a fine example of complex behavior resulting from an apparently simple signal. Under such circumstances a rabbit dominant in its home range looks "nervous" and becomes subordinate even to juvenile rabbits belonging to the foreign territory (see "Territorial Marking by Rabbits," by Roman Mykytowycz). An example of an equally complex response to a simple auditory signal is seen in vervet monkeys, which produce three distinctive warning calls to identify a hawk, a snake, or a leopard: each pattern of sound evokes very different evasive tactics. It is easy to imagine how natural selection has led to the association of a stimulus (such as the sighting of a hawk) with a response (emitting a specific sound) so that appropriate behavior by other individuals that can recognize the sound takes place.

The study of rabbit territoriality has raised at least two unanswered questions. First, it is not clear how each local population acquires a characteristic odor. Presumably each individual rabbit produces unique odors; the combination scattered around one warren may be the territorial smell. It is also possible that local inbreeding within each small territory might allow distinctive, group-specific odors to appear; this alternative does not seem likely, but it has not been ruled out.

Perhaps more intriguing is the question of what controls dominance and hypertrophied odor-producing glands. Mykytowycz points out that a dominant rabbit is not necessarily the largest rabbit in the territory, but its anal and chin glands are of extraordinarily large size and may be bigger than the glands of larger subordinate rabbits. One might guess that hormones cause this differential growth and the resultant increased scent-producing capacity, as well as aggressiveness and social dominance.

The article "The Language of Birds" by W. H. Thorpe is a good general treatment of bird song and provides examples of the diverse ways in which songs and calls are used. Since the article was published, it has become clearer that the slight variations in song observed between different birds of one species may be individual recognition markers. It is hard to generalize about as diverse a topic as bird song, but it does seem probable that the characteristics of the notes, or the syllables of the song are varied by individuals, while the basic time spans between the notes are kept relatively constant in order to provide species-recognition information. Since pitch, frequency modulation, and amplitude can all be varied, it is not difficult to imagine how even minute differences may identify each bird, and so allow pair maintenance, recognition, and so on to operate.

As a result of a number of recent experiments, we are able to determine quite precisely the stage at which young birds "learn" or acquire their songs. The zoologist Peter Marler and his collaborators have investigated populations of white-crowned sparrows living north, south, and east of San Francisco Bay. Each population sings its own dialect of the basic white-crowned sparrow song. A subsong (as defined by Thorpe), or a full song unlike that of any dialect, will develop in cage-reared, isolated white-crowned sparrows. If a mixed group of young from the three populations is never allowed to hear parental songs, the birds will develop their own unique dialect, which can in turn be taught to their offspring.

Normally a newly hatched bird hears its own dialect being sung for the first two or three months of life. Then in the fall and winter the older birds of the population stop singing. Several months later when spring time approaches, the maturing bird begins singing, and soon perfects the parental dialect. After a series of experiments in which captured young birds were raised in isolation, it was found that the period of learning the dialect occurs between about two weeks and two months of age. From then on, the bird "remembers" in some way what it heard early in life.

As might be expected, a nestling from one population placed with another group acquires the new dialect and sings it the following spring.

This is an extraordinary feat! The young nestling acquires the song early, by listening. It does not practice or receive any reward for learning the song. Then months elapse before singing starts, and the bird practices and varies its song until it finally duplicates what it heard months before.

It is of interest, therefore, to investigate the relationship of hearing to dialect. A bird deafened at birth can at best sing only the species subsong. If a bird is deafened at two months of age, we might guess that it had heard the dialect for a sufficient length of time and that no interference with singing would occur. However, this is not true, because the dialect song has not been perfected. In fact, the experiments show that a bird must be able to hear during the weeks that it is perfecting its dialect song. Thus it appears that the bird must compare its own song noises with those that were heard months before, matching those it produces to the original sounds to produce the correct dialect. After the song has been perfected, deafening has little effect except over several months when the song gradually drifts away from the original melody; apparently, some feedback from hearing acts to maintain the normal dialect song.

Perhaps the most surprising example of this type of learning has been observed in female white-crowned sparrows. Normally, they never sing, but like the males, they are exposed to dialect singing during youth. A female injected with testosterone (a male gonadal hormone) soon breaks into song and before long is singing the dialect! Thus she too has retained the memory of early sounds, although as a rule she would never emit them. The utility of such retention is obvious if she can use it also to identify males of her regional population when pair formation and breeding take place.

One of the most fascinating variations on bird song is antiphonal singing. Some shrikes, warblers, and barbets use antiphony for pair identification and location under conditions of limited visibility, particularly in tropical habitats. One bird begins by singing notes or groups of notes; the mate breaks in with its song; then the first may repeat, and so on. Precision of timing of the portions coming from each bird is the critical feature of the process. As W. H. Thorpe (1963) has noted, "...the timing of the singing is normally so perfect that in no case would one suppose that two birds were actually involved unless one sees them or until one happens actually to come between them and hear sound coming from two different directions." In the dense thickets or forest habitat of these birds the duets are repeated again and again, so that each bird is kept informed of the whereabouts of its mate. Although a bird normally sings only its own part during a duet, it does know all of the notes so that, when one bird wanders away, the mate begins to sing the whole duet alone. What better means than this to call back a straying mate: for what else can the other bird surmise, when it hears its own part being sung, than that it has a competitor that is singing with its partner?

When pairs are being established, unique duets are worked out. The repertoire and learning capabilities are great: one pair of shrikes was heard to sing seventeen distinctive duets in the course of one day. Presumably, this capacity for great song variation is simply an extension of the common ability to vary timing, frequency, and other properties of bird song.

Antiphonal singing is of particular interest because of the exceedingly short reaction times between emission and response of notes. Whereas a human being may require roughly 440 milliseconds to respond to a foreign speech sound by making a different sound, a black-headed gonolek needs only 135 milliseconds to begin singing its portion of a song after its mate emits a note. Not only is the reaction time extraordinarily fast for vertebrate hearing, but the length of the time interval between one bird's notes and those of the mate is exceedingly precise; even though the song is repeated again and again, the standard deviation in the length of time between responses is very slight. In contrast, a human being, if subjected to repeat trials, would be about one-eighth as accurate in attempting to allow a constant time interval to elapse before response. This precise timing and rapid response is somewhat reminiscent of the hypothesis that a bat's auditory system is programmed to identify echoes with the same characteristics as the sound emitted immediately before from the larynx. Perhaps analogous programming operates in antiphonal duets to speed and coordinate the singing.

It is probable that the use of antiphonal singing as a form of personal identification and location has arisen in species in which territoriality is not rigidly enforced. Mixing, both between and within species, is much freer in the tropical habitats than in more strict territorial regions of the temperate zones. Consequently, accurate pair identification signals may have become so important that antiphony evolved. Examples of an extreme form of the imitative abilities of antiphonal singers are seen in the parrots and mynah birds, which have an amazing imitative repertoire. They too may have acquired such capabilities in order to have distinctive nuances in song for individual identification.

Figure 1. The duet pattern on a pair of shrikes recorded on the Mozambique Coast. This is a duet of intermediate complexity; the A and B birds alternate as shown. After repeating this duet a number of times the birds may suddenly change to another song in their repertoire. On rare occasions W. H. Thorpe has heard three birds participating in a trio, but the biological function of such behavior is a mystery. The scientific pitch shown in this illustration is 256 hertz; the bar length equals 1.5 seconds. [From Thorpe, W. H., and North, Myles W., *Nature*, **208**, 1965.]

34

Territorial Marking by Rabbits

ROMAN MYKYTOWYCZ · May 1968

Over the past few years it has become increasingly apparent that one of the principal ways animals communicate is by means of odorous glandular secretions that have been given the name pheromones. The best examples of such chemical communication are found among the ants, some species of which use pheromones to lead their fellows to food, to warn them of danger and to organize social behavior in the nest [see "Pheromones," by Edward O. Wilson; SCIENTIFIC AMERICAN Offprint 157]. It has also been shown that pheromones play an important role in the social behavior of mammals (perhaps including man), although exactly how they do so has been somewhat obscure. My colleagues and I have been investigating such mechanisms in the wild rabbit of Australia (*Oryctolagus cuniculus*), and we have been able to demonstrate a clear-cut relation between the animal's social behavior and pheromone-secreting glands.

As is well known, the rabbit was introduced into Australia about 100 years ago, and since that time it has become a serious pest. Over the past two decades the Division of Wildlife Research of the Australian Commonwealth Scientific and Industrial Research Organization has conducted a broad ecological study of the wild rabbit in order to gain a better understanding of the life of the species and to provide a basis for the development of more effective methods of controlling the rabbit population. One result of this study is that we have been able to detect a distinct social organization within the rabbit colony. The role individual animals play in such a society is reflected both in the size of certain glands and in the extent to which the glands secrete pheromones. These substances probably serve a number of functions. They may communicate in-

formation about age, sex, reproductive stage and group membership. They may also warn of danger, and they definitely serve to define the "territory" of the rabbit.

The area within which an animal confines its activities is not necessarily the same as its territory; in a strict sense the term territory refers to that part of an animal's home range which it protects, sometimes by fighting. The size, form and character of a territory of course vary according to the animal's way of life. Some animals occupy a territory permanently; others hold it only during a particular season when, for example, breeding or nesting takes place. The possession of a territory, and therefore available shelter and food, makes breeding possible for some individuals of a species and prevents breeding by other individuals. Hence territoriality is an important factor regulating the density of a population.

Many mammals are known to mark out a territory with substances manufactured by specialized glands. Indeed, nearly all species of mammals possess scent-producing glands, often in several places on the body. In the dromedary the glands are at the back of the head, in the elephant at the temples, in a number of deer species below the eyes (the American deer and some other species have such glands near the hoof and on the leg). The chamois's glands are around the horns, the golden hamster's between the ribs, the peccary's in the loin. The pika (mouse hare) and marmot (woodchuck) employ glands behind and under the eyes and on the cheek for territorial marking. We have identified odor-producing glands on the chest of the kangaroo, and other workers in Australia have found similar glands on the chest of the koala and the brush-tailed

possum. The rabbit has scent glands in the anal region, in the groin and under the chin.

In order to study the territorial behavior of the rabbit it was necessary to follow the activities of individual free-living animals. As in the study of other wild animals, there were certain difficulties. It is not easy to identify individual rabbits, even in daylight, and the animal is largely nocturnal. Live rabbits are hard to catch, and it was necessary to examine them regularly. To minimize these problems we confined our rabbit colonies within fenced areas. Each enclosure was small enough to allow close observation (from an elevated hiding place nearby) but not so small as to interfere with the rabbit's normal behavior. To facilitate the recognition of individual animals each one was marked with black dye in a distinctive pattern; tags of different shapes were also affixed to the rabbits' ears. We used a colored light-reflecting tape to mark the tags in a variety of patterns; at night under spotlights the rabbits could easily be identified. To keep track of the animals' movements in their burrows we drilled a few holes down to the burrow tunnels. When we were not using the holes to check the location of rabbits underground or to catch them, they were plugged with earth enclosed in wire netting.

When a rabbit was born in an enclosure, its ears were permanently marked by tattooing; in this way the behavior of the animal could be followed for its lifetime. The rabbits were observed every day and on certain occasions continuously for a 24-hour period. Some studies were continued for three years, which is twice the average lifespan of a free-living wild rabbit in Australia.

It was established by these observa-

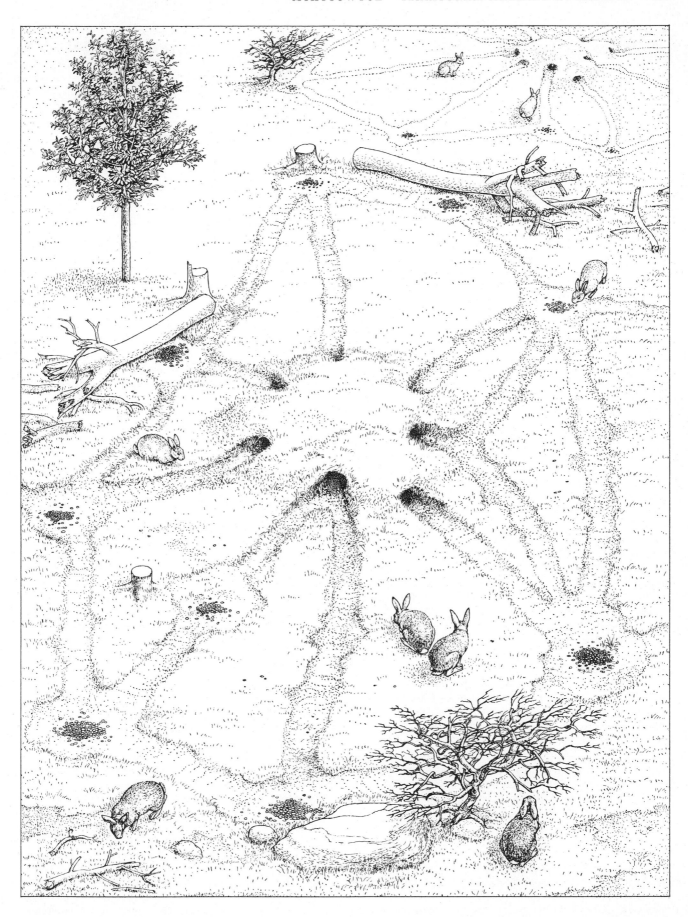

RABBIT TERRITORY, somewhat idealized in this drawing, lies around a central warren. Radiating from the entrances are intersecting runs. On the runs are small mounds of fecal pellets deposited by the rabbits of the colony. At top right a rabbit from another colony sniffs at a mound of pellets. It is warned by odor of an anal-gland secretion on the pellets that the territory is occupied.

RABBIT EXPERIMENT followed the behavior of individual wild rabbits (*Oryctolagus cuniculus*) aboveground and underground. Holes dug down to the burrow tunnel gave access to the animals; when not in use, the holes were plugged with earth enclosed in wire

tions that the rabbit lives in small groups, each consisting of eight or 10 animals, depending on the density of the overall rabbit population. A group of rabbits occupies a distinct territory, with a warren—a burrow with a number of entrances—as its center. At the onset of the breeding season the males establish a hierarchy of descending dominance by fighting. The same is done by the females. The most dominant male and female rule over the group and its territory, which is defended by its occupants and recognized by rabbits of other groups. The rabbit hierarchy is constantly reinforced by chasing and submission.

The advantages of having a territory were evident in the different breeding patterns of female rabbits. High-ranking females give birth frequently and regularly, housing the young in a special breeding chamber dug as an extension to the burrow. Their young have a much higher survival rate and growth rate than the young of low-ranking females. Some of the subordinate females are chased away from a warren and forced to drop their litters in isolated breeding "stops"—short, shallow burrows dug at a distance of 10 to 50 yards from the warren. Both in the stop and later, when they come out of it, the young of such litters are vulnerable to predators, particularly foxes and crows. When they try to enter the central warren, they are attacked by the resident females and their young. Some subordinate females, although they are physi-

ologically fit, never give birth; the embryos they conceive do not develop to full term but are absorbed in the uterus.

It could also be seen that not all rabbit territories are of equal quality: some offer more protection and a better food supply than others. The most dominant animals tend to occupy the better territories. The breeding stops of subordinate females are often in places that are susceptible to flooding, another factor that contributes to the lower survival rate of their young.

A rabbit that crosses the border between its own territory and a neighboring one is immediately aware that it has done so. No matter how frequent and regular the visits, the animal's behavior changes. In its own territory it moves freely; it feeds and examines objects confidently. In a foreign territory the animal seems always on the alert. Its neck is stretched, the movement of its nostrils indicates that it is sniffing continuously and it does not feed. Although the interloper may be dominant in its own territory, when it is challenged outside by a rabbit permanently attached to the foreign territory, it will offer no resistance. It will not resist even if the challenger is half-grown.

It is not difficult to believe that a rabbit territory becomes saturated with the characteristic smell of the group and that within the area in which this group smell prevails the animals feel at home, much as a man may be able to perceive the odor of another man's home as be-

ing strange in contrast to the familiar smell of his own. Specific odors associated with an individual group or colony have been demonstrated in many social insects and also in some fishes. Apart from the effect on the odor of the food eaten by the animals, genetic factors are undoubtedly involved as well.

One component of a rabbit territory's odor is the smell of urine. During amatory behavior the males can be seen urinating on the females, and the animals also urinate on each other during aggressive displays. Young rabbits so marked by adult members of their group are identified with it. The smell of foreign rabbit urine releases aggression; females may even attack their own young when they have been smeared with foreign urine.

Another component of the territory odor comes from feces. The marking out of territory with feces seems to be common among animals, as has been pointed out by Heini Hediger of the University of Zurich. Among certain animals the odor of the feces comes not from the excrement itself but from the pheromone of anal glands; such glands have been identified in more than 100 species of mammals. Some animals whose anal glands are highly developed—for example the gray squirrel, the marten, the dormouse and the hyena—use the anal pheromone alone, rather than in combination with feces, for territorial marking.

The anal glands of the rabbit are well developed. They consist of two clusters netting. Each adult animal was marked with dye in a distinctive pattern and wore an identification tag in its ear. The ears of rabbits born during the experiment were tattooed. To house their young, rabbits dig special breeding chambers as extensions to the burrow.

of brownish tissue forming a saddle-like mass around the end of the rectum. The secretions of the glands flow through a few ducts into the rectum, where they coat the pellets of feces passing out of the anus. Until recently it was generally accepted that the secretion facilitated the passage of the hard fecal pellets. We have found, however, that when the rabbit's anal glands are removed, defecation is not affected.

Our studies indicate that the fecal pellets serve to distribute the rabbit's anal pheromone.

When one examines a rabbit territory, one can see a number of places in which the animals have repeatedly deposited feces. Around a typical warren it is usual to find about 30 of these small dunghills. They are interconnected by paths that all the rabbits use in moving around the area. When a strange rabbit enters the territory, it inevitably encounters a dunghill—a warning signal that the area is occupied. It then displays the wary behavior I have described.

A similar warning is deposited at the entrances to breeding stops. When a stop contains young, it is sealed by the female with soil. Once a day the female reopens the burrow, enters it and suckles the young. When the entrance

CHINNING rabbit enclosed in an experimental pen was photographed at night, when the animal is active. As the rabbit presses against a wooden peg, droplets from its submandibular (underchin) glands are forced through pores of the skin, "marking" the object.

UNDERCHIN of the rabbit is the site of the subcutaneous glands that, together with the anal glands, function in territorial marking. The fur under the chin of the female rabbit (*top*) displays no trace of a glandular secretion. Under the male rabbit's chin (*bottom*) the fur is matted from the secretion, which the male produces more copiously than the female.

is resealed, the female is likely to deposit a few fecal pellets and some urine on top of the seal. It is remarkable that these earth seals are almost never disturbed by other rabbits. (The exceptions occur under abnormal circumstances, such as when the density of a confined population becomes exceptionally high and competition for breeding sites is intensive.)

Certain of our experiments support the idea that the rabbit's feces serve a communicative function, and indicate that the pellets of a dunghill differ from those that are randomly deposited around a territory. We presented a group of rabbits with artificial dunghills consisting of turf sprinkled with some of the pellets found at random locations in the territory of other rabbits. Around these artificial dunghills (and also on pieces of turf used as a control) the animals engaged mainly in digging and eating. When they were confronted with an actual dunghill from foreign territory, however, they did not eat, they sniffed intensely and they produced marking feces of their own. These pellets were similar to dunghill pellets in that their "rabbity" odor was (according to 30 human judges) decidedly stronger than the odor of the randomly distributed pellets. Presumably the difference between the two odors is perceived even more sharply by rabbits.

There is a highly significant relation between the size of a rabbit's anal gland and the place of the animal in the social hierarchy of a warren. The largest glands belong to dominant individuals, the smallest to subordinate animals. (Body weight is not the main factor determining glandular size.) The secretory activity of the anal gland also is higher in the dominant animals. Indeed, we found that the social rank of an individual rabbit could be guessed with a fair degree of accuracy merely from the appearance of the gland in section. It is also significant that the size and secretory activity of the gland were greatest during the breeding season—the period when territorial activity is most intense.

Male rabbits are mainly responsible for establishing dunghills (in Australia about 80 percent of the animals caught in traps set on dunghills are males), and the anal gland of the male rabbit is larger than the anal gland of the female. Our experiments indicate that the activity of the gland is under the control of sex hormones. When male rabbits were castrated before puberty, the growth and activity of the anal gland were inhibited; when the ovaries were removed from female rabbits, the size and activity of the gland were somewhat enhanced. When male sex hormones were given to both male and female rabbits, the gland grew larger and produced more secretion.

The rabbit's anal pheromone and its urine thus serve to establish its overall territory. For marking localized features such as logs, branches and blades of grass the animal employs a pheromone secreted by its chin gland. If one looks under the chin of a female rabbit, one cannot find any conspicuous marks, although the fur may be slightly moist or matted. Under the male rabbit's chin, however, there is a distinct yellowish encrustation and matted fur. One can feel the glands under the skin, and if pressure is applied, droplets of secretion can be forced out through a semicircular row of external pores. With this secretion (which is odorless to humans) the male rabbit marks not only objects that would be difficult to mark with feces or urine but also the entrances to its burrows, the fecal pellets of other rabbits, its own weathered pellets and its females and young. To describe marking with this gland we use the term "chinning."

Within its own territory a rabbit chins freely and frequently, particularly if it is a male. When it is in a foreign territory, it does not chin; when it is confronted on its own ground with foreign feces, it chins intensely. We have found that the individuals in a rabbit hierarchy that are most dominant chin more often than the subordinate animals. In fact, the frequency of chinning can

ANAL-GLAND ACTIVITY can be determined from the appearance of the gland in section. In the less actively secreting gland shown at top the tubules (*dark areas with light centers*) are smaller than those in the intensely secreting gland that appears below it.

CHIN-GLAND ACTIVITY is also reflected in contrasting size of tubules in less active gland (*top*) and more active one (*bottom*). These four photomicrographs were made by E. C. Slater of the Commonwealth Scientific and Industrial Research Organization.

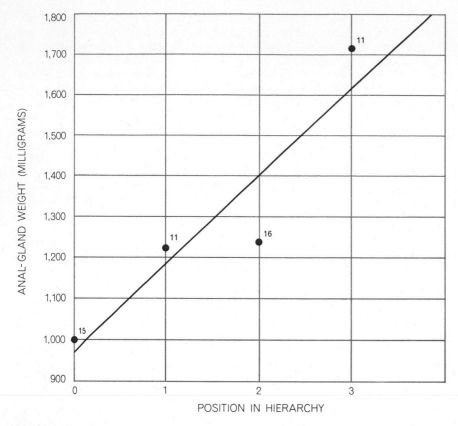

RELATION BETWEEN ANAL GLAND AND SOCIAL BEHAVIOR was established from observations of the activities of rabbits. The most dominant animals of a warren hierarchy (*here given the rating "3"*) were found to possess the heaviest anal glands. The number above a dot indicates the number of rabbits in the sample; the trend is indicated by a line.

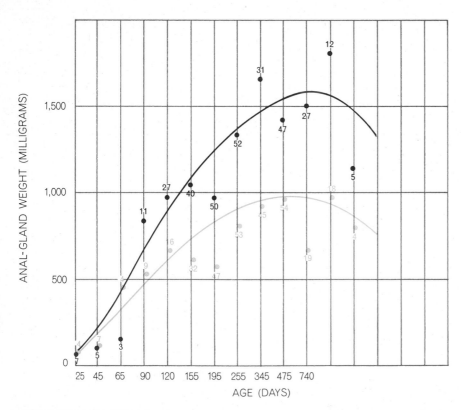

SEXUAL DIFFERENTIATION appears when the weight of the anal gland of male rabbits (*black*) is compared with that of female rabbits (*color*). The number of animals sampled is shown adjacent to a dot; the curves indicate the trend in the measurements. Age of the rabbits was estimated from the weight of the eye lens and is uncertain beyond 740 days.

be used as an indication of potential dominance: when two males completely strange to each other were brought together, the male with the highest chinning score always established his dominance over the other animal.

The rabbit's chin gland, like its anal gland, is larger and secretes more abundantly in dominant animals than in subordinate ones. This gland too, being larger in males than in females, appears to be under the control of sex hormones. Moreover, its activity, like that of the anal gland, fluctuates with the seasons; it secretes most freely at the time when the rabbit's territorial activity is at its most intense. Thus the animals that are dominant in the hierarchy are the ones most concerned with the demarcation and defense of territory. Indeed, their territorial behavior is rooted in their physiology.

Additional support for the territorial function of the anal and chin glands has come from the study of an animal that is closely related to the rabbit but that behaves differently with respect to territory. This animal is the European hare (*Lepus europaeus*), which like the rabbit has become widely distributed throughout Australia since being introduced there. Although a fully grown hare is four times as heavy as a rabbit and most of its glands (such as the thyroid and lachrymal glands) are larger, the anal and chin glands of the hare are only a tenth the size of those in rabbits.

This difference between the two animals reflects a difference in their territorial behavior. Unlike the rabbit, the hare does not live in a social group; it is a solitary animal and its home area is large. The hare protects only that part of its home range which is in its immediate vicinity, and it does not retain such a territory permanently. Although the animal makes dunghills (apparently at the sites it visits most frequently), the number of them is small compared with the number in a rabbit territory. There is no difference between the anal gland of the male hare and the gland of the female. In short, it appears to be unnecessary for the hare to mark its territory by odor.

Another difference in the glandular makeup of the hare and the rabbit also appears to have behavioral significance. The animals have similar glands in the groin, but in the hare these glands are larger than they are in the rabbit (and they are somewhat larger in the female hare than they are in the male). Observations of the hare's mating behavior suggest that the glands in the groin are the source of a powerful sexual attractant: when the solitary-living female hare is in estrus, she attracts males from some distance. The female of the gregarious rabbit species obviously has no need of a long-range attractant.

What we have learned about the wild rabbit in Australia is supported by studies of American species. The swamp rabbit (*Sylvilagus aquaticus*), a strongly territorial species, chins more frequently than the weakly territorial cottontail rabbit (*Sylvilagus floridanus*). Our examination of gland tissue from these species indicates that the anal and chin glands are larger in the swamp rabbit than in the cottontail. The social behavior of the two species was studied by Halsey M. Marsden and Nicholas R. Holler of the University of Missouri.

The pheromones of rabbits and other mammals have not yet been chemically separated and identified, as has been done with certain insect pheromones. With knowledge of the composition of specific odors it will be possible to establish their role in the life of a mammalian species. This will undoubtedly lead to a better understanding of the species' behavior. Some insect pheromones have even been synthesized; incorporated in traps, they have been used successfully· in pest control. The synthesis of mammalian pheromones would no doubt be helpful in developing effective controls for mammals that are economically undesirable.

The existence of glands that function specifically and solely for territorial marking emphasizes the importance of territory and social organization in the life of an animal. In today's crowded world the question of space and territory is of interest not only to students of animal biology but also to all who are concerned with man's problems of overpopulation. The theory that in animals population control is achieved through social behavior of which territoriality is an integral part has been advanced by V. C. Wynne-Edwards of the University of Edinburgh [see "Population Control in Animals," by V. C. Wynne-Edwards; SCIENTIFIC AMERICAN Offprint 192]. More and more we are coming to realize that it is not only the availability of food that determines the size of a human population but also our own behavior and spacing, and that these factors must be considered in speculating on the fate of the human species. Every animal has, in addition to minimum requirements of things such as food, minimum requirements of living space and distance from others of its own species.

DEFENSE ACTION of small birds against a predator takes two forms, which require different types of audible message. When the enemy is perched in a tree (*upper drawing*) the small birds may practice "mobbing." They swarm around the larger bird, uttering sharp, easily located "chinks" to advertise its presence. Against a hawk on the wing (*lower drawing*) the little birds take cover under foliage, and their warning cry is now the high-pitched, drawn-out "seeet" which is difficult to trace (*see diagrams on opposite page*).

35

The Language of Birds

W. H. THORPE · October 1956

If birds were suddenly eliminated from the world, the absence of their song would at once change the whole aspect of nature out of doors. The reasons why we appreciate bird song so keenly are several. We are attracted by its beauty, by its association with spring and all the promise which that time of the year suggests. Perhaps strongest of all is the feeling expressed by W. H. Davies in the lines:

> I could not sleep again, for such
> wild cries,
> And went out early into their green
> world:
> And then I saw what set their little
> tongues
> To scream for joy—they saw the
> East in gold.

The idea that bird song is often an expression of irrepressible joy actually has some scientific justification. But we are apt to overlook the fact that bird songs and calls are not merely a spontaneous emotional outlet, that they are in fact the language in which the chirpers communicate with one another.

The sounds that birds make have two main functions: to arouse an emotional state (by way of warning, wooing, etc.) and to convey precise information. The sounds themselves can conveniently be divided into two categories: call notes and true song. In general the characteristic call notes of a species are inherited, whereas the true songs may be either entirely inherited, partly inherited and partly learned or almost entirely learned. We have been making a detailed study of bird songs and calls for several years at the Madingley Ornithological Field Station of the University of Cambridge. In this investigation we have enlisted the help of tape recorders and

electronic equipment for analyzing sound. The chief bird partner in our study has been the common English chaffinch (*Fringilla coelebs*). The calls and the songs of the chaffinch illustrate very beautifully some of the chief generalizations we are now able to draw

concerning the musical language of birds.

A bird's call note, in contrast to its song, is a brief sound with a relatively simple acoustic structure. Its main function, in the case of small birds, is to sound a warning of the presence of a dangerous enemy, such as a hawk or

WARNING CALLS differ according to the circumstances of their use (*see drawing opposite*). "Chink" (*top oscillogram*) is easy to locate because of its long wavelength, brief duration and abrupt beginning and end. "Seeet" (*bottom oscillogram*) has short wavelength, long duration and begins and ends imperceptibly, making its direction difficult to trace.

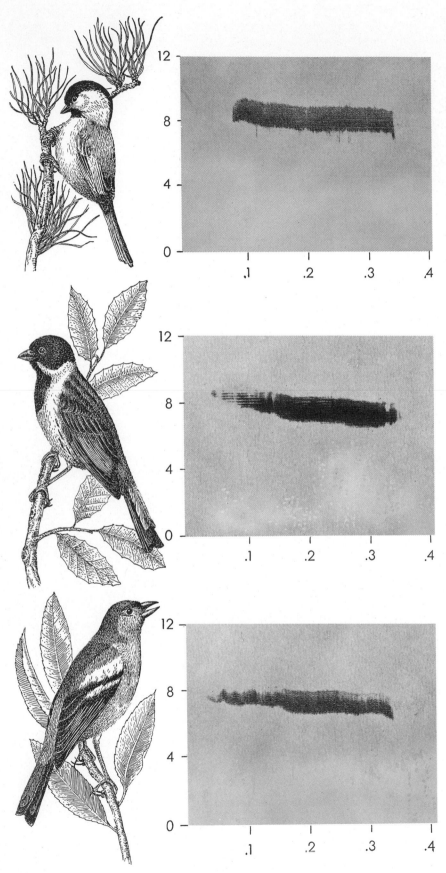

CALLS OF DIFFERENT SPECIES are sometimes remarkably alike. Above are sketches of three small birds (the blue tit, a close relative of the American chickadee, top, the bunting, center, and the chaffinch, bottom) together with oscillograms of their "seeet" calls. The oscillograms show time in seconds horizontally and kilocycles per second on the vertical axis.

owl. If the bird of prey is perched conspicuously in a tree, the small birds will often make themselves conspicuous too by behavior known as "mobbing." They set up a chorus of cries which points out the predator, so to speak, to all and sundry. If the bird of prey is in flight, on the other hand, the small birds race to the nearest bush or other cover, and utter their warning cries from that haven. Now the calls are very different in the two cases. Chaffinches mobbing a perched predator give forth relatively low-pitched sounds known as "chink" calls. But when they have fled to cover, the males give a high, thin note designated as the "seeet" call, the effect of which is to cause other chaffinches also to dash for the nearest shelter, and to peer cautiously upward looking for the hawk in the sky.

The significant difference between the two calls is that the "chink" note is easy to locate whereas the "seeet" is extremely difficult. The low frequencies of the "chink" sound are of a wavelength which allows the two ears of a hawk (or a man) to detect phase differences; the call also gives clues to its direction in the form of intensity and time of arrival of the sound at the two ears—the latter because the sound comes as clicklike pulses. On the other hand, the "seeet" call is composed of certain high frequencies which probably permit no clues to its location by phase or intensity difference, and it probably also fails to give a time clue, because it begins and ends imperceptibly, instead of coming as a sharp click [*see spectrograms on page 343*]. So it seems that the "seeet" call is admirably adjusted to avoid giving positional clues of any kind to predators. Yet it is just as effective as any other sound would be in warning neighboring chaffinches.

The full song of the male chaffinch performs the function of keeping other males from its territory and attracting unmated females. It is not too inadequately described by the mnemonic jingle *chip-chip-chip; tell-tell-tell; cherry-erry-erry; tissy-chee-wee-oo.* As sound spectrograms show [*see opposite page*], the chaffinch song is sufficiently complex not only to identify the species but also to allow wide individual variation, so that individual birds are recognizable, even by human beings, by their personal signature tune.

Study of these songs is extremely interesting from the standpoint of heredity and learning. We have found evidence that even complex songs may depend primarily on the inherited makeup of a bird. For example, the spectrograms of the songs of the European wren and of the American winter wren are remarkably alike. It appears that the song pattern of some birds must rest upon an inborn pattern of activity in the central nervous system.

On the other hand, everyone who has listened to bird songs attentively and with a trained ear has detected individual differences. We have lately proved, by experiments with chaffinches, that these individual differences are not the expression of genetic differences but develop by learning during the early life of the bird. This problem fascinated field ornithologists in England and Germany as far back as the early 18th century, but its precise study has become possible only within the last few years, when apparatus for the accurate analysis of sounds became available.

When a young chaffinch is taken from the nest and reared separately out of hearing of all chaffinch song, its song development is greatly restricted. The bird eventually produces a song of about the normal length (two to three seconds), but it fails to divide the first part of the song into phrases, as a normally reared chaffinch does, or to end its song with the elaborate flourish—the *tissy-chee-wee-oo*—which is one of the most striking characteristics of the chaffinch song in the wild.

The simple, restricted song of the isolated bird can be taken to represent the inherited basis of a chaffinch's performance. Now if after babyhood two or more such birds are put together in a room, but still with no opportunity to hear experienced chaffinches, they develop more complex songs. The attempt to sing in company provides mutual stimulation which encourages the production of complexity. The group of birds will, by mutual imitation, build up a distinctive community pattern. The members of the group conform so closely to this pattern that it is barely possible to distinguish the songs one from another, even by the most minute electronic analysis. Their song may be quite as complex as that of a normal wild chaffinch. But it bears practically no resemblance to the characteristic chaffinch song!

There is a short and critical six-week period, at about the 11th month of life, during which the chaffinch develops its song pattern. Once this critical learning period is over, the song is fixed for life: no matter how much a bird is exposed to other chaffinch songs afterward, it continues year after year to sing only the song or songs it worked out as a youngster.

Such experiments make clear what is happening in the wild. In nature young chaffinches must certainly learn some details of song from their parents or from other adults in the first few weeks of life. At this stage a young bird absorbs the general pattern of division of the song into two or three phrases with a flourish at the end. But not until the critical learning period, during the following spring, does the bird develop the finer details of its song. This is the time when the young wild chaffinch first sings in a territory in competition with neighboring birds of the same species, and there is good evidence that it learns details of song from these neighbors. It may learn two or three different songs, sometimes even more, from neighbors on different sides of its territory. Many field naturalists have observed local dialects of the song of a given species.

So the full chaffinch song is a simple integration of inborn and learned song patterns, the former constituting the basis for the latter. While isolated chaffinches can, as we have seen, work out for themselves very strange songs, those in the wild are circumscribed by the general pattern of the chaffinch song characteristic of the locality, though they may develop individual variations in detail.

The chaffinch, like many other small birds, has a subsong consisting of an irregular sequence of chirps and rattles. This subsong, in contrast to the full song, is usually uttered from dense cover and appears to have little or no communicatory function. Heard in the early spring, it seems to be associated in some degree with rising production of sex hormones by the gonads. The subsong

SONGS OF DIFFERENT BIRDS of the same species have similar over-all patterns but may show striking individual differences. Above are oscillograms of the songs of three different chaffinches. The phrases into which the songs are divided are marked off by dotted lines.

DIRECTION from which a sound is coming may be judged in various ways. Wavelengths comparable to the width of the bird's head give phase differences at its two ears *(top)*. Shorter waves may be blocked by the head so that the more distant ear is in a "sound shadow" and receives little energy *(bottom)*.

in a sense constitutes the raw material out of which the true song is constructed. It contains a much bigger range of frequencies than does the full song, and the bird drops some of these frequencies in the full song. This suggests a similarity with the way in which human children learn to speak. A baby will produce at random almost every conceivable sound its vocal mechanisms are capable of making, but as it grows it ceases to produce those sounds which it does not hear uttered by its parents and others around it.

Everyone knows that many birds are good mimics: besides the proverbial parrot there are the mockingbird in the U. S. and the starling and other species in Europe. To its own innate song such a bird adds notes and phrases from a wide variety of other species, and sometimes even sounds of inanimate origin. (The biological function of this imitation is still obscure: if the song of the starling, for instance, is a territorial proclamation like that of the chaffinch, to imitate many other species would seem merely to lead to confusion.) We have recently found that a chaffinch caged with, say, canaries may introduce a very good imitation of a phrase of canary song into its subsong, but never into its full song. How this restriction is maintained, we do not know. It is being studied, however, and we hope that its investigation will in due course throw light on the relationship between subsongs and full songs.

We have just commenced a very interesting study of the songs of hybrid birds—born of two different species. A curious and puzzling first result is that the hybrid is sometimes more imitative than either parent bird. For example, the song of a hybrid offspring from a goldfinch and a greenfinch is a virtually per-

INNER EAR of a bird contains the cochlea (A), or organ of hearing, and the highly developed semicircular canals (B) which provide acute sense of balance needed for flight.

fect imitation of a chaffinch song which the bird heard in its aviary.

It was said at the beginning that most people tend to think of bird song as a sort of emotional release rather than the process of communication that it usually is. Actually the possibility of birds singing for pleasure is by no means ruled out. The evidence is far from negligible that the songs of some thrushes, the warblers and the nightingale exhibit elaborate esthetic improvement far beyond what strict biological necessity requires. To be sure, the purity of tone which characterizes the best singers is potentially advantageous to them, for it helps to provide an additional dimension for distinctiveness. On the other hand, we have seen that in birds' imitation of song there seems to be no immediate or obvious biological reward, and that often the matching of sound patterns must itself constitute the reward. Much of it, of course, may be merely part of the trial-and-error process of learning, but in those cases of vocal imitation where new phrases are produced only after long delay and apparently without specific practice, another influence must be at work.

Biographical Notes
and Bibliographies

AN ESSAY ON VERTEBRATES

Bibliography

Altman, S. A., SOCIAL COMMUNICATION AMONG PRIMATES. Chicago, University of Chicago Press, 1967, p. 392.

Barrington, E. J. W., THE BIOLOGY OF HEMICHORDATA AND PROTOCHORDATA. London, Oliver and Boyd, 1965, pp. 1–176.

Campbell, B. G., HUMAN EVOLUTION, AN INTRODUCTION TO MAN'S ADAPTATIONS. Chicago, Aldine, 1966, p. 425.

Dobzhansky, T., MANKIND EVOLVING. New Haven, Yale University Press, 1962, p. 381.

Gordon, M. S., ANIMAL FUNCTION: PRINCIPLES AND ADAPTATIONS. New York, Macmillan, 1968, p. 560.

Hoar, W. S., GENERAL AND COMPARATIVE PHYSIOLOGY. Englewood Cliffs, N. J., Prentice-Hall, 1966, p. 815.

Howell, F. Clark, "Recent advances in human evolutionary studies." Quart. Rev. Biol. **42**, 1967, pp. 471–513.

Sturkie, P. D., AVIAN PHYSIOLOGY, 2nd ed. Ithaca, N. Y., Cornell University Press, 1965, p. 766.

Young, J. Z., THE LIFE OF VERTEBRATES, 2nd ed. New York, Oxford University Press, 1962, p. 820.

I · STRUCTURAL ADAPTATIONS OF VERTEBRATE BODIES

Introduction

Bibliography

Carter, G. S., STRUCTURE AND HABIT IN VERTEBRATE EVOLUTION. Seattle, University of Washington Press, 1967, p. 520.

Gray, J., "Studies in animal locomotion." J. Exptl. Biol. **13**, 1936, pp. 170–218. (A series of papers on physical and neurological aspects of swimming; some coauthored by A. Sand.)

Tobias, P. V., "Early man in East Africa." Science **149**, 1965, pp. 22–33.

Welty, J. C., THE LIFE OF BIRDS. Philadelphia, Saunders, 1964, p. 546.

1. How Fishes Swim

The Author

SIR JAMES GRAY was head of the Department of Zoology of the University of Cambridge for more than twenty years. In addition to his academic duties, he is the British Government's Development Commissioner for Fishery Research and a trustee of the British Museum. Born in 1891, he was elected a fellow of King's College, Cambridge, in 1914. A long-time student of animal movement, Sir James writes that he first studied fish as a result of trying to explain the movement of single cells. The lash of a spermatozoon's tail led him to observe eels, and eels led him to fishes and dolphins. As a result of this work on the mechanics of cellular and organismal movements, Gray played a leading role in changing the focus of zoological research in the twentieth century from evolutionary comparative anatomy to the function analysis of living animals. He is the author of several books, including the well-known *How Animals Move*.

Bibliography

ASPECTS OF THE LOCOMOTION OF WHALES. R. W. L. Gawn in *Nature*, Vol. 161, No. 4,080, pages 44–46; January 10, 1948.

THE PROPULSIVE POWERS OF BLUE AND FIN WHALES. K. A. Kermack in *The Journal of Experimental Biology*, Vol. 25, No. 3, pages 237–240; September, 1948.

STUDIES IN ANIMAL LOCOMOTION. VI: THE PROPULSIVE POWERS OF THE DOLPHIN. J. Gray in *The Journal of Experimental Biology*, Vol. 13, No. 2, pages 192–199; April, 1936.

WHAT PRICE SPEED? G. Gabrielli and Th. von Kármán in *Mechanical Engineering*, Vol. 72, No. 10, pages 775–781; October, 1950.

2. How Animals Run

The Author

MILTON HILDEBRAND is professor of Zoology at the University of California campus in Davis, California. He decided at the age of six that he wanted to be a zoologist. "As a boy," he reports, "I collected skeletons. My private teaching collection now includes about 1,000 specimens from all over the world." He took his B.A., M.A., and Ph.D. degrees at the University of California, and has also studied with various anatomists in England. During World War II he was an officer in the ski troops, and taught skiing, winter warfare, rock-climbing, and mountain combat. During the Italian campaign he served as a battalion pack officer in charge of mule transport in the Apennines.

Bibliography

HOW ANIMALS MOVE. James Gray. Cambridge University Press, 1953.

MOTIONS OF THE RUNNING CHEETAH AND HORSE. Milton Hildebrand in *Journal of Mammalogy*, Vol. 40, No. 4, pages 481–495; November, 1959.

QUADRUPEDAL AND BIPEDAL LOCOMOTION OF LIZARDS. Richard C. Snyder in *Copeia*, No. 2, pages 64–70; June, 1952.

SOME LOCOMOTORY ADAPTATIONS IN MAMMALS. J. Maynard Smith and R. J. G. Savage in *Journal of the Linean Society–Zoology*, Vol. 42, No. 288, pages 603–622; February, 1956.

SPEED IN ANIMALS. A. Brazier Howell. University of Chicago Press, 1944.

3.   The Antiquity of Human Walking

The Author

JOHN NAPIER is reader in anatomy at the Royal Free Hospital School of Medicine of the University of London and director of the school's Unit of Primate Biology and Human Evolution. Son of a former professor of tropical medicine at the University of Calcutta, Napier was educated in England, receiving a medical degree from St. Bartholomew's Hospital in London. In 1963 he obtained a D.Sc. from the University of London. Napier's principal interests are teaching and research in primate biology. With his wife, he has published a textbook on the primates. Napier has appeared on numerous television programs dealing with primates and human evolution.

Bibliography

THE APE-MEN. Robert Broom in *Scientific American;* November, 1949.

THE FOOT AND THE SHOE. J. R. Napier in *Physiotherapy*, Vol. 43, No. 3, pages 65–74; March, 1957.

A HOMINID TOE BONE FROM BED 1, OLDUVAI GORGE, TANZANIA. M. H. Day and J. R. Napier in *Nature*, Vol. 211, No. 5052, pages 929–930; August 27, 1966.

4.   The Evolution of the Hand

The Author

For information about JOHN NAPIER, see the preceding biographical note.

Bibliography

THE ANTECEDENTS OF MAN: AN INTRODUCTION TO THE EVOLUTION OF THE PRIMATES. W. E. Le Gros Clark. Edinburgh University Press, 1959.

MAN THE TOOL-MAKER. Kenneth P. Oakley. British Museum of Natural History, 1950.

THE PREHENSILE MOVEMENTS OF THE HUMAN HAND. J. R. Napier in *The Journal of Bone and Joint Surgery*, Vol. 38-B, No. 4, pages 902–913; November, 1956.

PREHENSILITY AND OPPOSABILITY IN THE HANDS OF PRIMATES. J. R. Napier in *Symposia of the Zoological Society of London*, No. 5, pages 115–132; August, 1961.

THE TROPICAL RAIN FOREST. P. W. Richards. Cambridge University Press, 1957.

5.   Bird Aerodynamics

The Author

JOHN H. STORER is a student of the aerodynamics of birds. He is author of the book *The Flight of Birds.*

Bibliography

THE FLIGHT OF BIRDS: ANALYZED THROUGH SLOW-MOTION PHOTOGRAPHY. John H. Storer. Cranbrook Institute of Science, Bulletin No. 28; 1948.

6.   Birds as Flying Machines

The Author

CARL WELTY is professor of zoology and Chairman of the Department of Biology at Beloit College in Wisconsin. He was brought up in Fort Wayne, Indiana, except for summers spent on a rundown fruit farm in Michigan. These summers left him with a taste for nature, and when he later went to Earlham College, a Quaker school in Indiana, he majored in biology. He took a master's degree at Haverford College in 1925, and went on to Parsons College, Iowa, where he taught biology and met his wife, a fellow teacher. Welty has been at Beloit College since 1934. In 1946 he took a year's leave to head a team of American Quakers engaged in postwar relief work in Coblenz, Germany.

Bibliography

THE BIOLOGY OF BIRDS. J. A. Thomson. The Macmillan Company, 1923.

THE BIRD: ITS FORM AND FUNCTION. C. W. Beebe. Henry Holt and Company, 1906.

FUNCTIONAL ANATOMY OF THE VERTEBRATES. D. P. Quiring. McGraw-Hill Book Company, Inc., 1950.

A HISTORY OF BIRDS. W. P. Pycraft. Methuen & Co., 1910.

7.   The Brain of Birds

The Authors

LAURENCE JAY STETTNER and KENNETH A. MATYNIAK are on the staff of Wayne State University; Stettner holds the rank of associate professor of psychology and Matyniak is a research assistant. Stettner is spending the year as a special research fellow of the National Institutes of Health, working in the laboratory of perinatal physiology of the National Institute of Neurological Diseases and Blindness in San Juan, Puerto Rico. He went to Wayne State in 1963 after receiving a Ph.D. from Stanford University. Earlier he had taken bachelor's and master's degrees at Brooklyn College. Matyniak was graduated from Wayne State in 1965. He has worked with Stettner since 1964.

Bibliography

BRAIN LESIONS IN BIRDS: EFFECTS ON DISCRIMINATION ACQUISITION AND REVERSAL. Laurence J. Stettner and William J. Schultz in *Science*, Vol. 155, No. 3770, pages 1689–1692; March 31, 1967.

EFFECTS OF ENDBRAIN LESIONS UPON VISUAL DISCRIMINATION LEARNING IN PIGEONS. H. P. Zeigler in *The Journal of Comparative Neurology*, Vol. 120, No. 2, pages 161–194; April, 1963.

OBSERVATIONS ON THE COMPARATIVE ANATOMY OF THE AVIAN BRAIN. Stanley Cobb in *Perspectives in Biology and Medicine*, Vol. 3, No. 3; Spring, 1960.

II · VASCULAR SYSTEM BIOLOGY

Introduction

Bibliography

Bevegard, B. S., and Shepherd, J. T., "Regulation of the circulation during exercise in man." *Physiol. Revs.* **47**, 1967, pp. 78–213.

Braunwald, E., "Heart." *Ann. Rev. Physiol.* **28**, 1966, pp. 227–266.

Fanelli, A. R., Antonini, E., and Caputo, A., "Hemoglobin and myoglobin." *Adv. Protein Chem.* **19**, 1964, pp. 73–222.

Riggs, A., "Functional properties of hemoglobins." *Physiol. Revs.* **45**, 1965, pp. 619–673.

8. The Physiology of Exercise

The Authors

CARLETON B. CHAPMAN and JERE H. MITCHELL are respectively professor and associate professor of medicine at the University of Texas Southwestern Medical School. Chapman, a native of Alabama, was graduated from Davidson College in 1936 and spent three years as a Rhodes scholar at the University of Oxford before obtaining a medical degree from Harvard University. He was on the medical faculty of the University of Minnesota for six years before assuming his present post. Mitchell was previously senior assistant surgeon in the laboratory of cardiovascular physiology at the National Heart Institute.

Bibliography

BEHAVIOR OF STROKE VOLUME AT REST AND DURING EXERCISE IN HUMAN BEINGS. Carleton B. Chapman, Joseph N. Fisher and Brian J. Sproule in *The Journal of Clinical Investigation*, Vol. 39, No. 8, pages 1208–1213; August, 1960.

THE PHYSIOLOGICAL MEANING OF THE MAXIMAL OXYGEN INTAKE TEST. Jere H. Mitchell, Brian J. Sproule and Carleton B. Chapman in *The Journal of Clinical Investigation*, Vol. 37, No. 4, pages 538–547; April, 1958.

THE PHYSIOLOGY OF MUSCULAR EXERCISE. F. A. Bainbridge. Longmans, Green and Co., 1919.

9. The Heart

The Author

CARL J. WIGGERS retired in 1953 as professor of physiology at Western Reserve University, where he had taught since 1913. Following retirement, he was honorary professor at the Bunts Educational Institute in Cleveland and editor of *Circulation Research*, a journal which he founded. Wiggers received his M.D. from the University of Michigan, taught there for several years, and did advanced work at the Physiological Institute in Munich before going to Western Reserve. He wrote *The Physiology of Shock* and *Circulatory Dynamics*, served as president of the American Physiological Society, and won the Gold Heart Medal of the American Heart Association, the Lasker Award and the Order of Southern Cross from Brazil. Dr. Wiggers died in 1963.

Bibliography

PHYSIOLOGY IN HEALTH AND DISEASE. Carl J. Wiggers. Lea & Febiger, 1949.

THE MOTION OF THE HEART: THE STORY OF CARDIOVASCULAR RESEARCH. Blake Cabot. Harper & Brothers, 1954.

10. The Heart's Pacemaker

The Author

E. F. ADOLPH is emeritus professor of physiology at the University of Rochester. He was graduated from Harvard College in 1916, obtained a Ph.D. from Harvard in 1920, and taught zoology at the University of Pittsburgh before going to the School of Medicine and Dentistry at the University of Rochester in 1925 as assistant professor of physiology. He has been interested in a number of regulatory processes in physiology, particularly the beginnings of such processes in the individual. In 1953 he was president of the American Physiological Society. Although he retired in 1960, he continues to work regularly in his laboratory at the University.

Bibliography

ACTIVITY IN A CRUSTACEAN GANGLION, II: PATTERN AND INTERACTION IN BURST FORMATION. Donald M. Maynard in *The Biological Bulletin*, Vol. 109, No. 3, pages 420–436; December, 1955.

CAPACITIES FOR REGULATION OF HEART RATE IN FETAL, INFANT, AND ADULT RATS. E. F. Adolph in *American Journal of Physiology*, Vol. 209, No. 6, pages 1095–1105; December, 1965.

HEART, BLOODVESSELS, BLOOD AND ENTODERMAL DERIVATIVES. W. M. Copenhaver in *Analysis of Development*, edited by Benjamin H. Willier, Paul A. Weiss and Viktor Hamburger. W. B. Saunders Company, 1955.

RANGES OF HEART RATES AND THEIR REGULATION AT VARIOUS AGES (RAT). E. F. Adolph in *American Journal of Physiology*, Vol. 212, No. 3, pages 595–602; March, 1967.

SOME OBSERVATIONS ON THE GROWTH AND FUNCTION OF HETEROPLASTIC HEART GRAFTS. W. M. Copenhaver in *Journal of Experimental Zoology*, Vol. 82, No. 2, pages 239–271; November 5, 1939.

11. The Microcirculation of the Blood

The Author

BENJAMIN W. ZWEIFACH says that he is a "complete product of New York City's public-school system." Upon graduating from the College of the City of New York in 1931, at the height of the depression, he found himself jobless, and so decided to enroll for a year in the New York University Graduate School. There he came under the influence of Robert Chambers, a pioneer in the microsurgery of cells. Chambers' work on the permeability of cell membranes led Zweifach immediately into the study of how the cells are nourished by the blood capillaries. Zweifach took his Ph.D. in 1936, was a research fellow at Tufts University for two years, then returned to N.Y.U., where (except for a period of a few years at the Cornell University Medical College) he worked until 1966. Since then, he has been at the University of California, San Diego, in the Department of Bioengineering.

Bibliography

THE ANATOMY AND PHYSIOLOGY OF CAPILLARIES. August Krogh. Yale University Press, 1929.

GENERAL PRINCIPLES GOVERNING THE BEHAVIOR OF THE MICROCIRCULATION. B. W. Zweifach in *The American Journal of Medicine*, Vol. 23, No. 5, pages 684–696; November, 1957.

THE ROLE OF MEDIATORS IN THE INFLAMMATORY TISSUE RESPONSE. W. Feldberg in *International Archives of Allergy and Applied Immunology*, Vol. 8, No. 1–2, pages 15–31; 1956.

12. The Lymphatic System

The Author

H. S. MAYERSON is the associate director of Touro Infirmary. He was professor and chairman of the department of physiology at Tulane University until his retirement in 1965. Mayerson obtained an A.B. from Brown University in 1922 and a Ph.D. in physiology from Yale University in 1925. He went to Tulane in 1926, becoming professor of physiology and chairman of the department in 1945. He was president of the Federation of the American Society of Experimental Biology in 1963, and president of the American Physiological Society in 1962. From 1954 to 1960 he served on the board of directors of the American Heart Association. Mayerson has also been associated with the National Research Council in various capacities: as a representative of the Biology and Agriculture Review Committee on the International Exchange of Persons, from 1955 to 1957; as a member of the Committee on Shock, from 1954 to 1961; and since 1961, as a member of the National Committee for the International Union of Physiological Sciences. He is still on the fellowship panel of the National Science Foundation and the graduate fellowship program of the National Academy of Sciences.

Bibliography

THE LYMPHATIC SYSTEM WITH PARTICULAR REFERENCE TO THE KIDNEY. H. S. Mayerson in *Surgery, Gynecology & Obstetrics*, Vol. 116, No. 3, pages 259–272; March, 1963.

LYMPHATICS AND LYMPH CIRCULATION. István Rusznyák, Mihály Földi and György Szabó. Pergamon Press Ltd., 1960.

LYMPHATICS, LYMPH AND LYMPHOID TISSUE. Joseph Mendel Yoffey and Frederick Colin Courtice. Harvard University Press, 1956.

OBSERVATIONS AND REFLECTIONS ON THE LYMPHATIC SYSTEM. H. S. Mayerson in *Transactions & Studies of the College of Physicians of Philadelphia*, Fourth Series, Vol. 28, No. 3, pages 109–127; January, 1961.

13. "The Wonderful Net"

The Author

P. F. SCHOLANDER is professor of physiology and director of the Physiological Research Laboratory at the Scripps Institute of Oceanography. Scholander was born in Örebro, Sweden, in 1905, and received an M.D. from the University of Oslo in 1932. After two years as instructor in anatomy at Oslo he acquired a Ph.D. in botany there in 1934. He did research in botany and physiology in Norway until 1939, when he came to this country to join the department of zoology at Swarthmore College. During World War II Scholander served as an aviation physiologist in the U.S. Army Air Force, returning to Swarthmore in 1946 to continue his studies on the comparative physiology of diving. He investigated climatic adaptations of arctic and tropical animals and plants at the Arctic Research Laboratory in Point Barrow, Alaska, and in Panama from 1947 until 1949, when he became a research fellow in the department of biological chemistry at the Harvard Medical School. In 1952 he joined the staff of the Woods Hole Oceanographic Institution, and in 1955 he was appointed professor of physiology and director of the Institute of Zoophysiology at the University of Oslo. He has been at the Scripps Institute since 1958.

Bibliography

COUNTER-CURRENT VASCULAR HEAT EXCHANGE IN THE FINS OF WHALES. P. F. Scholander and William E. Schevill in *Journal of Applied Physiology*, Vol. 8, No. 3, pages 279–282; November, 1955.

EVOLUTION OF CLIMATIC ADAPTATION IN HOMEOTHERMS. P. F. Scholander in *Evolution*, Vol. 9, No. 1, pages 15–26; March, 1955.

THE RABBIT PLACENTA AND THE PROBLEM OF PLACENTAL TRANSMISSION. Harland W. Mossman in *The American Journal of Anatomy*, Vol. 37, No. 3, pages 433–497; July, 1926.

SECRETION OF GASES AGAINST HIGH PRESSURES IN THE SWIMBLADDER OF DEEP SEA FISHES. II: THE RETE MIRABILE. P. F. Scholander in *The Biological Bulletin*, Vol. 107, No. 2, pages 260–277; October, 1954.

TEMPERATURE OF SKIN IN THE ARCTIC AS A REGULATOR OF HEAT. Laurence Irving and John Krog in *Journal of Applied Physiology*, Vol. 7, No. 4, pages 355–364; January, 1955.

14. The Ice Fish

The Author

JOHAN T. RUUD is professor of marine biology at the University of Oslo, an institution he has also served as dean of the science faculty and as rector. Born in a Norwegian seaport, Ruud went to sea in a merchant steamer before going to the University of Oslo as a student. There he became interested in the scientific problems of Norway's whaling industry, and after graduation he spent many seasons with the whaling and sealing fleets. That work led in 1938 to his appointment as director of the State Institute for Whale Research. Ruud has also served as chairman of the Norwegian Research Council for Science and the Humanities. He was the discoverer of the Chaenichthyidae, the family of fishes without red blood cells that is discussed in his article.

Bibliography

BLOOD AND PARENCHYMAL CELLS IN THE SPLEEN OF THE ICEFISH CHAENOCEPHALUS ACERATUS (LÖNNBERG). Finn Walvig in *Nytt Magasin for Zoologi*, Vol. 6, pages 111–120; 1958.

A CONTRIBUTION TO THE SYSTEMATICS AND BIOLOGY OF CHAENICHTHYID FISHES FROM SOUTH GEORGIA. Steinar Olsen in *Nytt Magasin for Zoologi*, Vol. 3, pages 79–93; 1955.

FISHES OF THE STANFORD ANTARCTIC BIOLOGICAL RESEARCH PROGRAM, 1958–1959. Hugh H. DeWitt and James C. Tyler in *Stanford Ichthyological Bulletin*, Vol. 7, No. 4, pages 162–199; 1960.

THE INTEGUMENT OF THE ICEFISH CHAENOCEPHALUS ACERATUS (LÖNNBERG). Finn Walvig in *Nytt Magasin for Zoologi*, Vol. 9, pages 31–36; 1960.

VERTEBRATES WITHOUT BLOOD PIGMENT: A STUDY OF THE FISH FAMILY CHAENICHTHYIDAE. Johan T. Ruud in *XVth International Congress of Zoology, London, 16–23 July, 1958: Proceedings*, Section 6, pages 526–528; 1959.

III · GAS EXCHANGE, THE LUNGS, AND ADAPTATIONS FOR DIVING

Introduction

Bibliography

Andersen, H. T., "Physiological adaptations in diving vertebrates." *Physiol. Revs.* **46**, 1966, pp. 212–243.
Fänge, R., "Physiology of the swim bladder." *Physiol. Revs.* **46**, 1966, pp. 299–322.
Pattle, R. E., "Surface lining of lung alveoli." *Physiol. Revs.* **45**, 1965, pp. 48–79.
Permutt, S., "Respiration." *Ann. Rev. Physiol.* **28**, 1966, pp. 177–200.

15. The Lung

The Author

JULIUS H. COMROE, JR. is professor of physiology and director of the Cardiovascular Research Institute at the San Francisco Medical Center of the University of California. He went to the institute in 1957 after 21 years as a member of the faculty at the Graduate School of Medicine of the University of Pennsylvania. Earlier he had received undergraduate and medical degrees from that University. Comroe is involved as writer, editor, or consultant in many activities related to his professional interests. He was president of the American Physiological Society in 1960–1961.

Bibliography

THE MECHANISM OF BREATHING. Wallace O. Fenn in *Scientific American*, Vol. 202, No. 1, pages 138–148; January, 1960.
THE PHYSIOLOGY OF EXERCISE. Carleton B. Chapman and Jere H. Mitchell in *Scientific American*, Vol. 212, No. 5, pages 88–96; May, 1965.
SURFACE TENSION IN THE LUNGS. John A. Clements in *Scientific American*, Vol. 207, No. 6, pages 121–130; December, 1962.

16. Surface Tension in the Lungs

The Author

JOHN A. CLEMENTS went to the University of California San Francisco Medical Center in 1961 as Professor of Pediatrics and American Heart Association career investigator. In 1952 he was assistant chief of the Directorate of Medical Research, a division of the Army Chemical Center in Maryland. Clements' research on the physiology of respiration and his association with the Directorate of Medical Research both began with a tour of duty with the Army from 1948 to 1951. On assignment to the Applied Physiology Branch during his first year, Clements began studying the effects of carbon dioxide, exercise, and heat on respiration. In 1951 he was assigned to the Clinical Investigation Branch. He has done research at the Chemical Defense Experimental Establishment in England, and the Roswell Park Memorial Institute in Buffalo.

Bibliography

MECHANICAL PROPERTIES OF LUNGS. Jere Mead in *Physiological Reviews*, Vol. 41, No. 2, pages 281–330; April, 1961.
THE PHYSICS AND CHEMISTRY OF SURFACES. Neil Kensington Adam. Oxford University Press, 1941.
SOAP-BUBBLES: THEIR COLOURS AND THE FORCES WHICH MOLD THEM. C. V. Boys. Dover Publications, Inc., 1959.

SURFACE PHENOMENA IN CHEMISTRY AND BIOLOGY. Edited by J. F. Danielli, K. G. A. Pankhurst and A. C. Riddiford. Pergamon Books. The Macmillan Company, 1958.

17. The Master Switch of Life

The Author

P. F. SCHOLANDER is professor of physiology and director of the Physiological Research Laboratory at the Scripps Institute of Oceanography. For additional information about him, see biographical note 12.

Bibliography

CIRCULATORY ADJUSTMENT IN PEARL DIVERS. P. F. Scholander, H. T. Hammel, H. LeMessurier, E. Hemmingsen and W. Garey in *Journal of Applied Physiology*, Vol. 17, No. 2, pages 184–190; March, 1962.
MESENTERIC VASCULAR INSUFFICIENCY: INTESTINAL ISCHEMIA INDUCED BY REMOTE CIRCULATORY DISTURBANCES. Eliot Corday, David W. Irving, Herbert Gold, Harold Bernstein and Robert B. T. Skelton in *The American Journal of Medicine*, Vol. 33, No. 3, pages 365–376; September, 1962.
RESPIRATION IN DIVING MAMMALS. Laurence Irving in *Physiological Reviews*, Vol. 19, No. 1, pages 112–134; January, 1939.
SELECTIVE ISCHEMIA IN DIVING MAN. R. W. Elsner, W. F. Garey and P. F. Scholander in *American Heart Journal*, Vol. 65, No. 4, pages 571–572; April, 1963.

18. The Diving Women of Korea and Japan

The Authors

SUK KI HONG and HERMANN RAHN are professors of physiology, Hong at the Yonsei University College of Medicine in Korea and Rahn at the State University of New York at Buffalo. Each is also chairman of the department of physiology at his institution. Hong was born and educated in Korea. He received the degree of M.D. at Severance Union Medical College (now part of Yonsei University) in 1949 and a Ph.D. from the University of Rochester in 1956. He then joined the faculty of the University of Buffalo School of Medicine (now the State University of New York at Buffalo). Before he left Buffalo in 1959 he and Rahn made plans for a long-term collaborative research program on physiological adaptations to diving. Rahn was graduated from Cornell University in 1933 and received a Ph.D. from the University of Rochester in 1938. He was a member of the department of physiology at Rochester until 1956, when he went to the State University of New York at Buffalo.

Bibliography

THE ISLAND OF THE FISHERWOMEN. Fosco Maraini. Harcourt, Brace & World, Inc., 1962.
KOREAN SEA WOMEN: A STUDY OF THEIR PHYSIOLOGY. The departments of physiology, Yonsei University College of Medicine, Seoul, and the State University of New York at Buffalo.
THE PHYSIOLOGICAL STRESSES OF THE AMA. Hermann Rahn in *Physiology of Breath-Hold Diving and the Ama of Japan*. Publication 1341, National Academy of Sciences–National Research Council, 1965.

IV · WATER BALANCE AND ITS CONTROL

Introduction

Bibliography

Norman, A. W., "The mode of action of vitamin D." *Biol. Revs.* **43**, 1968, pp. 97–137.

Potts, W. T. W., "Osmotic and ionic regulation." *Ann. Rev. Physiol.* **30**, 1968, pp. 73–104.

Poulson, T. L., "Countercurrent multipliers in avian kidneys." *Science*, **148**, 1965, pp. 389–391.

Salt, G. W., "Respiratory evaporation in birds." *Biol. Revs.* **39**, 1964, pp. 113–136.

Sharp, G. W. G., and Leaf, A., "Mechanisms of action of aldosterone." *Physiol. Revs.* **46**, 1966, pp. 593–633.

Thurau, K., Valtin, H., and Schnermann, J., "Kidney." *Ann. Rev. Physiol.* **30**, 1968, pp. 441–524.

Vander, A. J., "Control of renin release." *Physiol. Revs.* **47**, 1967, pp. 359–382.

19. The Desert Rat

The Authors

KNUT SCHMIDT-NIELSEN is James B. Duke Professor of Physiology at Duke University. He has long been interested in the water metabolism of animals, as indicated in the three articles included in this volume. He wrote *The Desert Rat* in collaboration with BODIL SCHMIDT-NIELSEN, who is the daughter of the Nobel laureate in physiology, August Krogh.

Knut Schmidt-Nielsen has received many honors. He was a Harvey Society lecturer in 1962, a regents' lecturer at the University of California in 1963, and received the Public Health Service Research Career Award in 1964. His studies on water metabolism have taken him to many places in the world; the work he describes on the camel, for instance, was the result of an expedition that he led to the Sahara Desert in 1953 and 1954 while on a Guggenheim fellowship.

Bibliography

THE WATER ECONOMY OF DESERT MAMMALS. Bodil and Knut Schmidt-Nielsen in *The Scientific Monthly*, Vol. 69, No. 3; September, 1949.

20. The Physiology of the Camel

The Author

For information on KNUT SCHMIDT-NIELSEN, see the preceding biographical note.

Bibliography

BODY TEMPERATURE OF THE CAMEL AND ITS RELATION TO WATER ECONOMY. Knut Schmidt-Nielsen, Bodil Schmidt-Nielsen, S. A. Jarnum and T. R. Houpt. Department of Zoology, Duke University, 1959.

THE CAMEL, ITS USES AND MANAGEMENT. Major Arthur Glyn Leonard. Longmans, Green and Co., 1894.

PHYSIOLOGY OF MAN IN THE DESERT. E. F. Adolph and associates. Interscience Publishers, 1947.

21. Salt Glands

The Author

For information on KNUT SCHMIDT-NIELSEN, see biographical note 19.

Bibliography

THE SALT GLAND OF THE HERRING GULL. Ragnar Fänge, Knut Schmidt-Nielsen and Humio Osaki in *Biological Bulletin*, Vol. 115, pages 162–171; October, 1958.

SALT GLANDS IN MARINE REPTILES. Knut Schmidt-Nielsen and Ragnar Fänge in *Nature*, Vol. 182, No. 783–785; September 20, 1958.

V · TEMPERATURE ADAPTATIONS

Introduction

Bibliography

Bartholomew, G. A., "Body Temperature and Energy Metabolism." *In* M. S. Gordon, Ed., ANIMAL FUNCTION: PRINCIPLES AND ADAPTATIONS. New York, Macmillan, 1968, pp. 290–354.

Hammel, H. T., "Regulation of internal body temperature." *Ann. Rev. Physiol.* **30**, 1968, pp. 641–710.

Hochachka, P. W., "Organization of metabolism during temperature compensation." *In* C. L. Prosser, Ed., MOLECULAR MECHANISMS OF TEMPERATURE ADAPTATION. Washington, D.C., American Association for the Advancement of Science, 1967, pp. 177–204.

Licht, P., "Thermal adaptation in the enzymes of lizards in relation to preferred body temperatures." *Ibid.*, pp. 131–146.

Waring, H., Moir, R. J., and Tyndale-Biscoe, C. H., "Comparative physiology of marsupials." *In* O. E. Lowenstein, Ed., ADVANCES IN COMPARATIVE PHYSIOLOGY AND BIOCHEMISTRY, Vol. 2, New York, Academic Press, 1966, pp. 237–376.

22. How Reptiles Regulate Their Body Temperature

The Author

CHARLES M. BOGERT is chairman and curator of the Department of Amphibians and Reptiles at the American Museum of Natural History in New York. He was born on a ranch at Mesa, Colorado. "The reptiles my elder brother—a trapper—brought in, particularly such rarities as a gaudily banded red, yellowish and black king snake (*Lampropeltis doliata*) left a lasting impression on me," he reports. After the family moved to California, Bogert would make frequent trips to the Mojave desert, "collecting tortoises, lizards and snakes, which I kept under observation in a large cage in the back yard." Bogert did undergraduate and graduate work at the University of California at Los Angeles, where he began a long collaboration with Raymond B. Cowles on thermoregulation in reptiles.

Bibliography

A PRELIMINARY STUDY OF THE THERMAL REQUIREMENTS OF DESERT REPTILES. Raymond Bridgman Cowles and Charles

Mitchill Bogert in *Bulletin of the American Museum of Natural History*, Vol. 83, Article 5, pages 265–296; 1944.

RATTLESNAKES: THEIR HABITS, LIFE HISTORIES, AND INFLUENCE ON MANKIND. Laurence M. Klauber. University of California Press, 1956.

THERMOREGULATION IN REPTILES—A FACTOR IN EVOLUTION. Charles M. Bogert in *Evolution*, Vol. 3, No. 3, pages 195–211; September, 1949.

TEMPERATURE TOLERANCES IN THE AMERICAN ALLIGATOR AND THEIR BEARING ON THE HABITS, EVOLUTION AND EXTINCTION OF THE DINOSAURS. Edwin H. Colbert, Raymond B. Cowles and Charles M. Bogert in *Bulletin of the American Museum of Natural History*, Vol. 86, Article 7, pages 331–373; 1946.

23. Adaptations to Cold

The Author

LAURENCE IRVING is director of the Institute of Arctic Biology and professor of zoophysiology at the University of Alaska. A graduate of Bowdoin College, he received a master's degree at Harvard University in 1917 and a Ph.D. at Stanford University in 1924. He has worked in Alaska since 1947, going there after more than 20 years of teaching, mostly at Swarthmore College. "I have long been inclined to study the physiological adaptations that enable men and animals to succeed in extreme natural conditions," he writes. "It turned out that the natural physiological reactions of arctic animals to cold were of dimensions large enough to demonstrate general principles of adaptation to various temperatures that we had been unable to ascertain in mild climates and by the use of domesticated animals."

Bibliography

BODY INSULATION OF SOME ARCTIC AND TROPICAL MAMMALS AND BIRDS. P. F. Scholander, Vladimir Walters, Raymond Hock and Laurence Irving in *The Biological Bulletin*, Vol. 99, No. 2, pages 225–236; October, 1950.

BODY TEMPERATURES OF ARCTIC AND SUBARCTIC BIRDS AND MAMMALS. Laurence Irving and John Krog in *Journal of Applied Physiology*, Vol. 6, No. 11, pages 667–680; May, 1954.

EFFECT OF TEMPERATURE ON SENSITIVITY OF THE FINGER. Laurence Irving in *Journal of Applied Physiology*, Vol. 18, No. 6, pages 1201–1205; November, 1963.

METABOLISM AND INSULATION OF SWINE AS BARE-SKINNED MAMMALS. Laurence Irving, Leonard J. Peyton and Mildred Monson in *Journal of Applied Physiology*, Vol. 9, No. 3, pages 421–426; November, 1956.

PHYSIOLOGICAL INSULATION OF SWINE AS BARE-SKINNED MAMMALS. Laurence Irving in *Journal of Applied Physiology*, Vol. 9, No. 3, pages 414–420; November, 1956.

TERRESTRIAL ANIMALS IN COLD: INTRODUCTION. Laurence Irving in *Handbook of Physiology, Section 4: Adaptation to the Environment*. American Physiological Society, 1964.

24. The Human Thermostat

The Author

T. H. BENZINGER is head of the Calorimetry Branch and the Bio-Energetics Division of the Naval Medical Research Institute in Bethesda, Maryland. He was born in Germany in 1905, and studied at the Universities of Tübingen and Munich and at the Stuttgart Institute of Technology. From 1927 to 1933 he studied medicine at Tübingen and the Universities of Berlin and Freiburg, receiving his M.D. degree from the latter institution. During World War II Benzinger was head of both the Medical Division of the German Air Force Test-

ing Center and the Medical Branch of the Research Division in the Air Ministry. After two years at the U.S. Air Force Aero-Medical Center in Heidelberg, he went to the Naval Medical Research Institute in 1947. His many contributions led to his being awarded the Golden Sheele Medal by the Chemical Society of Sweden in 1963.

Bibliography

ACTIVATION OF HEAT LOSS MECHANISMS BY LOCAL HEATING OF THE BRAIN. H. W. Magoun, F. Harrison, J. R. Brobeck and S. W. Ranson in *Journal of Neurophysiology*, Vol. I, No. 2, pages 101–114; March, 1938.

THE RELATION OF THE NERVOUS SYSTEM TO THE TEMPERATURE OF THE BODY. Isaac Ott in *The Journal of Nervous and Mental Disease*, Vol. XI, No. 2, pages 141–152; April, 1884.

THE ROLE OF THE ANTERIOR HYPOTHALAMUS IN TEMPERATURE REGULATION. R. S. Teague and S. W. Ranson in *The American Journal of Physiology*, Vol. 117, No. 3, pages 562–570; November 1, 1936.

25. The Production of Heat by Fat

The Authors

MICHAEL J. R. DAWKINS and DAVID HULL began their collaboration at the Nuffield Institute for Medical Research at the University of Oxford. On June 27, shortly before their article went to press, Dawkins died after a brief illness. He was 34 years old. Hull writes: "Michael was an exceptional person with great ability. He was highly qualified as a physician and practiced as a pediatric pathologist. His original work on the biochemical and physiological changes occurring after birth had already gained him a considerable reputation both in Britain and abroad." Dawkins, who was graduated from the University of Cambridge, had received his medical training at University College Hospital in London. At the time of his death he was senior lecturer in pathology at the Institute of Child Health in London. Hull, who is lecturer in pediatrics at the medical school of the University of Oxford, received degrees in physiology and medicine at the University of Liverpool. He writes that he is "currently investigating the problem of resuscitation of the newborn human." He took his present post in 1963.

Bibliography

BROWN ADIPOSE TISSUE AND THE RESPONSE OF NEW-BORN RABBITS TO COLD. M. J. R. Dawkins and D. Hull in *The Journal of Physiology*, Vol. 172, No. 2, pages 216–238; August, 1964.

BROWN FAT: A REVIEW. Bengt Johansson in *Metabolism: Clinical and Experimental*, Vol. 8, No. 3, pages 221–240; May, 1959.

ON THE ACTION OF HORMONES WHICH ACCELERATE THE RATE OF OXYGEN CONSUMPTION AND FATTY ACID RELEASE IN RAT ADIPOSE TISSUE IN VITRO. Eric G. Ball and Robert L. Jungas in *Proceedings of the National Academy of Sciences*, Vol. 47, No. 7, pages 932–941; July, 1961.

THERMOGENESIS OF BROWN ADIPOSE TISSUE IN COLD-ACCLIMATED RATS. Robert E. Smith and Jane C. Roberts in *American Journal of Physiology*, Vol. 206, No. 1, pages 143–148; January, 1964.

26. Desert Ground Squirrels

The Authors

GEORGE A. BARTHOLOMEW and JACK W. HUDSON were colleagues in the department of zoology at the University of California at Los Angeles. Bartholomew received his A.B. and M.A.

degrees from the University of California and, after wartime service as a scientist with the U.S. Navy, obtained his Ph.D. in 1947 at Harvard University. He then went to U.C.L.A., where he is professor of zoology. In 1961 Bartholomew went to Australia on a Guggenheim Fellowship and a National Science Foundation grant to study the physiology of marsupials and reptiles in Queensland. Hudson was graduated from Occidental College in 1948 and received his M.A. there the next year. While teaching biology at Occidental he did doctoral research under Bartholomew at U.C.L.A., receiving his Ph.D. in 1960. He was a lecturer in zoology there until 1962, when he went to Rice University, where he is now an associate Professor.

Bibliography

THE COMPETITIVE EXCLUSION PRINCIPLE. Garrett Hardin in *Science*, Vol. 131, No. 3409, pages 1292–1297; April 29, 1960.

EFFECTS OF SODIUM CHLORIDE ON WEIGHT AND DRINKING IN THE ANTELOPE GROUND SQUIRREL. George A. Bartholomew and Jack W. Hudson in *Journal of Mammalogy*, Vol. 40, No. 3, pages 354–360; August 20, 1959.

HEAT REGULATION IN SOME ARCTIC AND TROPICAL MAMMALS AND BIRDS. P. F. Scholander, Raymond Hock, Vladimir Walters, Fred Johnson and Laurence Irving in *The Biological Bulletin*, Vol. 99, No. 2, pages 237–258; October, 1950.

HIBERNATION. Charles P. Lyman and Paul O. Chatfield in *Scientific American*, Vol. 183, No. 6, pages 18–21; December, 1950.

WATER METABOLISM OF DESERT MAMMALS. Knut Schmidt-Nielsen and Bodil Schmidt-Nielsen in *Physiological Reviews*, Vol. 32, No. 2, pages 135–166; April, 1952.

VI · ORIENTATION AND NAVIGATION

Introduction

Bibliography

Griffin, D. R., LISTENING IN THE DARK. New Haven, Yale University Press, 1958, p. 413.

Kalmus, H., "Comparative physiology: navigation by animals." *Ann. Rev. Physiol.* **26**, 1964, pp. 109–130.

Kellogg, W. N., PORPOISES AND SONAR. Chicago, University of Chicago Press, 1961, p. 177.

Lang, T. G., and Smith, H. A. P., "Communication between dolphins in separate tanks by way of an electronic acoustic link." *Science* **150**, 1965, pp. 1839–1844.

Marler, P., MECHANISMS OF ANIMAL BEHAVIOR. New York, Wiley, 1966, p. 771.

Moncrieff, R. W., THE CHEMICAL SENSES. London, Leonard Hill, 1961, p. 760.

Pfeiffer, W., "The fright reaction of fish." *Biol. Revs.* **37**, 1962, pp. 495–511.

Rice, C. E., "Human echo perception." *Science* **155**, 1967, pp. 656–664.

Slijper, E. J., WHALES. New York, Basic Books, 1962, p. 475.

Storm, R. M., Ed., ANIMAL ORIENTATION AND NAVIGATION. Corvallis, Oregon State University Press, 1967, p. 134.

27. The Homing Salmon

The Authors

ARTHUR D. HASLER and JAMES A. LARSEN are both at the University of Wisconsin. Hasler is head of Wisconsin's Limnology Laboratory and professor of zoology. Born in Utah, he studied in Germany, graduated in 1932 from Brigham Young University, worked for two years as an aquatic biologist for the U.S. Fish and Wildlife Service in Chesapeake Bay, and in 1937 took his Ph.D. in zoology at the University of Wisconsin, where he has taught ever since. He spent a couple of summers as director of the Lake Geneva Institute of Natural Science before the war, and in 1945 the War Department sent him to Germany in its Strategic Bombing Survey. Hasler is a former vice president of the Society of Limnology and Oceanography. In 1955, he worked with Karl von Frisch at the Zoological Institute in Munich. He was at Helsinki in 1963 as an exchange professor. Larsen is the science editor of the University of Wisconsin News Service. He has done some research in animal and plant ecology, but his only part in the article here was as a collaborator with Hasler in writing it.

Bibliography

THE CHEMICAL SENSE. R. W. Moncrieff. John Wiley & Sons, Inc., 1946.

HOMING INSTINCT IN SALMON. Bradley T. Scheer in *The Quarterly Review of Biology*, Vol. 14, No. 4, pages 408–430; December, 1939.

THE MIGRATION AND THE CONSERVATION OF SALMON. Edited by Forest R. Moulton. American Association for the Advancement of Science, 1939.

SENSORY PHYSIOLOGY AND THE ORIENTATION OF ANIMALS. Donald R. Griffin in *American Scientist*, Vol. 41, No. 2, pages 209–244; April, 1953.

28. Electric Location by Fishes

The Author

H. W. LISSMANN is lecturer in the department of zoology at the University of Cambridge. Lissmann, who was born in Russia, studied in Germany, where he obtained a Ph.D. at the University of Hamburg. He received an M.A. from Cambridge in 1947 and became assistant director of research there the same year. Lissmann was elected a Fellow of the Royal Society in 1954. He was made lecturer in zoology at the University of Cambridge the following year and was also elected a Fellow and Lecturer of Trinity College, Cambridge. Lissmann is interested mainly in the behavior of animals, their movements, sense organs, and nervous systems. His studies of electric fishes, begun in 1950, are described in his article. Lissmann has found it "useful and illuminating" to collect his own fish in Africa and South America. Recently, he and his collaborators have extended their analysis of electric organs by using electronmicroscopy.

Bibliography

ECOLOGICAL STUDIES ON GYMNOTIDS. H. W. Lissmann in *Bioelectrogenesis: A Comparative Survey of its Mechanisms with Particular Emphasis on Electric Fishes*. American Elsevier Publishing Co., Inc., 1961.

ON THE FUNCTION AND EVOLUTION OF ELECTRIC ORGANS IN FISH. H. W. Lissmann in *Journal of Experimental Biology*, Vol. 35, No. 1, pages 156–191; March, 1958.

THE MECHANISM OF OBJECT LOCATION IN GYMNARCHUS NILOTICUS AND SIMILAR FISH. H. W. Lissmann and K. E. Machin in *Journal of Experimental Biology*, Vol. 35, No. 2, pages 451–486; June, 1958.

THE MODE OF OPERATION OF THE ELECTRIC RECEPTORS IN GYMNARCHUS NILOTICUS. K. E. Machin and H. W. Lissmann in *Journal of Experimental Biology*, Vol. 37, No. 4, pages 801–811; December, 1960.

29. More about Bat "Radar"

The Author

DONALD R. GRIFFIN has been interested in natural history since boyhood, and in bats since his undergraduate days at Harvard University. A specialist in the sensory physiology of animal orientation, he has devoted a great deal of study to the radar-like echolocation systems of bats and other animals. Born in Southampton, New York, in 1915, he was educated at Harvard and remained there during the war to do physiological research for the Government. In 1946 he joined the faculty of Cornell University. He returned to Harvard as professor of zoology in 1953 and served as chairman of the department of biology until 1965. Since then he has been at the Rockefeller Institute, where he and the animal behaviorist Peter Marler head an outstanding group of biologists working on animal behavior. Griffin is the author of one of the most fascinating and literate books written about biology in this century: it is about bats, and is called *Listening in the Dark*.

Bibliography

BATS. Glover Morrill Allen. Harvard University Press, 1939.

BATS. William A. Wimsatt in *Scientific American*, Vol. 197, No. 5, pages 105–114; November, 1957.

BIRD SONAR. Donald R. Griffin in *Scientific American*, Vol. 190, No. 3, pages 78–83; March, 1954.

LISTENING IN THE DARK: THE ACOUSTIC ORIENTATION OF BATS AND MEN. Donald R. Griffin. Yale University Press, 1958.

THE NAVIGATION OF BATS. Donald R. Griffin in *Scientific American*, Vol. 183, No. 2, pages 52–55; August, 1950.

30. The Navigation of Penguins

The Authors

JOHN T. EMLEN and RICHARD L. PENNEY are respectively professor of zoology at the University of Wisconsin and an investigator at the Institute for Research in Animal Behavior, which is sponsored jointly by Rockefeller University and the New York Zoological Society. Emlen was graduated from Haverford College in 1931 and obtained a Ph.D. in ornithology from Cornell University in 1934. He spent some years as a biologist with the U.S. Department of Agriculture and as a research associate at Johns Hopkins University before going to the University of Wisconsin in 1946. In addition to his work with penguins he has studied social and population control in gulls, swallows, blackbirds, mice, squirrels, and bats, and has made special studies of gorillas, bison, and porpoises. Penney took a bachelor's degree at St. Olaf College in 1957 and a doctorate in zoology at the University of Wisconsin in 1963. He was a postdoctoral fellow and assistant professor at Johns Hopkins before going to his present position in 1966.

Bibliography

BIRD NAVIGATION. G. V. T. Matthews. Cambridge University Press, 1955.

CURRENT PROBLEMS IN BIRD ORIENTATION. Klaus Schmidt-Koenig in *Advances in the Study of Behavior: Vol. I*, edited by Daniel S. Lehrman, Robert A. Hinde and Evelyn Shaw. Academic Press, 1965.

LONG-DISTANCE ORIENTATION. G. Kramer in *Biology and Comparative Physiology of Birds: Vol. II*, edited by A. J. Marshall. Academic Press, 1961.

VII · HORMONES AND INTERNAL REGULATION

Introduction

Bibliography

Farrell, G., Fabre, L. F., and Rauschkolb, E. W. "The neurohypophysis." *Ann. Rev. Physiol.* 30, 1968, pp. 557–588.

Gorbman, A., and Bern, H. A., A TEXTBOOK OF COMPARATIVE ENDOCRINOLOGY. New York, Wiley, 1962, p. 468.

Loomis, W. F., "Skin-pigment regulation of vitamin D biosynthesis in man." *Science* 157, 1967, pp. 501–506.

McCann, S. M., Dhariwal, A. P. S., and Porter, J. C. "Regulation of the adenohypophysis." *Ann. Rev. Physiol.* 30, 1968, pp. 589–640.

Proceedings of the Royal Society B. 170, pp. 1–111. "A discussion on polypeptide hormones." May, 1968. (A series of papers on thyrocalcitonin, neurophysin, and neurohypohseal hormones. Included is the data of Archer on hormone evolution.)

31. Hormones

The Author

SIR SOLLY ZUCKERMAN is Sands Cox Professor of Anatomy at the University of Birmingham. He was born in Cape Town, South Africa, and studied at the University of Cape Town and at University College in London. In 1928 he became research anatomist at the London Zoological Society. In Africa and at the Zoological Society Zuckerman studied baboon colonies, and in 1932 he published *The Social Life of Monkeys and Apes*, which is still one of the standard works in its field. In 1961 he published *A New System of Anatomy* and in 1962 edited *The Ovary*. Zuckerman found that the harem rank of female baboons depended on their sexual cycles; this led him into the study of endocrinology. He was a Rockefeller Fellow at Yale University in 1933–1934 and subsequently a university lecturer at the University of Oxford. During World War II he studied the biological effects of the London blitz. As a top scientific adviser to Air Marshall Lord Tedder and SHAEF, he defined the tactical and strategic purposes of aerial bombardment. He was awarded the Order of the Bath and the U.S. Medal of Freedom with Silver Palm.

Bibliography

HORMONES AND BEHAVIOR. Frank A. Beach. Paul B. Hoeber, Inc., 1948.

THE HORMONES IN HUMAN REPRODUCTION. George W. Corner. Princeton University Press, 1943.

THE HORMONES: PHYSIOLOGY, CHEMISTRY AND APPLICATIONS. Edited by Gregory Pincus and Kenneth V. Thimann. Academic Press, Inc., 1955.

HORMONES IN REPRODUCTION. *British Medical Bulletin*, Vol. 11, No. 2; May, 1955.

RECENT PROGRESS IN HORMONE RESEARCH: VOL. 12. Edited by Gregory Pincus. Academic Press, Inc., 1956.

32. The Pineal Gland

The Authors

RICHARD J. WURTMAN and JULIUS AXELROD are respectively associate professor of endocrinology and metabolism at the Massachusetts Institute of Technology and chief of the section on pharmacology in the Laboratory of Clinical Science at the National Institute of Mental Health. Wurtman majored in philosophy as an undergraduate at the University of Pennsylvania and was graduated in 1960 from the Harvard Medical School. There, he writes, he "became interested in the new field of neuroendocrinology, especially in how environmental factors such as light and stress influence glandular function and how circulating hormones affect nervous function and behavior." From 1965 to 1967 Wurtman was medical research officer in the Laboratory of Clinical Science at the Institute of Mental Health. He joined the staff at M.I.T. in 1967. Axelrod was graduated from the City College of the City of New York in 1933. He received a Ph.D. at George Washington University 22 years later, having in the interim spent 13 years in a commercial laboratory before joining the National Heart Institute in 1950 to work on "the fate of drugs and the enzymes involved in their metabolism." At the National Institute of Mental Health, which he joined in 1955, he has developed techniques for studying how hormones regulate the action of neurotransmitters.

Bibliography

CONTROL OF HYDROXYINDOLE O-METHYLTRANSFERASE ACTIVITY IN THE RAT PINEAL GLAND BY ENVIRONMENTAL LIGHTING. Julius Axelrod, Richard J. Wurtman and Solomon H. Snyder in *The Journal of Biological Chemistry*, Vol. 240, No. 2, pages 949–954; February, 1965.

MELATONIN SYNTHESIS IN THE PINEAL GLAND: EFFECT OF LIGHT MEDIATED BY THE SYMPATHETIC NERVOUS SYSTEM. Richard J. Wurtman, Julius Axelrod and Josef E. Fischer in *Science*, Vol. 143, No. 3612, pages 1328–1329; March 20, 1964.

THE PINEAL GLAND: A REVIEW OF THE PHYSIOLOGIC LITERATURE. Julian I. Kitay and Mark D. Altschule. Harvard University Press, 1954.

SOME CLINICAL, BIOCHEMICAL, AND PHYSIOLOGICAL ACTIONS OF THE PINEAL GLAND. Robert A. Cohen, Richard J. Wurtman, Julius Axelrod and Solomon H. Snyder in *Annals of Internal Medicine*, Vol. 61, No. 6, pages 1144–1161; December, 1964.

STRUCTURE AND FUNCTION OF THE EPIPHYSIS CEREBRI. Edited by J. Ariëns Kappers and J. P. Schadé in *Progress in Brain Research*, Vol. X. Elsevier Publishing Company, 1965.

33. The Parathyroid Hormone

The Author

HOWARD RASMUSSEN is professor and chairman of the department of biochemistry at the University of Pennsylvania. He was graduated from Gettysburg College in 1948 with a B.A. in chemistry. After receiving an M.D. degree from the Harvard Medical School in 1952, Rasmussen spent three years at Massachusetts General Hospital and another year at University College Hospital Medical School in London. He joined the Rockefeller Institute in 1956 and acquired his Ph.D. there in 1959. From 1959 to 1961, he was an assistant professor of physiology at Rockefeller Institute and associate physician at the hospital. From 1961 to 1965 he was with the department of biochemistry at the University of Wisconsin.

Bibliography

DIRECT RENAL ACTION OF A PURIFIED PARATHORMONE EXTRACT. T. N. Pullman, A. R. Lavender and I. Aho in *Endocrinology*, Vol. 67, No. 5, pages 570–582; November, 1960.

THE INFLUENCE OF PARATHORMONE ON CARTILAGE AND BONE IN VITRO. P. J. Gaillard in *Acta Physiologica et Pharmacologica Neerlandica*, Vol. VIII, No. 2, pages 287–289; June, 1959.

MOLECULAR BIOLOGY OF MINERALIZED TISSUES WITH PARTICULAR REFERENCE TO BONE. Melvin J. Glimcher in *Reviews of Modern Physics*, Vol. 31, No. 2, pages 359–393; April, 1959.

PARATHYROID HORMONE: NATURE AND MECHANISM OF ACTION. Howard Rasmussen in *The American Journal of Medicine*, Vol. XXX, No. 1, pages 112–128; January, 1961.

VIII · COMMUNICATION BETWEEN VERTEBRATES

Introduction

Bibliography

Symposium of the Zoological Society of London 8, "Evolutionary aspects of animal communication. Imprinting and early learning." 1962.

Marler, P., "Animal communication signals." *Science* **157**, 1967, pp. 769–774.

Thorpe, W. H., "Antiphonal singing in birds as evidence for avian auditory reaction time." *Nature* **197**, 1963, pp. 774–776.

Thorpe, W. H., and North, M. E. W., "Origin and significance of the power of vocal imitation: with special reference to the antiphonal singing of birds." *Nature* **208**, 1965, pp. 219–222.

34. Territorial Marking by Rabbits

The Author

ROMAN MYKYTOWYCZ is principal research scientist with the Division of Wildlife Research of the Commonwealth Scientific and Industrial Research Organization of Australia. Born in the Ukraine, he studied veterinary science at the Zootechnical and Veterinary Institute of Lvov and obtained a doctorate in veterinary medicine from the University of Munich in 1948. He writes: "I then went to Australia, and after joining the CSIRO in 1950 I became engaged in investigations of the epidemiology of diseases of wildlife species, including the rabbit, the kangaroo and the Tasmanian shearwater or muttonbird. I was associated with experiments to control plague populations of rabbits by biological means, using the virus disease myxomatosis. While studying the fluctuations of numbers of animals in free-living populations, particularly of rabbits, I came to recognize the importance of social and territorial behavior of the animal as a population-regulating factor and became interested in ethology."

Bibliography

ANIMAL DISPERSION IN RELATION TO SOCIAL BEHAVIOR. V. C. Wynne-Edwards. Hafner Publishing Company, 1962.

FURTHER OBSERVATIONS ON THE TERRITORIAL FUNCTION AND HISTOLOGY OF THE SUBMANDIBULAR CUTANEOUS (CHIN) GLANDS IN THE RABBIT, ORYCTOLAGUS CUNICULUS (L.).

R. Mykytowycz in *Animal Behavior,* Vol. 13, No. 4, pages 400–412; October, 1965.

OBSERVATIONS ON ODORIFEROUS AND OTHER GLANDS IN THE AUSTRALIAN WILD RABBIT, ORYCTOLAGUS CUNICULUS (L.), AND THE HARE, LEPUS EUROPAEUS P, I: THE ANAL GLAND. R. Mykytowycz in *CSIRO Wildlife Research,* Vol. 11, No. 1, pages 11–29; October, 1966.

PHEROMONES. Edward O. Wilson in *Scientific American,* Vol. 208, No. 5, pages 100–114; May, 1963.

35. The Language of Birds

The Author

W. H. THORPE is director of studies at Jesus College and a university lecturer in entomology at the University of Cambridge, from which he holds the degrees of Ph.D. and Sc.D. Born at Hastings in 1902, he developed his interest in bird behavior after a long and varied career studying the behavior of insect parasites, which has taken him to many parts of the world. He was a research fellow of the Rockefeller International Education Board at the University of California in 1927–1929 and Prather Lecturer in Biology at Harvard in 1951–1952. Among the other places in which he has conducted research are Hawaii, Panama, Trinidad, Tanganyika, Kenya, Southern Rhodesia, and the Yerkes Laboratory in Florida. Thorpe is now investigating bird song as a means of exploring the general relation between learned and inborn behavior. The Ornithological Field Station at Madingley, near Cambridge is the site of most of his observations on English birds. Thorpe was president of the Zoological Section of the British Association for the Advancement of Science and president of the British Ornithologists' Union. He was elected a Fellow of the Royal Society in 1951. He has written several books, including *Learning and Instinct in Animals, Bird Song,* and *Man and Morals.*

Bibliography

CHARACTERISTICS OF SOME ANIMAL CALLS. P. Marler in *Nature,* Vol. 176, No. 4470, pages 6–8; July, 1955.

COMMENTS ON 'THE BIRD FANCYER'S DELIGHT': TOGETHER WITH NOTES ON IMITATION IN THE SUB-SONG OF THE CHAFFINCH. W. H. Thorpe in *Ibis,* Vol. 97, No. 2, pages 247–251; April, 1955.

THE PROCESS OF SONG LEARNING IN THE CHAFFINCH AS STUDIED BY MEANS OF THE SOUND SPECTROGRAPH. W. H. Thorpe in *Nature,* Vol. 173, No. 4402, pages 465–469; March, 1954.

Index